D0275208

PRINCIPLES OF
GENERAL PHYSIOLOGY

PRINCIPLES OF
GENERAL PHYSIOLOGY

VOLUME ONE
The Physico-chemical Background

BY

L. E. BAYLISS

Department of Physiology
University College, London

JOHN WILEY & SONS INC
NEW YORK N.Y.

QP
34
.B295

Published throughout the World except the United States
by Longmans, Green and Co Ltd

V.1

Fifth-edition   Vol. I © L. E. Bayliss, 1959
Vol. II © L. E. Bayliss, 1960

PRINCIPLES OF GENERAL PHYSIOLOGY
by W. M. Bayliss, (1860-1924)

First published 1915
Second edition 1918
Third edition 1920
Fourth edition
revised by A. V. Hill and others . . 1924
New impression 1931
Fifth edition, in two volumes
by L. E. Bayliss . . . . Vol. I 1959
Vol. II 1960
New impression . . . . . Vol. I 1960

12902

Printed in Great Britain
by T. and A. CONSTABLE LTD., Hopetoun Street
Printers to the University of Edinburgh

PREFACE

In the earlier editions of *Principles of General Physiology* there were several chapters and parts of chapters which dealt with certain aspects of physical chemistry. The inclusion of these "background" subjects in a book on physiology was defended, in the Preface to the 2nd edition, in the following passage: "A word seems requisite with regard to certain discussions contained in the earlier chapters, especially some of the questions of physical chemistry. The text-books on the subject do not always give sufficient treatment of those aspects which are of great importance in physiology. Original papers must be referred to in order to disinter some particular fact, and it seemed to me that I could save a certain amount of time and trouble for my fellow-workers. It is true that some of these matters may not seem to belong to a treatise on 'General Physiology', but I know of no more appropriate name, and as far as I can find out these parts of the book have been found useful". The emphasis given to this aspect of general physiology—more by the readers, perhaps, than by the author—gave rise at one time to the danger that "general physiology" would be regarded as the application of physical chemistry to biology, and nothing else. It is the "nothing else" to which objection must be taken: chemistry may be regarded as an application of certain aspects of atomic and molecular physics, and physics as an application of mathematics; but this does not describe the whole contents of these subjects. The study of physical chemistry should be regarded as an essential foundation on which the study of living processes is based.

In the Preface to the 2nd edition, again, a number of passages are quoted from the writings of Claude Bernard (*La Science expérimentale*), and concluded by the following words: "The only interpretation that I can put upon these passages is that the reason why we make an independent science of physiology is because the laws of physics and chemistry exert their influence in a specially complex system. At present we are unable to analyse the workings of this machine to more than a limited extent. We know, for example, that glucose supplied to a living cell is burnt up and that the energy set free is used for particular purposes; but how this happens is as yet beyond our comprehension. Nevertheless, each step in analysis results in reducing some further stage to simpler laws. When we obtain an electrical current from a fish, we make use of a more complex manner of production than that from a galvanic battery, but we are not justified in saying that the vital production of an electrical current differs in any more fundamental way from that by a galvanic battery than this does from that by a thermopile or a dynamo-machine. From the philo-sophical point of view, of course, we know neither more nor less of the essential 'nature' of living processes than of those of chemical action or electricity". The developments in physiology during the past 40 years serve only to strengthen this view. There are many aspects of physical chemistry, moreover, which were not discussed in the earlier editions, but which have since become of great importance to physiology. Some, indeed, are new developments, since the 1st edition was prepared. The most obvious, perhaps, are: the whole concept of activation energy and the kinetics of chemical reaction, particularly in solution; the theory of strong electro-lytes and G. N. Lewis' concept of "activity"; and the applications of the quantum theory to photochemical reactions. Although the lack of suitable text-books has now been largely remedied, it seemed to me, when undertaking the preparation of a new edition of *Principles of General Physiology* that the discussion on physico-chemical subjects should not be omitted entirely.

With all this in mind, I felt that the important principles of physical chemistry, and applications which are widespread in all branches of biology, should be brought together and put into a separate volume. This may be found convenient, indeed, by those who wish to understand the physico-chemical background .before proceeding to study the principles of general physiology, treated more particularly in the second volume; and by those whose interests lie more, perhaps, in other aspects of biology. Two volumes, moreover, of moderate size, may be less formidable than a single volume whose very dimensions may be daunting. It must be confessed, however, that the dividing line between one volume and the other has been drawn somewhat arbitrarily in many places, and some duplication has been inevitable. The two parts of the book are now largely independent; but this is not alone responsible for its character not being what it was. The times, as well as the author, have changed: many of those unusual features, and what may, perhaps, be called "frills", which were responsible for so much of its personality and charm, have had regretfully to be omitted.

In the treatment adopted, the reader is assumed to have an elementary knowledge of physics, chemistry and biology. Many would say that all students of natural science should have this knowledge: it is essential that students of physiology should have it. Again, all students of science should have some familiarity with the appropriate branches of mathematics; and this, also, is assumed. In the 1st edition (p. 37) reference is made to "the view taken by some, that the introduction of mathematics into biological questions is mischievous". There cannot be many who now hold quite this view, although there may be some who doubt whether mathematics is necessary. When students of general physiology and experimental biology are concerned directly with the applications of physico-chemical principles, the advantages of such knowledge are obvious enough: the meaning and significance of these principles cannot be fully appreciated without mathematics. But biological studies of all kinds are becoming increasingly quantitative, even when they are not obviously physico-chemical. Although "it may seem hard to add an extra burden to the already large equipment necessary for the physiological investigator", mathematical treatment of biological investigations is often valuable. As Arrhenius has pointed out, the expression of experimental results in a formula, or equation, shows their relation to known laws in a way which is otherwise very difficult or impossible to attain; one is then enabled to see, also, whether all the factors have been taken into account. "A moderate amount of mathematics will probably have to suffice for most of us, enough to be able" (and willing) "to understand and use the fundamental equations". A working knowledge of the principles and uses of the infinitesimal calculus, for example, and of simple applications of the laws of probability, is as desirable in a physiologist as it is essential in a physicist. "A word of caution may be allowed. Although an equation may express in one line what would require pages of verbal description, it must not be forgotten that it is, after all, but a kind of shorthand, and must never be permitted to serve in place of a clear conception of the process itself". (1st edition, p. 40.) The experimenter is always well advised to consider carefully the physical meaning of any equations that he may encounter—particularly those that he has developed himself.

I am grateful to the many authors and publishers who have given permission for reproduction of illustrations which are new to this edition. A great many of these, and all those which have been retained from the previous editions, have been re-drawn, so that they should illustrate more concisely the matters discussed in the text, or that the quality of reproduction should be improved and a uniform style maintained. I am indebted, also, to Dr. M. Grace Eggleton, who has not only read the proofs and made suggestions for improving obscure passages, but also prepared the index. But the most valuable of all my assistance has come, whether they knew it or not, from my colleagues and students in the course of discussion and instruction.

References to some text-books and monographs on physical chemistry, pure and applied to biological studies, the contents of which are relevant to many different chapters, are given on p. viii. Some books are suggested, also, which should be useful to those who wish to start, or continue, studies on mathematics and statistics.

L. E. BAYLISS

University College, London, 1958

GENERAL LITERATURE

Elementary Physical Chemistry. Lowry and Sugden (1952); Findlay (1955).

Biological Applications of Physical Chemistry. Hitchcock (1953); Bull (1951); West (1956); Wallwork (1956); Dawes (1956); Mansfield Clark (1952); Johnson, Eyring and Polissar (1954).

More Advanced Physical Chemistry. Moore (1956); Moelwyn-Hughes (1956); Guggenheim (1957); Guggenheim and Prue (1955); (and many others).

Physico-chemical Methods. Oster and Pollister (1955, 1956); Reilly and Rae (1940, 1948).

Mathematics. Fleming (1938); Mellor (1912); Kynch (1955); (*More advanced*) Jaeger (1951); (and many others).

Statistics. David (1953); Fisher (1954); (and many others).

ACKNOWLEDGEMENTS

For permission for diagrams based on copyright material we are indebted to the following:—

The Clarendon Press for Figs. 5.3, 5.4, 5.9 from Adam: *Physics and Chemistry of Surfaces*; The Faraday Society for Figs. 5.6, 5.8, 6.2 from *Transactions of the Faraday Society*; The Rockefeller Institute of Medical Research for Figs. 6.3, 7.5, 10.3 (upper), 10.8 from the *Journal of General Physiology*; the American Chemical Society for Figs. 6.5, 9.3 from the *Journal of the American Chemical Society*; the Royal Society for Fig. 6.6 from *Proceedings of the Royal Society*; the Editor for Fig. 6.10 from *Biological Bulletin*; Longmans, Green & Co. Ltd. for Figs. 7.2. 7.4 from Haldane: *Enzymes*; Cambridge University Press for Fig. 9.6 from Lea: *Radiations on Living Cells*; and Fig. 10.2 from Davson and Danielli: *Permeability of Natural Membranes*; Long Island Biological Association for Figs. 10.1, 10.7 from *Cold Spring Harbour Symposia on Quantitative Biology*; J. & A. Churchill Ltd. for Fig. 10.4 from Bayliss: *Modern Views on the Secretion of Urine*; Pergamon Press Ltd. for Figs. 10.5, 10.6 from *Progress in Biophysics and Biophysical Chemistry*; American Society of Biological Chemists Inc. for Fig. 7.3 from *Journal of Biological Chemistry*; University of Chicago Press for Fig. 9.3 from *Botanical Gazette*; American Society of Plant Physiologists for Fig. 9.3 from *Plant Physiology*; The Botanical Society of America for Fig. 9.3 from *American Journal of Botany*.

We are also indebted to The Royal Society of London for the use of an extract from an article by D. Keilin from *Proceedings of the Royal Society*, Vol. 98, series B, 1925.

CONTENTS

I

ENERGY

In almost every branch of science we are concerned above all with the changes that occur in the systems studied, or the changes that have occurred in the past, bringing the systems into the particular states and conditions which they have reached. This is true for physiology and experimental biology even more, perhaps, than for any other branch of science: one of the most striking characteristics of living organisms is their perpetual state of change; and, indeed, continued existence is impossible without continual change.

Now, in general, systems do not change unless *forces* act on them, as Newton made clear in his laws of motion. But even if forces are present, they will not necessarily produce changes; if they do, *work* is performed, the amount of work depending on the magnitude of the force and the amount of change produced. Further, if the conditions are such that work can be done, the system is said to possess *energy*, whether or not any work is, in fact, actually done; energy, indeed, is frequently defined as the "capability of doing work". Just as the systems studied can change in many different ways—in their pressure, volume, temperature, electric charge, chemical properties, and so forth—so are there many different ways in which work can be done, and many different forms of energy. Study of the sources of energy, and of the laws that govern its conversion from one form to another must, then, be one of the most important foundations of physiology, as well as of most other kinds of science. Such studies are fundamental in that they are not concerned with the particular kind of machinery by which the work is performed, or any particular conceptions as to the behaviour of molecules in chemical reactions, for example, or the mode of action and existence of living organisms. It is an universal belief, justified by experience, that the laws governing the exchanges of energy are obeyed in principle in whatever system we are concerned with, however elaborate it may be.

Before proceeding further, we may note that in every form of work and energy, we have an "intensity" factor and a "capacity" factor and the quantity of work or energy is given by the product of the two, provided, of course, that they are properly chosen and expressed in appropriate units. The work to be obtained from a stream of water depends both on the height

A

from which it falls and on the quantity of water flowing. A mere trickle, even from a considerable height, can do little work. The quantity of water is the capacity factor, and the height above sea level, or velocity is the intensity factor. In electrical energy, the intensity factor is electromotive force or potential difference, and the capacity factor is quantity of electricity or electric charge. In heat energy, the intensity factor is temperature, but the capacity factor is *not* quantity of heat, as measured in a calorimeter. This, although called "quantity" is, in fact, a measure of heat energy. Since the product of the intensity factor by the capacity factor must give the amount of heat energy, the capacity factor must be defined as the quantity of heat, divided by the temperature; this is called "entropy", and its nature and properties will be discussed later. Heat energy, as we shall see, has peculiar properties of considerable importance.

In the sources of power dealt with by the engineer, work is ordinarily done as a result of a fall in the intensity factor, without change in the capacity factor. Thus the same amount of water emerges from a hydro-electric power station as enters it, but at a smaller pressure. But work may also be performed by a system as a result of a change in the capacity factor, at a constant value of the intensity factor. This may occur, for example, in chemical reactions and at interfaces between immiscible substances.

It will be noticed that the intensity factors are what are called "strengths", whereas the capacity factors are of the nature of spaces or masses; the latter sum together when combined, the former do not. If a litre of water at 50° be added to a second litre of water at the same temperature, the energy content of the mixture will be twice that of a single litre, due to doubling the capacity factor; the intensity factor, temperature, on the other hand, is not altered. Similarly, if we have a condenser at a certain electrical potential, and connect it to another at the same potential, the total charge available will be the sum of the two separate charges, but the potential will be unaltered.

In all physico-chemical studies, and particularly in those concerned with the properties of energy, the term "system" will frequently be encountered. The word has, indeed, already been used, and could hardly be avoided without great inconvenience. According to Lewis and Randall: "Whatever part of the objective world is the subject of thermodynamic discourse is commonly called a system" (1923, p. 8). Use of the word, however, is not restricted to thermodynamics. A system is bounded by walls, or surfaces, which, however, are not necessarily physical entities, but may be mathematical abstractions; it may—and usually does—contain matter, but need not; it may be homogeneous, or it may consist of several different "phases", each of which is homogeneous and separated from one another by discontinuities; the matter within it may undergo changes of state, chemical reactions and so forth.

Any particular system which may be considered will thus have external surroundings; it is defined as "isolated" if it cannot exchange either matter or energy with its surroundings; as "closed" if it can exchange energy, in the form of heat or work, for example, but cannot exchange matter; and as "open" if it can exchange both matter and energy. Each of the phases in a heterogeneous system may, of course, be treated as a system in itself; these may be open systems, for example, even though the whole is closed or isolated. "Classical" thermodynamics is concerned chiefly with closed systems. Open systems are rather more difficult to deal with by thermodynamical methods, but are of particular interest to the biologist, since all living organisms are essentially open systems.

THE LAWS OF THERMODYNAMICS OR ENERGETICS

There are two great laws which define quantitatively the manner in which energy may change from one form to another. The first law states that while energy may be of many kinds, kinetic, thermal, chemical, electrical and so on, which can be converted into one another, there is never any gain or loss. The first law is thus known as the *"Law of Conservation of Energy"*.

The fact that energy can neither be created nor destroyed is a matter of universal experience: but it could not become so until such phenomena as light, electricity, and particularly heat, were recognised as forms of energy not essentially different from the more obvious and recognisable form, mechanical energy. The inclusion of heat is of particular importance, since in practice it is never possible to convert one form of energy into another without also generating some heat. Although Boyle and Hooke, in the latter part of the 17th century, had the idea that all forms of energy (as we now regard them) could be conceived as forms of mechanical motion, this was not generally accepted. In the 18th century, heat was regarded as an "imponderable fluid", and called "caloric"; electricity and light were other such fluids. By the close of the 18th century, however, the idea that any "fluid" could be without weight was already becoming inconsistent with experimental observation, and unattractive. The investigations of Count Rumford, moreover, at the end of the century showed that heat could be generated as a result of the performance of mechanical work (and not only, therefore, as a result of combustion processes) and that there was a quantitative relation between work and heat. It is of interest, incidentally, that Rumford's observations and measurements were made during, and as a result of, his concern with the practice of boring cannon. This quantitative relation, however, and the general conception of heat as a form of energy, was not firmly and finally estab-

lished until the work of Joule; and the idea of the conservation of energy
was first expressed by him in a classical paper which appeared in 1847.

The second law of thermodynamics may be stated in several different
ways; and in none of them is its meaning and significance as simple and
obvious as is that of the first law. As stated in one form, the law defines
limits to the extent to which a given amount of heat energy can be converted into mechanical work. As Nernst (1923) put it: "while external work
and the kinetic energy of moving bodies can be transformed into one
another completely and in many ways, and can also be converted into heat,
as by applying the brakes to a railway train in motion, the reverse change
of heat into work is only possible under certain conditions". In fact, only
a fraction of the heat available in the engine of the train can ever be converted into useful work for driving it. That heat had this peculiar property
was first realised by Carnot in 1824, but the second law of thermodynamics
was not properly established until the latter half of the 19th century. Study
of the relation between heat and mechanical work led to the development of
"thermodynamics", as is implied by the meaning of the word; the work of
Joule, Helmholtz, Clausius and Kelvin being of particular importance in
this development. Such a study was very relevant during the 19th century,
owing to the development of the steam engine and the application generally of mechanical power to industrial processes. But just as the first law
applies generally to all forms of energy and not only to heat and mechanical energy, so also can the second law be expressed in a more general
way. As put by Clausius, the second law states that heat will never pass
spontaneously from one object or system to another which is at a higher
temperature—a statement which is supported by universal experience.
But it is equally a matter of common observation that water flows downhill,
not uphill, for example, and that a motor-car tyre will deflate spontaneously
but will never pump itself up. These, and other similar observations,
suggest and illustrate a very general way of stating the second law of
thermodynamics; "A system will change of itself only if it can do work in
the process." As thus stated, the law not only covers the facts of common
observation, but may be extended to the less obvious problems of chemical
reactions, and is of great value in predicting which reactions will go
spontaneously and which will not.

Since the study of thermodynamics involves all kinds of energy, and
not only those implied in the strict meaning of the word, and its laws are
of universal application, there is some reason, particularly when we are
studying physical chemistry rather than engineering, for using the word
"energetics". In the late 19th and early 20th centuries, "energetics" was
commonly used in place of "thermodynamics", but it seems now to be
rather out of fashion. To the biologist, the word "thermodynamics" seems
particularly inappropriate. As we shall see, application of the second law

makes it quite certain that living organisms, however they may work, cannot possibly operate as heat engines.

"Free" and "Bound" Energy

The restriction set by the second law to the fraction of the heat energy which can be converted into mechanical work, led Helmholtz, in 1882, to distinguish between "free energy" and "bound energy". Of all the energy contained in a system, that part which can be converted into other forms of energy is "free", and that part which cannot, and is thus of no practical value, is "bound". The statement of the second law, given above, can thus be put into the form: "Free energy always decreases, if it possibly can, but never increases." This fact, derived from universal experience, is sometimes known as the *Principle of Carnot and Clausius*. It does not follow, of course, that if a process results in a diminution of free energy, it will invariably occur at a measurable rate. The descent of a heavy object from the top storey of a house to the bottom is attended by a diminution of free energy, but it will not occur unless the supporting floors are removed. The reaction between hydrogen and oxygen involves a diminution of free energy, but it does not occur at room temperature to a detectable extent unless started by a spark. The second law does tell us, however, that if all constraints are removed from the heavy object, it will travel downwards, not upwards, and that no kind of "triggering" will result in a spontaneous decomposition of water into hydrogen and oxygen at room temperature.

In practice, it is impossible to convert one form of energy into another without generating heat (we shall consider this in more detail later); part, at least, of this heat will be "bound", and cannot be converted into other forms of energy. We can thus express the second law in still another form: "Bound energy always tends to increase, but can never decrease." The term "bound energy" is now little used, but the concept of "free energy", and its distinction from other kinds of energy which a system may contain, is one of considerable importance; it will be found essential in all our subsequent applications of thermodynamics, or energetics, to physico-chemical problems.

The Condition of Equilibrium. Two systems are said to be in true and complete (or "thermodynamic") equilibrium with one another when the circumstances are such that there is no net transfer of matter or energy from one to the other, in spite of the fact that there is no constraint on such a transfer. This does not mean that there is no transfer at all from one system to the other, but that the rate of transfer in one direction is identical with that in the other; in fact, the absence of constraint is shown by the existence of such a reciprocal transfer. The same definition applies, also, to the condition that a single system shall be in equilibrium with its

surroundings, and to the condition that the various constituents of a
system shall be in equilibrium with one another. It is clear from what has
just been said that two such systems in equilibrium with one another must
possess the same amount of free energy; if they did not, there would be
some change from one to the other. In these circumstances, we can make
a small, or more strictly an infinitesimal, transfer of heat, for example, or
of actual molecules from one of the systems to the other, without affecting
the free energies, or performing any work during the transfer. This is an
important generalisation, and we shall find this definition of a state of
equilibrium being used repeatedly in subsequent chapters.

Thermodynamic Probability and Entropy

A natural, or spontaneous, change can be described as one which proceeds
from a less to a more probable state. This is, to some extent, a self-evident
statement, but useful deductions can be made from it, if we consider what
are the properties of a state that make it more or less probable.

Suppose we had a completely empty box and inserted a single molecule
into it. If we then divided the box into two equal parts, and examined one
of them, the chance of finding the molecule would be one-half—i.e. if
we made a very large number of such examinations, the number of occasions on which we found the molecule would be the same as the number
on which we failed to find it. If we put two molecules in the box, the
probability that both would be in the same part, according to the laws of
chance, would be $\frac{1}{2} \times \frac{1}{2}$ or $\frac{1}{4}$: and if there were N molecules, the chance
would be $(\frac{1}{2})^N$. In the circumstances dealt with in ordinary practice,
therefore, where N is very large, it would be extremely improbable to
find all the molecules in one half of the box; and the most probable condition is that there should be a uniform distribution throughout the box,
i.e. that there should be a maximum degree of what Willard Gibbs has
termed "mixed-up-ness", but which may also be called "thermodynamic
probability". This principle is of quite general application. A system of
any kind which is less "mixed-up" in one state than another is also less
"probable"; it will change from the one state to the other if it is allowed to.
Conversely, a system can only be brought into a more "organised" or less
"mixed-up" state if work is performed on it.

Now the thermodynamic probability of a system is also a measure of
its entropy content. The connection between this very general meaning of
the term "entropy" and its particular meaning as a measure of the capacity
factor in heat energy, is not immediately obvious. In a later section, some
particular cases will be discussed in which the connection can easily be
seen. For the moment, we will merely note that according to the kinetic
theory of gases, to be considered later, heat is an expression of the kinetic

energy of random motion of the molecules; this motion, being random, is more probable than an ordered, or directed, motion which is capable of performing external work. If we have a system which possesses free energy, therefore, it will always tend to change, if allowed to, in such a way as to increase its randomness, with the production of heat and an increase in entropy. Once the energy is in this random, more probable, state, it will not spontaneously re-organise itself into a less probable state; the second law of thermodynamics may be stated in the form: "Entropy will never spontaneously decrease."

Reversible and Irreversible Processes

The unrestrained flow of energy from a high potential to a low potential, is an irreversible process: the randomness, and entropy, of the system is increased, and no alteration of the conditions will reverse the flow unless an external source of energy is provided. If, on the other hand, the tendency for the system to change is always opposed to such an extent that the change is only just permitted, then a very small (infinitesimal in the limit) increase in the opposition will reverse the change. In such a reversible process (which, of course, will only proceed at an infinitesimal rate) the flow of energy is controlled and ordered, and there is no degradation into chaotic motion; entropy is not increased. It is only by the use of a reversible process, in conditions such that the system is in thermodynamic equilibrium, that the free energy of a system can be converted into work, and measured.

Lewis and Randall (1923) instance as the most nearly reversible process encountered in practice, the measurement of the E.M.F. of a battery by means of a potentiometer and sensitive galvanometer. By continually adjusting the potentiometer so that a just perceptible current flows out of the battery, it would be possible to make the battery do very nearly the theoretical maximum amount of electrical work, although it would obviously take a very long time. If the opposing potential were made too great, no current would flow from the battery and no work would be done; if there were no opposing potential at all, no useful work would be done in spite of the fact that a very large current would flow, since electrical work is measured as the product of the current and the potential difference. There would probably be a large dissipation of energy in the resistance of the connecting wires, but this would be in the form of heat, and the entropy of the system would increase.

The Conversion of Heat into Work

We are now in a position to show, simply, how our first statement of the second law of thermodynamics, which puts restrictions on the conversion of heat into work, is an inevitable consequence of the other, more general statements given later. All heat energy is not necessarily "bound", as is demonstrated by the successful functioning of innumerable heat engines. Let us, therefore, consider the passage of heat from a hot body at a temperature T_1 to a colder body at a temperature T_2, as from the boiler of a steam engine to the condenser. Since this is a process which would occur spontaneously, it may be used to perform work. If we wish to ensure that all the energy made available is converted into external work, we must perform the transfer of heat by a reversible process—an imaginary conception, of course, which cannot be realised in practice; but if this is done, the entropy of the system will be unchanged. Now since we are taking heat from the boiler, we must also be taking entropy, and this must be quantitatively transferred to the condenser. Obviously the quantity of heat added to the condenser, q_2, must be less than the quantity taken from the boiler, q_1, if the engine is doing any work; by the first law of thermodynamics, the difference between q_1 and q_2 must be equal to the work W. We see from this, incidentally, that the same change in entropy, ΔS, is produced by taking a quantity of heat q_1 from the boiler at a temperature T_1, and by adding a smaller quantity of heat q_2 to the condenser at a lower temperature T_2; a given change in entropy is produced by a smaller addition of heat at a low temperature than at a high. This, indeed, is only to be expected if entropy is the capacity factor in heat energy; as already remarked (p. 2) the quantity of heat added to or removed from a system is measured by the product of the change in entropy and the temperature at which the change is carried out. In our ideal heat engine, the amount of entropy added to the condenser, ΔS_2, is equal to that taken from the boiler, ΔS_1. Thus:

$$\Delta S_1 = \Delta S_2 \text{ or } \frac{q_1}{T_1} = \frac{q_2}{T_2} \text{ or } \frac{q_1 - q_2}{q_1} = \frac{W}{q_1} = \frac{T_1 - T_2}{T_1} \,. \qquad . \qquad 1.1$$

Thus, unless the temperature of the condenser T_2 is zero (absolute) only a part of the heat drawn from the boiler can be used for performing work. Nothing would, in fact, be gained by attempting to use a heat engine working down to the absolute zero of temperature, or indeed, any temperature less than that of the earth's surface. The second law of thermodynamics, as put by Clausius (p. 4 above), states that the heat absorbed by the condenser will never pass spontaneously into surroundings which are at a higher temperature; in order to keep the condenser cool, we should have to do work in order to take the heat out of it, and thus lose all the extra work provided by the engine.

Discussion of the factors affecting the efficiency of heat engines is of more concern to the engineer than to the physiologist. As already remarked, the study of energetics has been regarded as synonymous with that of thermodynamics largely because of the practical importance of heat engines. It is the

necessary connection between the "efficiency" of a heat engine and the difference in temperature over which it operates that demonstrates that living
organisms cannot be heat engines.

THE INEVITABLE INCREASE OF ENTROPY

In spite of the theoretical importance of reversible processes, it is obvious
that in practice, processes which involve a flow of energy will almost always
be irreversible; if they were not, no appreciable changes would be produced
in a finite time. If the heat engine, just discussed, were to work in an
irreversible manner (as it would have to, in practice), there would be a
gain of entropy, the quantity q_2/T_2 would be greater than the quantity
q_1/T_1, and the ratio of the work done $(q_1 - q_2)$ to heat drawn from the boiler
(q_1), or the efficiency of the engine, would be reduced.

It follows from this analysis, that no work can be obtained from the
heat energy of a system the whole of which is at the same temperature. If
there are any parts of the system which are not at the same temperature,
there will be a spontaneous tendency for these differences to be equalised,
with or without the performance of work. The system will then be "run
down". Thus if there is any increase of entropy in an isolated system as a
result of irreversible, or imperfectly reversible, changes, all forms of energy
which it may contain will eventually be converted into heat, and in the end,
the temperature will become equalised throughout. Entropy, therefore, is
a measure of "run-down-ness". This conception of entropy is of particular
value in connection with chemical reactions. If a reaction is allowed to
proceed spontaneously—i.e. irreversibly in the thermodynamic sense—
the entropy will increase; a maximum value will be reached when the
reaction has ceased, either because the reactants have disappeared, or
because a state of equilibrium has been attained. In both cases, the system
has "run down". This provides us, incidentally, with an alternative, and
sometimes more convenient, criterion for the condition of equilibrium;
not only is there equality between the free energies of the systems, or
components of the system, but the entropy of the whole system, or systems,
concerned reaches a maximum value.

In a fundamental paper published in 1865, Clausius formulated the two
laws of thermodynamics as follows:

I. The energy of the universe is a constant quantity.

II. The entropy of the universe is always striving to a maximum.

Lord Kelvin, at about the same time, referred to the fact that free
energy tends to a minimum, and entropy to a maximum, as the law of
"Dissipation of Energy".

Stationary (or Steady) States. Although, as just remarked, an isolated
system must eventually run down, a closed system can be supplied with

A*

energy, in the form, say, of heat, radiation, or mechanical work, from the surroundings. If the rate of supply of this energy is equal to the rate of performance of work by the system, together with the rate of production of entropy by irreversible processes, a *stationary, or steady, state* will be reached. The heat engine, just considered, is a closed system, since the working fluid—by implication, steam and water—passes from boiler to condenser and *vice versa* without loss to, or gain from, the surroundings. The engine will be in a steady state when the supply of heat to the boiler is equal to the sum of the work done by the engine, the heat given up to the condenser, and the heat "lost" as a result of the existence of irreversible processes.

With an open system, a stationary state will be reached only if, in addition, the gain of matter from the surroundings is equal to the loss of matter, not necessarily in the same physical and chemical state. The energy needed to compensate for the performace of work and the production of entropy can now be supplied by the matter, as a result, say, of chemical reactions. The boiler and condenser of the heat engine, by themselves, are open systems; it is obvious that in order that they should be in steady states, not only must the rate of supply, or removal, of heat be appropriate, but also the rate of supply of water or steam must be equal to the rate of evaporation, or condensation, respectively. Stationary states are thus fundamentally different from equilibrium states, since there is a continuous flow of energy (and perhaps matter) through the systems considered. The entropy content of the system does not reach a maximum value; but it can be shown that as a stationary state is approached, the rate of production of entropy falls to a minimum value determined by the general operating conditions.

INTERNAL ENERGY AND TOTAL ENERGY

It is convenient to imagine that any system with which we are concerned possesses a certain amount of "internal energy", to which we give the symbol E (some authors use the symbol U for the same quantity). The system may gain or lose internal energy, as a result, for example, of work being done on it or by it, or of heat being added to it or lost from it. In a general way, we may consider the internal energy to be made up of a number of components. First, there is the free energy, which we denote by G; then there is a quantity which we may refer to as "bound" energy, and measured by the product of the temperature, T and the entropy, S, changes in which, in certain circumstances, as we have seen, are equal to the quantity of heat added to, or taken from, the system; and lastly, since any change in volume or pressure of the system will be associated with the performance of external work, we include a quantity which is the product of the capacity factor, the volume V, and the intensity factor, the pressure p. Thus from the law of conservation of energy, we can write:

$$E = G + T.S - p.V \qquad . \qquad . \qquad . \qquad . \qquad 1.2$$

We use the symbol G to represent free energy since we are using it in the sense defined by Willard Gibbs. Helmholtz, when he first introduced the conception of free energy, did not specifically consider the term $p.V$ and included it with the free energy. The Helmholtz free energy (denoted by F) is thus a measure of the *maximum work* that can be done by the system; the Gibbs free energy is a measure of *net work*, apart from that due to changes in volume or pressure. In the applications of the laws of energetics to physiological systems (and indeed to most physico-chemical systems) it is the Gibbs free energy that is of most value, and it is thus generally used.

The negative sign in front of the term $p.V$ is apt to cause confusion. A decrease in either of the other terms can only result from the loss of energy from the system to the outside, or from the performance of work by it. But if this work is done by, say, a general expansion of the system, the term $p.V$ increases, in spite of the fact that the total energy content decreases; the negative sign puts this right.

This equation may also be written in the form

$$E + p.V = H = G + T.S \qquad . \qquad . \qquad . \qquad 1.2a$$

where H is a quantity known as the "heat content" or "enthalpy". As we have seen, if a system is allowed to run down freely and come into equilibrium with its surroundings the changes in its energy content will appear as heat. But if the change occurs at constant pressure (the commonest condition in practice) we cannot prevent the system from doing work—positive or negative—as a result of its changes in volume: the term $p.V$ therefore, is incorporated in the heat content. We shall make use of this equation for the heat content of a system when we consider the energetics of chemical reactions in the next chapter.

We cannot actually measure the total energy content of a system in any particular conditions, nor can we measure the free energy or entropy content: we can only observe, and measure, *changes* in these quantities, consequent on changes in the conditions. It is more useful, therefore, to put equation 1.2 in the form of its general differential equation, which gives us an expression relating changes in the internal energy to changes in each of the component parts, the remainder being held constant, i.e.

$$dE = dG + T.dS + S.dT - (p.dV + V.dp) \qquad . \qquad . \qquad 1.3$$

We may note here that, in accordance with convention, we add the prefix "d" to the symbol of any quantity when we wish to indicate that we are considering only a very small (strictly, infinitely small) change in the magnitude of that quantity. It is implied in this that we can make such an infinitesimal change without affecting the magnitudes of any other quantities which are, or may be, affected by larger changes: the effects produced by such a change, also, are taken to be directly proportional to the change, whereas the effects produced by larger changes may be very complex. Over a very short period of time, we may assume that the distance travelled by any moving object is proportional to the period of time considered, i.e. that the velocity is constant: over a long period of time, the distance travelled may take any value, according to the nature of the moving body. The prefix, Δ, which we met in an earlier paragraph is used when we wish to describe a change in the magnitude of a quantity which is usually small, but not infinitesimal.

The internal energy of a system may change as a result of changes in any of the different physical sources of energy with which we are acquainted —gravitational, as in hydraulic power, electrical, or chemical, for example. But, as already emphasised, whether these changes result in changes in free energy, and the performance of work, or in changes in entropy, and "degradation" of the energy into heat, depends on the conditions in which they occur.

We may now apply a set of restrictions to the system which we shall encounter frequently in subsequent analyses. The system considered is supposed to be at a uniform temperature and pressure, and is in complete equilibrium with its surroundings. In these circumstances, as we have seen, we can make small changes in the volume of the system, or transfer small amounts of heat to it or from it, without changing the free energy content. In the above equation (1.3), therefore, dG can be put equal to zero, and since by definition dp and dT are also both zero, we have:

$$dE = T.dS - p.dV \quad . \quad . \quad . \quad 1.4$$

If we subtract this equation from the general differential equation 1.3, we get:

$$dG = V.dp - S.dT \quad . \quad . \quad . \quad 1.5$$

Thus in these particular conditions, when we can make changes in pressure, temperature, etc. in a thermodynamically reversible manner, we have the following relations:

at constant temperature:

$$(\partial G/\partial p)_T = V \quad . \quad . \quad . \quad . \quad 1.5a$$

and, *at constant pressure*:

$$(\partial G/\partial T)_p = -S \quad . \quad . \quad . \quad . \quad 1.5b$$

Combining equation 1.5b with equation 1.2a,

$$(\partial G/\partial T)_p = (G - H)/T \quad . \quad . \quad . \quad 1.5c$$

which, by a simple mathematical operation, may be transformed to:

$$(\partial(G/T)/\partial T)_p = -H/T^2$$
or
$$(\partial(G/T)/\partial(1/T))_p = -H$$

. . . . 1.5*d*

Since entropy is a positive quantity, equation 1.5*b* means that the free energy content of a system falls as the temperature rises: a greater proportion of the total energy present might be considered as becoming "randomised", and so more "bound" and less "free". Equations 1.5*c* and 1.5*d* are two forms of the "Gibbs-Helmholtz" equation; use of this equation enables us, in certain conditions, to deduce changes in free energy, in a chemical reaction for example, from changes in the heat content— i.e. the heat of reaction, as will be discussed in the next chapter. We shall make use of equations 1.5*a* and 1.5*b* in Chapter 3 in order to relate the partial free energy, or activity, of the solvent to the osmotic pressure and freezing point of the solution, respectively.

The fact that these equations, defining the rate at which free energy changes with pressure and temperature, respectively, are derived on the assumption that both pressure and temperature are constant, may appear a little confusing. We are, however, concerned only with the infinitesimal changes in free energy which accompany infinitesimal changes in pressure and temperature; the ratio of the one to the other can be finite, and its value will depend on the particular values of temperature and pressure at which it is determined.

The above elementary, and somewhat superficial, account of the principles of energetics is intended to provide a general idea of the conceptions involved, and the basic principles from which relations, to be introduced later, of "practical" importance are derived. Those readers to whom these conceptions are unfamiliar are recommended to turn back to this section when, in later chapters, they encounter the "practical" applications. Those who wish to go into the subject more fully. and in a more rigorous manner, should consult the appropriate text-books, of which there are several devoted to the physico-chemical applications of energetics, rather than the engineering; all serious students of the subject should read the important book by Lewis and Randall (1923). For an introduction to the application of thermodynamic principles to irreversible processes, the book by Prigogine (1955) may be consulted; an adequate familiarity with "classical" thermodynamics is required.

LIFE AND ENERGY

The physiologist and experimental biologist, for whom this book is primarily intended, will be concerned with the relevance, if any, of the principles of thermodynamics, or energetics, to the existence and activities of living organisms. In so far as these organisms may be regarded as physico-chemical "engines", the relevance is indirect, through the application of the laws of energetics to all kinds of physico-chemical problems; discussion of these applications will make up a large part of the remainder of this book. But there are also some more general points of relevance which we may now consider briefly.

The two chief characteristics of living organisms are that they "metabolise" all the time, and require a supply of energy; and that they possess "organisation", or highly specific structures, in respect both of gross and microscopic morphology, and of the molecular constitution of the "protoplasm" within the living cells. When an organism dies, its organisation vanishes, and its metabolism ceases. Living organisms are thus highly "improbable" thermodynamically; they are by no means "mixed-up" or "run-down". It is possible, as we have seen, to build up an improbable system, such as a mixture of hydrogen and oxygen, which will only run down with extreme slowness. Living organisms, however, are not like this, and they run down rapidly if a suitable supply of energy is not available. The tendency of living systems to become disorganised, with an increase in entropy, therefore, is ordinarily just balanced by the supply of energy from the exterior, by means of which directed, organised, arrangements can be created. The changes that occur in living systems are, for the most part, not thermodynamically reversible, and we are concerned, not with conditions of equilibrium, but with stationary or steady states. It is true that many of the conclusions reached by thermodynamical methods apply only to reversible systems, and equilibrium conditions; they may not be applicable to living systems, and it is, indeed, necessary always to bear this in mind. But the fundamental principles of thermodynamics apply also to irreversible systems; no practical heat engine is thermodynamically reversible, but the laws of thermodynamics are not, in consequence, useless to engineers.

The energy needed by living organisms is, in the last analysis, obtained from the radiant energy of the sun by the activity of the green plants. These, however, convert the radiant energy into chemical energy, and it is this which is actually used by the living cells. The fundamental reaction which supplies this energy is the reduction of molecular oxygen to water, with an associated oxidation of certain foodstuffs. In ordinary circumstances, if we reduce oxygen by burning some combustible substance, heat is released; this heat could be used to perform the work necessary to preserve the organisation of the living cell, but, as we have seen, only a very small fraction of it would be useful unless there were large differences in temperature. Such differences do not occur in living organisms, and, in fact, could not occur without destroying the organisms. The chemical energy made available in the metabolic reactions must, therefore, be released largely as free energy; and its release and utilisation must be arranged in such a way that the processes are, to some extent at least, reversible in the thermodynamic sense. As already pointed out, energy can be transferred in a strictly reversible manner only when the system is in equilibrium (the application of this general principle to the particular case of chemical reactions will be demonstrated later). In living cells, the reduction of oxygen occurs, not in one rather violent reaction, but in a number of stages. This does not affect the total amount of free energy made available, but by taking the reaction through what appears to be a roundabout path, the free energy is released little by little, each stage can be made more nearly reversible than is the complete reaction, and there is less increase in entropy; the living cells are thus able to utilise a greater fraction of the free energy than they would otherwise be able to.

Since entropy is a measure of the probability of the system, the law that entropy will spontaneously tend to increase, will apply, strictly, only to large numbers of molecules. It has been suggested that it may not apply to such very small units as living cells. There is, indeed, a reasonable probability that the free energy of a very small system should spontaneously increase, or the entropy spontaneously decrease (as, for example, if all the constituent molecules were to move in the same direction at the same time). But this condition could only last for a very short time; the second law of thermodynamics is applicable even to a single molecule if considered over a period of time which is large compared with, say, the interval between collisions (a very minute fraction of a second). Moreover, even the smallest cell almost certainly contains quite a substantial number of individual units (of the order of 10^{10} molecules, for example), the exact number relevant to this problem depending on the form of energy considered.

It has been held, in the past, by some writers that there is a special form of energy found only in living systems, and called "vital" or "biotic" energy. Experimental evidence makes it necessary to suppose, nevertheless, that "vital" energy can be converted quantitatively into other forms of energy, chemical, electrical, thermal and so on, and *vice versa*; the principle of conservation of energy must be supposed to hold even here. We have, however, no means by which we can measure the intensity factor of "vital" energy, as, for example, we can measure electrical potential, or temperature. We may feel, intuitively, that the "higher" animals and plants are more "alive" than the "lower"—that we ourselves, for example, have a greater "vital" potential than a sea anemone, or an oak tree more than a sea-weed—but we cannot express the difference numerically. It may be well to remember, on the other hand, that it is not so very long since the concept of chemical potential has been given a precise meaning and methods of measuring it established. It is, of course, now generally accepted that one of the aims of experimental biology— using the word in its widest sense—is to describe "vital" phenomena in the same terms as are used to describe chemical and physical phenomena. But in chemistry and physics, the aim is to describe chemical, electrical, thermal and even gravitational energy in terms of the properties of certain fundamental "particles", of which the atoms are composed; the biologist, it would seem, might be allowed to add "vital" energy. The chief argument against introducing such an hypothesis, however, is that there does not seem to be any particular need for it.

Aristotle put forward the view that the characteristic of all living things was their "form" ($\epsilon\iota\delta\sigma\varsigma$). It is this which shows that they are living, and the nature of the "form" allows us to recognise one kind of organism from another. Now the "form" was considered to be closely related to, if not identical with, the proportions ($\lambda\sigma\gamma\sigma\varsigma$), and the activity ($\dot{\epsilon}\nu\dot{\epsilon}\rho\gamma\epsilon\iota\alpha$), of the living material; that is, with what we may call its "organisation". We now know that the material substance of which a living being is composed is in continual flux: very few of the molecules of which it is composed at any moment remain within it for the whole life-time. What constitutes the living being is not any particular material, but the orderly way in which ordinary material is put together, and the orderly sequence of changes which it undergoes. We are thus in agreement on this with Aristotle.

Further, that great body of physiological doctrine which was based on the teachings of Galen, held that living things only remained alive so long as they possessed an "innate heat": this was something entirely different from the "elemental heat" of ordinary experience. Jean Fernel in his "Physiology" (1542) wrote: " . . . is there not within all living things a heat which cherishes what they are, a heat which is even of the same nature as the sun's? Death is the extinction of this heat, which is the innate heat. The coldness of old age dominates the material heat, the elemental heat, which is of the temperament; but old age cannot, so long as there is life, overcome the innate heat itself." And again: "The innate heat is superior to the elemental heat. Elemental cold avails against elemental heat, but it avails nothing against this more excellent heat which is the innate heat of living things." (The translation from the Latin is that given in Sherrington's book on Fernel (1946).) Without the innate heat there can be no "total substance", and "total substance" is identical with Aristotle's "form". In modern terminology, we should say that without a supply of free energy (innate heat) from the sun, the organisation of living things breaks down, and the entropy (lack of "form") increases. The innate heat was believed to be concentrated in the heart—a view which was discredited by Harvey's observations, by the subsequent work of Hooke, and Lavoisier and by the whole development of modern physiology. Nineteenth century thermodynamics, also, introduced a new and better terminology, but the basic ideas are not very much changed.

MOLECULAR KINETIC ENERGY AND THE GAS LAWS

The properties of the various forms of energy, as described in terms of the "thermodynamical functions", free energy, entropy, and so forth, are independent of the physical and chemical nature of any particular material system which may be considered. They are, for this reason, generally related only indirectly to properties which can actually be observed and measured. We will now introduce some applications of these fundamental conceptions to actual material systems. We begin, as is conventional—and indeed necessary—by considering the behaviour of "perfect" gases and of "ideal" solutions.

In a gas the molecules are in ceaseless movement, and the space that they occupy, or rather the space occupied by their spheres of action, is very small compared with the space unoccupied. Any one molecule will travel in a certain direction until it meets another one. Both molecules will rebound and each will then move off again in a different direction and with a different velocity, until further collisions occur. The kinetic energy of any individual molecule will thus vary from moment to moment, but will have a mean value over a period of time. Similarly, the distance travelled between collisions will vary about a certain value, called the "mean free path". Again, although no two molecules will have quite the same kinetic energy at any given moment, there will be an average value of the kinetic energy of all the molecules in a large assembly. Further, according to the second law of thermodynamics, any two molecules, or particles, in a system which is internally in equilibrium, must possess the same amount of free energy. This particular application of the law is known as the *principle of equipartition of energy*. In a gas, therefore, which is at a uniform temperature and pressure, the *average* value of the kinetic energy of any one molecule must be the same as that of any other molecule.

Similar statements apply to liquids, with the exception that the molecules are in such close relation that the cohesive forces of attraction come into play much more powerfully. The molecules can, as it were, change partners, but they cannot move right away from each other; the mean free path is very much smaller than it is in gases. In solids, the molecular movement must be supposed to be confined to oscillation about a mean position. The molecules of solids do not continually change their places, as in gases and liquids, and the mean free path is zero. In the ideal monatomic gases, the molecules possess no energy in any form other than that of translation from one point to another; they are supposed to behave like billiard balls (an old-established analogy) in violent motion, bouncing off one another—and off the walls of the containing vessel—when they hit, but occupying a negligible fraction of the space and having no attraction for each other. In other kinds of gas, and in liquids, the molecules also possess energy in other forms, i.e. of rotation and oscillation, both of themselves and of their constituent atoms, as well as that due to their mutual attraction; and in solids, all the energy of the molecules is in these forms, and there is no energy of translation.

Now the pressure exerted by a gas results from the bombardment of the walls of the container by its molecules. The pressure will thus depend on the kinetic energy of translation, as may be seen from the following considerations. Suppose we have a gram-molecule of a gas in a cube whose sides have a length l; there will be N molecules (the Avogadro number), and if the mass of each molecule is m, the molecular weight, M, will be $N.m$. Suppose, to begin with, and for simplicity, that all the molecules have the same velocity c. Although they must be travelling in all possible directions, we may imagine them to be divided into three equal groups, each group moving straight across from one of the sides of the cube to the other (this is equivalent to resolving the motion of each molecule into three components, and adding up the components of all the molecules). Each time a molecule hits the side, it suffers a change of momentum of $2.m.c$; it travels a distance $2l$ between each hit, so that the frequency of hits is $c/2l$. The total force acting on the side of the cube is thus

$$(N/3).(c/2l).(2m.c);$$

and this force, divided by the area l^2 is the pressure exerted p. We thus have:

$$p = \frac{N.m.c^2}{3l^3} = \frac{N.m.c^2}{3V} = \frac{1}{3} \cdot \frac{M.c^2}{V} \quad . \qquad . \qquad . \quad 1.6$$

V being the volume of the cube. The total kinetic energy of all the molecules is given by: $E_{tr} = N.m.c^2/2$. As already pointed out, however, the molecules do not in fact all have the same velocity, or the same kinetic energy. If $\bar{E}_{tr}$ is the *average* value of the kinetic energy of the molecules in one gram-molecule of the gas, we may write:

$$\bar{E}_{tr} = M.\bar{c}^2/2 \quad . \qquad . \qquad . \qquad . \quad 1.7$$

where $\bar{c}^2$ is the mean value of the square of the velocity ($\bar{c}$ being the "root mean square velocity") of the molecules. Equation 1.6 may thus be written:

$$p = \frac{1}{3} \cdot \frac{M.\bar{c}^2}{V} \text{ or } p.V = M.\bar{c}^2/3$$

and inserting equation 1.7, we get:

$$p.V = 2.\bar{E}_{tr}/3 \quad . \qquad . \qquad . \qquad . \quad 1.8$$

Now the kinetic theory of gases states that the average kinetic energy of the molecules depends only on the temperature of the system. It is clear from equation 1.8, then, that the product $p.V$ must also depend only on the temperature.

It is interesting to note that, although the first actual publication of the kinetic theory was made, independently, by Kroenig in 1856 and by Clausius in 1857, a complete development of the theory had been sent to the Royal Society in 1845 by J. J. Waterston. This paper was not printed until 1892, having been found by Lord Rayleigh in the archives.

The Gas Laws. Boyle's law states that the volume of a given mass of gas is inversely proportional to the pressure, if the temperature remains constant; and the law of Charles (or of Gay-Lussac) states that the volume is proportional to the absolute temperature if the pressure remains constant. In symbols, we may combine these two laws, and write:

$$V = R \cdot \frac{1}{p} \cdot T \qquad \text{or } p.V = R.T \qquad . \qquad . \qquad . \qquad 1.9$$

where T is the absolute temperature, and R is a numerical quantity called the "gas constant"; its value depends on the units in which the other factors are expressed, and will be found in the Table of Constants on page 495 of this book. The fundamental gas laws, of Boyle and Gay-Lussac, are thus a direct consequence of the kinetic theory of gases; although they were, of course, actually discovered empirically. These same laws were shown by van't Hoff to apply to dilute solutions, the pressure concerned now being the osmotic pressure, and the volume being the volume of the solution which contains one gram-molecule of the solute. This will be considered further in Chapter 3. By combining equations 1.8 and 1.9, we see that the average energy of translation, per gram-molecule of gas, $\bar{E}_{tr}$, is given by:

$$\bar{E}_{tr} = 3RT/2 \qquad . \qquad . \qquad . \qquad . \qquad 1.10$$

Avogadro's Hypothesis. Suppose we have a confined space containing two different kinds of molecule; let the mass of each kind of molecule be m_1 and m_2 respectively, and the root mean square velocities be $\bar{c}_1$ and $\bar{c}_2$. Then according to the principle of equipartition of energy, the average kinetic energy of one kind of molecule must be equal to that of the other kind, i.e.:

$$m_1 \bar{c}_1^2 / 2 = m_2 \bar{c}_2^2 / 2$$

Moreover, suppose that the number of molecules in a gram-molecule is N_1 for one kind, and N_2 for the other kind. Since both kinds are supposed to be together in the same space, they must be at the same pressure, and the product $p.V$ must be the same for both. Thus the average kinetic energy of all the molecules in a gram-molecule, denoted $\bar{E}_{tr}$ above, must be the same for both (equation 1.8), and consequently:

$$N_1 m_1 \bar{c}_1^2 / 2 = N_2 m_2 \bar{c}_2^2 / 2$$

and thus: $N_1 = N_2$, and Avogadro's hypothesis, that the number of molecules in a gram-molecule is a constant, independent of the nature of the molecules, follows necessarily from the kinetic theory of gases.

The simple gas laws, of Boyle and Gay-Lussac, are only approximations, applying to "perfect" gases and "ideal" solutions. If the behaviour of gases is examined over a wide range of pressure, and particularly if they are made to approach their liquefying points, the simple gas laws no longer apply. As the molecules come closer together, the actual space that they occupy is no longer negligible, and the coherence forces of attraction between them becomes large enough to be significant; additional factors must therefore be introduced, and we get the van der Waals equation:

$$(p + a/V^2)(V - b) = RT \ . \qquad . \qquad . \qquad . \quad 1.11$$

where a/V^2 represents an apparent additional pressure due to the intermolecular forces, and b represents the effective volume occupied by the molecules. Similarly, in an "ideal" solution, it is implied that the solute molecules have no particular interactions with each other or with the solvent molecules. This is not, in general, true, and the simple law fails when applied to solutions which are not very dilute; this will be discussed more fully in Chapter 3.

Returning now to equation 1.3 (p. 11), relating changes in internal energy to changes in free energy and entropy, we see that if the system considered is a "perfect" gas or an "ideal" solution, the product $p.V$ is constant, at constant temperature; the quantity $(p.dV + V.dp)$ is thus zero. But in other systems in general, $p.V$ is not constant (as, for example, in most gases in practice, and in solutions which are not extremely dilute), owing to the existence of intermolecular and interatomic forces; these, therefore, may be regarded as contributing to the internal energy of the system.

The Free Energy Change and Work Done in Compressing a Gas. Suppose that we take a volume V of a gas at a pressure p, and compress it so that its volume is diminished by a minute fraction of its original volume, that is by dV. Let us compress it by means of a piston working in a cylinder of cross-sectional area A, moving through a distance dl. Now the work done is equal to the product of the force exerted by the distance moved; this is $p.A.dl$. But $A.dl = dV$, so that the work done, dW, is $p.dV$. Further, if we start with one mole of gas, occupying a volume V_2, and diminish the volume to V_1, the total work done, W, is the sum of all the minute portions, $p.dV$, between the limits of these two volumes. In the notation of the infinitesimal calculus:

$$W = \int_{V_1}^{V_2} dW = \int_{V_1}^{V_2} p.dV$$

(The symbol $\int$ is a lengthened "s", the first letter of "sum" and is used to indicate that we are making a summation of an infinite number of infinitesimal quantities.) This relation is perfectly general, and applies to any system, whatever its physical and chemical properties. We can evaluate it, however, only if we know how the pressure varies with the volume in the conditions considered. If we are considering a perfect gas, and suppose, for simplicity, that the temperature is kept constant, we have, from equation 1.9, $p = RT/V$, and hence:

$$W = RT \int_{V_1}^{V_2} \frac{dV}{V}$$

Inserting the value of this integral—a matter of straightforward mathematics—we get:

$$W = RT \ln(V_2/V_1) \quad . \qquad . \qquad . \qquad . \quad 1.12$$

or alternatively:

$$W = RT \ln(p_1/p_2) \text{ (from 1.9)} \quad . \qquad . \qquad . \quad 1.12a$$

As applied to an "ideal" solution, we replace the volume V containing one mole of the gas, by the reciprocal of the concentration, c, the number of moles in unit volume of solution. Hence we have:

$$W = RT \ln(c_1/c_2) \quad . \qquad . \qquad . \qquad . \quad 1.13$$

These equations will be found to be of considerable value, since it may be shown, in some cases, that a component of a system is in equilibrium with a gas phase containing this same component at a certain pressure; the change in free energy of this component when the system changes from one state, or condition, to another, must then be equal to the work done in changing its pressure in the gas phase in such a way that equilibrium is maintained. This, of course, follows from the definition of equilibrium given above (p. 5). We shall make use of this principle, and of equation 1.12a in the next chapter in order to estimate the free energy changes of the components of a solution.

The Entropy Change when a Gas Expands. From the first law of thermodynamics, a gas which expands and does work must lose a corresponding amount of energy. If the gas is a "perfect" one, the only source of this energy is the random motion of the molecules; thus if it is not supplied with heat from an external source, the kinetic energy of the molecules, and the temperature, will be reduced. Conversely, if heat is supplied in such a quantity q that the temperature remains constant, we shall have:

$$q = W = RT \ln(p_1/p_2)$$

Thus the change in entropy, ΔS, consequent on the expansion of one mole of a gas at constant temperature, is given by:

$$\Delta S = q/T = R.\ln(p_1/p_2) = R.\ln(V_2/V_1) \quad . \qquad . \quad 1.14$$

Now a gas in a vessel at a finite pressure will always expand into another vessel at a lower pressure if allowed to. This, as pointed out on

p. 6 above, is associated with an increase in the "probability" of the system. In general, therefore, the increase in entropy when a gas expands may be regarded as an expression of the increase in thermodynamic probability. In this particular case, moreover, we can readily show how the entropy change is related to the probability change. We saw on p. 6 above, that the probability of finding all N molecules in one-half of the box was $(\frac{1}{2})^N$, while that of finding them evenly distributed in the whole box was very nearly 1. If, in a more general case, we allowed the gas to expand from a volume V_1 to a volume V_2, similar reasoning shows that the ratio of the probabilities in the two conditions is:

$$P_1/P_2 = (V_1/V_2)^N \quad \text{or:} \quad \ln P_2 - \ln P_1 = N \ln.(V_2/V_1) \qquad . \quad 1.15$$

Comparison of this equation with equation 1.14 above, shows that

$$\Delta S = \frac{R}{N}(\ln P_2 - \ln P_1) \qquad . \qquad . \qquad . \quad 1.16$$

N now being the Avogadro number. The change in entropy is thus proportional to the change in the logarithm of the probability. This relation is, in fact, quite a general one, and is not limited to the particular example of the expansion of a perfect gas.

That entropy may be regarded either as a measure of the "randomness" of the system or as a measure of the capacity factor of heat energy, may also be seen in the changes of state between solid and liquid and between liquid and gas. In a solid, particularly a crystalline solid, the molecules are arranged in an orderly manner, and there is very little random movement; in a liquid the molecules can move about, relative to one another, in any direction; and in a gas, the motion of the molecules is almost entirely random and erratic, as already emphasised. Thus, from this point of view, we should expect an increase of entropy when a substance changes from the solid state to the liquid state, and a further increase when it changes from the liquid state to the gas. From the point of view of heat energy, we find that in order to change the state of a substance, we must add heat—the "latent heat" of fusion or evaporation, respectively. The addition of this heat does not raise the temperature of the substance, so long as the change of state has not been completed; since the intensity factor (temperature) is constant, the capacity factor (entropy) must increase.

MATHEMATICS IN PHYSIOLOGY

It will have become apparent already that little progress can be made in the study of the physico-chemical foundations on which that of biological phenomena must, in the end, be based, without some knowledge of mathematics. And even when we study the biological phenomena themselves, mathematics in some form will sooner or later be needed for their interpretation. This, perhaps is more obvious when experimental and quantitative methods are used, rather than observational and descriptive, but is by no means confined to them.

For those who are not sufficiently familiar with the subject, a little explanation may be useful at this point. The expression deduced in the previous section for the work done in compressing a gas (equation 1.12) contains a logarithmic term. Such logarithmic terms turn up in a great many phenomena, both in pure physical chemistry and in physiology, and in nearly all cases they arise from the fact that the process is one in which the "driving force", and the rate at which the quantity studied changes at any moment, is proportional, directly or inversely, to itself; or in other words, the rate depends on how much of the process has already been completed. In compressing a gas, the work needed to cause the same actual diminution in volume increases the more the gas has already been compressed; or, looked at from another point of view, the work needed in each successive step depends on the result of the preceding step. The rate of increase of money lent at compound interest similarly increases progressively as the capital sum becomes larger, and for this reason, the general law describing this kind of process was called by Kelvin the "*compound interest*" law.

If, in general, we are interested in how one quantity, y, changes when we vary another quantity, x, the "compound interest" law, in mathematical terms, states that each small change in x, dx, produces a change in y, dy, which is proportional to the product of dx and the value of y at that moment, i.e. $dy = A.y.dx$, or $A.dx = dy/y$. Both y and x may increase together, or y may decrease as x increases; the constant A may have either a positive or a negative value. The full equation relating y to x is then derived from the differential equation describing the relation between very small changes in the two quantities, by the mathematical process of integration. It is here that the logarithm comes in, since the differential coefficient of the logarithm of y to the base e (written $\ln y$) is $1/y$, so that $d(\ln y) = dy/y$; conversely, therefore, the integral of dy/y is $\ln y$. Thus, if we perform the integration between the limits y_1 and y_2, we have:

$$A.x = (\ln y_2 - \ln y_1) = \ln (y_2/y_1) \qquad . \qquad . \qquad 1.17$$

This may also be written in the form: $e^{A \cdot x} = y_2/y_1$, commonly, and more conveniently, written: $\exp (A.x) = y_2/y_1$, particularly when the exponent is a complicated expression. The equation describing the compound interest law, may thus be considered either as a logarithmic one, or as an exponential one.

The quantity e, chosen as the base of natural logarithms is one of the most important in mathematics. It is defined as the limiting value of the quantity $\left(1+\dfrac{1}{n}\right)^n$ when n is made infinitely large, and, by the use of the binomial expansion, can be expressed as the sum of an infinite series. The value of e can be obtained to as many places of decimals as required, and may ordinarily be taken as 2·72. If we expand $\left(1+\dfrac{1}{n}\right)^{n.x}$ or e^x, we get an expression which is identical with the expansion of $\left(1+\dfrac{x}{n}\right)^n$; and accordingly, the limit of the quantity $\left(1+\dfrac{x}{n}\right)^n$, when n becomes infinite, may be identified with e^x. It is sometimes convenient to develop an equation containing an exponential or logarithmic term by starting with such an infinite series, rather than with a differential equation, as in the previous paragraph. Two examples of this will be given in Chapter 8.

A further useful property of the exponential function is that $d(e^x)/dx = e^x$—i.e. the differential coefficient of an exponential function is identical with the function itself. It can be shown, also, that $d(\log x)/dx = (1/x)\log.e$, whatever base may be used for the logarithms, so that if we take e as the base, the arbitrary constant, $\log e$, vanishes. If, as is more usual in practice, we use logarithms to the base 10, we must divide them by $\log_{10}e$, i.e. by 0·4343, or multiply them by 2·30.

A very simple experiment to demonstrate these relationships can be performed in any laboratory. A capillary tube is fitted to an ordinary 50 ml. burette, its size being chosen so that the burette takes a couple of minutes or so to empty. It is best to take a fairly long capillary of relatively wide bore. The outlet end of the capillary is brought up so as to be level with the lowest graduation on the burette. The rate of emptying at various degrees of filling is first measured by finding the time taken by the meniscus to fall from 0 to 1 ml.; 10 to 11 ml.; 20 to 21 ml.; and so on. The rate of emptying will be found to be proportional to the volume left in the burette, and if one is plotted against the other, a straight line will be obtained. We thus infer that $dV/dt = k.V$, or $dV/V = k.dt$, where V is the volume in the burette at any moment. Next, the rate of flow is integrated experimentally by finding the total quantity which will flow out in 5, 10, 20, 40 seconds, or other convenient time units, starting each time with the burette filled. The logarithm of the volume remaining in the burette after any given time will be found to be proportional to the time that has elapsed since the flow started, i.e. that $\log V = k.t$. The results of the mathematical process of integration are thus confirmed experimentally.

RADIANT ENERGY AND THE QUANTUM THEORY

Before proceeding further, there is one general property of the exchange of energy from one form to another that must be discussed. In ordinary cases of chemical combination, as is well known, additions are made by not less than one atom at a time; similarly, electric charges on ions are added or removed by units of one electron at a time. Energy, also, is exchanged in discrete units, known as *quanta*, but these are not necessarily all of the same size. Fortunately the discontinuous nature of energy exchanges, although of fundamental importance, can often be neglected; the conclusions reached in the previous sections are valid, in spite of the fact that no account has been taken of the existence of quanta. The quantum theory, however, cannot be neglected when considering energy exchanges in single atoms, and, above all, when considering energy exchanges between matter and radiation.

Energy in the form of radiations can be emitted and absorbed by material bodies, in appropriate conditions, with increase or decrease in their internal energies; the increase in internal energy consequent on the absorption of radiation, as might be expected, will usually be followed by a release of free energy, by an increase in entropy, or more usually, by both together, according to circumstances. This will be discussed more fully in Chapter 8. At this point, however, we may note that classical theory predicted either that there could be no equilibrium at all between matter and radiation, or that practically all the radiant energy emitted by a material body would be concentrated in radiation of very short wave-length, whatever was the temperature of the body. Both of these conclusions are manifestly at variance with experimental observation; there is equilibrium between matter and radiation, and the maximum amount of radiation occurs at a wave-length which becomes smaller as the temperature of the radiating body becomes greater. This difficulty, as well as others of a somewhat different nature, was got over by Planck, who in 1901, suggested that radiant energy was emitted in *quanta*; the amount of energy in each quantum being proportional to the frequency (inversely proportional to the wave-length) of the radiation that is emitted or absorbed. If ϵ is the amount of energy in the quantum, and v is the frequency of the radiation, then $\epsilon = h.v$, where h is a universal constant. If, therefore, energy is emitted from a hot body in quanta, then the total energy in the radiation of very long wave-lengths (low frequencies) will be small, since the quanta are small; and the total energy in the radiation of very short wave-lengths (high frequencies) will also be small, for the very reason that the quanta are so large that there is only a small chance that the thermal energy of any of the molecules will, even momentarily, reach a sufficiently large value for a quantum to be emitted. In this way, the observed maximum in the curve relating the distribution of energy with wave-length, and its dependence on the temperature of the radiating body, can be accounted for.

It is a matter of experimental observation that atoms and simple molecules can only absorb, or emit, radiation at certain definite frequencies; their emission and absorption spectra consist of a number of discrete lines. This implies, in accordance with the quantum theory, that the internal energy of an atom can only change in a series of discrete jumps, from one "level" to another. The restriction, moreover, applies to the changes in internal energy that are brought about by any means, including those which occur when atoms combine to form molecules. We shall return to this in the next chapter. In a complex molecule, there is additional energy associated with the various modes of vibration and oscillation of the constituent atoms and groups of atoms with respect to one another; this, again, must in each case change discontinuously, but in general the jumps, or quanta, are smaller and more numerous than those associated with changes in the energy "levels" of the atoms. The emission and absorption spectra of complex molecules usually consist of broad bands, rather than distinct lines.

The kinetic energy of translation of the molecules of a gas is associated with quanta that are ordinarily so small as to be negligible. The frequency corresponding to the maximum of the energy distribution curve (and thus the size of the quanta) increases in proportion to the absolute temperature. At the ordinary temperature of our surroundings, this frequency is about 1/20 of that of, say, sunlight; and for most purposes, the finite size of the quanta becomes important only when the frequency becomes even greater than that of sunlight. Moreover, the total amount of energy radiated per unit time increases as the fourth power of the absolute temperature; at ordinary temperatures practically all the energy remains associated with the atoms and molecules, and is not radiated. Thus the interchange of energy between molecules is sensibly continuous; in the kinetic theory of gases, and the principle of the equipartition of energy among the various directions of translation, and types of rotation and oscillation of which the atoms and molecules are capable (the various "degrees of freedom"), the quantum theory is ignored. If, however, we cool a substance to a very low temperature, not far from the absolute zero, the total amount of energy within it falls to a very low value, and the finite size of the quanta becomes of increasing importance; the average content of each atom or molecule is of the same order of size as the quantum, even though this, of course, has become very small, and at any moment a substantial fraction will contain no energy at all. By application of the quantum theory, in fact, it is predicted that the specific heat of an element per gram atom (the "atomic heat") will fall as the temperature is reduced; this is observed experimentally, but is not predicted by the classical theory of continuous and smooth exchanges of energy.

LITERATURE

Doctrine of Energy—Historical. van't Hoff (1901); Ostwald (1912); Nernst (1923).

Thermodynamics, Energetics. Lewis and Randall (1923); Butler (1946); Glasstone (1956); Prigogine (1955); Guggenheim (1957); Wenner (1941).

2

CHEMICAL REACTION

In chemical reactions, certain "bonds" between the various atoms which unite them into molecules are ruptured, and fresh ones are formed; in this process, some energy is absorbed, and a greater or less amount is then released. The importance of the energy made available in chemical reactions for the growth and maintenance of living organisms has already been emphasised. Of the energy used to drive the many and various machines which are essential to modern civilised life, moreover, all but a small part is derived from chemical energy; in these, with negligible exceptions, the chemical energy is first converted into heat, with the result that only a fraction can then be further converted into mechanical, electrical or chemical work, as has already been discussed. Chemical energy, however, may be transformed into other forms of energy without passing through the form of heat. The primary battery converts chemical energy directly into electrical energy, and this, by means of a motor, may be converted into mechanical work. In the living world, mechanical work is performed by means of the activity of muscles and the like, and this, also, is derived directly from chemical energy; muscles are not heat engines—a fact which was familiar to Fick as long ago as 1882—although heat is unavoidably produced by them, and the "efficiency" is, indeed, much the same as that of modern heat engines. Even more important, perhaps, is the fact that in living organisms, the chemical energy released in one reaction is used directly to perform chemical work in "driving" another reaction.

As with other forms of energy, the quantity of chemical energy available will be determined by the product of a "capacity" factor and an "intensity" factor. The capacity factor is clearly the quantity of a substance which takes part in a reaction, expressed, of course, in terms of its equivalent, or combining weight. The intensity factor may be termed the "chemical affinity", although the name is sometimes used rather vaguely. Willard Gibbs, in 1878, introduced the term "chemical potential"; the chemical potential of some particular substance, in any given conditions, being defined in terms of its free energy content, per gram-molecule, as will be discussed more fully in a later section. The chemical affinity of one substance for another, may then be defined in terms of the total change of chemical potential that occurs when the two substances react.

In 1854, Thomson suggested that the chemical affinity might be identified with the amount of heat produced during the reaction, and this was supported in 1867, by Berthelot. But the fact that there are many reactions which proceed spontaneously, and thus, presumably with a reduction in the internal chemical energy, and yet *absorb* heat from the surroundings (i.e. have a negative heat of reaction) proves this suggestion to be unsound. It was largely due to the emphasis of van't Hoff, in 1883, that the chemical affinity became identified with the change in free energy of the system, and not with the heat of reaction. This, of course, is in accordance with the second law of thermodynamics, as expressed in the Principle of Carnot and Clausius (Chapter 1, p. 5).

The terms "exothermal" and "endothermal" for reactions in which heat is evolved, or absorbed, respectively, are well known. Coryell, in 1940, pointed out that in addition it would be useful to have terms that describe whether a reaction is accompanied by an absorption, or a release, of free energy; and he suggested that the terms "endergonic" and "exergonic" would be suitable. We shall frequently make use of these terms in later chapters.

CHEMICAL AFFINITY

From general principles, it will be clear that the "affinity" of one atom for another, and the stability of the molecule which is formed if, and when, they combine, will be determined by the relation of the internal energy of the molecule to the sum of the internal energies of the two atoms. A stable molecule will only be formed if there is a substantial reduction in the internal energy, and release of energy to the surroundings; this same amount of energy would have to be supplied to the molecule in order to make it break up into the atoms. We must first consider briefly, therefore, the internal structures of various kinds of atom, and the way in which the structure affects the energy.

Bohr, in 1913-15, put forward the conception, now generally accepted, that an atom consists of a small heavy positively charged nucleus, surrounded by a cloud of negatively charged electrons. In 1921-22 he further specified the number and arrangement of these electrons according to the position of the atom in the periodic table, and thus according to its physical and chemical properties. Each electron is present on one of several shells, the outermost one containing up to eight, and the remainder being fitted into inner shells according to a definite scheme which need not concern us here. The lightest atom, hydrogen, contains only one electron; the next, helium, contains two, both on the same shell; next comes lithium, with two on an inner shell and one on an outer. Continuing in this way along the top line in the periodic table, we come to fluorine with two electrons on the inner shell and seven on the outer, and finally to neon, with two on the inner shell and the full complement of eight on the outer. With the next element, sodium, a third shell is begun, containing one electron, and so on. As the total number of electrons to be included becomes greater, and the atoms heavier, the maximum number in the outer shells is increased, at first to 18 and then to 32; but this maximum is not attained in every case before a new shell is begun. All the elements in any one group of the periodic table have certain chemical properties in common; these properties are associated with the number of electrons on the outermost shell, all those in any one group containing the same number; lithium, sodium and potassium, for example, all containing one, and fluorine, chlorine and bromine all containing seven.

Bohr originally supposed that each electron moved round the nucleus in a certain *orbit*, the possible orbits in each atom being defined by a set of four *quantum numbers*; (1) the *principal* (n) which must be a small integer, and which is identical with the number of the shell, the innermost being 1, the next 2, and so on, up to 7, the number in the heaviest atoms; (2) the *subsidiary* or *azimuthal* (l) which may be any integer from 0 up to $(n-1)$, so that the larger is the principal quantum number, the more subsidiary numbers there are; (3) the magnetic (m) which may be any integer between $+l$ and $-l$, including 0; and (4) the "*spin*", which can have only one of two values, denoted $+\frac{1}{2}$ and $-\frac{1}{2}$ respectively. Each orbit is associated with a definite amount of energy, determined by its quantum numbers (hence the use of the word quantum), and it is obvious that the total number of possible electronic configurations, and thus of possible "energy levels" in the heavier atoms is very large. In the ordinary, or "ground" state, the electrons take up those orbits which lead to the atom containing the least amount of internal energy. But the atom may become "excited", by being raised sufficiently in temperature, by being placed in an adequate electric field, or by absorption of radiant energy, and an electron then moves into a new orbit with greater energy; on returning to the ground state, the energy is emitted as radiation with a wave-length determined, according to the quantum theory, by the magnitude of the energy change associated with the electron "jump".

One of the earliest justifications of Bohr's theory was the way in which it accounted for the main lines in the spectra of hydrogen and of ionised helium; in these, there is only one shell and only one electron in the shell, and thus only the principal quantum numbers are involved. The spectra of the more complex atoms have a "fine structure" which corresponds to jumps between energy levels determined by the subsidiary numbers, as well as the principal numbers.

The way in which the total number of electrons in an atom (which must be equal to the "atomic number") is divided among the various shells, is laid down by the *exclusion principle* of Pauli, enunciated in 1925.

This states that in any one atom (or molecule) no two electrons may be in identical states, as defined by all four quantum numbers. Taking into account the limitations to the possible values of the various numbers, it is possible to deduce immediately the maximum number of electrons which can be accommodated in each shell.

Only a few years after the Bohr theory was established, it became clear that just as light waves, from the point of view of energetics, behave as particles, each containing one quantum of energy, so, conversely, do electrons, and even atoms, behave like waves. One consequence of this is that it is impossible to define precisely the position and velocity of an electron at any given moment; one can only describe certain regions where it is most likely to be—a limitation which is embodied in the *uncertainty principle* of Heisenberg. We cannot, strictly, define orbits in which electrons move; but we can use the same quantum numbers to describe *orbitals* which define the probabilities that electrons should be in certain regions. The concept that both matter and radiation could behave either as particles or as waves, led to the establishment of the subject of wave mechanics; and in 1926, Schrödinger developed his fundamental "wave equation". This relates the parameters defining the various electronic orbitals to the energy levels of an atom and the masses and electric charges of the electrons and the nucleus. From the mathematical nature of the equation, the discontinuous nature of the changes in the energy levels and the limitations to the possible values of the quantum numbers, defining the orbitals, follow immediately. What had previously been somewhat arbitrary assumptions, became a necessary consequence of the quantum theory and of the properties of electrons as both particles and waves. The importance of the wave equations to a discussion of chemical affinity will appear below.

VALENCY

The property which defines the capacity of an atom to combine with one or more other atoms, and which limits the nature of these other atoms, is its *valency*. As ordinarily used, the word "valency" describes the number of chemical "bonds", by which the atom considered can be attached to other atoms. But, from the point of view of chemical affinity, we are concerned also with the magnitude of the force which holds two atoms together; it may be possible, from simple valency considerations, for two atoms to combine and form a molecule, but the attachment may be so weak, in the conditions considered, that in fact it does not occur. These two aspects of the concept of valency, as we shall see, are not essentially different. If the combination between the two atoms is of a kind ordinarily understood as "chemical", it results from forces associated with *primary valency*, of which there are two chief kinds—*electrovalency* and *covalency*.

If the combination lacks the specificity and simple numerical proportions characteristic of a chemical reaction, it results from forces of *secondary valency*. It is not possible to distinguish sharply between primary and secondary valency, and there are types of combination which are intermediate between them; and again, there are kinds of primary valency which have some of the properties of both electrovalency and covalency.

Electrovalency. There is always a tendency for the outer shell of electrons to become "perfect"—i.e. to contain the full complement of electrons, two if there is only one shell, eight if there are more than one. (This rule does not apply to the heavier elements, in which the "perfect" shell may have other numbers of electrons.) Elements such as lithium and sodium tend to lose the "lone" electron outside the "perfect" shell, and to become positively charged ions, while elements such as fluorine and chlorine tend to take up an extra electron and to become negatively charged ions. If, then, a sodium atom and a chlorine atom are brought together, they "combine" by the transfer of an electron from one to the other. In the crystalline state, X-ray analysis shows that each Na^+ ion is surrounded symmetrically by six Cl^- ions, and each Cl^- is surrounded by six Na^+ ions; the crystal is, in a sense, a single molecule. In aqueous solutions, also, there is good reason for supposing that only the ions, highly hydrated, are present. It is thus doubtful if such a compound as $NaCl$ really exists; the two ions are held together by electrostatic forces, and the chemical affinity, or potential, in such an electrovalent bond may be identified with the electrostatic potential. We shall discuss this in more detail in Chapter 3.

Covalency. There is an alternative way in which the "octet" of electrons can be completed. Suppose two fluorine atoms, each with seven electrons in the outer shell, come together. By sharing a pair of electrons between them, both can have, in effect, eight:

$$:\overset{\cdot\cdot}{\underset{\cdot\cdot}{F}}\cdot \; + \; \cdot\overset{\cdot\cdot}{\underset{\cdot\cdot}{F}}: \; \longrightarrow \; :\overset{\cdot\cdot}{\underset{\cdot\cdot}{F}}:\overset{\cdot\cdot}{\underset{\cdot\cdot}{F}}:$$

Or take an atom of carbon, with four electrons in the outer shell, together with four hydrogen atoms, each with one only:

$$\overset{\cdot\cdot}{\underset{\cdot\cdot}{C}} \; + \; 4(\cdot H) \; \longrightarrow \; H:\overset{\overset{\textstyle H}{\cdot\cdot}}{\underset{\underset{\textstyle H}{\cdot\cdot}}{C}}:H$$

A stable molecule of methane is thus formed. It will be noticed that each pair of electrons shared corresponds to a "bond" as it is ordinarily drawn. Such a type of combination is called "covalency"; it is the type of union present in most organic compounds.

The nature of the force which holds the two atoms together in a covalent bond is difficult to define in a simple manner. If two atoms approach one another, each nucleus, and each electron shell, will repel the other nucleus and the other electron shell, respectively. But each nucleus will attract the electron shell round the other nucleus, and thus indirectly the other nucleus itself. Whether the force of attraction is greater or smaller than the force of repulsion—i.e. whether the two atoms will combine to form a molecule or not—depends on whether, in the simplest case, an electron from one atom can "pair off" with an electron from the other atom, and both can enter the same orbital. If this is so, it can be shown, by

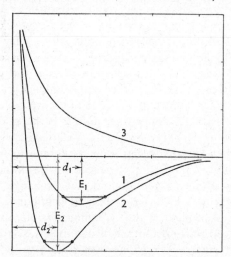

FIG. 2.1. POTENTIAL ENERGY DIAGRAMS FOR A PAIR OF ATOMS

The curves show the relation between the potential energy, as ordinates, and the distance between the atoms, as abscissae. In *Curves 1 and 2*, there is a minimum value of the energy when the atoms are a certain distance apart: the system will be stable, and the atoms will combine to form a molecule. Curves 1 and 2 might thus represent the energies of a pair of chlorine, or iodine, atoms, and a pair of hydrogen atoms, respectively (or, of course, of a molecule of hydrogen chloride, or hydrogen iodide). In *Curve 3*, there is no minimum value of the energy, and the atoms do not combine to form a molecule: they might be, say, a pair of argon atoms.

Ordinarily, the energy of the pair of atoms in a molecule oscillates about the minimum value, as indicated by the dots in the "trough" of the potential energy curves, the amplitude of the oscillation varying from moment to moment. The mean distance between the atoms, d_1 and d_2 respectively, is the *bond length*. If, at any moment, the amplitude is sufficient to take the energy of the atoms over the "potential barrier", and off the diagram to the right, the molecule will dissociate. The height of the "barrier", E_1 or E_2 as the case may be, is the *bond energy*.

means of quantum mechanics, that the potential energy of the system will have a minimum value when the nuclei are a certain distance apart. The curve relating potential energy to distance between the nuclei has a dip in it, as indicated by Curves 1 and 2 in Fig. 2.1. Any increase or decrease in the distance apart can only take place if work is done on the system; the two atoms are thus held together, and the compound is stable. One may imagine, crudely, that one or more pairs of electrons occupy an orbit which includes both the two nuclei, and that they then "belong" to both of them.

B

If two electrons are accommodated in a single orbital, three of the four quantum numbers must be the same for both. Consequently, by the exclusion principle, the electrons must have opposite "spins"; this is one of the factors which determines whether the two atoms will unite or not.

In principle, the difference between the energy associated with a common molecular orbital and that associated with the two atomic orbitals before combination—that is the magnitude of the "dip" in the potential energy curve (the *bond energy*)—as well as the distance between the two nuclei when the energy is at a minimum (the *bond length*), can be calculated by means of the Schrödinger wave equation. For a very simple reaction, such as the combination of two hydrogen atoms to form a hydrogen molecule, the calculation is not very difficult, and the values arrived at agree well with those discovered experimentally. For reactions which involve more complex atoms, the calculations are so complicated and laborious as to be virtually impossible, unless, perhaps, electronic calculating machines are used. Very few such calculations have yet been made.

Resonance. When two hydrogen atoms combine to form a molecule, the whole system of two nuclei and two electrons is symmetrical, and there is no reason why the electrons should not exchange nuclei; we may imagine, therefore, that there are two possible configurations, according as the exchange has taken place or not. It is not possible, in point of fact, to distinguish one electron from another by any means, so that it is not really possible to detect such an exchange; but it is a property of the wave equation that when, for example, the orbital of the hydrogen molecule is calculated in terms of the orbitals of the two hydrogen atoms, a term arises which represents the effect which would be produced by such an exchange of electrons. Owing to the presence of this term, the energy associated with the hydrogen molecule may be smaller or greater than the sum of the energies associated with the two atoms, according to whether the two electrons have opposite "spins" or the same "spin"—i.e. on whether they can or cannot enter the same orbital. This extra energy is known as *"resonance energy"*. It is, of course, of particular importance when it has the effect of reducing the total energy, so contributing to the "affinity" between the two atoms; indeed, in the hydrogen molecule, some 80 per cent. of the energy which holds the atoms together, as represented by the "dip" in the potential energy curve, results from the resonance effect. The remainder of the energy results from other more complicated interactions between the electrons and the nuclei.

The use of the term "resonance" in this connection implies the existence of two oscillating systems, of nearly the same natural frequency, which interact with one another; indeed, an electron which rotates round its nucleus in a definite orbit is such an oscillating system. But according to wave mechanical conceptions, we cannot picture the system so definitely. The wave equations, however, are formally similar to the equations describing the motion of an oscillating system. When two oscillators are coupled together, and resonate with one another, part of the energy—and it may be a large part—is associated with oscillations at the "beat" frequencies. When two wave equations are combined, the terms which describe the "exchange" effect arise in the same way as those which describe the amplitude of the oscillations at the "beat" frequencies.

Granting, then, that neither electron can be said to "belong" to either of the two atoms, but, in the old view, to exchange between one and the other, we can imagine them at any moment as being: (a) both on one atom; (b) both on the other atom; or (c) somewhere between the two. In conditions (a) and (b) one of the atoms will be negatively charged and the other positively charged, so that there will be an electrostatic attraction holding them together. In condition (c) the two atoms will be held together by reason of the electrostatic attraction between each positively charged nucleus and the negatively charged electrons between them. In the hydrogen molecule, there is little doubt that this last condition is by far the most probable, although some "ionic" interaction does occur.

Resonance effects occur, also, in more complicated systems, in which it is possible to make two or more arrangements of bonds, or paired electrons, all of which are equally likely. Such a state of affairs is by no means uncommon. In the anion of a carboxylic acid, for example,

$$R.C \begin{matrix} \diagup O \\ \diagdown O^- \end{matrix}$$

there is no particular reason why the negative charge should be ascribed to one of the oxygen atoms rather than the other. Indeed, there is reason to believe that the charge is divided between them. The extra electron does not "belong" to either oxygen atom, but to both simultaneously. Again, in a chain of carbon atoms, linked by alternating single and double bonds, it is often found that the single and double bonds can be made to change places without affecting the remainder of the links. The most obvious of these "co-ordinated" double-bond systems is to be found in the benzene ring:

Here, again, we should regard each carbon atom as being linked with both its neighbours equally, by something more than a single bond, but less than a double bond.

Where there is such "resonance" between two or more possible bond systems, it cannot properly be said that a single bond alternates rapidly between two positions, as was thought at one time. All that can be said is that when there are two or more possible electronic configurations in a molecule, the most stable state is one which is not that of any of them, but of something intermediate between them all. We shall refer to this again later.

Dative Covalency—Semi-polar Bonds. In certain circumstances, both the shared electrons can be contributed by one of the partners, which is then known as the "donor" of the electrons, the other partner being the "acceptor". The donor is thus left with a positive charge, and the acceptor acquires a negative charge. The whole molecule is electrically asymmetrical, and is known as a *dipole*. The separation of the electric charges, or polarity of the compound, is not so great as it is when there is an electrovalent bond; dative covalency is therefore regarded as producing a "semi-polar" bond. These occur most frequently when the electron acceptor lacks two electrons to complete the outer shell, as in oxygen. The donor usually contains one or more "lone pairs" of electrons, i.e. electrons in the outer shell which are not shared with another atom in a covalent link. Thus, if we consider hydrogen chloride, we see that by sharing a pair of electrons, the outer shells of both the hydrogen and the chlorine atoms are completed (the ordinary covalent bond):

$$H\cdot \; + \; \cdot \overset{..}{\underset{..}{Cl}}: \;\longrightarrow\; H:\overset{..}{\underset{..}{Cl}}:$$

But now, in the presence of oxygen, one of the lone pairs on the chlorine atom can be donated to the oxygen atom, and so complete its octet, giving us hypochlorous acid:

$$H:\overset{..}{\underset{..}{Cl}}: \; + \; \overset{..}{\underset{..}{O}}: \;\longrightarrow\; H:\overset{..}{\underset{..}{Cl}}{}^+:\overset{..}{\underset{..}{O}}{}^-:$$

the union between chlorine and oxygen is now by means of a semi-polar bond. Oxygen atoms will accept electrons, also, from nitrogen atoms, as in amine oxides and organic nitro-compounds, and from sulphur atoms, as in sulphoxides, sulphones and the oxides and oxy-acids of sulphur. All such compounds contain semi-polar bonds, and the forces acting are partly electrostatic, as is indicated by the presence of the positive and negative charges, and partly the same as those responsible for covalent bonds, as just discussed.

The presence of a dative covalency in a compound is often indicated by the use of an arrow, instead of the usual line, to represent the bond; the head of the arrow indicating the electron acceptor. Thus in the above examples, we should represent hypochlorous acid as H—Cl → O, and trimethylamine oxide as $(CH_3)_3N \rightarrow O$. Alternatively, if we wish to direct attention to the semi-polar nature of the bond, we add + and − to the formula, e.g. H—Cl$^+$—O$^-$.

The hydrogen ion, possessing no electrons, will accept a pair and complete a shell of two. For example, a nitrogen atom can form only three covalent bonds, and will thus combine with no more than three hydrogen atoms. There is still, however, a "lone pair" of electrons, which may be donated to a hydrogen ion, with the formation of an ammonium ion:

$$
\begin{array}{c}
\text{H} \\
\text{H}:\overset{\cdot\cdot}{\underset{\cdot\cdot}{\text{N}}}: \ + \ \text{H}^+ \ \longrightarrow \ \left(\text{H}:\overset{\cdot\cdot}{\text{N}}:\text{H} \right)^+ \\
\text{H} \qquad\qquad\qquad\qquad \text{H}
\end{array}
$$

Moreover, in the presence of water, the hydrogen ion will take a pair of electrons from the oxygen atom in a molecule of water:

$$
\begin{array}{c}
\text{H} \\
:\overset{\cdot\cdot}{\underset{\cdot\cdot}{\text{O}}}: \ + \ \text{H}^+ \ \longrightarrow \ \left(\text{H}:\overset{\cdot\cdot}{\underset{\cdot\cdot}{\text{O}}}: \right)^+ \\
\text{H} \qquad\qquad\qquad\qquad \text{H}
\end{array}
$$

The resulting ion, by analogy with the ammonium ion, is called the "oxonium", or "hydronium", ion. In a watery solution, indeed, there are, strictly, no hydrogen ions present as such, all being combined as oxonium ions. The oxygen atom is acting here as an electron donor, instead of an electron acceptor, as in the previous examples. It will also donate a pair of electrons to a carbon atom, as in carbon monoxide and the carboxylic acids, for example.

In the oxonium and ammonium ions, the three, or four, hydrogen atoms round the central oxygen, or nitrogen, atom, are completely symmetrical. It is not possible to say that any one of the bonds is the semi-polar one, and that the rest are covalent. The net positive charge must thus be ascribed uniformly to the whole system, as indicated in the above formulae; none of the bonds is thus, strictly, semi-polar. The whole bond system shows resonance, and thus acquires additional stability.

A somewhat similar type of linkage occurs in the combination of metals with organic compounds. Cobalt, for example, can lose three electrons to, say, three atoms of chlorine, and thus has three electrovalencies. The Co^{3+} ion can then accept a pair of electrons from the nitrogen atom in each of six molecules of ammonia, and thereby bring its outer shell of electrons to a stable number of 12. We thus get the "cobaltammine" ion, $Co(NH_3)_6^{3+}$. The nitrogen atoms, of course, may equally well be incorporated in organic compounds such as amines. Similar types of compound may be formed in which the electron donors are oxygen atoms. It is not essential, moreover, that such "metallo-organic" compounds should be ionised. In beryllium and magnesium, for example, the two electrons in the outer shell may "pair" with electrons from a carbon, oxygen or other atom in a true covalent bond. Two further pairs of electrons can then be accepted, as dative covalent bonds, from a nitrogen or an oxygen atom. It is possible, also, even for a sodium atom to be linked by a single true covalency and three dative covalencies. In many of these cases, the structure round the metal atom is symmetrical, with four oxygen atoms, or four nitrogen atoms, and, as before, it is not possible to define which of the bonds are the dative ones. Moreover, two of the nitrogen or oxygen atoms (or even, in some cases, all four) may be attached to the ends of, say, chains of carbon atoms (ethylene diamine, $NH_2 . CH_2 . CH_2 . NH_2$, is commonly given as an example). The chain is then bent round and closed by the two linkages attached to the metal atom, which thus has the appearance, in a structural formula, of being gripped in a claw (Formula I):

$$
\begin{array}{cc}
\text{I} & \text{II}
\end{array}
$$

NH₂ ... CH₂ ... CH₂ ... NH₂ ... Ca (I)

CH₂ ... CH₂COO⁻ ... CO ... N ... O ... Ca ... CH₂ ... CH₂ ... O ... N ... CO ... CH₂ ... CH₂COO⁻ (II)

If we use the more complex compound, ethylenediamine tetracetate (EDTA, or "versene"), the molecular chain is bent round even more, and becomes attached to the calcium atom (or other metal atom) by four bonds (Formula II). This compound is very stable, in neutral or alkaline solutions, and since the calcium is un-ionised it is very effective in removing calcium ions from solution. Such compounds are known as "*chelates*" and the particular type of combination as "chelation". There can be little doubt that these types of combination between metal atoms and organic compounds are of great importance in living systems. They occur, for example, in the metallo-porphyrins, as found in chlorophyll, haemoglobin and the cytochromes, and in many kinds of enzyme system, as will be discussed in later chapters.

Interactions in More Complex Molecules. So far, we have considered only those forces which hold together the neighbouring atoms in a molecule. But it is a fact of observation that the loss or gain of an atom, or group of atoms, in one part of a molecule, and thus a change in the electronic configuration of this part, may affect the electronic configurations, and thus the chemical reactivities, of some quite different parts. Such an effect may be produced by the operation of the Pauli exclusion principle; if one of the electrons is brought into such an orbital that it has the same four quantum numbers as those of some other electron, then this latter will have to change its orbital. More concretely, ionisation, for example, leaving the molecule with a free electric charge at one end, say, will make it less easy for ionisation to occur at some other point, and may create a field which distorts the arrangement of the electrons throughout the molecule, making more easy, perhaps, the formation of a semi-polar bond. Again, a change in one part of the molecule may introduce, or remove, the possibility of resonance throughout the molecule. And very large molecules may be so curled on themselves that apparently remote points may, in fact, be capable of interacting provided that the electronic arrangements at these points are suitable, and not otherwise.

Dipole Moments. As we have seen, in semi-polar bonds the linking electrons are mainly supplied by one of the atoms, which is thereby left positively charged, while the other atom becomes negatively charged. The dipole so produced in the molecule will tend to make it orientate itself in an electric field; the magnitude of the orientating force in a unit field is termed the Dipole Moment. In covalent bonds, since the linking electrons are shared by the two atoms, one would not expect a dipole to be formed; but in fact, when one of the atoms has its shell of electrons nearly completed, such as oxygen or one of the halogens—i.e. one of the "electro-negative" elements—the electrons appear to be attracted towards it, and the molecule is found to possess a dipole moment.

The possession of a dipole moment confers on the molecule properties which are termed *Polar*. In organic compounds the presence of one or more of the following groupings, for example, confers polar properties:

$$-OH \quad -COOH \quad -CHO \quad =CO \quad -NO_2 \quad -NH_2 \quad -CN \quad -Cl$$

Water is a highly polar substance, and its molecules are strongly held in the electrical fields of ions, as will be discussed further in Chapter 3. It also has an attraction for other substances which contain polar groups of all kinds, probably as a result of the electrical attraction between the dipoles, although hydrogen bonds, to be discussed below, also play a part. The non-polar groups, on the other hand, such as paraffin chains and benzene rings, have no attraction for water, with the result that the solubility of a substance in water is directly related to the proportion of polar and non-polar groups in the molecule. We shall find, also, that the polar properties of molecules are of great importance in connection with adsorption on surfaces and penetration through membranes.

The Determination of the Dipole Moment. We cannot here go into the detailed methods, and text-books of physical chemistry should be consulted. They depend on the fact that when molecules with dipole moments are orientated in an electric field, they affect the force exerted between the two electric charges which are separated by the substance under investigation. This force may be measured in terms of the *Dielectric Constant*. Moreover, by Maxwell's law, electromagnetic waves, such as light, radiant heat and wireless waves, are transmitted by the interaction of electric and magnetic forces, and hence the weaker are the electric forces, the more slowly will the waves travel. In a medium of high dielectric constant, therefore, the waves will travel slowly, and the refractive index will be large. This relation between the refractive index and the dielectric constant is of great value in determining the dipole moment. The presence of an electric field, however, will distort the molecules, tending to pull the nuclei and the electron shells apart. Thus even non-polar molecules will acquire an induced, or Distortion Polarisation. This, however, can be distinguished from the Permanent Polarisation by the following considerations. The permanent dipoles will only orientate themselves in the electric field to the extent that they are not prevented from doing so by their random motion due to thermal agitation, and by constraints imposed on them by neighbouring molecules. Thus the effects due to permanent polarisation fall with rise in temperature, while those due to distortion polarisation are independent of temperature; for a given substance, also, the former are greater in the gaseous than in the liquid state, and greater in the liquid than the solid. In solutions, again, the calculated dipole moment for a given molecule will increase as the solution becomes more dilute.

The Hydrogen Bond. Since the hydrogen atom has only one electron, it should be capable of being united with one other atom only, and should always be univalent. This is, indeed, true in that it has only one electrovalency, and can form only one covalent bond. Nevertheless it is found that a hydrogen atom, already firmly united by a pair of electrons to another atom, is capable, apparently, of becoming attached to another atom as well, by what is known as a "hydrogen bond". This bond is a weak one, as compared with a covalent bond (see Table 2.1, p. 65 below), and is only formed when the hydrogen atom is already united to a strongly electronegative element such as oxygen, nitrogen or fluorine; and the additional linkage is formed only with electronegative elements.

The hydrogen bond is exemplified in the union between the water molecules in a crystal of ice. X-ray analysis shows that in ice, each hydrogen atom is placed between two oxygen atoms, although not mid-way between them, and that each oxygen atom is surrounded by four hydrogen atoms, so:

the various water molecules being held together by hydrogen bonds be-tween each one and its neighbour (shown dotted in the diagram). Such association between adjacent molecules occurs very generally in com-pounds containing —OH groups, as in the rather loose end-to-end union of a pair of carboxylic acids, for example. The hydrogen bond plays an important part in uniting the molecules of long-chain compounds, such as proteins in particular, through various groups attached to the side chains; and in joining together pairs of side-chains on the same main chain, so holding it in a folded condition.

The origin of the force responsible for the hydrogen bond is not com-pletely known, but there seems little doubt that it is chiefly electrostatic in nature. The primary bond is always in a polar molecule, and is often, in fact, a semi-polar bond; the hydrogen atom will have a positive charge, and the atom to which it is attached will have a negative charge. The other molecule will also have a dipole moment, as already discussed, so that the atom on the opposite side of the hydrogen atom will also have a negative charge. The two negatively charged atoms will thus be held together through their mutual attraction for the positively charged hydrogen atom.

Secondary Valency. In addition to the primary valence forces which lead to the union between atoms to form molecules, in the chemical sense, there are attractive forces between molecules which are less powerful and less specific. It is these secondary valence forces that are responsible, for example, for the cohesion between the molecules in the liquid and solid states; and, since it is these forces that were introduced by van der Waals in 1873 in order to extend the applicability of the simple gas laws into regions of greater condensation, they are often known as "van der Waals forces". Primary valence forces are strong, but of short range: the magni-tude of the force falls off very rapidly with distance, and is quite negligible at a distance from an atom equal to its own diameter. Secondary valence forces, on the other hand, are weaker, but of longer range, being appreci-able sometimes over several atomic distances.

The origin of the van der Waals forces is still somewhat uncertain. When the molecules possess dipoles, an electrical attraction between them is to be expected. Similarly, a dipole in one molecule may induce a dipole in another, even though the second molecule ordinarily has no dipole moment. Such electrical forces, however, would not be expected to be of very great range; and, moreover, secondary valence forces are known to exist between molecules neither of which has a dipole moment. But if two atoms approach each other, there will be a certain amount of interaction between the electrons in their outer shells, and the perturbations in the motion of the electrons can be shown to result in a force of attraction between the atoms. Such a force, moreover, would have a relatively long

B*

range, and would be of about the same order of strength as are the van der Waals forces.

The distinction between primary and secondary valence forces must not be regarded as complete. We have already shown how the union between water molecules, and between other molecules containing —OH groups, for example, is brought about by hydrogen bonds. The cohesive forces in water, and the forces leading to the solution of a substance in water, therefore, are partly the result of forces between the atoms that are of the same general nature as those ordinarily regarded as responsible for the primary valence forces. Water, in addition, has a strong dipole moment, so that electrical forces are partly responsible for cohesion and solution. Many cases of adsorption, again, are now regarded as cases of union through a hydrogen bond: indeed, as we shall see in Chapter 5, there is a complete gradation between strong chemical combination and weak physical adsorption, and no hard and fast line can be drawn between them.

It is possible to give here only a very brief outline of the electronic theory of valency, and of the forces acting between atoms and molecules. It is not possible to appreciate fully the development of this subject without a knowledge of wave mechanics and an adequate familiarity with the necessary mathematics. The compounds and chemical reactions with which physiologists have to deal are, for the most part, so complex, however, that the physical chemists are far from being able to treat them theoretically. Those readers who wish to go more deeply into the matter should consult the appropriate text-books and monographs, such as those by Speakman (1955), which gives an elementary introduction to the subject, by Pauling (1948) and by Coulson (1952).

ISOTOPES

We may appropriately break into the study of chemical energy at this point with a brief account of the nature and importance of isotopes. Description of their nature necessitates reference to the internal structure of atoms; and their importance, in biological studies, lies chiefly in the way that they are used to study chemical reactions and the movements of chemical substances.

We ordinarily speak of "the" atomic weight of an element, but in fact, each element may have one of several atomic weights. These varieties—as we may call them—or *isotopes* of the same element all have the same chemical properties, since their outer electron shells are identical: the central nuclei, however, are different, and thus, also, many of their physical properties, notably their densities, rates of diffusion, vapour pressures and, above all, radioactivities. The elements as they occur in nature (usually, of course, in combination with each other) consist of mixtures of the stable, or non-radioactive isotopes. Separation can be effected by means of the physical properties mentioned. This is relatively easy when the atomic weight is small, as in hydrogen, but becomes increasingly difficult as the atomic weight rises. Of the ordinary elements (apart from those needed for providing atomic energy) the isotopes of hydrogen, carbon, nitrogen, oxygen and sulphur have so far been separated in this way. The radioactive isotopes, which are unstable and disintegrate in a greater or less time (a few seconds to millions of years) are for the most part created by bombardment of atoms of the right kind with particles of very great energy (such as neutrons) most usually in a nuclear fission reactor (atomic pile). Some of those with very long lives, such as that of potassium, occur in nature.

There can be little doubt that the availability of isotopes of so many of the elements of importance to the living cell has been of immense value in investigating the processes in which they take part. The replacement of one of the constituent atoms of a compound by an isotope different from that occurring naturally, has the effect of "labelling" this atom: it can be traced in the protoplasm of those cells into which the compound can penetrate; and in the products of any metabolic reactions which the compound may undergo. Although the chemical properties of all the isotopes of a given element are the same, it must not be taken for granted that substitution of one isotope for another will necessarily be entirely without action on a living organism. The rates at which the various reactions proceed are not the same; and, for example, substitution of deuterium (the isotope of hydrogen of atomic weight 2) for hydrogen in certain organic compounds has been shown to result in a reduction in the rate of enzymic reactions in which they take part. The radioactive isotopes, also, emit radiations and charged particles, which are known to have deleterious actions on protoplasm: but owing to the delicacy of the analytical procedures available for radioactive substances, they need be present only in very small concentration, and there is good reason to believe that the intensity of the radiation is too small to affect the cells.

The methods used for detecting the presence of an abnormal isotope, and of estimating its concentration, vary with the properties of the atom concerned.

First, since all isotopes of any one element must have different atomic weights, the replacement of an atom in some compound by one of its isotopes will change the density. Such a difference, however, is only large enough for analysis, even by the most refined methods, if the compound contains relatively few other elements, and if the isotopes themselves have relatively small atomic weights.

Secondly, the radioactive isotopes are estimated by means of the charged particles and radiations which they emit. The instrument most often used is the *Geiger-Müller counter*, which consists of two electrodes, at different potentials, in a partially evacuated chamber. The radiation emitted on the breakdown of a radioactive atom, on entering the chamber, causes ionisation in the gas, and a pulse of current passes between the electrodes. The gas is usually a mixture of argon and alcohol vapour at a suitable, rather low, pressure, such that the primary ionisation is amplified by the secondary ionisation of the gas atoms; the momentary drop in potential between the electrodes operates a counter through a valve amplifier. The chamber in which the electrodes are placed must, of course, be provided with a window through which the particles or radiation emitted by the substance under analysis can pass. The actual process of taking a count is extremely simple; but there are many precautions which must be observed in order to ensure that the count represents the concentration of the radioactive isotope in the material under investigation.

Alternatively, and for some purposes preferably, the radiations and charged particles emitted by the radioactive substance may be arranged to fall on a suitable fluorescent screen, similar to that used in a cathode ray tube. The minute flash (or *scintillation*) produced is detected by a photo-electric cell and amplifier of sufficiently high sensitivity, and the electrical pulses counted, as with the Geiger-Müller tube. This arrangement can be made to record the breakdown of nearly every radioactive atom, whereas the Geiger-Müller tube records only a small, but when properly set up, constant, fraction.

Lastly, the most universal instrument is the *mass spectrometer*; it is, however, elaborate and somewhat difficult to use. In principle, the atoms concerned are evaporated and ionised *in vacuo*, and then projected at high velocity under the influence of an electrical potential gradient. These "positive rays" are deflected sideways by electrical and magnetic fields, which are so adjusted that the final deflection from the direct path is a function of the mass of the ion only. The ions are arranged to fall on a photographic plate, the position of the line on the mass spectrum so formed indicating the mass of the ion, and its intensity (amount of blackening of the photographic emulsion) its concentration. Or better, the ions of any desired mass—and of that mass only—may be arranged to fall on a small ionisation chamber; the relative concentrations of the atoms of different mass are then measured in terms of the relative ionisation currents.

For further information as to the production, separation and analysis of isotopes, the monographs by Whitehouse and Putman (1953), by Francis, Mulligan and Wormall (1954) and by Kamen (1957) should be consulted.

THE KINETICS OF CHEMICAL REACTION—
ACTIVATION ENERGY

Most chemical reactions proceed at definite and measurable rates. It is true that there are reactions which go so rapidly as to cause explosions, and that reactions involving electrovalencies mostly go too rapidly for the speed to be easily measured; but these may be regarded as exceptional. It would seem, therefore, that there must be something in the nature of a chemical "resistance" which opposes the chemical "force", or affinity, and so limits the speed of the reaction. The very rapid reactions do not necessarily occur between substances which have particularly large affinities for each other, so that the magnitude of the "resistance" must vary according to the nature of the reaction.

Let us consider, to begin with, a very simple reaction in which the molecules of an unstable substance break up into two or more different molecules. It is intuitively reasonable—and indeed almost obvious—that the more molecules there are in the system considered, the more will break up in any given period of time, i.e. the greater will be the rate of dissociation. If the system is a closed one, with a constant volume, then the total number of dissociating molecules will steadily fall as the reaction proceeds. We must, therefore, consider a very short period of time, dt, in which case the rate of dissociation may be expressed as dn/dt, where n is the number of molecules present at any given moment. We can thus write:

$$dn/dt = k_1.n$$

where k_1 is a constant, varying with the nature of the reaction, and known as the "velocity constant". If the volume of the system is V, we may divide both sides of the equation by V, and replace n/V by the partial pressure, p, if the substance is a gas, or by the concentration, c, if it is in solution. We thus get:

$$dc/dt = k_1.c \qquad . \qquad . \qquad . \qquad . \qquad 2.1$$

This is the "*law of mass action*" in its simplest form.

In order to use this equation for practical purposes, it must be integrated, since we can only observe the changes that occur in a finite and measurable time. We have here another case of the "compound interest law", referred to on p. 23 above, and the integrated expression may be put in the form:

$$k_1 = \frac{1}{t_2 - t_1} \ln . \frac{c_1}{c_2} \qquad . \qquad . \qquad . \qquad . \qquad 2.2$$

where c_1 and c_2 are the concentrations of the substance considered at times t_1 and t_2 after the commencement of the reaction. This is known as a *unimolecular reaction*.

Suppose next that the reaction is one in which two molecules combine together to form one or more different ones. This is a *bimolecular reaction*. It is again so reasonable as to be obvious that the molecules cannot combine unless they hit one another. Let us call the reactants A and B and the product of the reaction C. Suppose, first, that we vary the number of molecules of A in the system considered, leaving that of B constant. Then clearly the number of times that a molecule of B meets with one of A will be proportional to the number of A present; and conversely, if we vary the number of B present, leaving that of A constant, the number of collisions will be proportional to the number of B in the system. Consequently, if both are changed, and the volume of the space considered is constant, the velocity of the reaction will be proportional to the product of the concentrations of the two molecules, or:

$$d[C]/dt = k_2.[A] . [B] \quad . \qquad . \qquad . \qquad . \qquad 2.3$$

using square brackets to denote the instantaneous values of the concentrations of A, B and C. In practice, most cases of bimolecular reactions can be simplified for integration, since the concentrations of A and B can be made to change equally, in which case, the equation is:

$$d[C]/dt = k_2([A]_0 - [C])([B]_0 - [C])$$

where $[A]_0$ and $[B]_0$ are the initial concentrations of the two reactants, and $[C]$ is the amount of the resultant produced in time t. If equivalent concentrations are taken, this equation becomes:

$$d[C]/dt = k_2([A]_0 - [C])^2$$

since $[A]_0 = [B]_0$. The integral of this equation is:

$$k_2 = \frac{1}{t} \cdot \frac{[C]}{[A]_0([A]_0 - [C])} \qquad . \qquad . \qquad . \qquad 2.4$$

Expressed in the most general way, we can state that if a molecules of substance A react with b molecules of substance B, then the velocity of the reaction will be

$$d[C]/dt = k_2[A]^a[B]^b \quad . \qquad . \qquad . \qquad . \qquad 2.5$$

The velocity constant of a reaction, whether unimolecular or bimolecular, is defined as the rate at which the concentration of the resultant increases when the reactant, or reactants, are at unit concentration. One of the factors which affects the rate of the reaction is thus eliminated, and the velocity constants of different reactions may be used as measures of the "chemical resistance" in these reactions.

The assumption made above, that the rate at which the molecules break up, or combine with one another, is proportional only to the total number present, implies that it does not depend on the extent to which they are packed together. If we are considering a perfect gas, or an ideal solution, this is justified, since, in these systems there are no forces of interaction between the molecules—they may be said to be indifferent to each other unless they actually collide; only then do they either repel each other *in toto* and bounce off again, or attract each other so strongly that chemical reaction occurs. In general, as we have seen, there are more distant interactions between the reacting molecules themselves, and, in a solution, between these and the molecules of the solvent. The law of mass action, as stated above, is, strictly, only an approximation in other than "ideal" conditions. We shall consider the more general case in the next chapter.

Chemical Equilibrium. It is well known that many reactions in which two molecules combine to form one or more different molecules, will proceed in either direction, A and B, say, forming Y and Z, or Y and Z combining to give A and B; the reversal being brought about by suitable adjustment of the conditions of temperature, pressure, concentration etc. We thus ordinarily write such a reversible reaction as:

$$A+B \rightleftharpoons Y+Z$$

Although reversibility is not obvious or apparent in every known reaction, it is highly probable that this is due merely to the imperfections of our observation; the difference between "reversible" and "irreversible" reactions is thus quantitative, not qualitative. Nernst (1923) wrote: "There can be no doubt that by suitable adjustment of the conditions of experiment, it would be possible to make a reaction take place, now in one direction, now in the opposite, that is *in principle every reaction is reversible.*" One of the most obvious of these conditions is that of temperature, as in the well-known case of the dissociation of ammonium chloride. Under ordinary conditions, however, the position of equilibrium may be so near the state of complete change in one direction that the reaction seems to go only in one direction.

Now if a reversible reaction is started by mixing two of the reactants— such as A and B in the above example—these will combine at a rate which depends on their concentrations and the velocity constant of the reaction. Immediately, however, the resultants, Y and Z, will also begin to react at a rate set by their concentrations and the velocity constant of the reverse reaction. A time will thus arrive when the forward and reverse reactions are proceeding at equal rates, and the concentrations of the reacting substances will then remain unchanged. A state of equilibrium has been attained. The actual position of the equilibrium, i.e. the relative concentrations of the reacting substances, is decided by the relative values of the two velocity constants. The ratio of these constants is obviously also a constant, and is known as the *equilibrium constant*.

In the most general case, supposing that the reaction involves a molecules of A, b molecules of B, y molecules of Y, and z molecules of Z, the velocity of the forward reaction would be

$$d[X]/dt = k_f[A]^a[B]^b$$

as we have seen already. Similarly, the velocity of the reverse reaction would be:

$$d[A]/dt = k_r[Y]^y[Z]^z$$

At the equilibrium position, these two velocities are equal, and we must have:

$$\frac{[Y]^y \cdot [Z]^z}{[A]^a \cdot [B]^b} = \frac{k_f}{k_r} = K, \text{ the equilibrium constant} \quad . \quad . \quad 2.6$$

The equilibrium position may thus be defined in two ways: either from the dynamical point of view, by the ratio of the two velocity constants; or from the statical point of view, as the ratio of the relative concentrations of the components. The equilibrium position, however defined, is not to be supposed as a static condition; the two reactions are still proceeding, the various molecules are continually changing their partners, but, in a given time, the number of changes in one direction is equal to that in the opposite direction. This conception that equilibrium is *dynamic*, not static, seems to have been first clearly expressed by A. W. Williamson in 1850.

It must be emphasised at this point, that the expression "dynamic equilibrium", used in this sense, does not refer to a "steady state". Some authors describe a steady state as a dynamic equilibrium, although the use of the expression is unfortunate. As discussed in the previous chapter, in a steady, or stationary, state there is a continuous flow of energy, or matter, through the system, and, in the thermodynamic sense, the processes are usually irreversible. A system in equilibrium is, by definition, thermodynamically reversible.

It is hardly necessary, though perhaps advisable, to make it clear that the chemical reversibility of a reaction has no necessary relation to its thermodynamic, or energetic, reversibility; a reaction may proceed towards its equilibrium condition, from either direction, in a manner which is thermodynamically irreversible.

A few notes on the history of the law of mass action may be of interest. Before the time of Berthollet (1799), it was generally held that the course of chemical action had nothing to do with the quantity of reacting matter. This chemist, however, pointed out how the reaction:

$$CaCl_2 + Na_2CO_3 \longrightarrow CaCO_3 + 2NaCl$$

was reversed, on the shores of certain Egyptian lakes, by the presence of great excess of calcium carbonate, thus accounting for the deposits of sodium carbonate. As he wrote: "an excess of quantity can compensate for a weakness of affinity," and "the result of a chemical reaction depends not simply on the strength of the affinities, but also on the amount of the active reagents" (p. 5 of the reprint in Ostwald's "Klassiker"). This point of view was not accepted for more than half a century. In 1850 Wilhelmy applied mass action in a quantitative manner to the hydrolysis of cane sugar by acid, and established the fact that the rate of action at any moment is proportional to the amount of substance undergoing change. Harcourt and Essen in 1856 obtained similar results; but it was Guldberg and Waage (1864) who formulated and applied the idea in its full significance, and in a clear and systematic manner. Nevertheless, their work remained for a long time unknown, so that the law of mass action was developed independently by Jellet in 1873 and by van't Hoff in 1877.

The Frequency of Molecular Collisions

We may now proceed a stage further, and calculate the frequency with which the reacting molecules may be expected to collide, and thus the expected velocity of a bimolecular reaction. The frequency of collision will be determined not only by the numbers of the two molecular species present in a given volume, but also on their sizes and on their average velocities in any given direction. From the kinetic theory of gases, considered in the previous chapter, we know that the average energy of translation of the molecules is proportional to the absolute temperature; and we can write:

$$\bar{E}_{tr} = \tfrac{1}{2}M.\bar{c}^2 = 3RT/2 \qquad . \qquad . \ 1.7 \text{ and } 1.10$$

and thus

$$\bar{c} = \sqrt{3RT/M}$$

We are concerned, however, not with the root mean square velocity, $\bar{c}$, but with the average velocity, $\bar{u}$, in some given direction—that joining the centres of the molecules just before they collide. It is assumed that the molecules move about in a random manner, and collide with each other purely by chance; the distribution of velocities among them at any moment will be described by an equation similar to that of the "normal law of errors", or "Gaussian distribution of errors" (Maxwell's law of the distribution of velocities, given below, p. 53). It can thus be shown that $\bar{u} = \bar{c}/\sqrt{6\pi}$. In this way, we find that there is a simple relation between the average velocity of the molecules, their masses, and the temperature of the system.

Where there are two different kinds of molecule present, with different molecular weights, as is usual when a chemical reaction is occurring, we must take account of the numbers, sizes and velocities of both of them. The frequency of collision, z, will be proportional to: (a) the numbers, n_1 and n_2, of the two kinds of molecule present; (b) the area at which contact can be made, $4\pi(r_1+r_2)^2$, where r_1 and r_2 are the radii of the molecules; and (c) on the velocities of the molecules, $\bar{u}_1$ and $\bar{u}_2$. From above, we see that $\bar{u} = \sqrt{RT/2\pi M}$, and we thus deduce that:

$$z = n_1 n_2 (r_1 + r_2)^2 \sqrt{8\pi RT(1/M_1 + 1/M_2)} \qquad . \qquad . \ 2.7$$

The radii of the molecules are approximately 3×10^{-8} cm., so that if, for example, we consider a substance in solution at a concentration of 1 molar, the actual value of z is about $1\cdot5 \times 10^{32}$ per second in each cubic centimetre; or, inserting the Avogadro number, about $2\cdot5 \times 10^{11}$ gram-molecules of solute collide per second in each litre of solution. This figure is the collision frequency for a gram-molecule of substance in whatever volume it is present. It is approximately the same for all kinds of molecule over a wide range of temperature; light molecules have a larger velocity than heavy ones, but this is balanced by the fact that they have smaller diameters, and so are less likely to hit each other.

If chemical reaction occurred at every collision, the velocity constant should be identical with the collision frequency when 1 mole of the substance is present in a volume of 1 litre, or in 1 molar concentration. There are a few reactions in which the velocity constant is such that some 10^{11} gram-molecules react in each second; but in the vast majority the reaction velocity is only a minute fraction of this. Thus only a very small proportion of the collisions can be accompanied by chemical reaction. Moreover, if all the collisions resulted in chemical reaction, the velocity constant would be proportional to the square root of the absolute temperature, and would thus increase by about $1\cdot5$ per cent. for a rise of temperature of $10°$ C. at room temperature; actually, in most reactions, the velocity constant is doubled, or trebled, when the temperature rises by $10°$ C. The "chemical resistance" clearly falls rapidly with rise in temperature, and the fraction of collisions that lead to reaction must increase.

The Concept of Activation Energy

In order to understand what it is that decides whether a reaction will occur when two molecules collide, we will first consider the behaviour of a single pair of reacting molecules in a homogeneous gas reaction, such as:

$$H_2 + I_2 \rightleftharpoons 2HI$$

In order that this reaction may occur, in either direction, molecules of hydrogen and of iodine on the one hand, or of hydrogen iodide on the other hand, must dissociate into the constituent atoms. Now a molecule of hydrogen, for example, is stable because the two atoms attract one another, as already discussed in an earlier section; the potential energy of the pair falls as the nuclei approach each other, and work must be done to separate them. If they get too close together, however, the attraction is changed to a repulsion, and the curve of potential energy against distance between the nuclei has the shape shown in Curve 1, Fig. 2.1 (p. 33). Ordinarily the two atoms are vibrating relatively to each other with an amplitude depending on the energy content of the particular molecule considered; as a result of its collisions with other molecules, this amplitude, and the energy content, of the molecule will vary from moment to moment.

Similarly, the energy content of any particular iodine molecule will vary from moment to moment. If, at the moment of collision, the amount of energy associated with either the hydrogen molecule or the iodine molecule or with both taken together, happens to be sufficiently large, it will be possible for both molecules to divide, and for the atoms then to re-combine into two molecules of hydrogen iodide. We may picture the amplitudes of vibration in the hydrogen and iodine molecules as being so large that, at the moment of collision a hydrogen atom comes closer to an iodine atom than either of them is to its partner atom. Conversely, if two molecules of hydrogen iodide collide, and have together a sufficient amount of energy, they will dissociate and the atoms will re-combine into molecules of

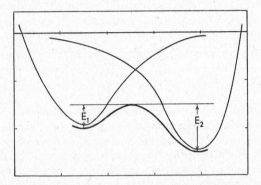

FIG. 2.2.   THE ACTIVATION ENERGY IN A CHEMICAL REACTION

The curves show the relation between potential energy and distance between a pair of atoms, as in Fig. 2.1; *on the left*, of two molecules of the reactants, say H_2 and I_2; and *on the right*, reversed right to left for convenience, of two molecules of the resultants, say 2HI. At the instant of collision between two molecules of the reactants (or between two molecules of the resultants) the potential energy curve of the whole system has the shape shown by the heavy line. The "potential barriers" in the system then have a height E_1 for the reactants, and a height E_2 for the resultants: these heights represent the *activation energies* of the forward and reverse reactions, respectively.

hydrogen and iodine. In each case, the amount of energy which the reacting molecules must possess if the atoms are to change partners and a chemical reaction occur, is known as the *"activation energy"* of the reaction.

We may draw potential energy diagrams for each of the systems $(H_2 + I_2)$ and $(HI + HI)$, and they will have the shape of Curve 1 in Fig. 2.1 —i.e. there will be a "dip" or "trough" indicating the inherent stability of each system. At the moment of collision, we are concerned with a potential energy curve which is a combination of both of these curves, as indicated in Fig. 2.2. The curve on the left represents the sum of the potential energies of the hydrogen and iodine atoms in their respective molecules; that on the right represents the sum of the potential energies of the hydrogen and iodine atoms in two molecules of hydrogen iodide.

In both, the energy is plotted against the distance between the atoms, the curve on the right being reversed for convenience in pictorial representation. The combined potential energy curve—i.e. that of the instantaneous "complex" of atoms at the moment of collision—is shown, in the region between the troughs, by the heavy line. The magnitude of the activation energy is indicated by the "potential barrier" between the two troughs, its height, above each trough, being defined by the activation energy, E_1 or E_2, of the forward or reverse reaction, respectively. If the trough defining E_2 is deeper than that defining E_1, the energy released on the combination of the hydrogen atom with the iodine atom will be greater than the activation energy for the dissociation of the hydrogen and iodine molecules. Free energy will be released when the combination occurs. Also, the number of hydrogen iodide molecules which acquire the necessary activation energy to lift them over the barrier in a given time, will be smaller than the corresponding number of hydrogen and iodine molecules. The reaction on the whole, therefore, will proceed in the direction $H_2 + I_2 \longrightarrow 2HI$, i.e. in the direction in which free energy falls.

It will, perhaps assist in understanding these points if we use an illustration due to Ostwald (*Lehrbuch der allgemeine Chemie*, 1902, II, p. 1087), who compares the system to that of a wedge-shaped block standing with its narrow edge upwards. In this position the system would remain indefinitely if undisturbed, although by falling on its side energy would be given out. To cause this to take place, there must be a certain expenditure of energy upon the block in order to tip it over; in this process, its centre of gravity is raised and the energy required to do this is given out again when the block falls over. Another illustration that might be given is that of a billiard ball lying in the concavity of a clock glass on the top of the tripod. Although energy would be given out by the fall of the ball if the glass were to melt away, no change actually takes place unless the ball is first raised over the edge of the glass by the application of a certain amount of energy. If there are many balls in the clock glass, all oscillating from side to side, and colliding with each other, it will occasionally happen that a particular ball acquires an exceptionally large amount of energy, and the amplitude of its oscillation becomes great enough to take it over the edge of the glass.

These conceptions, then, show that in general chemical reaction occurs only when there is a collision between two molecules which possess the necessary amount of activation energy—or between "active" molecules, as they were called by Arrhenius. As Moelwyn-Hughes has expressed it: "Molecules which are to react chemically do not generally walk towards one another, as in diffusion and other physical changes, but rush at one another." (*Kinetics of Reaction in Solution*, 2nd edn., p. 264.) Of all the collisions that take place, as we have said, only a small fraction is between molecules that are "active". It will be realised, without elaborate calculations, that the chance of a third molecule colliding with a pair of "active" molecules during the short time that they are in contact is extremely small; and that the chance that in such a collision the third molecule should itself be "active" is vanishingly small. Reactions are known which proceed at rates determined by the product of the concentrations of three, or sometimes four, different substances, and thus, kinetically, of the third or fourth order. But owing to the extreme improbability of collisions between three or more "active" molecules, it is reasonably certain that, in fact, these reactions occur in several stages, each of which is of the second, or first, order.

In a unimolecular reaction, we are not, at first sight, concerned with the frequency of collisions between molecules. Nevertheless, the energy content of any particular molecule will vary from moment to moment as a result of collisions with other molecules; and it will undergo chemical change only when it happens to have enough energy, and when this energy is associated with the particular bond which is broken. In the simplest possible kind of unimolecular reaction, such as the dissociation of a hydrogen molecule into two hydrogen atoms, the activation energy will be the same as the bond energy, and so very large; the dissociation will occur only very rarely, and, indeed, cannot be detected at all in ordinary conditions. More usually, however, unimolecular reactions consist of re-arrangements of more complex molecular structures. Here the potential barrier which must be surmounted before the bond is broken is lowered by the presence of a trough on the other side, another bond being created at the same time as the first is broken; the potential energy diagram is similar to that shown in Fig. 2.2. Many other reactions which are kinetically unimolecular actually take place only as a result of interaction with other molecules, such as those of the solvent, or of catalysts and enzymes, as will be seen in more detail in Chapter 7.

The relation between the magnitude of the activation energy and that of the reaction velocity constant may be deduced in one of two ways. In the first place, we can regard the reacting system kinetically, and inquire what fraction of all the molecules present at any moment may be expected to be active. If we consider a simple reaction in a gaseous system, and regard the molecules as so many billiard balls, we require to know what fraction of the total number present will possess an amount of kinetic energy equal to, or greater than, some quantity E, the activation energy. According to Maxwell's law of the distribution of molecular velocities, of all the N molecules present, the number dN which have a velocity between some value v and a slightly larger value $(v + dv)$ is defined by the equation:

$$\frac{dN}{N} = \frac{4}{\sqrt{\pi}} \cdot \frac{v^2}{a^2} \cdot \exp \cdot \left(-\frac{v^2}{a^2}\right) \cdot d\left(\frac{v}{a}\right) \qquad . \qquad . \qquad 2.8$$

where a is the most probable value of the velocity, that of most of the molecules at any one instant. Now molecules with velocity v will have kinetic energy E, given by $E = Mv^2/2$, where M is the molecular weight. The constant a^2 may be expressed as $2\bar{c}^2/3$, where $\bar{c}^2$ is the mean square velocity; and, as we have seen, we can put $\bar{c}^2 = 3RT/M$. Thus we can replace the quantity (v^2/a^2) by the quantity (E/RT). In the simple case of a collision between two molecules, we are concerned only with their velocities in the direction of the line joining them just before the impact; the general case is concerned with their velocities in all three dimensions of space. The equation representing Maxwell's law may thus be reduced to a somewhat simpler form, and can be expressed, in terms of the energies, as:

$$\frac{dN}{N} = \frac{1}{RT} \exp\left(-\frac{E}{RT}\right) \cdot dE$$

Thus the fraction of the molecules which are "active", i.e. have energy equal to, or greater than, E, will be given by:

$$\frac{N_a}{N} = \frac{1}{RT} \cdot \int_E^\infty \exp\left(-\frac{E}{RT}\right) \cdot dE$$

$$= \exp(-E/RT) \qquad . \qquad . \qquad . \qquad . \qquad . \qquad 2.9$$

This is the *Boltzmann law of the distribution of molecular energies*. (The quantity N_a/N may also be considered as the chance that a given molecule should possess energy equal to or greater than E, so that the presence of the exponential term may be expected—compare Chapter 9, p. 375.) If the frequency of collisions, expressed as gram-molecules per second, as already calculated (equation 2.7), is z, then the velocity constant of the reaction will be equal to the frequency of collisions between *activated* molecules, i.e.:

$$k = z \cdot \exp\left(-E/RT\right) \qquad . \qquad . \qquad . \qquad . \qquad 2.10$$

The exponential quantity (the "Boltzmann factor") is, in most cases, very small, and we can identify the "chemical resistance" with the large number of molecules which collide without having enough energy to permit them to react.

The restriction that the reaction considered is between two simple molecules in a gaseous state, implies that the activation energy must be kinetic. The same expression (equation 2.9) also applies, however, to the case of a single molecule which dissociates when the energy of vibration of some constituent parts exceeds a certain value. But in general we are more usually concerned with more complex molecules, usually in solution; and here there may be little kinetic energy, but much energy distributed among various types of rotation and oscillation, of the molecules themselves, and of the constituent atoms and groups within the molecules relative to each other. Each of these modes of rotation or oscillation is known as a "degree of freedom", and it at once appears intuitively reasonable that the more degrees of freedom there are—i.e. the more complex is the molecule—the more likely it is that the necessary amount of activation energy should appear in one or other of them. The mathematical treatment of the problem is rather complicated, but we find that if a molecule has s degrees of freedom altogether, then we must modify the Boltzmann factor, given above, by the addition of a further term. The fraction of the molecules which are active at any moment is then given by:

$$\frac{N_a}{N} = \exp(-E/RT) \cdot \frac{(E/RT)^{(s-1)}}{(s-1)!} \qquad . \qquad . \quad 2.11$$

and the velocity constant of the reaction, k, will, as before, be equal to this quantity multiplied by z, the collision frequency. The influence of this additional factor may be very large; as pointed out by Moelwyn-Hughes (1947), if s is increased from 1 to a value of, say, 7, the chance of a molecule acquiring the quite reasonable activation energy of 21 kcals./mole is increased by a factor of some $2\frac{1}{2}$ million.

We shall consider in a later section the manner in which the activation energy is usually discovered. The obvious method is to compare the observed velocity with which any given molecules react, with the frequency of the collisions. But this does not always give very reliable results, partly because the expression for the collision frequency assumes the reacting molecules to behave like billiard balls. In addition, very large discrepancies may occur as a result of the reaction being more complex than would appear at first sight. Moelwyn-Hughes' monograph (1947) should be consulted for further information.

In the second place, an alternative way of looking at the process is that developed by Eyring and his co-workers, although the basic conceptions are implicit in the original views of Arrhenius in 1889. A full account will be found in the monograph by Glasstone, Laidler and Eyring (1941). Active molecules of the reactants are conceived as uniting into an "activated complex" by the reversible reaction:

$$A + B \rightleftharpoons A^*B^*$$

This complex then breaks down either into molecules of the reaction products:

$$A^*B^* \longrightarrow C + \text{etc.}$$

or into molecules of the reactants again without chemical reaction having occurred. The essential point is that the activated complex is in chemical equilibrium with the (unactivated) reactants, so that we can write (equation 2.6):

$$\frac{[A*B*]}{[A] \times [B]} = K_a$$

square brackets indicating concentrations. Moreover, the rate at which the products of the reaction are formed at any moment is directly proportional to the concentration of the activated complex at that moment, i.e.:

$$d[C]/dt = B \cdot [A*B*] = B \cdot K_a[A] \times [B]$$

This, in turn, is equal to the concentration of the reactants multiplied by the equilibrium constant of the activation reaction. The rate of reaction when the reactants are at unit concentration, therefore—or the velocity constant of the reaction—is directly proportional to this equilibrium constant.

We are now considering a system in equilibrium, and can apply thermodynamic methods. As we shall see in a later section (p. 71), if K_a is the equilibrium constant of the activation reaction, we can write (equation 2.22)

$$RT \cdot \ln K_a = -\Delta G \qquad . \qquad . \qquad . \quad 2.22$$

where ΔG is the change in free energy associated with the formation of the activated complex. But from equation 1.3 we have

$$\Delta G = \Delta E + p \cdot \Delta V - T \cdot \Delta S \qquad . \qquad . \qquad . \quad 1.3$$

where ΔE is the change in total energy, ΔV is the change in volume and ΔS is the change in entropy, on formation of the activated complex, and p and T are the pressure and temperature of the system, respectively (assumed constant). Remembering that the velocity constant, k, is proportional to the equilibrium constant of the activation reaction, K_a, we can write:

$$k = B(T) \exp\left[\frac{(-\Delta E - p \cdot \Delta V + T \cdot \Delta S)}{RT}\right] \qquad . \qquad . \quad 2.12$$

The constant $B(T)$ is expressed in this way so as to indicate that it is a function of the temperature.

This expression, as will be seen, has a close formal similarity with that deduced from kinetic considerations. In order to bring a molecule into the "active" state, work must be done on it; free energy is thus needed for activation. In the simplest case, where there are no internal degrees of freedom from the kinetic viewpoint, all the energy in the molecule is kinetic, and thus capable of doing work. Again, when there is no change in volume or entropy associated with the formation of the activated complex, from the thermodynamic viewpoint, the change in total energy is identical with the change in free energy. In both cases, the exponential function contains only a single energy term. It is not unreasonable, also, to imagine that when there are additional degrees of freedom, there is likely to be a change in entropy; a system with many degrees of freedom is more probable than one with few, and will thus have a greater entropy content.

SOURCES OF ACTIVATION ENERGY

Although the kinetic energy of the molecules, as represented by their temperature, is the commonest, and most obvious, source of the energy needed for activation, it is not the only one. The internal energy of the molecules may be affected by changes in the pressure of the system, or by the presence of electrical fields: activation may occur as a result of the absorption of radiation, as will be discussed in Chapter 9; or in consequence of the presence of catalysts, including enzymes, as will be discussed in Chapter 7. The products of an exergonic reaction, again, are likely to be in an "active" state, since they will contain, at least temporarily, the energy released in the reaction as well as the original activation energy. It seems possible that this energy may, in suitable conditions, be handed on to other atoms, or groups of atoms, which are thus made "active". This may result in a "chain reaction", or the "coupling" of one reaction with another, as will be discussed further in connection with catalysed reactions in Chapter 7, and with photo-chemical reactions in Chapter 9. At this point, we will discuss only the effects of temperature and pressure.

The Effect of Temperature on the Velocity of Reaction. The fraction of molecules which are active at any moment will be expected to increase rapidly with a rise in temperature, owing to the exponential term in both equation 2.10 and equation 2.12; the rate of reaction will thus be affected very markedly by temperature. The total number of collisions in unit time, on the other hand, will increase very slightly when the temperature rises, so that the temperature coefficient of the reaction will be determined almost entirely by the size of the activation energy.

In the simplest conditions, the velocity constant, k, is given by the expression:

$$k = z(T) \cdot \exp(-E/RT) \qquad . \qquad . \qquad . \quad 2.10$$

writing $z(T)$ to remind us that z itself varies with temperature; the rate of variation, however, is much smaller than that of the exponential factor. In the thermodynamic treatment, $z(T)$ is replaced by $B(T)$, and this quantity, also, does not vary rapidly with temperature; it expresses the rate of decomposition of a complex which is already activated, and Eyring considers it to be a linear function of the temperature. As a first approximation, the variation with temperature of either $z(T)$ or $B(T)$ may be neglected. We thus find, by differentiation that the rate of change of k with temperature is given by:

$$-\frac{d(\ln k)}{d(1/T)} = E_A/R = \text{constant} \qquad . \qquad . \qquad . \quad 2.13$$

Hence, if we plot the logarithm of k against the reciprocal of the temperature, we shall get a straight line. This relation is known as the *Arrhenius equation*, and originally, it was deduced empirically from studies on the effects of temperature on the velocities of many different chemical reactions.

The work of Arrhenius was of fundamental importance in many branches of the physical chemistry of solutions, and in their application to biological systems. In addition to his studies on the effect of temperature on the velocity of chemical reaction, an account of which will be found in his book on "Immunochemistry" (1907), he was responsible for the "electrolytic dissociation theory". This will be discussed in Chapter 4.

In spite of the fact the Arrhenius equation (2.13) can really be only an approximation when applied to most chemical reactions, it is, in fact, nearly always possible to draw a reasonably good straight line relating $\ln k$ to $1/T$ over quite a wide range of temperatures as shown in Fig. 2.3; we can thus deduce the value of the activation energy (the slope of the line multiplied by the gas constant, R). This, indeed is the most usual way in which the activation energy is discovered. But since it can only be an approximation, holding over a relatively small range of temperatures, the value so obtained is known as the *apparent (or Arrhenius) activation energy*, and given the symbol E_A.

By differentiating the more exact expressions for the velocity constant, given above, we find that from the kinetic method of treatment, we have

$$E = E_A + (s-1)RT \qquad . \qquad . \qquad . \quad 2.14$$

and from the thermodynamic method of treatment, we have

$$\Delta E = E_A - p.\Delta V + RT.\Delta S \qquad . \qquad . \qquad . \quad 2.15$$

E_A in both expressions being defined as $R\dfrac{d(\ln k)}{d(1/T)}$.

We thus see that it is to be expected that the apparent activation energy should decrease with temperature at a rate determined by the value of $(s-1)RT$, or of $\Delta S.RT$, as the case may be. Such a decrease is, indeed, very often observed, but it is doubtful whether the decrease is strictly linear with temperature, as is predicted by the above expressions. There are still unresolved complexities when the finer details of the problem are examined.

Conclusions are sometimes drawn as to the nature of a particular process from the value of the temperature coefficient. This quantity varies so much, not only according to the position on the scale of temperature at which the reaction happens to take place, but also in individual cases, that, on this ground, caution must be exercised. If a reaction has an activation energy such that it proceeds at a measurable rate at about room tempera-

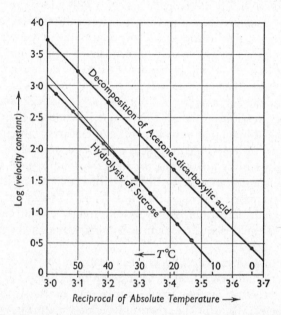

FIG. 2.3. THE EFFECT OF TEMPERATURE ON THE VELOCITY OF CHEMICAL REACTION

Upper line: the decomposition of acetone-dicarboxylic acid, $CO(CH_2COOH)_2 \rightarrow CO(CH_3)_2 + 2CO_2$. The observed values of $\log_{10} k$, where k is the velocity constant of the reaction, are plotted against $1/T$, where T is the absolute temperature. They lie very closely on a straight line, and the simple Arrhenius equation (equation 2.13) is obeyed, the slope of the line indicating that the activation energy is 23,200 calories.

(Data of Wiig, 1930.)

Lower line: the hydrolysis of sucrose in the presence of 0·19 M. hydrochloric acid. The observed values of $\log_{10} k$, where k is the velocity constant divided by the HCl concentration, do not lie on a single straight line. The apparent activation energy falls as the temperature rises, and obeys, approximately, equation 2.14, i.e. $E_A = 52,400 - 46 RT$.

(Data of Moelwyn-Hughes, 1934.)

ture, it is found that the rate is very often about doubled by a rise in temperature of 10° C. i.e. the Q_{10} value, as it is often written for short, is about 2. Purely physical processes are usually said to be much less affected by temperature, and, indeed, many of them proceed at a rate which is proportional to the absolute temperature, so that a rise of 10° C. from room temperature would only change it by about 3 per cent. The rule, however, that chemical processes are extremely sensitive to temperature, while physical processes are not, is, in both cases, honoured almost as much in the breach as in the observance. The attempts that have been made to segregate physiological processes into those primarily of chemical origin, and those primarily of physical origin, on the basis of the temperature coefficient alone, are mostly quite unreliable.

Living systems are heterogeneous, consisting of various solid and liquid phases; when not coarsely heterogeneous, they are at least colloidal, or ultra-microscopically heterogeneous. Not only are there many purely chemical processes going on together, but in addition there are the more physical processes of diffusion and adsorption. Some may have large values of the activation energy, some may have small, or none at all. The velocity of the process as a whole will be conditioned by the complex interaction of all these processes. One of them may be such that its velocity will virtually control that of the remainder, and thus act as a "limiting factor", to use Blackman's expression, although this is not inevitable. This factor may, for example, be diffusion at one range of temperatures, so that the temperature coefficient of the whole process is small; and some chemical reaction at another range of temperatures, so that the temperature coefficient is large. But it is most unwise to deduce either that there is a "limiting factor", or, still more that its nature has changed, solely on the grounds that the apparent activation energy is different over different ranges of temperature. That this can occur in a homogeneous chemical reaction is shown in Fig. 2.3.

The Effects of Pressure. The kinetic treatment of the mechanism of chemical reaction does not lead us to suppose that changes in the pressure applied to a reacting system would necessarily have any effect on the reaction velocity. But in the thermodynamic treatment, we find the pressure entering explicitly into the equations. On differentiating equation 2.12 with respect to pressure, we get

$$\frac{d(\ln k)}{dp} = -\Delta V/RT \; . \qquad . \qquad . \qquad . \quad 2.16$$

If, therefore, the formation of the activated complex is attended by a change in the volume of the reactants, the velocity constant of the reaction will vary with the applied pressure.

Now the whole conception of active molecules, and activated complexes, implies that they are formed with a gain in energy, and accordingly that a rise in temperature will increase the rate of reaction. But there is no *a priori* expectation that the molecular volume of the activated complex should be greater than, equal to, or less than that of the reactants: and, accordingly, we find that a rise in pressure may decrease, have no effect on, or increase, the rate of reaction. The pressure effects are in any case, small, and pressures amounting to hundreds of atmospheres must be used in order to obtain measurable effects.

ENERGY CHANGES IN CHEMICAL REACTIONS

If, in an isolated system, a chemical reaction is allowed to proceed "irreversibly" in the thermodynamic sense, the change in the internal energy of the atoms consequent on the rupture of some of the bonds and the formation of others, is all, in the end, converted into heat. If the reaction is one of oxidation, the amount of heat released is often known as the "*heat of combustion*", but more generally, it is the *heat of reaction*. As emphasised in the previous chapter, however, the amount of energy made available for the performance of work—mechanical, electrical or chemical— is decided by the change in free energy during the reaction, that is, by the chemical affinity of the substances concerned, or by the change in the chemical potential. In practice, however, it is not possible to convert the whole of the free energy change into work. Chemical "engines" are no different from heat engines, or other machines in which one form of energy is converted into another; if the energy of a chemical reaction is to be released at a sufficient rate to be "useful", the reaction must be irreversible, in the thermodynamic sense, but not necessarily, of course, in the chemical sense, and the entropy of the system, and of its surroundings, will increase.

A system in which there is a continuous production of entropy, as pointed out in the previous chapter, will tend to "run-down". This may be prevented, in an "open" system, such as a living organism, by supplying matter, in the form of chemical substances which react within the system, with the production of entropy, and leave again in different chemical or physical states. If the system is in a stationary state, the mass of the substances leaving in a given time must be equal to that entering; but the amount of entropy leaving the system must be greater than that entering it, since entropy is being produced. The entropy content per unit mass of the end-products of the chemical reactions must thus be greater than that of the substances which react; the arrangements of atoms and molecules may be said to become "degraded" as they pass through the system, or their energy "dissipated".

Any system in which there are chemical reactions may also be prevented from "running down" by means of a supply of energy. A green plant, for example, absorbs radiant energy from the sun, and converts water and carbon dioxide into oxygen and carbohydrates; these contain *less* entropy per unit mass than the water and carbon dioxide from which they were formed. If, in some other part of the plant, the oxygen and carbohydrates re-combine (as, in fact, they do to a considerable extent) water and carbon dioxide will be formed again, with a production of entropy. A green plant, therefore, could behave as a "closed" system, fixed quantities of hydrogen, oxygen and carbon going round a cycle of chemical reactions, and the necessary entropy being provided only by the degradation or dissipation of the radiant energy into heat of chemical reaction. (Plants do not, in fact, behave as closed systems, since their tissues are, in general, either growing or dying away, and there must, therefore, be either a gain or loss of matter; few living organisms, indeed, are strictly in a stationary state.) In any case, the cells, or parts of cells, which contain chlorophyll, and those which do not, must each constitute "open" systems, since matter passes from one to the other. Although the matter leaving a cell which contains chlorophyll may have a smaller specific entropy than that entering it, there must, nevertheless, be a net production of entropy in the whole photosynthetic process; only a small fraction of the radiant energy can be "trapped" in the products of photosynthesis, the remainder being degraded into heat.

It is thus clear that heats of combustion, or of reaction, are not the most important quantities which describe the energy changes in chemical reactions, including those that occur in living organisms. It so happens, however, that in the case of the oxidation of the simple food materials, such as carbohydrates and fats, there is no very great difference between the free energy change and the heat of reaction. We do not make any serious error if we calculate, for example, the minimum food requirements of a man from the heats of combustion rather than from the changes in free energy. But when we come to consider the various intermediate reactions concerned in the controlled release of this energy, the difference may become important.

The three quantities, heat content (or enthalpy), free energy, and entropy, are not independent, as is made evident in the fundamental equation of thermodynamics given in the previous chapter (equation 1.2a, p. 11). As given, this equation applies to the heat, free energy and entropy contents of each of the reactants and resultants in the reaction considered, taken separately. An equation of exactly similar form may thus be applied to the *change* in these quantities when the reaction proceeds, i.e.:

$$\Delta H = \Delta G + T \cdot \Delta S \qquad . \qquad . \qquad . \qquad . \qquad 2.17$$

Of these quantities, the heat of reaction is ordinarily the most easily measured; but knowing this, we need only measure either the change in free energy or the change in entropy.

STANDARD HEAT CONTENTS, FREE ENERGIES AND ENTROPIES

It is not always convenient, or even possible, to measure directly the heat of every reaction with which we are concerned; still less is it possible to measure the free energy and entropy changes. It is not, moreover, necessary. Suppose two substances A and B react to form two other substances Y and Z, with the evolution of heat. The sum of the heat contents of Y and Z must obviously be less than the sum of the heat contents of A and B by an amount equal to the amount of heat released in the reaction; if, therefore, we know the heat contents per mole of all the reactants and of all the resultants, and the number of moles of each that takes part—i.e. the stoichiometric equation of the reaction concerned—we could deduce the heat of any reaction desired. A similar argument is obviously applicable to the changes in free energy and entropy.

In any actual chemical reaction, however, there are likely to be changes in the heat contents, free energies and entropies of the reactants and resultants due to changes in factors other than the chemical reaction itself, such as changes in temperature, pressure or concentration, and changes in physical state from solid to liquid, liquid to gas, or from solution to the free state. In order to derive values which refer only to the formation and rupture of chemical bonds, we must imagine the reaction to occur in such a way that the reactants and resultants are all in some *standard state*, and correct the observed values accordingly. We have no means of knowing the absolute values of the heat content, or free energy or entropy of any substance in any given conditions. It is assumed, however, that for every crystalline substance, the values of all three quantities become zero at the absolute zero of temperature and at one atmosphere pressure. The changes in the values when the temperature or pressure is altered (which are all that can be measured) can be fitted to empirical equations, extrapolated to $0°$ K and 1 atm. pressure, and absolute values obtained. When considering heats and free energies of chemical reaction, however, is it convenient to assume, by convention, that the heat content and free energy per gram-molecule of every element is zero when it is at a pressure of 1 atmosphere, at a temperature of $25°$ C., and in its most stable state (crystalline if solid) at this temperature and pressure; this is then regarded as the "standard state". Clearly, if a compound can be formed by direct reaction of its constituent elements in their standard states, the heat content of the compound will be equal to the heat of formation. But such direct combination of the elements occurs rather rarely, and a more indirect method must be applied, making use of the particular application of the law of conservation of energy known as "Hess' Law", put forward in 1840; this states that the heat of reaction between two substances is the same whether they are made to react directly with one another, or whether they are taken through any number of intermediate stages. The heat of any reaction is an expression of the difference between the heat absorbed when reactant molecules A and B disrupt into their constituent atoms, and the heat evolved when these atoms re-combine with the formation of resultant molecules Y and Z. By studying the heats of a number of reactions involving some particular substance (together with the heats associated with changes of state etc.) and subtracting one from another, we can eventually arrive at a value for the heat of formation of that substance. A similar process may be applied to the free energy and entropy of formation. In this way, we can build up Tables of Standard Heat Contents, Free Energies and Entropies, which will be found in books of physico-chemical constants, and less completely in appropriate text-books of physical chemistry, such as those by Glasstone (1957) and by Bull (1951).

Chemical Potentials. We can now define more precisely what is meant by the chemical potential (or molar free energy) of a substance in any given conditions. It is given by the change in free energy that is associated with the formation of a gram-molecule of the substance from its elementary constituents, together with the algebraic sum of the free energies of these constituents—i.e. their standard free energies multiplied by the number of moles that take part in the reaction, corrected for any changes consequent on bringing them into the particular conditions considered. When several different substances are present in the same system, the chemical potential of each may be affected by the presence of the others. We must then define the chemical potential of each one as the rate of change of the free energy of the system with change in the number of moles of the particular substance considered, the number of moles of all the other substances, and the temperature and pressure, being constant; chemical potential is thus the *partial* molar free energy. The chemical potential of a substance A, is then defined as:

$$\mu_A = (\partial G/\partial n_A)_{T_1 p_1 n'} \qquad . \qquad . \qquad . \qquad 2.18$$

n' referring to all molecules other than those of A. We shall refer to this again in the next chapter.

Bond Energies. Having deduced the heats of formation of a number of compounds from the heats of the various reactions in which they take part, we can take a step further. Knowing the structures of a number of compounds, and their heats of formation, we can ascribe a definite value to the energy of formation of each type of bond. Such a process of course, can only be possible if the energy of formation of a bond between any two atoms a and b is independent of the nature of any other bonds attaching a and b to, say, c and d. On the whole, this is true, and a consistent set of values of *Bond Energy* can be produced, as is indicated in Table 2.1. It is to be noted that these figures give the amount of energy which is liberated when the bond, or bond system, is formed. Conversely, therefore, this amount of energy must be supplied from some external source if the bonds are to be ruptured. Thus the higher the bond energy, the more stable is the bond.

TABLE 2.1

Standard Bond Energies

Bond	Energy Liberated on Formation, kcals. per mole
H—H	103
O—H	110
O=O	96 (48 per bond)
O—O	35
C—H	87
C—O	70
C=O	$\begin{cases}149 \text{ in aldehydes} \\ 152 \text{ in ketones}\end{cases}$ (average 75 per bond)
O—C=O	250 (83 per bond)
O=C=O	337 (84 per bond)
C—C	59
C=C	100 (50 per bond)
C—C=C	172 (57 per bond)
C—N	49
N—H	84
S—S	64
Hydrogen	4–8
Ionic	ca. 5
van der Waals	ca. 0·5

The above figures are those given by Pauling (1940). There is some uncertainty about the values to be assigned to bonds involving carbon atoms, and
some authors give values which are greater than those above by about 10 kcals.
per mole for C—C and C—H bonds, and by about 7 kcals. per mole for the
C—O bond.

The values of the bond energies deduced in this way should, of course,
be identical with the values of the change in internal energy of the atoms
when combination takes place, as deduced from their electronic structures
by means of the wave equation. Such calculations, from fundamental
physical principles, as already remarked, can at present be performed only
for the very simplest atoms. Valuable information as to the natures and
properties of the bonds between the atoms in a molecule—and in some
cases, values of the actual bond energies—can, however, be obtained by
purely physical measurements, without observing any actual chemical
reaction. The whole subject is too complex for detailed consideration here.
Briefly, however, from observations on molecular spectra, and the application of the quantum theory, it is possible, in some cases, to deduce the
bond energies between the atoms in the molecule; some aspects of this will
be discussed in Chapter 9. From the molecular spectra, also, as well as

c

from measurements of X-ray and electron diffraction, it is generally possible to deduce the *bond lengths* and *bond angles* in a molecule, and thus, very often, the arrangement of its constituent atoms. It is found that the length of a covalent bond between two atoms, of the same kind, or of different kinds, may be expressed as the sum of the *Bond Radii* of these atoms. The bond radius is thus a property of the atom; it increases with the number of electron shells, and decreases as the positive charge on the nucleus becomes greater, and the shells consequently shrink. If there is a double bond between the atoms, the bond length is less than the sum of the bond radii. The bond lengths, on the whole, increase as the bond energies decrease, as might reasonably be expected; but the inverse relation is not perfect, as, again, is only to be expected.

Further information as to the structures of molecules is obtained from their orientation in electric and magnetic fields. We have already referred to the former in the paragraph on Dipole Moments; but molecules may have magnetic dipole moments as well as electric, and these may provide information as to their electronic structures. Any more detailed discussion of this— or, indeed, of any of the physical methods for determining molecular structure —would take us too far into a very complicated subject.

It will be noted, on studying the values of bond energies in Table 2.1, that there are certain anomalies. Double bonds, for instance, may be associated with either more or less than twice the energy of a single bond between the same two atoms. But more important for our purposes are the anomalies which are found in molecules whose structure is capable of resonance. Thus, as shown in Table 2.1, the co-ordinated double bond structure $C\!-\!C\!=\!C$, as found in the benzene ring, has an energy which is greater than the sum of that in the single $C\!-\!C$ bond, together with that in the double $C\!=\!C$ bond. In accordance with this, the average bond length is less than that between two carbon atoms united by a single covalent bond, but greater than that between atoms united by a double bond. Again, we see that the energy of the $O\!-\!C\!=\!O$ group, found in carboxy-acids, is quite substantially greater than three times the energy of a single $C\!-\!O$ bond. This extra energy, which is indicative of a high degree of stability in the structure, is characteristic of *resonance*, which has already been referred to in an earlier section. The complete symmetry of the carboxylate ion leads to a considerable degree of resonance, and a large amount of resonance energy, probably some 36 kcals. per mole, or a little more. In the undissociated state, there is much less symmetry, the resonance being between the structures:

i.e. between a system of entirely covalent bonds, and one which contains two semi-polar bonds. The resonance energy is now reduced to 28 kcals. per mole. Further reduction in symmetry, by esterifying the carboxyl group, leads to a further reduction in resonance energy, to 24 kcals. per mole. We shall see in a later chapter that this resonance energy is of some importance in the mechanisms whereby the energy released in biological oxidation systems is used in building up the organisation of the living cell.

By using the values of the bond energies, it is possible to calculate, with a reasonable degree of accuracy, the heat change in any desired reaction. From the structural formulae of the reactants and the resultants, it will be obvious that some bonds between atoms must be broken in the reaction, and other bonds, between different atoms, must be formed; the energy which must be supplied in order to break the existing bonds is subtracted from that which is released when the new bonds are formed. Some examples of this will be given in Chapter 7. It is not possible to derive a similar set of consistent values for free energy changes; these, in most cases, depend on the whole structures of the molecules concerned in the reaction, and not only on the particular bonds that are ruptured or created.

Methods of Determining Heats, Free Energies and Entropies

The measurement of the *heat of reaction* is, in principle at least, straightforward. It consists essentially in measuring the rise in temperature of the reaction mixture, and subsequently its heat capacity; this is usually done by generating a known amount of heat electrically, and again measuring the rise in temperature. There are, of course, many points of practical detail with which we need not concern ourselves here.

Alternatively, if the reaction considered reaches an observable condition of equilibrium, use can be made of the *van't Hoff Isochore*, relating the heat of reaction to the rate of change of the equilibrium constant with temperature. The derivation of this relation will be discussed later. This method is often of great value in conditions where direct measurement of the heat of reaction is difficult or impracticable.

The measurement of the *free energy change* in a chemical reaction is a more difficult matter. Direct measurement is possible only in certain particular kinds of reaction, and in others, it is necessary to derive it from the heat of reaction by the application of thermodynamical formulae.

(1) In reactions between ionised substances in solution, involving electrovalencies, the free energy change may be directly estimated in terms of the electrical potential difference between suitable electrodes, as will be seen in Chapter 4.

(2) Similarly, in certain oxidation—reduction reactions, the free energy change may be estimated in terms of electrical potential differences, as will be seen in Chapter 8.

(3) More generally, the relation between the heat of reaction and the free energy change in the reaction may be deduced by means of the *Gibbs-Helmholtz equation* (equation 1.5d, p. 13). As applied to the changes in free energy and heat content during the reaction, we get:

$$\left(\frac{\partial(\Delta G/T)}{\partial T}\right)_p = -\frac{\Delta H}{T^2}$$

or

$$\left(\frac{\partial(\Delta G/T)}{\partial(1/T)}\right)_p = \Delta H$$

. . . 1.5d

In order to solve this equation, in either form, we must know the value of ΔH over a range of temperatures, and either work out an empirical equation relating ΔH to T, or perform the integration graphically.

(4) If we are concerned with a reaction which reaches an observable state of equilibrium, the change in free energy in the standard state may be calculated directly from the value of the equilibrium constant, as will be discussed later.

The *entropy change* in a chemical reaction may be deduced from the heat of reaction and the free energy change by means of the general equation (equation 1.2a) already introduced. It is possible, also, to evaluate the standard entropy of a substance from measurements of the specific heat, and thus, conversely, to deduce the standard free energy from the heat content. Suppose we add a small quantity of heat dq to a system at a constant pressure and temperature (the amount being so small that there is no appreciable change in either), the change in the entropy, by definition, is given by:

$$dS = dq/T$$

There will, however, be an infinitesimal change in temperature, dT, and the ratio dq/dT, which will be finite, is defined as the specific heat (or heat capacity) at constant pressure, C_p. Thus

$$dS = (C_p/T).dT$$

On integrating this from zero temperature upwards, we get:

$$S = \int_0^T C_p.d(\ln T) + S_0$$

. . . . 2.19

where S_0 is the entropy of the system at the absolute zero of temperature. According to the "heat theorem" put forward by Nernst in 1906, the entropy change in any reaction is zero at the absolute zero of temperature: this was extended by Planck in 1912 into the *third law of thermodynamics*, which states that the entropies of all solids and liquids are not only the same at the absolute zero of temperature, but are all zero, provided that they become "perfectly crystalline" (i.e. are not solid solutions or amorphous glasses). We may thus put $S_0 = 0$; and, accordingly, the entropies of a great many pure substances can be discovered by integrating the right hand side of equation 2.19. We must remember, however, that the heat capacity is not independent of the temperature: it must be measured down to as low a value of temperature as possible, and either plotted against the logarithm of the temperature and the integration performed graphically, or fitted to an empirical equation, which can be integrated. If the substance under investigation undergoes transition from one crystalline form to another, melts, or evaporates as the temperature is raised, the entropy of transition, fusion or evaporation must, of course, be included.

We may note, incidentally, that the statement that the entropy of a crystalline substance is zero at the absolute zero of temperature is in accordance with the concept of entropy as thermodynamic probability. In a crystalline substance, the arrangement of the atoms or molecules is unique, and thus highly improbable: and there are no random movements of thermal origin to increase the probability.

Free Energy Changes and the Equilibrium Constant

If a chemical reaction has reached a state of equilibrium, it follows from the second law of thermodynamics, as pointed out in the previous chapter (p. 5), that the free energy of the reactants must be equal to that of the resultants; or, expressed in another way, the sum of the chemical potentials of the reactants must be equal to the sum of the chemical potentials of the resultants. In the equilibrium condition, the components of the reaction will not, in general, be in their standard states; their concentrations, for example, will be determined by the value of the equilibrium constant, which in turn, will depend on the temperature. If we could discover the amount of free energy needed to bring them to their standard states, we should have a value of the free energy change which would be associated with the reaction supposing that all the components were in their standard states; this could be regarded as characteristic of the particular reaction considered. There is no general method by which this change in free energy can be calculated, although it can be done in certain special cases, and is relatively simple when all the reactants and resultants are "perfect" gases, or in "ideal" solution.

Let us consider the general case of the reaction:

$$aA + bB \rightleftharpoons yY + zZ$$

all the reactants and resultants being perfect gases, their partial pressures, in the conditions considered, being p_A, p_B, p_Y and p_Z atmospheres, and the reaction proceeding at the standard temperature. Then the free energy to be associated with each mole of A or the chemical potential of A, μ_A, will be the free energy per mole in the standard state G_A°, together with the work done on the system when the pressure is brought to the value p_A, i.e. $RT \ln . p_A$. (From equation 1.12a, p. 21; p_A is put in place of p_1, and in the standard state, the pressure is 1 atmosphere, so that $p_2 = 1$.) The total free energy of the reactants will thus be given by:

$$a\mu_A + b\mu_B = a(G_A^\circ + RT \ln p_A) + b(G_B^\circ + RT \ln p_B)$$

An analogous expression will give the free energy of the resultants. The total change in free energy consequent on the chemical reaction will be given by the difference between the chemical potentials of the resultants and the chemical potentials of the reactants, i.e. by:

$$\Delta G = (yG_Y^\circ + zG_Z^\circ) - (aG_A^\circ + bG_B^\circ)$$
$$+ RT(y.\ln p_Y + z.\ln p_Z - a.\ln p_A - b.\ln p_B)$$
$$= \Delta G^\circ + RT \ln . \frac{p_Y^y \cdot p_Z^z}{p_A^a \cdot p_B^b} \quad . \qquad . \qquad . \qquad . \qquad 2.20$$

where ΔG° is the change in free energy that would be observed if all the components were in the standard state. But if equilibrium has been reached, ΔG must be zero. Thus:

$$\Delta G^\circ = -RT \ln . \frac{p_Y^y \cdot p_Z^z}{p_A^a \cdot p_B^b} \quad . \qquad . \qquad . \qquad 2.21$$

In applying physico-chemical theory to physiological problems, we are concerned almost entirely with reactions that occur in solution. The calculation of the free energy changes of substances in solution is somewhat complicated, and will be considered in the next chapter. As will be shown, however, if the solution in which our reaction is occurring can be considered "ideal", van't Hoff's theory may be applied, and the pressure terms replaced by concentrations. The expression within the logarithm term would then be identical with the expression derived in a previous section for the equilibrium constant K (equation 2.6, p. 48). Now at constant temperature, ΔG° is constant, independent of the particular conditions of the reaction; we have thus demonstrated by a thermo-dynamical method that in a chemical reaction in equilibrium, this particular function of the concentrations of the reactants and resultants is constant.

In any conditions, "ideal" or otherwise, the equilibrium state, and thus the value of the equilibrium constant, is determined by the free energies of the reactants and resultants, even though we may have to use partial pressures or concentrations for simplicity of treatment, or for the purpose of chemical analysis. We thus have the important, and quite general, relation:

$$\Delta G° = - RT \ln K$$
$$= -1\cdot36 \log K \quad \text{kcals./mole at 25° C.} \qquad . \qquad 2.22$$

This relation is of great value in enabling us to calculate the free energy changes in many reactions for which no other methods are available, and we shall make use of it on many occasions. We learn, also, that if a reaction can be observed to be reversible under ordinary laboratory conditions— if, say, the concentration of the components on one side of the equation is not less than 1 per cent. of that of the components on the other side— then the change in free energy cannot be greater than about 2·5 kcals./mole. Conversely, reactions which involve large changes in free energy cannot be observed to be reversible, and the equilibrium state cannot be shifted by changes in the relative concentrations of the components.

THE EFFECT OF TEMPERATURE ON THE EQUILIBRIUM CONSTANT

The quantitative relation between the effect of temperature on the position of equilibrium in a reversible chemical reaction, and the heat of the reaction can be deduced from the fundamental principles of thermodynamics; the resulting expression is often known as *van't Hoff's Isochore*, since it was first deduced by van't Hoff in 1884. The change in free energy (ΔG) and the change in heat content (ΔH) associated with some chemical reaction, are related to one another by means of the Gibbs-Helmholtz equation:

$$\frac{d(\Delta G/T)}{d(1/T)} = -\Delta H \qquad . \qquad . \qquad . \qquad 1.5d$$

Inserting the relation between the change in free energy and the equilibrium constant, deduced in the previous section (equation 1.31), we get:

$$\frac{d(\ln K)}{d(1/T)} = \frac{-\Delta H}{R} \qquad . \qquad . \qquad . \qquad 2.23$$

This is one form of the van't Hoff isochore. We see that if we plot the logarithm of the equilibrium constant of the reaction, against the reciprocal of the absolute temperature, we should get a straight line, although in practice the line is often not quite straight when the range of temperatures is large: but in any case, the slope of the line at any temperature, multiplied by the gas constant will be equal to the heat of reaction.

Qualitatively, the significance of this relation between the heat of reaction and the effect of temperature on the equilibrium constant may be seen by considering a simple reversible reaction which may be represented:

$$A \rightleftharpoons Y$$

In one direction, A reacts in such a way as to give rise to Y, the velocity constant of the reaction being k_f; in the reverse direction, Y becomes A, with a velocity constant k_r. If the formation of Y from A is exothermic, with the evolution of heat, ΔH is negative (heat is lost from the system), and from the van't Hoff isochore, K, or the ratio k_f/k_r, increases as $1/T$ increases, or as T decreases. Thus if the temperature falls, the concentration of Y rises, while that of A falls (compare equation 2.6, p. 48), and there is an evolution of heat which tends to counteract the fall in temperature. Conversely, if the temperature rises, Y will be converted into A, with an absorption of heat; one may say that since the reaction requires heat in order to proceed, an extra supply, consequent on raising the temperature, will help it on. These qualitative conclusions as to the direction in which the equilibrium constant changes when the temperature changes, were put by van't Hoff into a general rule, known as the "Principle of Mobile Equilibrium". It may be expressed briefly as follows: Any change of the temperature of a system in equilibrium is followed by a reverse thermal change within the system.

Since the rule holds for physical as well as chemical phenomena, it may easily be remembered by considering the condensation of water vapour (A) to liquid water (B), which is accompanied by evolution of heat. The law states that raising the temperature will increase the quantity of steam (A), as every one knows. Lowering the temperature, conversely, reduces the rate of evaporation. If the rate of heat supply is constant, evaporation will occur until the temperature has fallen to such a value that the rate of absorption of heat in evaporation is equal to the rate of supply from the surroundings. If the liquid is a very volatile one, such as ether, the temperature may fall very considerably.

The principle was stated by Le Chatelier in 1884 in a more general form, in which it can be seen to be comprehended in the second law of thermodynamics: When any influence or factor capable of changing the equilibrium of a system is altered, the system tends to change in such a way as to oppose and annul the alteration in this factor. If it be temperature, for example, the effect is to decrease the change in temperature. As applied to matter, the law states that addition of one of the components of the reaction to a system in chemical equilibrium will cause a shift in the position of equilibrium such as to remove this component; this, of course, follows equally from the law of mass action.

Confusion sometimes arises between the effect of a rise in temperature in increasing the *rate* of a change, and its effect on the position of equilibrium in a reversible reaction. The rate of any reaction, exothermic or endothermic, is increased by a rise of temperature. On the position of equilibrium, its effect will depend on the nature of the heat changes in the reaction, as we have just seen. From the purely kinetic standpoint, we have two balanced opposing reactions, and the rise of temperature may increase the rate of one more than it increases the rate of the other. An instructive case to consider in this connection is that of the uptake of a dye by a substance which is stained by it, such as paper, or the tissues of an animal or plant in the process of histological staining. The amount of dye which a piece of paper of a certain size will take up from a given solution of Congored, for example, if allowed to remain until no further amount is taken up, is *less* at 50° C. than at 10° C., as is shown by the curves in Fig. 2.4,

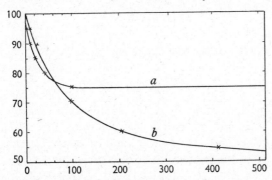

FIG. 2.4 THE ADSORPTION OF CONGO-RED BY PAPER
     The total amount of dye left unadsorbed at any moment is plotted against the time in minutes: *curve a* at 50° C., *curve b* at 10° C.
     At the higher temperature the *rate* of adsorption is greater, but the *total amount* adsorbed when equilibrium is reached is smaller.   (W. M. Bayliss, 1911.)

although the rate at which the uptake occurs is greater. At the higher temperature, equilibrium was attained, in this experiment, in about 100 minutes (Curve *a*), whereas at the lower temperature (Curve *b*) it was not quite complete in 24 hours. The amount taken up at the lower temperature was about one-half of that originally present in the solution; at the higher temperature, only one-quarter.

CHEMICAL AFFINITY AND THE VELOCITY OF REACTION

The change in free energy associated with a chemical reaction, denoted ΔG in the previous sections, is sometimes defined as the "affinity" of the reaction, A. In the example previously considered, we have:

$$\Delta G = y\mu_Y + z\mu_Z - (a\mu_A + b\mu_B)$$

or, in general:

$$A = -\Sigma(r\mu_R)$$

c*

where r refers to the number of molecules of any reactant or resultant, R, which take part in the reaction, considered positive for resultants, the number of which increases, and negative for reactants, the number of which decreases. The negative sign in front of the summation sign ensures that the affinity is positive for reactions which proceed spontaneously, with a liberation of free energy, or a reduction in the free energy content of the system. As used in this sense, it is obvious that the "affinity" becomes zero when equilibrium is reached, and its value depends on the extent to which the concentrations of the reactants differ from their values in the equilibrium condition. It thus represents the "net" affinity.

If we combine equations 2.20, 2.21, and 2.22 in the earlier section, we get the relation:

$$\Delta G/RT = \ln K \frac{p_A^a \cdot p_B^b}{p_Y^y \cdot p_Z^z}$$

This may be written in the form:

$$\exp(A/RT) = \frac{k_f}{k_r} \cdot \frac{p_A^a \cdot p^b}{p_Y^y \cdot p_Z^z} = \frac{v_f}{v_r}$$

replacing ΔG by the affinity A; K, the equilibrium constant, by k_f/k_r, the ratio of the forward and reverse velocity constants; and introducing v_f and v_r, the actual velocities of the forward and reverse reactions, respectively. The net velocity of the reaction, v, is thus given by:

$$v = v_f - v_r = v_f(1 - v_r/v_f) = v_f(1 - \exp(-A/RT)) \qquad . \quad 2.24$$

In the equilibrium conditions, $v = 0$ and $v_f = v_r = v_e$, the actual velocity of both the forward and reverse reactions. If the reaction is nearly in equilibrium, A will be small and A/RT small compared with unity. We then have, approximately:

$$v \doteqdot v_e.A/RT \qquad . \qquad . \qquad . \qquad . \quad 2.24a$$

The net velocity v, in these circumstances, will be nearly proportional to the net affinity of the reaction, A. When A/RT is large, however, as when the reaction is well removed from the equilibrium position, the quantity $\exp(-A/RT)$ will be nearly zero, and the velocity of the reaction will be independent of the affinity. This is in accordance with the conclusions reached earlier in this chapter that the velocity of reaction between two substances depends only on the frequency of collisions and the magnitude of the activation energy.

If no heat is being supplied to, or lost from, the system in which a chemical reaction is occurring, the heat content will be constant. For the chemical reaction itself, then, we have, from equation 22.17 (p. 62):

$$T\Delta S = -\Delta G$$

for each mole of substance reacting. Thus, if dn molecules react in time dt, the rate of entropy production will be given by:

$$T \frac{dS}{dt} = - \Delta G \frac{dn}{dt} = A.v \qquad . \qquad . \qquad . \quad 2.25$$

A being the affinity and v the velocity of the reaction. In a given reaction, at a given temperature, the rate of entropy production, as is to be expected, will increase as the conditions depart from those corresponding to the equilibrium state—i.e. to those corresponding to thermodynamic reversibility; the rate of increase, moreover, is likely to be very rapid, since both A and v increase together. In a number of different reactions, all proceeding at the same rate in terms of molecules reacting per unit time— as for example, in a series of consecutive reactions in a system which has reached a steady state—the rate of entropy production by each will be proportional to its net affinity; that is, to the standard free energy change of the reaction and the extent to which the concentrations of the reactants depart from their equilibrium values.

LITERATURE

Valency, Affinity and Chemical Energy. Speakman (1955); Pauling (1948); Coulson (1952); Prigogine (1955).

Kinetics of Chemical Reactions. Moelwyn-Hughes (1947); Arrhenius (1907); Glasstone, Laidler and Eyring (1941); Guldberg et Waage (1867).

Isotopes. Kamen (1957); Whitehouse and Putman (1953); Francis, Mulligan and Wormall (1954).

3

SOLUTIONS

Living cells consist largely of substances in watery solution: the great majority are immersed in watery solutions, and acquire energy from substances that reach them in those solutions and that are carried away by them. It is important, therefore, that we should consider the general properties of solutions, with particular reference to the properties of aqueous solutions.

When it is said that chemistry has been built up almost entirely on aqueous solutions, it is not that water has been used as a solvent merely because of its cheapness and accessibility; actually, there is no other liquid capable of dissolving so great a variety of substances. Very few inorganic salts are soluble in any other liquid; more organic substances are to be found which require alcohol, ether, and so on for solution, but even here, the majority can be dissolved in water.

As to what happens in the actual process of solution, we are still very much in the dark. Why, for example, sodium salts are nearly all soluble in water, whereas certain corresponding potassium salts are insoluble; and why the nitrates of practically all metals are freely soluble, but the chlorides of only some of them, is not explained. The question has, from the first, been closely connected with that of chemical affinity. In solutions there is undoubted evidence of combination of some kind between solvent and solute, "hydration" or "solvation". One of the factors concerned is the presence of appreciable electrical fields around the molecules both of solute and of solvent: roughly speaking, polar substances, with large dipole moments, are soluble in polar liquids which also have large dipole moments, and non-polar substances are soluble in non-polar liquids. Water is a highly polar substance, and all substances which have a sufficient proportion of polar groups in their molecules will dissolve in it. A more important factor, however, is the ability of the water molecules to become attached to the solute molecules by means of hydrogen bonds; the constitution of water is particularly favourable for this type of attachment, as discussed in Chapter 2, p. 40.

The physical properties of water are not at all such as would be expected in a simple compound, containing three molecules only, of gases with extremely low boiling points. In fact, comparing water with similar compounds, the freezing point would be expected to be about $-150°$ C., and the boiling point about $-100°$ C., instead of the observed values of $0°$ C. and $+100°$ C., respectively. The molecular weight of water, then, would appear to be greater than 18; it must be a polymerised, or associated liquid, in which a number of molecules are united together. This tendency for water molecules to associate results at least partly from the presence of a large dipole moment. Each molecule of water possesses a strong positive charge at one end and a strong negative charge at the other end. An assembly of such molecules would behave somewhat as an assembly of small bar magnets, and would stick to each other end to end and side to side in all three directions of space. It is to be expected, also, that as in ice, there would be more powerful attachments between the water molecules owing to the formation of hydrogen bonds (cf. Chapter 2, p. 40). The union of one water molecule with another, however, whatever may be its exact nature, must be relatively weak and frequently broken as a result of thermal agitation; otherwise, water would not behave as a fluid. In the presence of a dissolved substance, some of the attachments between the water molecules will be broken, and replaced by attachments to the solute molecules. These, therefore, must be the more powerful, and the water molecules so attached will be less "free" than the remainder.

CONCENTRATION

The composition of a solution is described quantitatively in terms of its concentration; preferably, for ordinary purposes, in terms of the *molal concentration*, i.e. the number of gram-molecules of the solute in 1000 grams of the solvent. Not uncommonly, however, the concentration is expressed in terms of the total volume of the solution, i.e. as the number of gram-molecules of the solute present in one litre of the solution. This is less desirable, since there is no simple relation between the weight or volume of the solvent and the volume of the solution; it depends on the nature of the solute and on the concentration. The term "molar" is not infrequently used indiscriminately for concentrations in terms of the volume of the solution or the weight of the solvent. The term *"molal"* should, properly, be used for the latter. In very dilute solutions of substances of low molecular weight, the volume concentration does not differ much from the weight concentration; and for many biological purposes, the distinction may be neglected in most of the solutions of crystalloids with which we are concerned. When, however, the solution contains colloids, such as proteins, the distinction becomes important, and weight concentration should always be employed.

When considering the energetics of solution, the most useful and convenient description of the concentration is in terms of the *mole fraction*, i.e. the ratio of the number of moles of each particular component to the total number of moles of all the components present. Thus if we have a solution in which n_1 moles of solvent have dissolved n_2 moles of one kind of solute, n_3 moles of another kind, and so on, the mole fraction of the solvent is $n_1/(n_1+n_2+n_3+ \ldots)$, that of the first solute is $n_2/(n_1+n_2+n_3+ \ldots)$ and so on for all the components of the solution. The symmetry of these fractions has the advantage of reminding us that the distinction between solute and solvent is an arbitrary one; but a convenient one because we ordinarily deal with relatively dilute solutions in which a small quantity of one component is present in a much larger quantity of another. In dilute solutions, the ratio $n_2/(n_1+n_2)$ is approximately equal to the ratio n_2/n_1, since n_2 is small compared with n_1. If M_1 is the molecular weight of the solvent, and if we consider a volume of solution such that there are 1000 grams of solvent present, i.e. such that $M_1 n_1 = 1000$, then the molar fraction is related to the molar concentration (m) as follows:

$$n_2/(n_1+n_2) \fallingdotseq n_2/n_1 = m.M_1/1000 \qquad . \qquad . \qquad . \qquad 3.1$$

For solutions in water, the value of $1000/M_1$ is 55·5. For a molar solution, therefore, where $n_2 = 1$, the error in assuming n_2 to be negligible as compared with n_1 is 1·8 per cent.; it is, of course, correspondingly smaller for more dilute solutions.

PARTIAL QUANTITIES

When dealing with systems containing more than one component, such as solutions, it is often necessary to consider the consequences of altering the amount of one of the components only, the rest being unchanged. We therefore need to know what fraction of the particular property of the system that is being observed, such as density, specific heat, and so on, is to be attributed to each of the components present.

In a mixture of perfect gases, Dalton's law states that each gas exerts the same pressure as it would exert if it were present in the same space by itself: in other words, the *partial* pressure exerted by a given quantity of each gas in the mixture is the same as the total pressure exerted by the same quantity of that gas when in the pure state. The other properties of the perfect gases are similarly independent of the presence or absence of each other. In solutions, however, the situation is more complicated. Everyone who has made up solutions of known composition must have observed that the final volume of the solution is very rarely the same as the sum of the volumes of the two components. Sometimes, indeed, the volume of an aqueous solution is less than the volume of the water before the solute was dissolved in it, as in the case of potassium hydroxide. In other words, the volume occupied by a given mass of the solvent (the partial specific volume) has a value after the solute has dissolved which is different from the specific volume of the pure solvent. Similarly, the partial specific volume of the solute is not the same in the solution as in the pure state.

In solutions, then, the contribution by a given component to some particular property is not, as a rule, simply proportional to its concentration; this contribution, also, will depend on the nature and concentration of all the other components that may be present. We are concerned, therefore, mainly with what are known as *partial molar quantities*: these are defined as the change in the magnitude of some particular property of the whole system that is being considered, when a small change is made in the number of gram-molecules of one of the components only (i.e. the particular one under investigation), the number of gram-molecules of all the other components remaining constant.

FREE ENERGY IN SOLUTIONS

It is one of the cardinal principles of energetics that a system will change in such a way that its free energy falls, provided, of course, that it is free to do so; many examples of this principle have been given in the previous two chapters. In solutions, we may apply the same principle to each of the components separately; but we must use, as criterion, the change in the *partial* free energy in the particular conditions considered. Two of the components will react with each other if the sum of the partial free energies of the reactants is greater than that of the resultants: any one component will move from one part of the solution to another part where its partial free energy is smaller. The partial free energies of the components are thus the fundamental quantities which determine the dynamic behaviour of the solution as a whole. It is convenient for many purposes, also, to use Willard Gibbs' term "chemical potential" (p. 64), the partial molar free energies of the components of a solution being identical with their chemical potentials.

Experimentally, we find that if we place one solution in contact with another of different composition, each component passes from the one in which it is more concentrated to the one in which it is more dilute. The partial free energy of each component thus appears to be lowered by the presence of the other components; and, further, the greater is the concentration of the others, the greater is the reduction of its partial free energy. In the limiting case, we may consider only two components, and one of the two solutions may have zero concentration of one of them: we then have a solution containing one solute only, in contact with the pure solvent, and we find that the solute passes into the pure solvent, while the solvent passes into the solution. To some extent, this mutual lowering of the partial free energy is due to the fact that a given volume of a solution contains molecules of all the components, and thus less of any one of them than it would if this one were present alone, the conditions being otherwise unchanged. If this were all, however, we should expect the partial free energies, and, also, other quantities such as the partial specific volumes, to obey some simple law analogous to Dalton's law for perfect gases—i.e. each component would have the same partial free energy, for example, as it would if, without altering the number of its molecules in a given space, all the other components were taken away. This is not so, even approximately, except in very dilute solutions; in general, there are mutual interactions between the components of the solution which complicate the situation very considerably.

Suppose we take some solute—say sucrose—and dissolve it in some solvent—say water. The system (sucrose + water) becomes converted into the system (sucrose dissolved in water); on general principles, it is to be expected that there may, accordingly, be changes in heat content, free energy and entropy. Since these will appear not only when a solution is made up from its components, but also when the concentration of an existing solution is changed, they are known as the *heat*, *free energy* and *entropy*, *of dilution*. These quantities must be related to one another according to the fundamental equation of thermodynamics:

$$\Delta H = \Delta G + T.\Delta S \quad . \quad . \quad . \quad 1.2a, 2.17$$

In an "ideal" solution, as in a perfect gas, the molecules, both of solvent and solute, do not attract or repel one another (apart from bouncing off when they actually collide); there is no kind of chemical or physical "reaction" between them, and ΔH is zero. The entropy change, ΔS, moreover, is a measure only of the change in "randomness" consequent on dispersing the molecules of the solute amongst those of the solvent, and *vice versa*; it is analogous to the increase in entropy of a perfect gas when it is allowed to expand. We shall return to this later. In general, however, owing to the interactions between one solvent, or solute, molecule and another, and between a solvent molecule and a solute molecule, the heat of dilution is not zero, and the entropy of dilution depends upon more complicated factors than the random distribution of molecular "billiard balls". Our knowledge of the nature and magnitude of the forces between molecules of the same or different kinds, is not sufficient to allow us to calculate the free energy of dilution, and the changes in the partial free energies of the components of a solution, except in a few special cases.

FREE ENERGY AND VAPOUR PRESSURE

Suppose that we have a solution which is in equilibrium, at constant temperature and pressure, with its vapour. The partial free energies of the components of the solution must then be equal to the partial free energies of the vapours, otherwise there would not be a state of equilibrium. This is an important point, since, provided that we can apply the gas laws to the behaviour of the vapours, we can readily calculate the work done in transferring a gram-molecule of any one component from the vapour in contact with one solution to that in contact with another solution of different composition. The relevant equation has already been derived in Chapter 1. From the definition of free energy, this must be equal to the difference between the partial free energy of the component considered in the vapour in contact with one solution, and that in contact with the other solution; and thus, also, in the solutions themselves. Let the vapour pressure of this component over one solution be p, and over the other solution be p'. Then the work done in transferring one gram-molecule from one vapour to the other must be given by $RT \ln (p/p')$ (equation 1.12a, p. 21). If $\bar{G}$ and $\bar{G}'$ are the partial molar free energies of this component in the two solutions, we thus have:

$$\bar{G} - \bar{G}' = RT \ln (p/p') \qquad . \qquad . \qquad . \qquad 3.2$$

Let us now consider two special cases. First, suppose that one of the components of the solution is a gas at ordinary temperatures and pressures. We can then apply Henry's law, which states that the concentration of a gas in solution is directly proportional to its partial pressure in the gas phase with which the solution is in equilibrium. This law can readily be derived, both from kinetic and from thermodynamic considerations, provided that the solution is "ideal", by methods similar to those used in deriving Raoult's law (see below). We can thus write:

$$\bar{G} - \bar{G}' = RT \ln (m/m') \qquad . \qquad . \qquad . \qquad 3.3$$

where m and m' are the concentrations of this component in the two solutions considered. This simple relation between the partial molar free energy of a component in solution and its molal concentration is, in fact, extended to cover all kinds of solute, whether gaseous or not, *provided that the concentrations are sufficiently small*. We shall return to this later.

Secondly, let us consider a dilute solution containing for simplicity, one solute only, which may be of any kind; and let us compare the partial free energy of the *other* component—i.e. of the *solvent*—in this solution with its free energy in the pure state at the same temperature and pressure. We now write equation 3.2 as:

$$\bar{G}_1 - G_1^{\circ} = RT \ln (p_1/p_1^{\circ}) \qquad . \qquad . \qquad . \qquad 3.4$$

(It is conventional to use the subscript $_1$ when the solvent is referred to, and the subscripts $_2$ or $_3$ etc. for the solutes. Partial quantities are identified by the use of a bar over the symbol concerned, so that $\bar{G}_1$ represents the partial molar free energy of the solvent: if the pure solvent is being referred to, the symbol is given a superscript $^\circ$, so that G_1° represents the molar free energy of the pure solvent.)

Now the solution is supposed to be dilute, so that p_1 will differ only slightly from p_1°, by an amount which may be written Δp_1. Thus:

$$\bar{G}_1 - G_1^\circ = \Delta\bar{G}_1 = RT \ln\left(1 - \Delta p_1/p_1^\circ\right) \doteqdot -RT(\Delta p_1/p_1^\circ) \qquad . \qquad 3.4a$$

The fraction $\Delta p_1/p_1^\circ$ is known as the "fractional lowering of the vapour pressure". Since it is supposed to be small, simple mathematics shows that the quantity $\ln\left(1 - \Delta p_1/p_1^\circ\right)$ is approximately equal to $-\Delta p_1/p_1^\circ$. Further, experimental observations on the relation of the vapour pressure of the solvent to the concentration of the solute have shown that for sufficiently dilute solutions, the fractional lowering of the vapour pressure is equal to the relative number of solute and solvent molecules. This law, first enunciated by Raoult in 1886 and known by his name, may be expressed in symbols as:

$$\Delta p_1/p_1^\circ = \Delta n_2/n_1 \qquad . \qquad . \qquad . \qquad . \qquad 3.5$$

the Δ signs emphasising that the quantities are small. By comparing equations 3.4a and 3.5, we see that

$$-\Delta\bar{G}_1 = RT(\Delta n_2/n_1) \qquad . \qquad . \qquad . \qquad . \qquad 3.6$$

In dilute solutions, therefore, the reduction in the partial free energy of the solvent is proportional to the concentration of the solute.

That Raoult's law is intrinsically reasonable may be shown from kinetic considerations similar to those used by Langmuir for deriving his adsorption equation (Chapter 5, p. 185). Consider a dilute solution in which the mole fraction of the solute is $\Delta n_2/(n_1 + \Delta n_2)$; let it be in equilibrium with its vapour, the vapour pressure of the solvent being $p_1^\circ - \Delta p_1$, where p_1° is the vapour pressure of the pure solvent. Then we may consider that the rate of condensation at the interface between liquid and vapour will be proportional to the vapour pressure, and may be written $A(p_1^\circ - \Delta p_1)$; while the rate of evaporation may be considered to be proportional to the fraction of the surface occupied by solvent molecules, i.e. may be written $B \cdot n_1/(n_1 + \Delta n_2)$. Since the system is in equilibrium, we must have:

$$A(p_1^\circ - \Delta p_1) = B.n_1/(n_1 + \Delta n_2)$$

At an interface between pure solvent and its vapour, we should have: $A.p_1^\circ = B.n_1/n_1$. Thus:

$$1 - \Delta p_1/p_1^\circ = 1/(1 + \Delta n_2/n_1) \doteqdot 1 - \Delta n_2/n_1$$

or: $\qquad\qquad \Delta p_1/p_1^\circ = \Delta n_2/n_1.$

It is assumed implicitly in this treatment that the presence of the solute molecules has no action on the solvent molecules other than occupying part of the interface, and so interfering with their evaporation. Except in dilute solutions, this is by no means true.

We may also deduce the relation expressed in equation 3.6 and thus, by using equation 3.4a, Raoult's law, from thermodynamic considerations. In an "ideal" solution, as already remarked, the heat of dilution is zero, so that the free energy and entropy of dilution are related by the equation: $-\varDelta G = T.\varDelta S$. Suppose we add $\varDelta n_2$ moles of solute to n_1 moles of solvent; if we assume that the molecules do not interact with one another in any way, the only effect is that the molecules, both of solvent and solute, now become distributed over a greater volume than before. If we assume, also, that all the molecules are of the same size, we can replace the ratio (V_2/V_1) in equation 1.14 (p. 21), by the reciprocal of the mole fraction. Thus, for the solvent:

$$\varDelta \bar{S}_1 = R . \ln \left(\frac{n_1 + \varDelta n_2}{n_1} \right)$$

so that
$$-\varDelta \bar{G}_1 \fallingdotseq RT . \frac{\varDelta n_2}{n_1}.$$

ACTIVITY

The simple relations between the concentration of the solute and the changes in the free energy both of the solute and of the solvent, apply only to quite dilute solutions. In more concentrated solutions, there is no such simple relation; and, indeed, there is no relation at all which applies universally to all kinds of solute. The physico-chemical behaviour of a solution, however, depends upon the partial free energies of its components and only indirectly on their stoichiometrical concentrations. It is necessary, therefore, to abandon the attempt to describe the physico-chemical behaviour of solutions in terms of the concentrations of the components, and to adopt the concept of *activity*, introduced first by Lewis and Randall in 1923.

If the partial molar free energies of a substance in two solutions of different composition are $\bar{G}$ and $\bar{G}'$, then its activities in those two solution, a and a', are given by the equation:

$$\bar{G} - \bar{G}' = \varDelta \bar{G} = RT \ln (a/a') \qquad . \qquad . \qquad . \qquad 3.7$$

The introduction of the logarithmic relation and of the factor RT mean that the ratio of the activities of a substance in two different solutions is identical with the ratio of its partial vapour pressure, so long as the gas laws may be applied to the vapours, as may be seen by comparing equation 3.7 with equation 3.2.

It will be noted that it is not possible to define the activity of a component in a solution without reference to the activity of the same component in some standard state. This results from the close relation between activity and free energy: the energy content of a substance must always be referred to its energy content in some standard state, and no absolute values can be given, as we have seen in Chapter 2. For the solvent, the activity in a solution is referred to the activity of the pure solvent at the same temperature and pressure; this is taken as unity. We can thus write:

$$RT \ln a_1 = \bar{G}_1 - G_1^\circ \quad . \quad . \quad . \quad . \quad 3.8$$

where G_1° is the molar free energy of the solvent in the pure state, and $\bar{G}_1$ is the partial molar free energy of the solvent in the solution considered. Further, by combining equation 3.4 with equation 3.8, we get:

$$RT \ln a_1 = RT \ln (\bar{p}_1 / p_1^\circ)$$

or
$$a_1 = \bar{p}_1 / p_1^\circ \quad . \quad . \quad . \quad . \quad 3.9$$

where $\bar{p}_1$ and p_1° are the partial vapour pressure of the solvent in equilibrium with the solution, and the vapour pressure of pure solvent, respectively.

In dilute solutions, where Raoult's law may be assumed to hold, equations 3.6 and 3.8 may be combined to give:

$$-\Delta(\ln a_1) = -\Delta G_1 / RT = \Delta n_2 / n_1 \quad . \quad . \quad . \quad 3.10$$

or
$$-\Delta(\ln a_1) = \Delta m.M_1 / 1000 \text{ (from equation 3.1)} \quad . \quad . \quad 3.10a$$

$$= 0.018 \Delta m \text{ for aqueous solutions.}$$

In more concentrated solutions, this relation does not hold; it may be modified, however, by introducing an empirical correction known as the "*osmotic coefficient*", and given the symbol ϕ. We thus get, in place of equation 3.10:

$$-\ln a_1 = \phi(\bar{n}_2 / n_1) = \phi.\bar{m}.M_1 / 1000 \quad . \quad . \quad . \quad 3.11$$

$$= 0.018 \, \phi.\bar{m} \text{ for aqueous solutions.}$$

The concentration, $\bar{m}$, is here taken to be that of all the independently active particles in the solution, any association or dissociation of the molecules being taken into account: for electrolytes, for example, we must put $\bar{m} = (\nu_+ + \nu_-)m$, where m is the molar concentration and $(\nu_+ + \nu_-)$ is the total number of ions formed on complete dissociation. It must be remembered that the value of the osmotic coefficient depends on the concentration of the solute, and is different in different kinds of solute; it has no theoretical foundation, and its value must be discovered empirically.

For the solute, we define the standard state to which the activities are to be referred by assuming that in very dilute solutions the activity of the solute is equal to its concentration (or, more strictly, its mole fraction). This assumption is a reasonable one. If a component has zero concentration, it must have zero activity; and as its concentration is increased, it is assumed that at first the activity increases equally. As the concentration becomes greater, however, the activity becomes more and more affected by the interactions of the solute molecules with each other, and with the solvent molecules. Thus we can define the activity of the solute by the equation:

$$\bar{G}_2 - (\bar{G}_2)_0 = RT \ln (a_2/(m)_0) \qquad . \qquad . \qquad . \qquad . \qquad 3.12$$

where $(m)_0$ is the molar concentration of the solute in a solution which is so dilute that m approaches zero, and $(\bar{G}_2)_0$ is the partial molar free energy of the solute in this solution.

As in the case of the solvent, if the solution is "ideal", we may write:

$$-\varDelta G_2 = T . \varDelta S_2$$

and

$$\varDelta S_2 = -R . \ln \left(\frac{\varDelta n_2}{\varDelta n_2 + n_1} \right)$$

Thus

$$\varDelta G_2 = RT . \ln \left(\frac{\varDelta n_2}{\varDelta n_2 + n_1} \right) .$$

This is the molar free energy change when $\varDelta n_2$ moles of the solid solute are dissolved in n_1 moles of the solvent. In solutions of different concentration, therefore, the partial molar free energy of the solute will be proportional to the logarithm of the mole fraction.

The ratio of the activity of a substance to its mole fraction (or, alternatively, to its molal concentration) is known as the *activity coefficient*. Since the activity of the solute is taken to be equal to the concentration in very dilute solutions, the activity coefficient of the solute approaches unity as its concentration is reduced. Since, moreover, the activity of the pure solvent is assumed to be unity, and its molar fraction is also unity, the activity coefficient of the solvent also approaches unity as the concentration of the solute becomes smaller.

The ratio of the activity to the mole fraction is the "rational" activity coefficient, given the symbol f; the ratio of the activity to the molal concentration is the "molal" activity coefficient, given the symbol γ. The relation between them is given by:

$$f = \gamma (1 + 0 \cdot 001 \ m . M_1)$$

where m is the molal concentration and M_1 is the molecular weight of the solvent. If the solvent is water, f is 1 per cent. greater than γ when m is $0 \cdot 556$ M. In the same way, the "rational" osmotic coefficient, g, is to be distinguished from the "molal" osmotic coefficient, ϕ.

Some figures for the activity coefficients in solutions of cane sugar in water are given in Table 3.1; the methods by which they were determined will be discussed in the next section. Solutions of cane sugar are among the most nearly "ideal" solutions of any known, and it will be noticed that the activity coefficient of the solvent does not depart appreciably from unity until the concentration becomes greater than about $3M$. The activity coefficient then falls, showing that the solute does more than merely occupy the space which would otherwise be occupied by the solvent, but reduces the partial free energy of each solvent molecule. The activity coefficient of the solute, on the other hand, departs from unity at concentrations greater than about $0.8M$, and then rises steadily.

TABLE 3.1

The Activity Coefficients of Water and Cane Sugar in Aqueous Solutions at 50° C.

Molar Concentration per kg. water	Mole Fraction of Water	Activity Coefficient of Water	Activity Coefficient of Cane Sugar
0·333	0·994	0·9999	1·000
0·767	0·986	1·007	1·000
0·99	0·983	0·997	1·134
1·93	0·966	0·995	1·437
3·33	0·944	0·985	1·847
6·77	0·891	0·935	2·801

(From data by Perman, 1928)

THE MEASUREMENT OF ACTIVITY

We will assume, for simplicity in description, that the solutions considered are aqueous, and contain non-volatile solutes only. In such solutions, the activity of the solute can only be determined directly in certain special cases, notably that of many kinds of electrolyte which will be considered in the next chapter. It can, however, be calculated from that of the solvent, provided that we have sufficiently extensive information, owing to the fact that there is a general relation between partial quantities, of any kind, in any system.

Suppose we have a certain volume of a solution containing n_1 moles of solvent and n_2 moles of some solute. The free energy of the solution as a whole will be made up by the contributions of the solvent and the solute in proportion to the amounts present, so that:

$$G = \bar{G}_1 . n_1 + \bar{G}_2 . n_2 \qquad . \qquad . \qquad . \qquad 3.13$$

where $\bar{G}_1$ and $\bar{G}_2$ are the partial molar free energies of the solvent and the solute, respectively, in the conditions of the particular solution considered. These quantities, of course, are not necessarily constant, and, indeed, are rarely so, except in very dilute solutions.

Now, suppose that we increase n_1 and n_2 by very small amounts dn_1 and dn_2. $\bar{G}_1$ and $\bar{G}_2$ will then remain sensibly constant, and the change in the free energy of the solution may be represented by:

$$dG = \bar{G}_1 . dn_1 + \bar{G}_2 . dn_2 \qquad . \qquad . \qquad . \qquad 3.14$$

If, for example n_2 is kept constant, then $dn_2 = 0$ and we have:

$$\bar{G}_1 = (\partial G / \partial n_1)_{n_2}.$$

Similarly, if n_1 is kept constant, we have:

$$\bar{G}_2 = (\partial G / \partial n_2)_{n_1}.$$

This notation expresses concisely the definition of a partial quantity as given already (p. 79).

It is a consequence of the way in which partial quantities are defined that an equation such as equation 3.14 must describe *completely* the change in the free energy of the solution; it is what is known as an "exact" or "complete" differential. But if, without considering any special properties of the quantities involved, we differentiate equation 3.13 quite generally, we get:

$$dG = G_1 . dn_1 + G_2 . dn_2 + n_1 . dG_1 + n_2 . dG_2 \qquad . \qquad . \qquad 3.15$$

Since, however, equation 3.14 must be true, we deduce that:

$$n_1 . dG_1 + n_2 . dG_2 = 0 \qquad . \qquad . \qquad . \qquad . \qquad 3.16$$

This is an important, and quite general, relation between partial quantities; it is not restricted to partial molar free energies, although we shall make use of it in this form.

This deduction may, perhaps, appear to rest on a mathematical "sleight of hand". It is possible, however, to evaluate, for example, the partial molar volumes, $\bar{V}_1$ and $\bar{V}_2$, of, say ethanol and water in mixtures of the two substances in known proportions, from measurements of the densities of the mixtures. It is found that as the ratio of n_1 to n_2 is changed, $\bar{V}_1$ and $\bar{V}_2$ change in opposite directions, as is required by equation 3.16, and that when n_1 is small and n_2 large, a large change in $\bar{V}_2$ is accompanied by a small change in $\bar{V}_1$, and *vice versa*.

If we now replace the partial free energies by the corresponding activities, we get:

$$n_1.d(\ln a_1) + n_2.d(\ln a_2) = 0 \qquad . \qquad . \qquad . \quad 3.17$$

By integrating this equation, we can derive the ratio of the solute activities in two solutions A and B of different concentrations, i.e.

$$(\ln a_2)_A - (\ln a_2)_B = \int_A^B \frac{n_1}{n_2} d(\ln a_1) . \qquad . \qquad . \quad 3.18$$

The sign of integration emphasises that we must know the solvent activities, not only in solutions A and B, but also in solutions of all the intermediate concentrations. We must, in fact, know how the activity of the solvent varies with the concentration of the solute throughout the whole range between that of solution A and that of solution B. The form of this relation varies from solute to solute, and is usually of such a nature that the integration is best performed graphically. It is usual, of course, to arrange that one of the solutions, say solution A, is very dilute, so that $(a_2)_A$ can be put equal to $(m)_A$. In equation 3.17, the activities may be replaced by the activity coefficients f_1 and f_2. We get:

$$n_1.d(\ln f_1) + n_2.d(\ln f_2) + n_1.d(\ln N_1) + n_2.d(\ln N_2) = 0$$

where $N_1 = n_1/(n_1 + n_2)$ and $N_2 = n_2/(n_1 + n_2)$ and are the molar fractions of the solvent and the solute, respectively. Application of the elementary principles of the differential calculus shows that

$$n_1.d(\ln N_1) + n_2.d(\ln N_2) = 0.$$

Equation 3.18 may thus be put in the form:

$$(\ln f_2)_B - (\ln f_2)_A = \int_A^B \frac{n_1}{n_2} d(\ln f_1) \qquad . \qquad . \quad 3.18a$$

This is often the more convenient form of the expression, since if one solution is very dilute, the activity coefficient of the solute in this solution is unity, and the second term on the left-hand side vanishes.

There are several different methods of measuring the activity of the *solvent*, all of which, however, depend on the same principle. Owing to the close theoretical connection between activity and vapour pressure, the most fundamental method is to measure the vapour pressure of the solvent in equilibrium with the unknown solution, and in equilibrium with the pure solvent, respectively. This method can, of course, be used also for determining the activity of a *volatile* solute. But when we are dealing with solutions which contain only non-volatile solutes, the free surfaces of the solution and the pure solvent may be considered as acting as barriers which allow the solvent molecules to pass through, but not those of the solute. In the presence of such a barrier, we may change the temperature or pressure of either the solution or the pure solvent, and thus change the free energy so that with respect to the solvent the two systems are in equilibrium. Two other forms of barrier may also be used. We may interpose a "semi-permeable membrane" between the solution and the pure solvent, and we can then prevent the solvent passing through it into the solution by raising the hydrostatic pressure of the latter. This pressure is known as the *osmotic pressure* of the solution. Alternatively, the barrier may be formed by the surface of the solid solvent at its freezing point; we find that in order just to prevent the solvent from melting, we have to lower its temperature to a value below the freezing point of the pure solvent.

THE VAPOUR PRESSURE OF AQUEOUS SOLUTIONS

We will consider first the use of the vapour phase to separate the solution from the pure solvent. If both are at the same temperature, water will evaporate from the pure solvent and condense on the solution: but this may be prevented by lowering the temperature of the former, or raising that of the latter. If we choose to raise the temperatures of both solvent and solution so that the vapour pressures are equal to the atmospheric pressure—i.e. so that they boil—the temperature of the solution will be found to be greater than that of the pure solvent. This is the principle of the method by which the molar concentration of a solution is estimated by means of the elevation of the boiling point. The relation between the difference in temperature necessary to equalise the vapour pressures (at any value), and the fractional lowering of the vapour pressure in the solution, can be calculated theoretically, using the same principles as those used for calculating the depression of the freezing point, which will be outlined later; it may also be discovered by comparison with other methods of measuring the vapour pressure. Data for most simple solutions will be found in tables of physical and chemical constants, such as the International Critical Tables. It is common in practice, however, to proceed by finding, by trial and error, a solution of known solvent activity which is in equilibrium with the unknown solution when both are at the same temperature. Solutions of sodium chloride are ordinarily used.

The concept of solvent activity is less familiar than that of concentration. It is common, therefore, particularly when dealing with solutions containing many different kinds of solute, and whose composition may not be completely known, to describe the solvent activity in terms of the *total molecular concentration*, sometimes called *osmolar concentration*. This is the molar concentration of a solution of sodium chloride which, after multiplication by the appropriate osmotic coefficient, has the same solvent activity as has the unknown solution under examination. Measurement of this concentration is important in the study of the conditions of equilibrium and steady state between the various fluids that are met with in relation to living organisms: between the fluid within the living cells and the fluid immediately outside them; and between this fluid and the fluid outside the organism as a whole, and any fluids which may be produced by the organism, possibly as a result of "secretion".

The Measurement of Vapour Pressure. The earliest method used was to introduce the solution under investigation into the vacuum at the top of a barometer tube, and to measure the reduction in the height of the mercury column. This method clearly cannot be used when the solution contains dissolved gases or other volatile solutes, since they would come out of solution in the vacuum. The most direct method, but one which can only be used in certain cases, is to analyse chemically the gas in equilibrium with the solution, and to calculate the partial pressure exerted by the vapours by means of Henry's law.

A more generally useful method is that of measuring the *Dew Point*. A highly polished capsule is inserted into the vapour and cooled (usually by means of the evaporation of ether) until dew just forms on it. The temperature of the capsule is then measured. This, clearly, is the temperature to which the pure solvent must be cooled in order that it may be in equilibrium with the solution. At lower temperatures, dew continues to form, so that water must evaporate from the solution; at higher temperatures, the dew evaporates off and condenses on the solution.

When only very small quantities of the solution are available, and great accuracy is not required, the *method of Barger* will be found useful, and easily carried out. It is based on the fact that the solvent will pass from a solution which is less concentrated to one which is more concentrated: the unknown solution is matched against a series of solutions of known concentration until one is found with which there is no interchange of solvent. Alternate drops of one of the known solutions and the unknown solution are placed in a capillary tube as shown in Fig. 3.1 (A); and their lengths measured under a microscope. A number of such tubes are made up with different known solutions, and the change in the lengths of the drops measured over a period of 24 hours or more; the tubes being placed in a water-bath during this period. By interpolation, one can then discover the concentration of, say, sodium chloride in the known solution which would occasion no change in the length of any of the drops. Strictly, the passage of the solvent from one drop to another does not take place solely, or even chiefly, through the vapour phase; there is considerable diffusion in the film of fluid on the walls of the tube. The method has been improved in respect of accuracy by the modifications introduced by Urspring and Blum; details and references will be found in the monograph by Krogh (1939).

The most accurate determinations, when only small volumes of solution are available, are made by the *thermo-electric* method. This was developed by A. V. Hill as a result of his work, and that of his colleagues, on the heat production of muscles, necessitating the use of highly sensitive thermopiles and galvanometers. A small piece of filter-paper, soaked in the unknown solution,

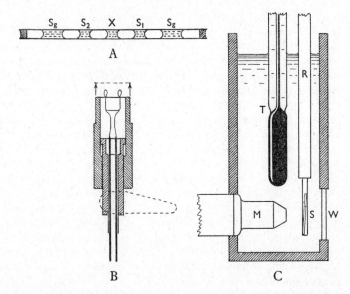

FIG. 3.1. THE MEASUREMENT OF VAPOUR PRESSURE AND FREEZING POINT

A. *Barger's Method for Vapour Pressure.* A capillary tube, of hard glass, some 0·3 to 1 mm. diameter, contains a drop of the unknown solution, X, in the middle, with a drop of some standard solution (usually of NaCl in known concentration) on each side of it, S_1 and S_2; beyond these, again, are "guard" drops, S_g, also of the standard solution. (The drops are inserted into the tube in succession, from one end.) The ends of the tube are sealed with soft wax. Several such tubes are prepared, each with a standard solution of slightly different concentration, mounted close together on a microscope slide, and placed in a water bath. The lengths of the drops are measured under a microscope at intervals of 12 to 24 hours, and the concentration of S is found, by interpolation if necessary, such that the lengths of drops X, S_1 and S_2 remain unchanged. This gives the equivalent concentration of the unknown solution X.   (Barger, 1904.)

B. *Thermo-electric Method of Hill and Baldes.* The two loops at the top contain thermo-junctions. A drop of the unknown solution is placed in one, and a drop of a standard solution in the other. The walls of the shield, which can be lowered for insertion of the drops and raised to protect them from draughts, are covered with filter paper soaked in the standard solution. The whole is placed in an accurate and well lagged thermostat, and the leads from the thermo-junctions connected to a suitable, very sensitive galvano-meter. The deflection is read after an interval, when thermal equilibrium has been established. Several such measurements are made, with different concentrations of standard solution, and, by interpolation, the concentration is found at which there is no difference in temperature between the two drops.   (From Krogh, 1939.)

C. *Measurement of Freezing Point (Ramsay).* The sample under investigation is con-tained within a fine capillary tube, some 20 to 70 μ diameter, which is inserted in a larger tube, some 1 mm. diameter, partly filled with liquid paraffin. This is shown at S, mounted on a brass rod R. The sample tube, S, and a Beckmann thermometer, T, graduated in 0·01° C., are contained in a chamber filled with 30 per cent. alcohol, cooled initially to about $-5°$ C., and stirred continuously. The ice crystals in the sample are observed by a microscope, M, mounted in the wall of the chamber opposite a window, W. The whole is placed in an outer box which is itself surrounded by a lagged jacket, containing 30 per cent. alcohol at $-5°$ C. A coil of resistance wire (not shown) is wound round the inner chamber, so that by passing a suitable current, its temperature can be raised at any desired rate (some 0·005° per minute as the final crystals of ice are melted). The tem-perature is then read on the thermometer.   (After Ramsay, 1949.)

is placed in contact with one set of junctions in the thermopile, and another similar piece, soaked in a sodium chloride solution of known concentration, is placed in contact with the other set of junctions. The whole thermopile is placed within a chamber whose walls are covered with filter paper soaked in the solution of known concentration, and the whole chamber is immersed in an accurate thermostat. Suppose, for example, that the unknown solution is more concentrated than the known solution. Water will distil from the walls of the chamber and condense on the unknown solution: the thermojunctions with which it is in contact are consequently warmed as a result of the latent heat of condensation. In principle, the equilibrium difference in temperature would be that which would raise the vapour pressure of the solution to a value equal to that of the known solution on the walls of the protecting chamber: actually, however, heat is lost by conduction through the walls and wires of the thermopile, and a steady state is reached when the difference in temperature is considerably smaller than this. The concentration of the known solution is adjusted, in successive trials, until it has nearly the same vapour pressure as the unknown solution, and the residual difference is estimated from the deflection of the galvanometer connected to the thermopile; the apparatus is calibrated by placing solutions of known concentration in contact with both sets of thermojunctions.

In an improvement of the method, made by Baldes, a single pair of junctions, made of very fine wire, and of materials with a low heat conductivity such as constantan and manganin, is used. The wires are bent into loops as shown in Fig. 3.1 (B), and a drop of the fluid under examination, which may be as small as $0 \cdot 1 \mu l$ in volume, is placed in one of the loops, and a drop of a solution of known concentration is placed in the other. The drops must be placed on the thermojunctions in an atmosphere which is kept saturated with water vapour, in order to guard against the very rapid rate of evaporation of these very small drops. Further improvements in the general design have been made by Krogh; descriptions of the apparatus and references to the original papers will be found in his monograph (1939). The use of the thermo-electric method is apt to be limited by the fact that the galvanometer must have more than ordinary sensitivity; it must be of low resistance (not more than 10 ohms) and give a deflection of at least 1 mm. for a current of 10^{-9} ampere.

Descriptions of methods not specially intended for use with very small volumes will be found in the book by Robinson and Stokes (1955).

The *elevation of the boiling point* is a method much used by chemists, but it is only applicable when the components of the solution under examination are stable at the boiling point. Few solutions of interest to the physiologist, however, are completely unaffected by boiling, so that the method is rarely used by them.

THE OSMOTIC PRESSURE OF SOLUTIONS

Suppose that we have a mixture of nitrogen and carbon dioxide consisting of one-fifth nitrogen and four-fifths carbon dioxide at atmospheric pressure.

If such a mixture is put in a bell-shaped vessel with a wet parchment paper tied over the large end, and pure carbon dioxide is placed on the outer side of the membrane, carbon dioxide will pass in more rapidly than nitrogen will pass out, since it is more soluble in the wet paper. If we have a manometer connected to the interior of the bell-jar, we shall observe that the pressure inside will rise until the partial pressure of carbon dioxide is the same inside and out. But since the influx of carbon dioxide will dilute the nitrogen, and so change its partial pressure, it is better for the sake of quantitative description to imagine that, before immersion in the carbon dioxide atmosphere, we have raised the internal pressure by forcing in more of the gaseous mixture until the partial pressure of the carbon dioxide is one atmosphere, and there is thus no flow of carbon dioxide inwards or outwards. In order to do this, the total pressure must be increased by a factor of 5/4, and will thus become 1·25 atmospheres. We have attained equilibrium by making the partial pressure of carbon dioxide the same on both sides of the membrane; and the necessary increase in pressure (0·25 atm.) is a measure of the ratio of the partial pressure of nitrogen in the mixture to the partial pressure of carbon dioxide (1/5 to 4/5), and thus of the "concentration" of nitrogen, the indiffusible component.

Let us now make an analogous experiment with a liquid system. A membrane of copper ferrocyanide is freely permeable to water, but refuses passage to cane sugar in solution. If, therefore, a solution of cane sugar in a closed vessel is separated from pure water by such a membrane, water will pass into the solution; and it will continue to do so unless and until the hydrostatic pressure of the solution is increased to such an extent that something that might be called the "effective partial pressure" of the water in the solution is made equal to that of the pure water. This will occur, as we have seen, when the partial molar free energy of the water in the solution is equal to the molar free energy of the pure water. We have to inquire, therefore, how the partial free energy varies with the hydrostatic pressure, and how this varies with changes in the concentration of the cane sugar, or other solute. The latter is, of course, of greater practical importance than the former, and historically, was investigated first. But the problem cannot be treated generally and, without restriction to particular conditions, without considering the free energies.

The process by which water passes through a membrane from a solution on the one side to another solution on the opposite side has been known, since the time of Dutrochet, who first studied it in 1827, as "endosmosis" or "exosmosis", so that the pressure due to this passage of water was naturally called "*osmotic*". Quantitative observations on the relation of the osmotic pressure to the concentration of the solute were first made by the botanists Pfeffer and de Vries, in 1877 and 1884, in connection with the phenomena of plasmolysis and turgor in plant cells. (By "plasmolysis" is meant a just detectable shrinking of the living proto- plasts which surround the central vacuoles of plant cells, so that they become detached from the cellulose envelopes; by "turgor" is meant the hydrostatic pressure within the vacuoles. Both phenomena depend on the relation between the osmotic pressure of the vacuolar contents and that of the solution outside them, the living protoplasts providing almost perfect "semi-permeable" membranes.) The experiments of Pfeffer served as the starting-point of subsequent work on osmotic pressure, especially as they formed the basis of the theory of solutions put forward by van't Hoff. He found that the osmotic pressure was directly proportional to the concentration of the solute, and to the absolute temperature. The simi- larity of this relation to the corresponding one in gases is obvious; and it was emphasised, and precisely formulated, by van't Hoff in 1885. Van't Hoff showed that the osmotic pressure developed by, say, one mole of a substance in solution in a given volume of solvent, is identical with the pressure which it would exert if present as a gas in the same total volume and at the same temperature. Thus if V is the volume of solvent which contains 1 mole of the solute, and Π is the osmotic pressure, we can write, for dilute solution:

$$\Pi.V = RT \qquad . \qquad . \qquad . \qquad . \quad 3.19$$

where R has the same value as it has in the well-known equation of state for perfect gases: $pV = RT$.

In equation 3.19, the volume V is, of course, the reciprocal of the molar concentration expressed in terms of 1 *litre* of solvent. If the solvent is water, this is sensibly identical with the molar concentration, m, expressed in terms of 1 kilogram of water. We can thus write equation 3.19 in the alternative form:

$$\Pi = RT.m \qquad . \qquad . \qquad . \qquad . \quad 3.19a$$

Van't Hoff originally took V to represent the volume of *solution* which contains 1 mole of solute, i.e. as the reciprocal of the volume concentration, c. Actual measurements, both of relatively concentrated solutions of such substances as cane sugar, and of all solutions of colloidal substances such as proteins, agree better with the simple theory if the concentration is expressed as moles per kilogram of water, rather than as moles per litre of solution. In such solutions, there is a considerable difference between the two methods of expressing concentration.

On account of the importance of van't Hoff's theory, the actual words of the author himself may be given:

1. "*Loi de Boyle pour les Solutions.*—La pression osmotique est pro- portionnelle à la concentration, si la température reste invariable.

2. *"Loi de Gay-Lussac pour les Solutions.*—La pression osmotique est proportionnelle à la température absolue, si la concentration reste invariable.

Ce sont là les analogies qui ont été démontrées et vérifiées en détail dans le travail cité; elles ont rapport à la variation de la pression avec les circonstances. Je vais ajouter maintenant une troisième proposition, ayant rapport à la grandeur absolue de cette pression, et n'étant, en réalité, autre chose qu'une extension de la loi d'Avogadro.

3. *"Loi d'Avogadro pour les Solutions.*—La pression exercée par les gaz à une température déterminée, si un même nombre de molécules en occupe un volume donné, est égale à la pression osmotique qu'exerce dans les mêmes circonstances la grande majorité des corps, dissous dans les liquides quelconques." ("Une propriété générale de la matière diluée." *Kon. Svenska Vetenskaps-Akad. Handl.* vol. 21, No. 17, pp. 42 and 43, 1885.)

At normal temperature and pressure, 1 mole of a gas occupies 22·4 litres, so that if 1 mole of a solid is dissolved in 22·4 litres of water, its osmotic pressure should be 1 atmosphere. Further, if 1 mole of a gas is made to occupy 1 litre, it will have a pressure of 22·4 atmospheres, by Boyle's law; the osmotic pressure exerted by a 1 M. solution is thus 22·4 atmospheres. Let us take an example from one of Pfeffer's experiments. A 4 per cent. solution of cane sugar gave at 15° C. an osmotic pressure of 208·2 cm. Hg. By Gay-Lussac's law, supposing it to apply, this would be, at 0° C., $208 \cdot 2 \times 273/(273+15)=197 \cdot 4$ cm. Hg. One mole of the sugar weighs 342 g., so that the number of litres of a 4 per cent. solution which contain 1 mole is $342/40=8 \cdot 55$. Hence its osmotic pressure should be $76 \times 22 \cdot 4/8 \cdot 55=199$ cm. Hg., a very close agreement, considering the difficulty of the measurement.

This rather surprising identity between the constants of proportionality in the two equations arises from the existence of a necessary and close relation between osmotic pressure and the fractional lowering of vapour pressure, as was demonstrated by van't Hoff himself. If a solution is in equilibrium with the pure solvent at a semi-permeable membrane, it must be at a greater hydrostatic pressure than the solvent, the difference being the osmotic pressure, Π. Now in order to transfer 1 mole of solvent from one system to another which is at a greater pressure, work must be done; if the pressure difference is Π, and the volume occupied by 1 mole is v_1^o (the specific volume), the work will be $v_1^o.\Pi$ (assuming v_1^o to be independent of the pressure). Since the solution and the solvent are in equilibrium when the solution is at a pressure Π, the partial free energy of the solvent must be the same on both sides of the semi-permeable membrane. In the absence of the hydrostatic pressure, therefore, we may conclude that the partial free energy of the solvent in the solution is less than that of the pure solvent by an amount equal to the work term; if the solution is very dilute, this may be taken to be equal to $v_1^o.\Pi$. (In the same way, we concluded in an earlier section that the difference between the partial free energy of the solvent in the solution and that in the pure solvent was equal to the work done in compressing the vapour from its partial pressure in equilibrium with the solution to its partial pressure in equilibrium with the solvent.) Thus we have:

$$\bar{G}_1 - G_1^\circ = -v_1^\circ.\varPi.$$

But we have already seen in an earlier section that:

$$\bar{G}_1 - G_1^\circ = RT \ln (p_1/p_1^\circ) \qquad . \qquad . \qquad . \qquad 3.4$$

where p_1 and p_1° are the vapour pressures of the solvent in equilibrium with the solution and with the pure solvent, respectively. Thus:

$$v_1^\circ.\varPi = -RT \ln (p_1/p_1^\circ) \doteqdot RT(\varDelta p_1/p_1^\circ)$$

If we now insert Raoult's law (equation 3.5), we get:

$$v_1^\circ.\varPi = RT(\varDelta n_2/n_1)$$

Now $n_1 v_1^\circ$ is the volume occupied by n_1 moles of solvent. Since this contains $\varDelta n_2$ moles of solute, we have: $n_1 v_1^\circ/\varDelta n_2 = V$, where V is the volume of solvent (in litres) which contains 1 mole of solute. Thus:

$$\varPi.V = RT \qquad . \qquad . \qquad . \qquad 3.19$$

Raoult's law and van't Hoff's law are thus mutually related; either may be deduced from the other.

This simple relation, applicable strictly only in quite restricted conditions, is, on the whole, adequate for most physiological purposes. It is clear, however, from the previous paragraph, that the osmotic pressure of a solution is a measure of the activity of the *solvent* in that solution; it has no direct and necessary relation to the concentration of the solute. The *activity* of the solute can, however, be calculated by means of the general differential equation given above (equation 3.18). If a less rigid and precise treatment is adequate, and the solution is too concentrated for the simple van't Hoff equation to be accurate enough, we may introduce the "osmotic coefficient", using equation 3.11 in place of equation 3.10 for the relation between solvent activity and solute concentration. We then get:

$$\varPi = \phi RT.m \qquad . \qquad . \qquad . \qquad 3.20$$

The value of ϕ may, of course, be derived from measurements of solvent activity by any of the methods available. It was, however, first introduced as an empirical correction to the van't Hoff equation.

The derivation of the relation between osmotic pressure and lowering of vapour pressure (and thus of solvent activity) given above is not strictly correct. If the solution is not very dilute, we must replace the specific volume of the pure solvent, v_1^o, by the partial specific volume of the solvent in the particular solution considered, $\bar{v}_1$. The effect on the free energy of a system of changing its pressure was considered in Chapter 1 from pure energetic considerations, and we may now apply equation 1.5a. The partial free energy of the solvent, therefore, will vary with the applied pressure according to the relation:

$$dG_1 = \bar{v}_1 . dp \qquad . \qquad . \qquad . \qquad . \qquad 1.5a$$

Hence, if the pressure of the solution must be raised from p_0 to p in order to maintain the solvent within it in equilibrium with the pure solvent, the change in the partial free energy will be given by:

$$\int_{p_0}^{p} dG_1 = (G_1)_p - (G_1)_{p_0} = \int_{p_0}^{p} \bar{v}_1 . dp$$

But since the system is in equilibrium, the pressure p must have been chosen so that $(G_1)_p = (G_1^o)_{p_0}$, where $(G_1^o)_{p_0}$ is the molar free energy of the pure solvent at the pressure p_0.

Thus
$$(G_1^o)_{p_0} - (G_1)_{p_0} = \int_{p_0}^{p} \bar{v}_1 . dp = \bar{v}_1 . \Pi \qquad . \qquad . \qquad . \qquad 3.21$$

where Π is the osmotic pressure. The integration assumes that $\bar{v}_1$ is independent of the pressure: this is not strictly true, although the error introduced is small except in solutions with very large osmotic pressures. In concentrated solutions, also, the value of $\bar{v}_1$ varies with the concentration of the solution; it must be derived from the slope of the volume-concentration curve of the substance investigated, and not taken as the volume occupied by 1 mole of solvent at one particular concentration.

Further, from the definition of activity, we have:

$$(G_1)_{p_0} - (G_1^o)_{p_0} = RT(\ln a_1)_{p_0} \qquad . \qquad . \qquad . \qquad 3.8$$

so that
$$-\bar{v}_1 \Pi = RT \ln a_1 \qquad . \qquad . \qquad . \qquad . \qquad 3.22$$

In Table 3.2 are given some figures for the osmotic pressure of cane sugar solutions, as observed, and as calculated. Even at a concentration of 0·1 molar, the observed values differ quite appreciably from those calculated from the simple van't Hoff equation; and at higher concentrations the discrepancy is large. If, however, the activity is calculated from measurements of the vapour pressure, and the value of the osmotic pressure is then calculated by means of equation 3.22, we find a remarkably good agreement with the values obtained by direct measurement, even at quite high concentrations.

D

TABLE 3.2

The Osmotic Pressures of Cane Sugar Solutions

as directly observed, and as calculated from the van't Hoff relation (equation 3.19) and from the solvent activity (equation 3.21).

Concentration moles/kg. water	$\bar{v}_1$ per gram	$-\ln a_1$	Osmotic Pressure, atm.		
			Observed	Calculated	
				Eqn. 3.19	Eqn. 3.22
0·1	—	—	2·59	2·39	—
0·3	—	—	7·61	7·17	—
0·5	—	—	12·75	11·95	—
0·8	—	—	20·91	19·12	—
1·0	—	—	26·64	23·90	
1·65	0·99515	0·03516	43·84	—	43·91
2·38	0·99157	0·05380	67·68	—	67·43
3·28	0·98690	0·07983	100·43	—	100·53
4·12	0·98321	0·10669	134·71	—	134·86

The upper five lines are from data by Morse and Fraser, the lower four lines are from data by Berkeley, Hartley and Burton.

The Measurement of the Osmotic Pressure. This may be done either by Pfeffer's method of measuring the pressure produced in the osmometer when one side of the membrane is immersed in water at atmospheric pressure, or by that of Berkeley of measuring the pressure necessary to be applied to the solution in order to prevent the passage of the solvent in either direction. The measurements are of considerable experimental difficulty, when crystalloidal solutions are used, and can only be done in certain cases, owing to the fact that we know of so few appropriate semi-permeable membranes. Copper ferrocyanide, supported within the walls of a porous pot is one of the best; and gelatin, hardened in tannin may also be used. The pressures developed may be very great, and elaborate precautions are necessary to prevent leakage. This problem can be avoided by balancing the osmotic pressure of the unknown solution inside the osmometer by that due to a solution of cane sugar, or other suitable substance, in known concentration, outside. This involves, of course, an accurate knowledge of the osmotic pressure of the compensating solution. Direct measurements of osmotic pressure are now rarely made, except with colloidal solutions, since the measurement of vapour pressure is technically easier. The use of osmotic pressure measurements for determining the molecular weight of a colloidal substance will be considered in Chapter 6.

Since dyes of the molecular weight of Congo-red are just sufficiently large to be unable to pass through parchment paper, collodion or cellophane, and yet give considerable osmotic pressures, they form very useful substances for the investigation of many problems relating to osmotic pressure. The difficulty of preparing reliable copper ferrocyanide membranes, and of dealing with very large pressures, is thus avoided. A 0·01 M. solution of Congo-red has an osmotic pressure of about 170 mm. Hg., and that of Chicago-blue is nearly double. Both substances are colloidal electrolytes, and the osmotic pressure will be affected by the presence of other electrolytes, this point will be discussed in Chapter 6.

Knowledge of the actual magnitude of the osmotic pressure is of interest to plant physiologists, since it is this which is largely responsible for the production of turgor in the cells, and perhaps, also, to some extent for the ascent of sap. The animal physiologist is less concerned with the large osmotic pressures which may be developed by crystalloidal solutions, since animal cells will not withstand such pressures and they consequently do not occur. But he is greatly concerned with the smaller pressures developed by colloidal solutions. The various fluids mentioned earlier in connection with the importance of measurements of the total molecular concentration, are mostly separated from each other by membranes or sheets of tissue cells which are impermeable to colloids. Osmotic pressures may thus be developed which affect considerably the passage of water from one of these fluids to another.

The Depression of the Freezing Point

Experimental observations over the course of some 150 years have provided two empirical laws. In 1788 Blagden put forward his law which states that the lowering of the freezing point of a solution is proportional to the concentration of that solution; and in 1883 Raoult stated that equimolecular quantities of various substances in the same solvent lowered its freezing point by the same amount. The position is thus very similar to that of the lowering of the vapour pressure.

These laws can be deduced from considerations of pure energetics provided, once more, that simplifying assumptions are made. At the freezing point, the pure solid solvent is in equilibrium with the liquid solvent, and their molar free energies must therefore be the same. But in a solution, the partial molar free energy of the solvent is less than the molar free energy of the pure solvent. If the temperature is changed, the free energies of both the pure solid solvent and the liquid solvent in the solution will change; and at some particular temperature it is possible that they will become equal. For this to occur, the change in temperature needed will be determined by the rates of change of free energy with temperature in the solid solvent and in the liquid solvent in the solution, respectively. The system is thus more complicated than that considered in connection with the vapour pressure; and the full equations relating the freezing point depression to the free energy changes are thus rather elaborate.

We start with the relation between the free energy content of a system and its temperature, at constant pressure, which was derived in Chapter 1, i.e.

$$dG/dT = -S \qquad . \qquad . \qquad . \qquad . \qquad 1.5b$$

Let T_0 be the temperature at which pure water freezes, and T be the temperature at which the solution under consideration freezes; $\Delta T (= T_0 - T)$ is thus the freezing point depression. Thus for the ice, we deduce that:

Thus
$$(G_s)_{T_0} - (G_s)_T = -\int_T^{T_0} S_s dT \qquad . \qquad . \qquad . \qquad 3.23$$

Similarly for the water:

$$(\bar{G}_1)_{T_0} - (\bar{G}_1)_T = -\int_T^{T_0} \bar{S}_1 dT \qquad . \qquad . \qquad 3.24$$

S_s being the molar entropy of ice and $\bar{S}_1$ the partial molar entropy of the water. But since the ice is in equilibrium with pure water at the temperature T_0, and with the water in the solution at the temperature T, we must have:

$$(G_s)_{T_0} = (G_1^\circ)_{T_0} \text{ and } (G_s)_T = (\bar{G}_1)_T$$

Subtracting equation 3.24 from equation 3.23, and inserting these equalities, we get:

$$(G_1^\circ)_{T_0} - (\bar{G}_1)_{T_0} = -\int_T^{T_0} (\bar{S}_1 - S_s) dT \qquad . \qquad . \qquad 3.25$$

But from the definition of activity in equation 3.8, the left-hand side of this equation is identical with $RT.\ln a_1$, where a_1 is the activity of the water at the freezing point. Further, in the discussion in Chapter 1 on the various forms of energy, we deduced the relation:

$$H = G + T.S . \qquad . \qquad . \qquad . \qquad 1.2a$$

Thus for ice and water in equilibrium at any temperature, we have:

$$\bar{S}_1 - S_s = (\bar{H}_1 - H_s)/T . \qquad . \qquad . \qquad 3.26$$

since $\bar{G}_1$ must be equal to G_s. We now make the assumption that

$$\bar{H}_1 - H_s = H_1^\circ - H_s = \Delta H \qquad . \qquad . \qquad 3.27$$

where ΔH is the change in the heat content when a mole of ice becomes water, i.e. the latent heat of fusion of ice. It can be shown that this assumption, that the partial molar heat content of the solvent in the solution is identical with the molar heat content of the pure solvent, means that the final expression (equation 3.28 below) gives the activity of the solvent at the freezing point of the solution, and not at that of the pure solvent. In ordinary aqueous solutions, not highly concentrated, the difference is negligible. We may note here, in parenthesis, that ΔH is positive, and heat is absorbed when the solid melts; the entropy of the liquid must thus be greater than that of the solid—a fact which is in accordance with the greater degree of disorder in the liquid, the solid being often, or even usually, crystalline. We infer, also, referring back to equation 1.5b with which we started, that the rate of change of free energy with temperature will be greater in the liquid than in the solid. Now the free energy contents of both liquid and solid rise as the temperature falls, and that of the liquid will thus overtake that of the solid at some temperature below the freezing point of the pure solvent.

Returning now to equation 3.25, and making the substitutions given in equations 3.26 and 3.27, we have:

$$RT_0 \ln a_1 = -\int_T^{T_0} \frac{\Delta H}{T}\, dT$$

This expression cannot be integrated as it stands, since ΔH depends on T. The relation between these quantities is known; but since we have already had to suppose the solution to be a dilute one, there cannot be much difference between T and T_0, and ΔH cannot depart widely from ΔH_0, the value at the freezing point of pure water. We thus have, approximately:

$$RT_0 \ln a_1 = -\Delta H_0 \ln (T_0/T)$$
$$= -\Delta H_0 (\Delta T/T_0)$$

the logarithmic term being removed by the same approximation as was used when calculating the fractional lowering of the vapour pressure (p. 82 above).

Hence
$$-\ln a_1 = \frac{\Delta H_0}{RT_0^2} \cdot \Delta T \qquad . \qquad . \qquad . \qquad . \qquad 3.28$$

$$= 0 \cdot 0097 \Delta T \text{ for aqueous solutions.}$$

If we introduce a correction for the variation of the latent heat of fusion with temperature, we get:

$$-\ln a_1 = 0 \cdot 0097 \Delta T (1 + 0 \cdot 00172 \Delta T)$$

For all ordinary purposes, this correction is negligible. If we compare equation 3.28 with the equation relating the solvent activity to the molar concentration of the solute (equation 3.11, p. 84), we see that it follows that:

$$\Delta T = \phi \cdot \frac{M_1}{\Delta H_0} RT_0^2 \frac{m}{1000} \qquad . \qquad . \qquad . \qquad 3.28a$$

$$= 1 \cdot 860 \phi.m \text{ for aqueous solutions.}$$

Here m is the concentration of the solute in moles per kilogram of solvent, M_1 is the molecular weight of the solvent, and ϕ is the osmotic coefficient. Equations 3.28 and 3.28a can, of course, be applied to the depression of the freezing point in any solvent, provided that the appropriate values of the constants are inserted.

The laws of Blagden and of Raoult are thus to be expected from energetic considerations provided that the solution is sufficiently dilute. Simplifying assumptions, however, have been made even when deriving equation 3.28; and these are different from those made when deriving the corresponding equations for vapour pressure and osmotic pressure. In relatively concentrated solutions, the value of the osmotic coefficient derived from equation 3.28a may not be identical with that derived from, say, equation 3.20, particularly when solutions of different composition are being compared. Equation 3.28 may, however, be used for calculating solvent activities in solutions of interest to the physiologist, including sea water and the body fluids of marine organisms, without introducing appreciable error: but it must be remembered that measurement of the depression of the freezing point gives the value of the activity of the solvent *at the freezing point*, and that this is not precisely the same as that at higher temperatures.

The Measurement of the Freezing Point. In theory, it is only necessary to insert a thermometer into the solution, and to reduce the temperature until ice begins to separate out. In practice, there are many difficulties. First, the temperature difference to be expected, as may be seen from equation 3.28a, is likely to be only a fraction of a degree; a very sensitive thermometer is required. Secondly, there is a great tendency for the solution to supercool, i.e. to become cooled to a temperature considerably below the true freezing point before any ice separates out. This is particularly apt to occur with solutions of biological interest containing proteins or other colloids. A relatively large quantity of ice then forms suddenly, so that if the original volume of the solution is small—as it is likely to be—its concentration is appreciably increased, and the freezing point, as measured, is erroneously low. This can be overcome by deliberately supercooling the solution until a considerable quantity of ice has formed, and then allowing it to warm up slowly, the temperature being measured at the moment that the last crystal of ice just disappears. Great care must be taken, of course, that the solution is well stirred, so that it is uniform as regards both composition and temperature.

The method can be used with very small volumes of fluid (less than $1 \mu l$). The solution is contained in a capillary tube and immersed in a freezing mixture, the temperature of which can be accurately controlled and measured; the disappearance of the ice crystals being observed by means of a microscope. Ramsay (1949) has developed the method so that it can be used with volumes as small as $0{\cdot}1$ $m\mu l$ (10^{-4} ml.); there are, indeed, some advantages in using very small volumes. The general arrangement of the apparatus is shown in Fig. 3.1 (C).

It may be emphasised at this point that the value of the concept of activity lies in its universal applicability to all problems of equilibrium, and, as we shall see, of diffusion, in solutions. Activity coefficients determined by vapour pressure, osmotic pressure or freezing point measurements, or, in the case of electrolytes as we shall see in the next chapter, by electrical measurements, are of general application. The constants of empirical equations describing the results of, say, osmotic pressure measurements, apply only to such measurements. In Fig. 3.2 are plotted curves showing the reduction in the activity of the solvent produced by the presence of several different solutes, in aqueous solution. It will be noted that the solutes fall into three classes, according as they are non-electrolytes, or electrolytes with two ions or three ions, each of which acts as an independent unit. As the concentration is reduced, the curves all tend to the value to be expected from Raoult's law (equation 3.10). But with nearly all the electrolytes, the departure from this value is appreciable at quite low concentrations.

ACTIVITY AND CHEMICAL REACTION

We are now in a position to deal rather more completely with the kinetics of chemical reaction in solution, and the conditions of equilibrium. As stated in Chapter 2, the velocity of a reaction depends on the free energy change associated with it; the velocity will depend, therefore, on the activities of the reactants. The law of Mass Action, as originally expressed, states that the velocity of a reaction depends on the "active masses" of the reactants; these, therefore, must be identified with their activities, rather than with their concentrations. In general, then, the equilibrium constant of the reversible reaction considered in Chapter 2 should be defined by the relation

$$K = \frac{(a_A)^a \times (a_B)^b}{(a_Y)^y \times (a_Z)^z}$$

concentrations being replaced by activities; although it is often more convenient to retain the concentrations, and multiply them by the activity coefficients.

We may now treat more generally the problem of the relation between the equilibrium constant of a reversible reaction in solution, and the change in free energy, if the reactants and resultants were all in their standard states. The changes in free energy needed to bring each reactant and resultant from the states of concentration, temperature and pressure at

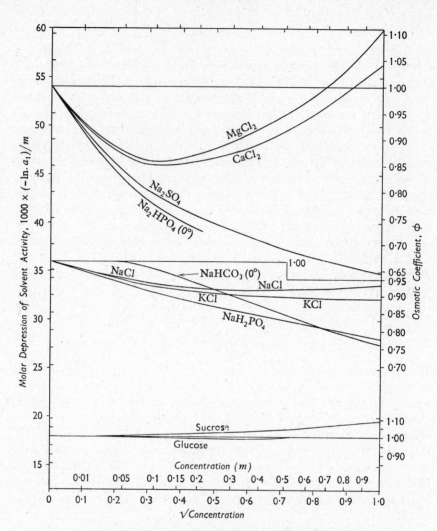

FIG. 3.2. THE RELATION BETWEEN THE ACTIVITY OF THE SOLVENT AND THE
CONCENTRATION OF THE SOLUTE IN AQUEOUS SOLUTIONS

The quantity plotted as ordinates, on the left-hand scale, is the observed reduction
in solvent activity at any given value of the solute concentration, divided by that concentration. The corresponding *Osmotic Coefficients* are given on the right-hand scale of
ordinates. Over the range of values plotted, $-\ln a_1$ may be considered numerically equal
to $(1 - a_1)$ without serious error.

Molar concentrations are plotted as abscissae, on a square root scale.

The activities have been derived from vapour pressure measurements wherever
possible, and refer to a temperature of 25° C. except where indicated. The values for
NaH_2PO_4 and $NaHCO_3$ are derived from freezing point measurements and are likely to
be some 2–4 per cent smaller than the corresponding values at 25° C.

(Data from Robinson and Stokes, 1949; and
International Critical Tables, Vols. III and IV.)

which the reaction is in equilibrium, to the standard states can be written down directly in terms of the changes in activity. In place of equation 2.21, referring to a reaction between perfect gases and involving their partial pressures, we have an exactly similar expression, involving activities, i.e.

$$\Delta G^\circ = RT \ln \frac{(a_A)^a \times (a_B)^b}{(a_Y)^y \times (a_Z)^z} = \text{constant.}$$

Thus from the expression given above for the equilibrium constant we have:

$$\Delta G_1 = -RT \ln K \quad . \qquad . \qquad . \qquad . \quad 2.22$$

It may be noted that the standard state is defined so that the activity—and not necessarily the concentration—of each of the components of the reaction system is unity.

The activity coefficients in aqueous solution of a number of the more ordinary substances have been determined with considerable accuracy, so that it is possible to convert their concentrations, as determined by chemical analysis, into activities whenever necessary. Fortunately, however, most chemical reactions that we deal with in physiology occur in solutions which are sufficiently dilute that, for most purposes, we can take the activities as being sensibly identical with the concentrations. Care must be taken, however, when dealing with reactions in such organisms as marine invertebrates, where the concentrations are such that the solutions are far from "ideal".

DIFFUSION

The process of diffusion is of great importance in physiology; the final stages by which the living cell acquires the substances which provide it with energy, and the initial stages by which it loses the products of the reactions, are processes of diffusion. Unfortunately, the calculation of the rate of diffusion in any given circumstances is usually of considerable difficulty.

The phenomena were investigated by Graham (1850), who showed that the rate of diffusion in any given circumstances varied with the nature of the substance studied. Later investigations showed that the rate is inversely proportional to the size of the molecule (in gases, to the square root of the molecular weight), is directly proportional to the difference in concentration between the two places from and to which diffusion is proceeding, is inversely proportional to the distance between them, and is directly proportional to the cross sectional area of the path concerned.

The condition that all parts of a solution should be in equilibrium with one another is that each component should have the same partial free energy throughout the solution. If the partial free energy of any component

D*

is greater at one point than at another, this component will tend to move in the direction of the fall in partial free energy, at a rate which will depend on the rate of fall of free energy with distance between the two points considered. This, of course, is merely a more general statement of the process of osmosis: if there is a membrane which prevents the movement of the solute, the solvent only will move; if there is no such membrane, both solvent and solute will move. In these cases of free diffusion, however, attention is usually directed to the movement of the solute. The simultaneous movement of the solvent will, of course, tend to displace the solute, and assist in its diffusion.

Consider the diffusion of the solute over an area A, between two planes in the solution distant dx apart, the concentration in this region being m. If dn_2 is the number of moles present at any moment in the volume contained between these planes, then $dn_2 = A.dx.m$. If $\bar{v}$ is the mean velocity of diffusion per mole, then in a time dt, a mole diffuses through a distance dx such that $dx = \bar{v}.dt$. Thus, eliminating dx from the previous equation, we have: $dn_2 = A.m.\bar{v}.dt$. This may conveniently be written as: $\phi_2 = m.\bar{v}$, where ϕ_2 is the "*flux*" of the solute concerned—i.e. the rate of diffusion through unit area. Now the velocity with which the solute moves may be regarded as being determined by the force acting on it, divided by a "friction". The work done in carrying a mole over the distance dx is proportional to the difference in the partial molar free energy $d\bar{G}_2$; the force acting on it is thus $d\bar{G}_2/dx$—i.e. the partial molar free energy gradient. But, as we have seen already (from equation 3.8) we can write:

$$d\bar{G}_2/dx = -RT.d(\ln a_2)/dx$$

where a_2 is the activity of the solute. We may thus write:

$$\bar{v} = \frac{-RT.d(\ln a_2)/dx}{Nf_D} \qquad . \qquad . \qquad . \qquad 3.29$$

and
$$\phi_2 = -m \cdot \frac{RT}{N} \cdot \frac{d(\ln a_2)}{dx} \cdot \frac{1}{f_D}$$

where f_D is the frictional force on each molecule, and N is the Avogadro number. This expression may be written:

$$\phi_2 = -m \cdot \frac{RT}{N} \cdot \frac{d(\ln a_2)}{d(\ln m)} \cdot \frac{d(\ln m)}{dx} \cdot \frac{1}{f_D} \qquad . \qquad . \qquad 3.30$$

Collecting the constants, we get:

$$\phi_2 = -D \frac{dm}{dx} \cdot \frac{d(\ln a_2)}{d(\ln m)} \qquad . \qquad . \qquad . \qquad 3.31$$

where D is now the "diffusion coefficient". If the change in activity with concentration, over the range of concentrations considered, may be neglected—i.e. if $d(\ln a_2)/d(\ln m)$ may be put equal to 1—this equation expresses *Fick's law of diffusion*: it is, as can be seen, in agreement with the experimental observations already referred to. The diffusion constant will clearly vary with the absolute temperature, which has been incorporated into it. For non-electrolyte solutions, in the concentrations ordinarily met with in physiology, the variation of activity with concentration may certainly be neglected. But the diffusion of electrolytes is more complex, although in some respects more important and of greater interest—we shall discuss this in the next chapter.

The rate of change with time of the concentration at a given place, dm/dt, depends on the difference between the rate at which solute molecules arrive at that place and the rate at which they diffuse away. This may be expressed as the difference between the rate of diffusion at the place considered, and the rate at a place distant dx from it. Now the rate of change of the quantity (dn_2/dt) with x is expressed as $\dfrac{\partial}{\partial x}\left(\dfrac{dn_2}{dt}\right)$, so that the required difference in diffusion rate is expressed as $\dfrac{\partial}{\partial x}\left(\dfrac{dn_2}{dt}\right)dx$. From equation 3.31, neglecting the variation of a_2 with m, this is equal to $D.A.\dfrac{d^2m}{dx^2}.dx$. But the rate of change of concentration is equal to the rate of accumulation of solute molecules divided by the volume in which they accumulate, which in this case is $A.dx$. Thus we have:

$$dm/dt = D.(d^2m/dx^2) \quad . \qquad . \qquad . \qquad . \quad 3.32$$

The solution of such a general equation, of course, requires knowledge of the geometry of the system and of the boundary conditions: even in simple cases, highly complex expressions are obtained, and in many cases, the equation is insoluble. But if the conditions which determine the rate of diffusion in any given system remain constant for a sufficient period of time, a steady state will be reached. The equations which define the steady state are less complex than those which define the transient state which follows changes in the conditions of diffusion, and in many physiological applications (but by no means all) the steady state is of greater interest than the transient state. A general account of the process of diffusion, with particular reference to applications of physiological interest, will be found in the review by Jacobs (1935): the more recent paper by Roughton (1952) should also be consulted by those interested. References to other important work will be found in these papers.

In ordinary circumstances, such as would be convenient in the laboratory, diffusion appears to be a very slow process. Graham (1850) describes the following experiment: A glass cylinder, 11 in. high, was filled to one-eighth of its capacity with a saturated solution of calcium bicarbonate, which also contained 200 gr. of sodium chloride in 8 cub. in. The jar was then filled completely with distilled water in such a way as not to disturb the lower layer, covered with a glass plate, and left to stand in a uniform temperature for six months. Samples of different strata were then removed by a syphon, and it was found that equality of concentration had not been attained, even in so long a time. The ratio of the concentrations of the sodium chloride in the top and bottom layers was as 11 to 12, while that of calcium bicarbonate was as 1 to 4.

In another set of experiments it was found that in fourteen days the concentration of sodium chloride at the top of a column of 127 mm. was only 1/22 of that at the bottom, while sugar was only just to be detected at the top in that space of time, the uppermost 50 c.c. of solution contained only 0·005 g. of glucose. Complete equality of concentration will never, of course, be reached in a finite time by pure diffusion only. But the time taken for the concentration at the most distant point to reach a certain fraction (say 95 per cent.) of that at the point from which the substance is diffusing may be calculated. It is inversely proportional both to the diffusion constant and to the *square* of the distance between these points, the cross sectional area being supposed to be large compared with this distance.

In the tissues of living organisms we are concerned mainly with distances which are measured in fractions of a millimetre, not in tens of centimetres, as in Graham's experiments. At a distance of 10μ from the diffusing source, for example, the concentration will reach 95 per cent. of that at the source in a matter of a second or less after the diffusion has started: in these circumstances, diffusion may be considered a relatively rapid process. Conversely, of course, in large bodies of water such as rivers, lakes and above all the sea, diffusion equilibrium will be attained with immeasurable slowness. Over a distance of, say 10 metres, and in the complete absence of stirring by convection or wave action, it would take hundreds of centuries for concentration differences to be eliminated, even approximately.

ACTIVATED DIFFUSION

From the kinetic point of view, the process of diffusion in solutions differs fundamentally from that in gases. In the latter, diffusion takes place as a result of the collisions between the molecules, any given molecule being hit more often from the direction in which the concentration (or pressure) increases than from that in which the concentration decreases; the only resistance to diffusion results from the collisions of the molecule considered with those ahead of it, in the direction in which diffusion is taking place. In these circumstances, application of the kinetic theory of gases leads to the expectation that the diffusion constant would be inversely proportional to the square root of the molecular weight—as Graham observed experimentally. The chemical nature of the diffusing molecules has no influence on the rate of diffusion.

When we consider the diffusion of a solute molecule in a solution, however, it is necessary to take into account the behaviour of the solvent molecules which surround it. In the simplest case, the solute molecule may move from one place to another as a result of the movement of the solvent molecules, which have left a space into which it can be driven by other solvent molecules which surround it. But movement of the solute molecule may also occur as a result of its acquiring sufficient energy to tear itself away from its attachments to the neighbouring solvent molecules and to push away the solvent molecules in front of it. This is a process of *activated diffusion*, and will only occur when the diffusing molecule happens to acquire energy in excess of the necessary activation energy. This activation energy will be determined by the secondary valence and other forces between the solute and the solvent molecules—without which the solute molecule would not be in solution. Or, if the solute molecule moves together with its shell of solvent molecules, the activation energy will be determined by the association forces—secondary valencies, hydrogen bonds, etc.—between neighbouring solvent molecules.

The diffusion of any particular molecule will thus take place in a series of jumps, as it acquires the activation energy necessary to take it over the next step. But if the solute molecule is large compared with the solvent molecules, and if the total path over which diffusion is occurring is large compared with the dimensions of the molecules, there will be a very large number of steps, each of which will be small, and diffusion will be sensibly continuous.

The process of activated diffusion by a solute has been considered theoretically by Danielli and Turton, and the account to be given below is based on their treatment, as given in the monograph by Davson and Danielli (1952). Suppose for simplicity that the potential barriers to diffusion are all of the same height, and that each requires a minimum energy μ_e before it can be surmounted. Then, as we have seen in Chapter 2 (equation 2.9, p. 54), the fraction of all the molecules waiting to surmount the barrier which have sufficient energy is proportional to $\exp(-\mu_e/RT)$. If $(m)_r$ is the concentration at the rth barrier, the rate of passage of solute molecules over it will be

$$(\phi_2)_r = (m)_r.e$$

where e is a function of $\exp(-\mu_e/RT)$; and if the concentration on the other side of the barrier—i.e. between the rth and the $(r+1)$th barriers—is $(m)_{r+1}$, the rate of passage backwards is

$$(\phi_2)_{r+1} = (m)_{r+1}.e$$

Hence the net rate of flow in the direction of diffusion is

$$\phi_2 = e[(m)_r - (m)_{r+1}]$$

In the steady state, the same net rate of flow must occur across all the barriers, and this will be given by the sum of the flows across all the barriers divided by the number of barriers, say p. Hence we have:

$$\phi_2 = \frac{e}{p}[(m)_0 - (m)_p] \qquad . \qquad . \qquad . \qquad 3.33$$

Now if the distance between each barrier is λ, the total distance over which diffusion is taking place is $(p+1)\lambda$, and the concentration gradient is thus

$$\frac{(m)_0 - (m)_p}{(p+1)\lambda}$$

By Fick's Law

$$\phi_2 = D \cdot \left[\frac{(m)_0 - (m)_p}{(p+1)\lambda}\right] . \qquad . \qquad . \qquad 3.34$$

By comparison of equations 3.33 and 3.34, we see that

$$D = \frac{(p+1)\lambda}{p} \cdot e$$

Now if the system considered were a perfect gas, the kinetic theory of gases would indicate that e should have the value $\sqrt{RT/2\pi M} \cdot \exp(-\mu_e/RT)$, where M is the molecular weight of the gas and R and T have the usual significance (compare Chapter 2, pp. 49, 54). To allow for the facts that (a) we are not considering a perfect gas, without intermolecular forces, and (b) only a fraction of the molecules which possess the necessary activation energy will, in fact, surmount the barrier—some being wrongly orientated or otherwise in an unsuitable state—we multiply the above equation by an arbitrary factor r'. We thus reach the final expression for the diffusion constant:

$$D = \frac{p+1}{p} \cdot \lambda r' \sqrt{\frac{RT}{2\pi M}} \cdot \exp(-\mu_e/RT) \qquad . \qquad . \qquad 3.35$$

This expression cannot be more than approximate, owing to the introduction of the factor r'; but it shows that in general the rate of diffusion of a substance will depend upon its chemical properties, which affect the magnitude of the activation energy, as well as on its molecular weight. Diffusion across a very thin film, also, of thickness comparable with molecular dimensions, will be proportionately faster than diffusion over macroscopic distances. If, however, we consider diffusion over a relatively long distance, and if the solvent has a relatively low viscosity, the energy of association between its molecules will not be very large, and there will be a number of substances whose molecules in solution will diffuse as a result chiefly of the rupture of these solvent-solvent bonds, rather than of the more powerful solute-solvent bonds. The value of μ_e, therefore, will be very much the same for all these substances, and the diffusion constant will be very nearly inversely proportional to the square root of the molecular weight; there will be no effect of chemical constitution. This relation has, in fact, been shown to hold for a number of substances with molecular weights up to that of the hexoses, in solution in water and ethanol. It happens, also, to be the relation that one would deduce by assuming that dilute solutions behave as perfect gases—i.e. by ignoring the influence of the solvent altogether.

In these special circumstances, the rate of diffusion will not vary very rapidly with temperature (the activation energy is not very large), and the rate of variation with temperature will be much the same for all the substance concerned. On the other hand, if the rate of diffusion is slow, and the activation energy required is large, there will be a large variation with temperature, and different substances will have different values of the temperature coefficient. Thus diffusion in solution may, from its temperature coefficient, appear to be either a "physical" process or a "chemical" one, according to circumstances (compare Chapter 2, p. 59).

Facilitated Diffusion. It is conceivable that the activation energy required for a solute molecule to pass from one solvent molecule to another may be less than that required to break the bonds between the solvent molecules. This is likely to occur, for example, if there is an easily reversible chemical reaction between the particular solute and the solvent, and particularly if the solvent molecules are firmly attached to one another: in the limit, they may form some kind of structure over the surface of which the solute molecules are handed from point to point. In a system such as this, the rate of diffusion of molecules of some particular kind is likely to exceed greatly that of those of any other kind; their diffusion is said to be "facilitated". We shall have occasion to return to these considerations of activated and facilitated diffusion, and the effects of temperature on the rate of diffusion, when we deal with the permeability of membranes in a later chapter.

TRANSIENT OSMOTIC EFFECTS

The different diffusion rates of various substances may give rise temporarily to considerable differences of osmotic pressure between two solutions in an osmometer, even when the two solutions are actually of equal osmotic pressure to begin with, and separated by a membrane permeable to both solutes. Sodium chloride diffuses more rapidly than magnesium sulphate, so that, if we place solutions of the same concentration on the two sides of a membrane permeable to both solutes, the former will diffuse through the membrane faster than the latter, the molar concentration and osmotic pressure of the sodium chloride solution will diminish, while that of the magnesium sulphate will increase, and water will pass to the latter. The difference in concentration is, of course, only temporary, but may give rise to considerable changes in osmotic pressure.

Similarly, if we have a solution enclosed in a membrane through which the solute passes less rapidly than the solvent, in contact with the pure solvent, a transient inflow of solvent will take place. Later, both solute and solvent will pass out again, and both hydrostatic pressure and concentration will be equalised on both sides of the membrane. Phenomena of this nature are often encountered in physiology. We may instance the swelling of muscles on activity owing to the production of smaller molecules, such as those of lactic acid, from larger ones, such as glycogen. The lactic acid only slowly leaves the interior of the muscle and so water at first passes in. The effect of injections of concentrated solutions into the circulation of a mammal and the consequent withdrawal of water from the tissues into the blood stream is another example of transient osmosis. Such effects do not, strictly, require the presence of a membrane, but are not easily noticed without one. In the absence of a membrane it is not easy to define the boundary of the more concentrated solution.

When we have a solution of an electrolytically dissociated salt in contact with water, if the anion and cation move at different rates, it is clear that there will be a difference of potential between the front and back of the advancing surface of the diffusing column, the faster moving ions giving the sign of their charges to the front layer. Owing to electrostatic forces, the one set of ions cannot outdistance the other set further than their kinetic energy can carry them in opposition to the electrostatic attraction. This phenomenon is a possible source of potential differences in living tissues, and will be discussed in the next chapter.

THE VISCOSITY OF SOLUTIONS

The subject of viscosity is, strictly speaking, not quite in place here, since it concerns liquids in general and not only water and watery solutions. But since, in physiological work, the liquids with which we have to deal are, almost entirely, solutions or suspensions in water, we may be allowed to take the subject at this stage, as a convenient one.

As was pointed out by Newton, the particles of liquids are not free to move about without resistance due to their "adherence" to one another. This gives rise to friction, so that the viscosity, or internal friction, of a liquid is proportional to the velocity with which these particles are moving past one another, and also to the extent of the rubbing surfaces. More precisely, if two neighbouring layers of a liquid are not moving with the same velocity, there will be a force between them acting so as to increase the velocity of the more slowly moving layer, and decrease that of the more rapidly moving layer. The magnitude of this force per unit area of the two layers is proportional to the difference in their velocities, and to their distance apart (i.e. to the velocity gradient); and the constant of proportionality is known as the coefficient of viscosity.

The viscous property of liquids is of importance in physiology, as in ordinary life, chiefly in relation to the flow through tubes. The internal friction of the blood, for example, gives rise to what is often called the "peripheral resistance" of the vascular system: the magnitude of the resistance determines the magnitude of the arterial pressure necessary to produce the required flow of blood, and so, also, the amount of power exerted by the heart.

The first point to be noted is, that when a liquid is being caused to flow through a tube by the pressure applied at the inlet end of the tube being greater than that at the outlet, the layer in immediate contact with the wall of the tube is at rest, while that in the middle has the greatest velocity; each layer experiences friction at its contact with the neighbouring layer, so losing in velocity progressively until the outermost layer is reached, where the velocity disappears entirely. We see, then, that the friction is between the parts of the liquid itself and not between the liquid and the wall of the tube. These considerations, applied to the flow in a tube of circular cross section, lead to the well-known Poiseuille's law. This states that the volume of a given fluid that will pass through a uniform tube in unit time is proportional: (a) to the difference in hydrostatic pressure between the two ends of the tube (p); (b) inversely to the length of the tube (l); and (c) directly to the fourth power of the radius of the tube (a). Expressed in symbols, this becomes:

$$F = \frac{V}{t} = \frac{\pi}{8\eta} \cdot \frac{p}{l} \cdot a^4 \quad . \quad . \quad . \quad . \quad 3.36$$

Poiseuille actually discovered this relation empirically in 1840. The fact that the constant of proportionality takes the form $\pi/8\eta$ depends upon the definition of the coefficient of viscosity (η) as given above: the first precise theoretical derivation of the equation was given by Hagenbach in 1860. It will be found in many text-books of physics, and in monographs dealing with viscometry, such as that by Barr (1931).

The *methods* used for the determination of viscosity consist either (a) in measuring the resistance offered to the movement of a surface passing through the liquid, or more usually, the force exerted by a moving liquid on a stationary surface with which it is in contact (the *rotating cylinder* method); or (b) in measuring the resistance offered to the passage of the liquid through a narrow tube (the *capillary tube* method). The latter method is a simple one, and requires merely the determination of the time taken by a given amount of the liquid, under a given pressure, to run through the tube. Full descriptions of the various types of apparatus which have been developed for various purposes will be found in the monographs by Barr (1931) and by Scott Blair (1949).

It can be shown theoretically (as was done by Einstein in 1909) that under ideal conditions, the viscosity of a solution or suspension, expressed as a product of the viscosity of the solvent or suspending fluid (the *relative viscosity*) depends primarily on the total volume occupied by the solute or disperse phase in unit volume of the solution or suspension; and secondarily on the shape of the dispersed particles. It is independent of the size of the particles provided that these are so far away from one another— i.e. that the solution or suspension is so dilute—that they do not interfere with each other's motion. In the general case of particles of any shape, we can write:

$$\eta_{sp} = \eta/\eta_0 - 1 = v.\phi \quad . \qquad . \qquad . \qquad . \quad 3.37$$

where η_{sp} is known as the *"specific viscosity"* of the suspension; η being the observed viscosity of a suspension in which the suspended particles occupy a volume ϕ per unit volume of the suspension, η_0 the viscosity of the suspending fluid (η/η_0 therefore, being the relative viscosity) and v a constant depending on the shape of the particles. For spheres, $v=2\cdot5$, as Einstein showed. For spheroids which are too large to show Brownian movement, the value to be assigned to v depends on what assumptions are made as to the orientation of the particles during flow; it is, however, always less than $2\cdot5$. If the suspended particles are sufficiently small to show considerable Brownian movement, there can be no particular orientation, and departure from the spherical shape leads to an increase in the relative viscosity by an amount which depends both on the relative volume of the dispersed phase, and on the ratio of the longer axis to the shorter axis of the particles (for ellipsoids of revolution). The Brownian movement has the effect of making the effective volume occupied by each particle approximate to the sphere swept out by its longest axis. Of particular interest is the case of rigid rods in strong Brownian movement, such as long chain macro-molecules. Many equations, both theoretical and empirical, have been developed, involving various functions of the axial ratio, and most have been found to give reasonably consistent results on proteins, celluloses and nitro-celluloses in suitable solvents. Details will be found in the book by Alexander and Johnson (1949): a theoretical treatment of the subject will be found in the article by Sadron (1953 *a*).

It cannot be too strongly emphasised that these considerations as to the effect of the shape of the particles on the specific viscosity can only be applied to very dilute solutions and suspensions, in which the particles are widely separated from one another. For more concentrated suspensions, even when the particles are spherical, theoretical considerations show that a further term in ϕ^2 (and terms in higher powers of ϕ) must be added in equation 3.36. According to Guth and Simha, the coefficient of ϕ^2 should be 14·1. It has not, so far, been possible to treat the case of asymmetric particles in more concentrated suspensions. But from an empirical standpoint, and quite generally, we may consider the constant ν in equation 3.36 to be a function of the relative volume of the particles (ϕ) as well as their shape: many different functions have been proposed, each of which has been found suitable in the appropriate circumstances. A general review will be found in the monograph by Scott Blair (1949).

The relation between the specific viscosity and the concentration and shape of the dissolved or suspended particles is of considerable importance in the study of colloidal systems. Complications and anomalies appear, however, and the subject will be considered in a later chapter.

The Influence of Temperature on Viscosity. Rise of temperature leads to a considerable decrease in the viscosity of all fluids, as, indeed, is a matter of common experience. The increase in temperature increases the kinetic energy of thermal motion, and the molecules more frequently break the secondary valence bonds which attach them to their neighbours. Liquids which possess powerful association bonds between the molecules, such as water, have a greater temperature coefficient of viscosity than have non-associated liquids.

The *relative* viscosity of a solution or suspension is, in general, independent of the temperature—as, indeed, it should be from theoretical considerations. There may, however, be secondary effects due to changes in the degree of hydration of the particles; and if these are small and asymmetric, the increased Brownian movement with rise in temperature will result in a diminished degree of orientation, and thus in a rise in the relative viscosity.

LITERATURE

Thermodynamics. Lewis and Randall (1923).
Methods. Krogh (1939—Appendix); Ramsay (1949); Robinson and Stokes (1955).
Diffusion. Graham (1850); Jacobs (1935); Davson and Danielli (1952); Roughton (1952).
Viscosity. Barr (1931); Scott Blair (1949); Alexander and Johnson (1949); Sadron (1953 *a*).

4

ELECTROLYTES

Suppose that we take a solution of hydrochloric acid in water and pass an electric current through it, we find free chlorine is separated at the anode, where the current enters, and free hydrogen at the cathode, where the current leaves the solution. One of the constituents of the solute, which is called an "electrolyte" when it conducts electricity, "wanders" in one direction, the other in the other direction. Faraday was the first to use the name "electrolyte," and he showed that this is actually the way in which the electric current is carried through the solution of a substance which is capable of conducting it. Each constituent of the electrolyte carries a definite quantity of electricity; in our case, the hydrogen carries positive electricity from the anode to the cathode, and the chlorine carries negative electricity from the cathode to the anode. The name used by Faraday (1834, pp. 78 and 79, and 1839, I. pp. 197, 198) for these electrically charged atoms, or molecules, was "ions" (ἰών, participle of εἶμι, "going"), those carrying a positive charge, which they give up at the cathode, being "cations" (κατά = down), and those with a negative charge "anions" (ἀνά = up), in accordance with the direction in which they move in relation to the current, regarded as of positive electricity. The electrodes are "anode" and "cathode" (ὁδός = way). In order to conduct a current, then, the solute must be decomposed into positively and negatively charged parts, that is, *"electrolytically dissociated"*.

It is obvious from the facts of electrolytic conduction that hydrogen and chlorine are capable of existence in forms which have quite different properties from those which they possess in their ordinary familiar forms. While they are engaged in carrying electric charges through the solution in which a current passes, they cannot be recognised as hydrogen and chlorine.

Now in the previous chapter it was shown that the lowering of the freezing point of a solution, and its osmotic pressure, were, in dilute solution, both directly proportional to the molar concentration; and the early experiments of Raoult in 1878, and of Pfeffer in 1877 and de Vries in 1884-88, which demonstrated this relation, were referred to. But both Raoult and de Vries had, in fact, found that this applied only to certain substances, such as sugar, mannitol and some others. Substances such as sodium chloride or potassium nitrate produced effects which were greater than was to be expected from their molar concentrations. For a given value of freezing point lowering or osmotic pressure, then, the concentration of a "normal" substance such as sugar, has to be greater than that of an "anomalous" substance such as sodium chloride. The ratio of the one to the other is called the *isotonic coefficient* of the anomalous substance concerned; van't Hoff in 1885, when formulating the laws of osmotic pressure, gave this coefficient the symbol i. If, for example, we make a solution by adding 1 gram-molecule of potassium chloride to 10 litres of water, we find that its osmotic pressure is about 1·8 times that of a solution made with 1 gram-molecule of cane sugar in the same volume of water. Since the osmotic pressure is roughly indirect proportion to the number of molecules of the solute present in unit volume, it appears that there are more osmotically active elements in the solution of potassium chloride than in that of cane sugar; the number of active "molecules" would seem, somehow to have increased. We must suppose, therefore, that each molecule has split up or "dissociated" so as to increase the total number present.

But what sort of dissociation are we to suppose that such a salt as potassium chloride undergoes in water? Looking at the lists of substances in the two classes referred to, we are at once struck by the fact that those substances which give an abnormally high osmotic pressure and are, thus "dissociated" in solution in water, are all good conductors of electricity, whereas the "normal" ones are non-conductors. Further, it is found that if a substance which is a good conductor and gives an anomalous osmotic pressure in water, is dissolved in a solvent in which it no longer conducts electricity, as, for example, hydrochloric acid in benzene, its osmotic pressure is normal, or, at any rate, not greater than normal.

Arrhenius, on considering these various facts, was led to see that the anomalous osmotic pressures of solutions of electrolytes could be very simply explained by the assumption that the dissociation into ions is not merely the state during the passage of a current, but is the normal condition of the solution of an electrolyte under any circumstances. This is the "electrolytic dissociation theory" which plays so large a part in science at the present day.

In his classical paper *Ueber die Dissociation der in Wasser gelöster Stoffe* (1887, p. 637), Arrhenius gives the evidence for the acceptance of two hypotheses, which are:

"1. The Law of van't Hoff applies not only to the greater number of substances, but to all, including those which had been considered to be exceptions (electrolytes in watery solution)."

This law of van't Hoff, which is a generalisation of Avogadro's law, has already been quoted (p. 94), but, for reference, it may be repeated here:

"The pressure which a gas possesses at a given temperature, when a definite number of molecules are present in a definite volume, is of the same value as the osmotic pressure which is exerted, under the same conditions, by the greater number of substances, when they are dissolved in any kind of liquid."

The second hypothesis of Arrhenius states that:

"2. All electrolytes (in solution in water) consist partly of molecules which are active (in electrolytic and chemical relationships), and partly of inactive molecules. The latter, however, on dilution, are converted into active molecules; so that in infinitely diluted solutions only active molecules are present."

We may now venture to call these hypotheses "laws", although objections have not been wanting.

The modern views on the physical chemistry of electrolyte solutions are treated very fully in the book by Robinson and Stokes (1955). Those wishing for a more detailed and more advanced discussion of the subject than can be given here, should consult this book.

THE CONDUCTION OF ELECTRICITY THROUGH SOLUTIONS

The passage of an electric current through a solution being due to the ions present between the electrodes, it is clear that the amount of current that will pass through a given solution will depend, in the first place, on the size of the electrodes—the larger they are, the more ions there will be between them. The current that passes, other things being equal, is in direct proportion to the area of the electrodes when the column of solution between them is of the same cross section as the electrodes, so that no spreading of the current takes place. In the second place, owing to the fact that the velocity with which the ions move is finite, the greater the distance between the electrodes the longer it will take for an ion to carry its charge to the opposite electrode and the less electricity will be carried in unit time, i.e. the current will be less. In comparing the conductance of one solution with that of another, it is therefore necessary to agree to some arbitrary dimensions. The unit of conductance is taken, accordingly, as that of a body of which a column one centimetre long and one square centimetre in cross section has a resistance of one ohm. The resistance is the reciprocal of the conductance; if one solution has twice the resistance of another, only half the current will pass through it, so that its conductance is half that of the other.

If the resistance of a solution between electrodes of area s and distant d apart, is R ohms, then the resistance that it would have if the electrodes were of standard dimensions and the standard distance apart can be calculated; it is $R.s/d$. This would be the *specific resistance*, or *resistivity*, ρ. The reciprocal of the specific resistance $(1/\rho)$ is the *specific conductance* or *conductivity*, κ. Since resistance is measured in ohms, conductance is measured in reciprocal ohms, sometimes called "mhos" (ohm spelt backwards). Note that while the resistance and the conductance of a given solution depend on the dimensions of the electrode system, the specific resistance and conductance do not; they are properties only of the solution. It is convenient, also, to have an expression in which the molar concentration is taken into account. The *equivalent conductivity* is now understood as the specific conductance divided by the concentration in gram-equivalents per cubic centimetre, i.e. $\dfrac{1000\kappa}{m}$ and is denoted by Λ. It is clear that the conductivity of the solution of an electrolyte depends on its concentration, since it is the ions into which the solute dissociates that conduct the current, and the more there are in the space between the electrodes, the more current will pass. The value of taking gram-equivalents instead of gram-molecules is that salts with multivalent ions are more readily compared with those with univalent ions. Thus, if equimolar solution of KCl and K_2SO_4 are compared, we must remember that the second salt, at an equal degree of dissociation, has twice the conducting power of the first, since it gives ions with four charges, two negative and two positive, while the first only gives one negative and one positive.

The *methods of measuring electrical conductivity* may be considered briefly. What is actually measured is the electrical resistance of a layer of solution lying between electrodes of known area separated by a known distance. In practice, however, it is often convenient to use an electrode vessel whose dimensions cannot easily be measured accurately; such a system must be calibrated in terms of the observed resistance when a solution of known electrical conductivity (ordinarily 0·1 M. KCl) is placed within it. Two forms of electrode vessel suitable for use in physiological investigations are illustrated in Fig. 4.1 (A_1 and A_2). The electrical resistance is measured by the usual Wheatstone bridge method, familiar to physicists and electrical engineers, with certain modifications. These modifications are necessary, owing to the fact that if a current is sent for any appreciable time between metallic electrodes immersed in an electrolyte solution, the current falls off progressively, owing to the development of *polarisation*, as will be discussed in Chapter 5 (p. 200). The difficulty is avoided by using alternating currents in the bridge, instead of continuous (direct) currents, as was first done by Kohlrausch in 1876; each electrode is thus made anode and cathode in turn, and any incipient polarisation in one direction is almost immediately annulled by the incipient polarisation in the opposite direction. In addition, the electrodes are made partially "non-polarisable" by being coated with platinum-black (compare the "hydrogen electrode", p. 153 below); this adsorbs any hydrogen or

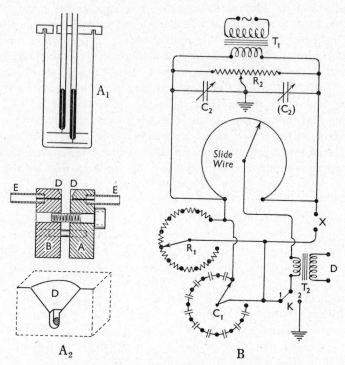

FIG. 4.1.   THE MEASUREMENT OF ELECTRICAL CONDUCTIVITY

A_1 *and* A_2. *Drawings of two forms of conductivity cell.* A_1 is the pattern used by Arrhenius. The electrodes are circular, and can easily be removed from the simple glass tube which contains the solution. Their distance apart can be increased or decreased, according as the solution has a large or a small conductivity (they must, of course, be firmly fixed during the course of the measurement); and within limits, the size of the vessel and of the electrodes can be made to suit the volume of solution available. A_2 is a pattern designed for use with very small volumes of solution (about 1 μl). The solution is placed in the small recess, cut in the face of one of the two ebonite blocks, A and B, and provided with a conical opening, D, for filling. The electrodes consist of the ends of two platinum wires, about 0·3 mm. diameter, which pass through the blocks; electrical connection is made through the tubes E, which contain mercury.

B. Circuit diagram of Wheatstone bridge for use with alternating currents. The conductivity cell is connected to terminals X. The bridge is supplied with alternating current through the transformer T_1, and the null-point detector (telephone, or cathode ray tube with suitable amplifier) is connected to the transformer T_2. Approximate balance is obtained by selecting an appropriate "standard" resistance by means of the selector switch R_1, and final balance by adjustment of the contact on the slide wire. Detection of the balance point may be made more precise by inserting a small capacitance by means of selector switch C_1.

The adjustable capacitance C_1 is primarily intended for use when the capacitative *reactance* of X is to be measured, as well as the resistance (see Chapter 10, p. 466). The null-point detector must then be such as to indicate the phase of the out-of-balance voltage, as well as its magnitude.

The variable resistance R_2 and capacitance C_2 constitute one form of the "Wagner earth", by means of which errors due to stray leakages to earth may be eliminated. After a preliminary balance has been obtained, the key K is put into position 2, instead of position 1, and R_2 and C_2 are adjusted until there is no signal in the null-point detector (C_2 may have to be put on one side or the other of the earth connection). K is then returned to position 1 and the balance of the bridge re-adjusted if necessary.

oxygen that may be released by the current and catalyses their re-combination. Originally, a small induction coil was used; alternating currents being induced in the secondary coil when the current in the primary coil is interrupted by a rapidly vibrating contact-breaker. Nowadays, a low-voltage transformer, connected to the alternating current mains may conveniently be used; but the frequency (50 c./sec.) is too small, if great accuracy is required, and a thermionic valve oscillator, with a frequency not less than 1000 c./sec. is preferable. Some instrument which responds to alternating currents must be used as a detector of the balance point of the bridge, in place of the galvanometer ordinarily used. A telephone is often used, or, more conveniently, an amplifier and loud speaker. Most convenient of all however, is an amplifier followed by one of the small cathode ray tubes that are used in wireless receiving sets as tuning indicators, and sometimes known as "electric eyes". Any cathode ray oscilloscope may, of course, be used equally well. The use of alternating currents of relatively high frequency may introduce considerable errors as a result of stray capacitances between the various components of the bridge, and between the bridge as a whole and earth. Precautions must always be taken to eliminate these. The circuit diagram of one form of alternating current bridge is shown in Fig. 4.1 B; for further details as to the circuit, and the method of operation, appropriate text-books should be consulted, such as that by Hague (1957).

IONIC CONDUCTIVITY

The equivalent conductivity, or the number of ions into which a gram-equivalent is dissociated, increases as the solution is diluted. By plotting successive values of the equivalent conductivity at increasing dilutions in the form of a curve, the value at infinite dilution can be extrapolated. In strong electrolytes, however, it is found that the equivalent conductivity reaches a maximum at low, but finite, concentrations. It is supposed that complete dissociation into ions has now occurred.

Let us take the equivalent conductivity of the following series of salts in 0·0001 molar concentration as given by Kohlrausch and Maltby.

			Chloride	*Nitrate*
K	.	.	129·05	125·49
Na	.	.	108·06	104·53
Li	.	.	98·06	94·38

The precise units in which these are expressed does not matter for our present purpose, since all are in the same units.

The difference between KCl and NaCl is 20·99 and between KNO_3 and $NaNO_3$ is 20·96, practically identical. Again, the difference between KCl and LiCl is 30·99 and between KNO_3 and $LiNO_3$ is 31·11. What does this imply? Obviously that it does not matter whether, in changing Na or Li for K, we take a chloride or a nitrate; that is, the metallic part of the salt makes a certain contribution to the conductivity which is independent of the acidic radical associated with it. Similarly, the difference between KCl and KNO_3 is 3·56, between NaCl and $NaNO_3$ 3·53, and between LiCl and $LiNO_3$ 3·68, so that the same consideration applies to the other radical. This fact may perhaps be clearer if put in a symbolic form:

$$(K + Cl) - (Na + Cl) = (K + NO_3) - (Na + NO_3)$$

and
$$(K + Cl) - (K + NO_3) = (Na + Cl) - (Na + NO_3)$$

can only hold, if K, Na, Cl and NO_3 each has a definite value independent of that of any of the others.

We may conclude, then, that the conductivity of a highly diluted solution is made up of the independent conductivities of the individual ions and, if this is so, these ions must be present as separate entities. Kohlrausch expresses this in what is generally known as his *law of the independent migration of the ions*. The symbol u_+ is given to the part contributed by the cation and u_- to that contributed by the anion, so that the equivalent conductivity at infinite dilution of a binary electrolyte (that is, one that dissociates into two univalent ions) is $u_+ + u_-$. These values are known as the "mobilities" of the ions (or "ion conductances") and are the same from whatever salts they may be derived.

If we now refer back to the values of equivalent conductivity just given, we must infer that the mobility of the lithium ion is less than that of the sodium ion, and this again is less than that of the potassium ion. Since each of these ions carries the same charge, it follows that they must travel at different rates. A little consideration will show that, if this be so, after electrolysis there will be a different concentration of the electrolyte around the two electrodes, and by this means, measurements were made by Hittorf of the fraction of the total current carried by each of the ions (the "transport numbers"). From this it is possible to deduce the individual ionic mobilities. Some values are given in Table 4.1.

TABLE 4.1

The Mobilities of Some Ions
(from the *International Critical Tables*, vol. 6)

cations	H^+	K^+	Na^+	Li^+	NH_4^+	Ag^+	$\frac{1}{2}Ca^{++}$	$\frac{1}{2}Mg^{++}$
u_+	315·2	64·2	43·2	33·0	64·3	53·8	51	45
anions	OH^-	Cl^-	Br^-	I^-	NO_3^-	ClO_3^-	CH_3COO^-	$\frac{1}{2}SO_4^{--}$
u_-	173·8	65·2	67·3	66·25	61·6	54·9	35	68

The practical use of these facts is that we can calculate the values of the molecular conductivity at infinite dilution in cases where it cannot be obtained experimentally. Thus ammonium hydroxide, even when diluted so far that the accuracy of the measurements becomes uncertain, is a considerable distance from complete dissociation. But from the law of Kohlrausch we can obtain the value as the sum of those of the constituents, NH_4^+ and OH^-.

The actual rate of movement of the various ions is of some interest. The mobility of an ion, derived from the equivalent conductivity of the solution in which it is contained, is measured in terms of the rate of flow of electric current in the standard conditions, under a potential gradient of 1 volt/cm. Since each gram-ion carries an electric charge of 96,500 coulombs, the actual rate of movement (under the same potential gradient) will be given by the mobility divided by 96,500. For the most rapidly moving ion, the hydrogen ion, this comes out to 0·0033 cm/sec.; the potassium ion, in the same conditions, moves at a rate of 0·00067 cm/sec.

THE DEGREE OF ELECTROLYTIC DISSOCIATION

Suppose that we find that a certain binary salt at a known concentration has an equivalent conductivity which is only half that which we obtain from Kohlrausch's law as the limiting value at infinite dilution; we should then infer that only half of its molecules were taking part in the conduction of the current. Thus we can equate the ratio of the equivalent conductivity at any given concentration to the equivalent conductivity at infinite dilution, i.e. Λ/Λ_∞, with an "apparent" degree of dissociation, a. The reason for introducing the word "apparent" will appear later.

The next step, clearly, is to apply the law of Mass Action to this dissociation. Consider a salt MA which dissociates into the ions M^+ and A^-. Let the concentration of MA before dissociation has occurred be m and let the degree of dissociation be a, i.e.

$$\frac{[M^+]}{[MA]} = \frac{[A^-]}{[MA]} = a$$

Then by the law of Mass Action

$$\frac{[M^+] \times [A^-]}{[MA]} = K$$

or

$$\frac{a^2 m}{1-a} = K \quad . \quad . \quad . \quad . \quad . \quad 4.1$$

This relation was worked out by Ostwald (1881) and is known as his "Dilution law".

The degree of dissociation is quite simply related to i, the isotonic coefficient of van't Hoff. For complete dissociation of uni-univalent salts, for example, $a=1$ and $i=2$, so that $a=i-1$. More generally, if each molecule of the electrolyte gives rise to $\nu_+ a$ cations and $\nu_- a$ anions, leaving $(1-a)$ undissociated molecules, the total number of independent particles is $1+(\nu_+ + \nu_- - 1)a$: this equals i. The *osmotic coefficient*, ϕ, is related to the isotonic coefficient by the equation

$$\phi = \frac{i}{(\nu_+ + \nu_-)} \qquad . \qquad . \qquad . \qquad . \qquad 4.2$$

STRONG ELECTROLYTES

The Ostwald dilution law describes satisfactorily the behaviour of the "weak electrolytes", i.e. those that have low electrical conductivities, such as weak organic acids and bases. It is very far from describing the behaviour of the "strong electrolytes", such as strong acids and bases and neutral salts. Moreover, the degree of dissociation calculated from the isotonic coefficients should, on this hypothesis, be the same as those calculated from the electrical conductivity. This is quite reasonably true for the weak electrolytes, but is by no means true for the strong electrolytes.

Now it is a remarkable fact that although the calculated values of the degree of dissociation lead us to expect that undissociated molecules of the strong electrolytes should exist in solution, they appear to have no properties. Calcium salts have a particular action on the muscle of the heart, and it is found that it does not matter what salt is taken. Again, hydrochloric acid has no properties peculiar to itself; it tastes sour, turns litmus red, dissolves metals, inverts cane-sugar, in common with all acids. It precipitates silver salts in common with all chlorides. These supposed undissociated molecules, also, absorb no light, even when the solution is strongly coloured. The nitrate, chloride and bromide of copper are all blue in dilute solution in water, but in alcohol, where very little dissociation is to be expected, they are blue, green and brown respectively. The absorption spectra of the permanganates of zinc, cadmium, ammonium, tin, potassium, nickel, magnesium, copper, hydrogen, aluminium, sodium, barium and cobalt, in dilute solution, all show an absorption band in the same position; various salts of dyes show the same behaviour. Furthermore, in some strong electrolytes, we find that in high concentrations the apparent degree of dissociation is greater than 1; this, of course, is ridiculous on Arrhenius' simple theory, and some totally different factors must be involved.

Now, as we have seen in Chapter 2, the electronic theory of valency leads us to expect that ions will often be more stable than the atoms from which they are derived. Thus the atoms of the alkali metals have a lone electron in the outermost shell, which is very readily lost, leaving the positively charged ion. The halogens possess seven electrons in the outer shell, and so readily take up an extra electron to complete the octet, and to form a negatively charged ion. We would expect, therefore, that if, say, atoms of sodium and chlorine were brought together, a transfer of an electron would take place immediately, with the formation of Na^+ and Cl^- ions. X-ray analysis of the crystals shows that such indeed does occur. There is no such thing as a molecule of NaCl, unless the whole crystal is considered to be one. Such is the case with the crystals of all the strong electrolytes. If undissociated molecules do not exist in the crystalline state, why should we assume that they are formed in solution? The present practice is to make no such assumption, and to account for the apparent partial dissociation by supposing that the activities of the ions fall as the concentration is increased.

We have seen in the previous chapter that with non-electrolytes the activity may be considered to be identical with the concentration in dilute solutions, but that as the concentration becomes greater, this identity breaks down, the partial free energies of both solute and solvent becoming appreciably affected by intermolecular forces. In a solution of a strong electrolyte, we have, in addition to these intermolecular forces of rather unknown nature and short range, the much longer range electrical forces between the ions. In considering the partial free energies, and thus the activities, of the ions, we must take into account the magnitude of the *electrical* potential as well as that of the chemical potential, as defined in the previous chapter.

In the crystal, the electrical forces maintain the ions in fixed positions relative to each other. In the presence of a solvent, the forces become weakened, and the ions become able to move apart from one another, and to behave, to some extent, as individual units. Nevertheless the electrical forces will result in the positive ions being surrounded by clouds of negative ions, and the negative ions by clouds of positive ions. The more ions there are, of both kinds, in a given volume, i.e. the more concentrated is the solution, the denser will be the clouds. We are thus led to expect, on general grounds, that the activity coefficients of the ions will depend on the concentration, and on the magnitude of the electrical forces between ions of opposite signs. By reason of these electrical forces, also, we should expect that the activity would differ appreciably from the concentration even in relatively dilute solutions.

The Effect of the Dielectric Constant of the Solvent. Since all ions of the same valency have the same charge, the magnitude of the electric force between any two ions of a given valency a given distance apart, will depend only on the dielectric constant of the medium between them.

Two oppositely charged bodies, as is well known, attract one another with a certain force, which can be measured. This force is greatest when the two charged bodies are in a vacuum, and is reduced if any material substance is interposed, as was discovered by Faraday. The ratio of the force exerted *in vacuo* to that exerted when some particular substance is inserted is defined as the dielectric constant of that substance.

The potential of a charged body is defined in terms of the work that must be done in bringing unit charge up to it from an infinite distance, and is thus directly related to the electrical force exerted. The contribution of the electrical potential to the activity of an ion will thus depend on the dielectric constant of the solvent. Of all liquids, with the exception of hydrogen cyanide, hydrogen peroxide and formamide, water has the highest dielectric constant, about 80, while the majority of other liquids have values which vary between 40 for nitromethane and 6·5 for acetic acid. When a substance is soluble in more than one of these various liquids, it is found that its electrical conductivity and the activities of its ions, which we may, for the moment, express as the degree to which it appears to be dissociated, is greater the greater the dielectric constant of the solvent, as is to be expected from the above considerations. The figures given in Table 4.2 will serve as illustrations of this; the solute is tetra-ethyl-ammonium iodide, on account of its solubility in a wide variety of organic solvents.

TABLE 4.2

The Electrolytic Dissociation of Tetra-ethylammonium Iodide in Various Solvents

Solvent	Dielectric Constant	Apparent Degree of Dissociation in 0·01 M. Concentration
Formamide . .	84	0·93
Water . .	81	0·91
Nitromethane . .	40	0·78
Acetone . .	21	0·50
Salicylic Aldehyde .	14	0·34

Solvation of the Ions. At the surface of an ion, the electric field is extremely large, and it has been calculated that it is no less than 2 million volts per centimetre at a distance of 3×10^{-8} cm. from a univalent ion in water. Now as we saw in Chapter 2, substances with large dielectric constants, such as water, also have large dipole moments, and their molecules will possess charges of opposite sign at their two ends. These molecules, therefore, will be orientated in the electric field around the ions, and since the field is not uniform, will be firmly held there. There may also be other forces of attachment as well as the electrical ones, when the water molecules are very close to the ion; hydrogen ions, as we saw in Chapter 2, actually unite with water molecules by means of dative covalent bonds, forming "oxonium" ions. This association between the ions and the solvent molecules, whether purely electrical or partly covalent, may be imagined as insulating, as it were, the ions of opposite charge from one another.

When we look at the values of the ionic mobilities, given in Table 4.1 (p. 122), for example, we are struck by the fact that they have little relation to the size of the ion concerned, as indicated by its atomic weight; indeed, as far as the cations are concerned, the mobilities tend to be more nearly *inversely* related to the size, in spite of the fact that one might expect the larger ions to experience greater friction than the smaller. This apparent anomaly results from the solvation of the ions; the smaller the ion, the denser is the electric field around it, and so the greater is the number of water molecules attached to it. Multivalent ions, for a similar reason, are more heavily hydrated than univalent ions, other things being equal.

It is unfortunate that different methods of estimation give different values for the degree of hydration, but the general order in which various ions are placed is more or less the same. The order is:

$$Al^{3+} \gg Mg^{2+} > Ca^{2+} > H^+ > Li^+ > Na^+ > K^+ \approx Cl^- > Br^- > I^-$$

This order, also, is roughly that of *decreasing size* of the hydrated ions, as they occur in solution. It is difficult, or perhaps even impossible, to state precisely the number of water molecules which are "bound" to each ion— and this is one of the reasons why different methods of estimation give different values; but for univalent ions it is about 5 to 10, and for multi-valent ions about 10 to 20, although the figures are rather uncertain. There will be a single layer of molecules immediately surrounding the ions, and tightly bound to it; although even these will exchange, to some extent, with "free" water molecules, the frequency of exchange depending on the magnitude of the electric field. Outside this layer will be a varying number of much more loosely attached water molecules which must be considered as only partially "bound"; there may be a second layer of relatively tightly attached water molecules round multivalent ions which contain only one atom each. Although it is thus impossible to define precisely the term "degree of hydration", the existence of hydration affects very considerably both the electrical conductivity and the ionic activity, as will be seen in later sections.

It will be observed that the hydrogen ion is shown as the most highly hydrated, and thus the largest, of the univalent cations; whereas in Table 4.1, it is seen to have the greatest mobility. This anomaly results from the particularly close association between hydrogen ions and water molecules, already referred to. The mobility given in Table 4.1 is not that of the oxonium ions being dragged among water molecules in the same way as are the hydrated sodium ions, for example; a hydrogen ion can transfer quite readily from one water molecule to another, and does not have to carry water molecules with it. We thus have an example of " facilitated diffusion", discussed in the previous chapter.

The Mean Activity of a Salt

Since, in practice, we can never deal with a solution of one kind of ion without also having present an equivalent number of ions of the opposite sign, it is convenient to make use of the mean activity of the salt as a whole. We will consider, first, the case of a uni-univalent electrolyte. If a_+ and a_- are the activities of the two ions, the partial free energy of the whole salt will be the sum of the partial free energies of the ions. In other words, since partial free energy it proportional to log (activity), we can write

$$\log a_2 = \log a_+ + \log a_- = 2 \log (a_\pm)$$

where $a_\pm$ is the mean ionic activity. Thus $a_\pm = \sqrt{a_+ . a_-}$. By similar reasoning, we define the mean ionic activity coefficient as $\gamma_\pm = \sqrt{\gamma_+ . \gamma_-}$ and hence $\log a_2 = 2 \log (\gamma_\pm m)$ where m is the molar concentration of the electrolyte. For electrolytes of other valency types it can easily be shown that

$$\log a_2 = \nu_+ \log (\gamma_+ m) + \nu_- \log (\gamma_- m) = (\nu_+ + \nu_-) \log (\gamma_\pm m) \quad . \quad 4.3$$

where ν_+ and ν_- are the numbers of positive and negative ions in a molecule of the salt considered.

The Change of Activity with Concentration

It was found, empirically, almost as soon as a sufficient number of determinations had been made, that the activity coefficients of a large number of salts varied with the concentration according to an expression of the form:

$$\log \gamma_\pm = \beta m^{0.5} + \alpha m \quad . \quad . \quad . \quad . \quad 4.4$$

where the constants β and α depend on the valency type of the salt, as well as on the temperature etc. The methods by which the mean ionic activity coefficients are determined will be considered in later sections.

It was also established experimentally that the activity of an ion of a given kind is modified by the presence in the same solution of ions of a different kind. Thus the mean ionic activity of, say, HCl, has a different value in solutions of, say, KCl or K_2SO_4, from that in pure water. The effect of a bivalent salt, moreover, is four times as great as that of a uni-valent salt. In dilute solution, in fact, the activity of a given ion is affected, not by the chemical nature of the other ions present in the solution, but only by their valency and total concentration. This, of course, is only to be expected if the effect is due primarily to the electrical interaction with the other ions of the same sign, and with the surrounding cloud of ions of opposite sign. Lewis and Randall, accordingly, introduced the conception of *Ionic Strength*. The concentration (m) of each ion is multiplied by the square of its valency (z), all the products so obtained are added together, and the sum divided by 2—this last so that the ionic strength of a uni-univalent salt shall be equal to its total molar concentration. In symbols

$$I = \Sigma(mz^2)/2 \qquad . \qquad . \qquad . \qquad . \qquad 4.5$$

The practical use of this conception is that the mean ionic activity co-efficient of a given salt will be the same in all dilute solutions of the same ionic strength, whatever their chemical composition.

The assumption of complete dissociation, and the modification of the ionic activities by the electrical forces, makes it possible to calculate the mean activity coefficients of an electrolyte solution. Debye and Hückel in 1923 made the calculation in a mathematical form which was sufficiently simple to be useful, although it is too complex to be given in full here. In principle, the problem is to calculate the work done in bringing an ion of given charge from an infinitely dilute solution, into one of the given concentration. This work must determine the free energy of the ion in the solution, and hence its activity. Now the work done in such a process is the product of the charge and the potential at the point to which it is finally brought, or, more strictly, since the potential of this point is affected by the presence of the ion, by the integral of all the elements of work that are done as the charge is brought up in infinitesimal fractions at a time.

Thus the work is given by the integral expression, $W = \int_0^{ze} \psi \, . \, de$, where ψ is the potential, e is the ionic charge and z the valency. We have first, therefore, to calculate the potential at any point close to an ion in an electrolyte solution. Now if we know the total charge at any point—i.e. the density of the ionic cloud—we can deduce the way in which the poten-tial varies at this point by means of a theorem in classical electrostatics (Poisson's equation). But we can also relate the density of ions at any point to the potential at that point by means of Boltzmann's principle of the random distribution of energy among the individual molecules (or ions) in a large assembly (Chapter 2, p. 54). From the combination of these two principles we deduce that the potential at any point in the neighbourhood of an ion is a function of a quantity κ. This quantity, which is proportional to the square root of the ionic strength, may be

E

regarded as being the reciprocal of the equivalent radius of the ionic cloud—i.e. if the whole cloud were concentrated on a shell of radius $1/\kappa$, the potential at any point under consideration would be unchanged. We thus arrive at the conclusion that the potential at a distance r from the centre of an ion is given by the expression:

$$\psi = \frac{ze}{\epsilon r} - \frac{ze}{\epsilon} \cdot \frac{1 - \exp(-\kappa r)}{r} \qquad . \qquad . \qquad . \qquad 4.6$$

where ϵ is the dielectric constant.

The mathematical treatment necessary for the derivation of this equation will be found in most of the more advanced text-books of physical chemistry, such as that by Moore (1957), and in the monograph by Robinson and Stokes (1955).

The change in free energy associated with the transfer of a single ion from a very dilute solution, in which the activity coefficient is unity, to a more concentrated solution, may be regarded as being composed of two parts: (a) that due to the change in concentration *per se*, the solution being imagined "ideal"; and (b) that resulting from the work done against the electric forces. The activity coefficient in the more concentrated solution, therefore, is determined only by the second part. Moreover, in equation 4.6, the first term represents that part of the potential due to the presence of the ion itself, and the second term, that part due to the cloud of ions of opposite sign: it is only the latter which varies with the ionic strength, and affects the activity coefficient. For convenience equation 4.6 is simplified by assuming that the quantity $[1 - \exp(-\kappa r)]$ approximates to κr. This is only justified if the solution is very dilute. Integration of the original equation for the work done in bringing an ion up to the point considered, thus yields an expression for the activity coefficient of a single ion. This is converted into an expression for the mean ionic activity coefficient— which is the quantity which we can determine experimentally—by making use of the general relation given above (equation 4.3). We thus finally arrive at the expression:

$$-\log_{10}\gamma_{\pm} = \sum \frac{\nu_1 z_1{}^2}{\nu_1 + \nu_2} \cdot \frac{A\sqrt{I}}{(\epsilon.T)^{3/2}} \qquad . \qquad . \qquad . \qquad 4.7$$

Or, if the solvent is water and the temperature 15° C., we have:

$$-\log_{10}\gamma_{\pm} = \sum \frac{\nu_1 z_1{}^2}{\nu_1 + \nu_2} \cdot 0 \cdot 50 \sqrt{I} \qquad . \qquad . \qquad . \qquad 4.7a$$

A is a constant involving the electronic charge, the gas constant and the Avogadro number. ϵ is the dielectric constant of the solvent. ν_1 is the number of ions of valency z_1 and ν_2 is the number of ions of valency z_2: ν_1 and z_1 refer to the ion of higher valency, if the two are not the same. The valency factor within the summation sign has the value 1 for uni-univalent salts such as KCl, the value 2 for uni-bivalent salts such as K_2SO_4 or $CaCl_2$, the value 4 for bi-bivalent salts such as $CaSO_4$, and so on. The value of the constant A rises slowly with rise in temperature; at 25° C. it is 0·509, and at 38° C., it is 0·522.

Strictly, this expression relates to the "rational" activity coefficient $(f_{\pm})$, the ratio of the mean ionic activity to the *mole fraction* of the solute. The relation between the rational and molal activity coefficients is given by:

$$f_{\pm} = \gamma_{\pm}[1 + 0 \cdot 001(\nu_1 + \nu_2)m.M_1]$$

where M_1 is the molecular weight of the solvent, and m is the molal concentration of the solute. Clearly, for dilute solutions, the term within the brackets is very nearly unity.

The relation expressed by equation 4.7, which is known as the Debye-Hückel *limiting* law, agrees very well with experimental observations in very dilute solutions, but fails in somewhat more concentrated solutions, as, indeed, it might well be expected to, owing to the approximations that are made in its development. In particular, it fails to account for the rise in activity coefficients that occurs in quite concentrated solutions, since it does not contain the linear term (am) that was found necessary in the empirical equation given above (equation 4.4). This is shown in Fig. 4.2. Better agreement with experiment is obtained when more complicated expressions are used.

(1) The exponential term in equation 4.6 $[1 - \exp(-\kappa r)]/r$ is more closely approximated by the expression $\kappa/(1 + \kappa r)$.

(2) It is then necessary to take into account the fact that an ion has a finite radius, a, and that we are concerned with the potential at its surface, or more strictly, at a point defined in terms of the "distance of closest approach" of a pair of ions. We must, therefore, insert into the denominator of equation 4.7, an additional term involving a, and κ or alternatively $\sqrt{I}$, and get:

$$\log . \gamma_{\pm} = \Sigma \frac{\nu_1 z_1^2}{\nu_1 + \nu_2} \cdot \frac{A\sqrt{I}}{1 + B.a\sqrt{I}} \qquad . \qquad . \qquad . \qquad 4.8$$

If the solvent is water, the constant B has a value of 0·33 between 15° C. and 38° C. The value of a, of course, varies with the nature of the electrolyte considered, but less so than might be expected, since it is the radius of the *solvated* ion that is concerned. For sodium and potassium chlorides, it is about 4, and for calcium chloride, it is about 3 (expressed in Ångström units). This expression fits the observed values well up to an ionic strength of about 0·1; for sodium chloride, it is in error by no more than about 6 per cent. at a concentration of 0·5 M, and may thus be used for most solutions of biological interest.

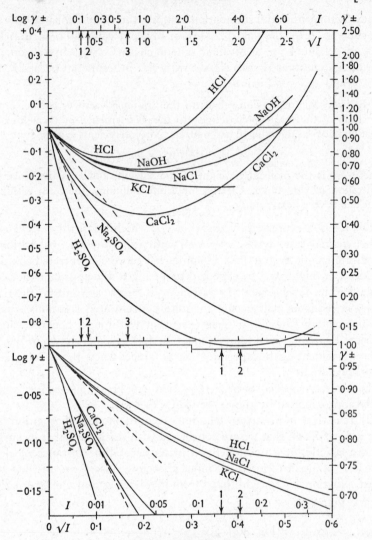

FIG. 4.2. THE MEAN IONIC ACTIVITY COEFFICIENTS OF SOME ELECTROLYTES
IN AQUEOUS SOLUTION

Ordinates: right-hand scales, activity coefficients ($\gamma_\pm$).
          left-hand scales, $\log_{10}$ ($\gamma_\pm$).

Abscissae: Ionic strength (I) and $\sqrt{I}$.

The lower figure gives the values for dilute solutions plotted on larger scales. The
broken lines give the expected relation on the basis of the Debye-Hückel theory for a
uni-univalent electrolyte and a uni-bivalent electrolyte, respectively. The relation is
obeyed reasonably well up to an ionic strength of about 0·01.

The arrows indicate the approximate ionic strengths of:
          1 Ringer's solution (frog)
          2 Ringer-Locke solution (mammalian)
          3 Sea water.

(Plotted from figures given by Conway, 1952.)

(3) The presence of an electric field around each ion affects the properties of the solvent molecules in its neighbourhood. This has two consequences: (a) the value of the dielectric constant to be inserted in the constants A and B in equation 4.8, for example, will not be that of pure water, and will vary with the ionic concentration; and (b) the ions are not simple charged spheres of constant radius, but are enclosed in a shell of firmly held water molecules, which are "immobilised" as it were, by the ions, as already discussed. If we assume that the number of these water molecules round each ion is independent of the concentration, we can derive an expression for the effect of this solvation on the mean ionic activity coefficient in terms of the reduction in the number of "free" solvent molecules per unit volume, and the activity of the solvent. This last can be calculated by means of equation 3.17 (p. 88), or less precisely by means of equation 4.9, in the next section, provided that we know the mean ionic activity coefficient over a range of concentrations; or it can be directly measured by any of the methods discussed in Chapter 3. The addition of a term derived in this way to equation 4.8 results in an expression which fits the observed values up to concentrations of at least 1 M., and with some electrolytes, up to 5 or 6 M. With this method of approach, it is assumed that the water molecules which are in the strongest electric fields are, in effect, parts of the ions themselves, and are not acting as the dielectric medium between the charges; the problem of the value of the dielectric constant to be used is thus avoided.

We note that the activity coefficients of strong electrolytes, as given in Fig. 4.2, for example, are less than unity, except in very high concentrations, whereas those of non-electrolytes (such as cane-sugar, as given in Table 3.1) are greater than unity. The activity coefficients of the non-electrolytes express the interactions between solute and solvent, whereas those of the electrolytes express primarily the electrostatic interactions between one solute ion and another. But in high concentrations the solute-solvent interactions also become appreciable in electrolyte solutions; and this leads to an increase in the activity coefficients.

In a solution containing two or more different electrolytes, the activity coefficient of each will not, in general, be the same as it would be in a pure solution of the same total concentration, except when the solutions are so dilute that the simplest form of the Debye-Hückel equation can be used. This applies, also, to the osmotic coefficients. The theory of mixed electrolytes is very complicated and has not yet been worked out adequately; the activity coefficients in most solutions of biological importance—and particularly in those of relatively high concentration, such as sea-water—cannot be predicted theoretically with any great confidence. But no very great error is likely to arise, certainly in the osmotic coefficients, if the value for each component is taken as that corresponding to an ionic strength calculated from the concentrations and valencies of *all* the components of the solution.

THE RELATION BETWEEN OSMOTIC AND ACTIVITY COEFFICIENTS

We saw in the previous chapter that there is no simple and necessary relation between the activity of the solvent and that of the solute, but that they are related by a differential equation (equation 3.17, p. 88) which, however, cannot in general be integrated. In sufficiently dilute solutions of electrolytes, however, the Debye-Hückel expression provides a relation between the mean ionic activity coefficient and the ionic concentration, and integration becomes possible. We thus get the explicit relation between the osmotic coefficient and the mean ionic activity coefficient:

$$-\ln \gamma_{\pm} = 3(1 - \phi) \qquad . \qquad . \qquad . \qquad 4.9$$

If we insert equation 4.3 into equation 3.17, we get:

$$-d(\ln a_1) = (n_2/n_1) \cdot (\nu_+ + \nu_-) \cdot d(\ln \gamma_{\pm}m) \qquad . \qquad 3.17, 4.3$$

Also, we have: $n_2/n_1 = mM_1/1000$, where M_1 is the molecular weight of the solvent; and from equations 4.5 and 4.7 we can write: $\ln \gamma_{\pm} = -B'\sqrt{2m}$, where B' includes the valency factors appropriate to the particular salt concerned. We thus have an equation relating $\ln a_1$ to m, which can be integrated, giving:

$$-\ln a_1 = (\nu_+ + \nu_-) \cdot (mM_1/1000) \cdot (1 - B'\sqrt{2m}/3)$$
$$= (\nu_+ + \nu_-) \cdot (mM_1/1000) \cdot [1 + (\ln \gamma_{\pm})/3] \qquad . \qquad . \qquad 4.10$$

Comparing this with equation 3.11 (p. 84), we see that:

$$\phi = 1 + (\ln \gamma_{\pm})/3$$
$$\text{or } -\ln \gamma_{\pm} = 3(1 - \phi).$$

Strictly, equation 4.9 only holds when the solution is sufficiently dilute for the Debye-Hückel equation to be obeyed, i.e. so long as $-\ln \gamma_{\pm}$ is proportional to $\sqrt{m}$. It will hold with quite a fair degree of approximation, however, at higher concentrations, since we do not require to know accurately the value of the activity coefficient at any one value of the concentration, but only the integral of the relationship between these quantities from zero concentration up to the concentration considered: it is adequate if the relation holds over most of this range.

SOLUBILITIES AND ACTIVITY COEFFICIENTS

The activity coefficients of sparingly soluble salts can be determined from their solubilities in solutions of other salts that have a common ion. Since all saturated solutions of a given substance are in equilibrium with the solid solute, they must, by definition (see pp. 5, 83) all have the same activity, even though the concentration may be changed by varying the concentration of some additional solute that has a common ion. Thus we plot the concentration of the sparingly soluble salt, when in saturated solution, against the total concentration of the solution, and extrapolate to zero total concentration. (Or better, we plot the reciprocal of the first concentration against the square root of the second.) We thus discover the rather strange mathematical fiction of the solubility of a salt in a solution of zero concentration. The activity coefficient in this case, must be unity, and so we can calculate the activity coefficient at any other concentration, since we know that the *activity* of the sparingly soluble salt is not changed.

THE ELECTRICAL CONDUCTIVITY OF SOLUTIONS OF STRONG ELECTROLYTES

As already pointed out, the equivalent conductivity of a strong electrolyte solution falls as the concentration increases. This was accounted for on Arrhenius' theory by assuming that there was a fall in the degree of dissociation, i.e. that the number of ions per mole of electrolyte diminished. The mobility of the ions, or their rate of movement in the electric field, was supposed to be independent of the concentration. If, on the other hand, we suppose that strong electrolytes are always completely dissociated we must account for the variations in equivalent conductivity by assuming variations in the mobility. The conception of the existence of an ionic cloud, whose density depends on the ionic strength of the solution, allows one not only to predict that there will be a variation of the mobility with the concentration, but also to calculate its magnitude. Two factors are concerned in this variation. In the first place, each ion, as it moves in the electric field, will drag the neighbouring water molecules with it, and along with them, any other ions which may be sufficiently close. Since these will mainly be of the opposite sign, and moving in the opposite direction, the effect will be to reduce the net velocity of all the ions. In the second place, as the ion moves under the influence of the electric field, the ionic cloud will have to be built up in front of it, and to diffuse away behind it; it is reasonable to suppose that these processes take an appreciable time, so that at any moment while the central ion is moving in the electric field, the cloud is incomplete in front of it, and excessively dense behind it. This asymmetry in the distribution of the charges of the opposite sign will act as a drag on the motion of the central ion. The actual time taken for the cloud to form and to disappear is very small, of the order of 10^{-9} seconds, and so the asymmetry produced is small; but the charges involved are very large, and the effect is quite important. Both the first of these effects—the *electrophoretic* effect—and the second—the *relaxation* effect—will increase in magnitude as the concentration, and the density of the ionic cloud, increase.

Mathematical treatment of the problem leads to rather complex equations, involving the dielectric constant of the solvent, the absolute temperature, the valency of the ions, and some universal constants. They may be written in the form:

$$\Lambda_c = \Lambda_0 - (c.\Lambda_0 + D)\sqrt{I} \qquad . \qquad . \qquad 4.11$$

and for a uni-univalent electrolyte in water at 25° C. reduce to:

$$\Lambda_c = \Lambda_0 - (0\cdot228\Lambda_0 + 59\cdot8)\sqrt{c} \qquad . \qquad . \qquad 4.11a$$

where Λ_c is the equivalent conductivity of a solution of concentration c (or ionic strength I), and Λ_0 is the equivalent conductivity at zero concentration, as estimated by extrapolation if necessary. This equation was worked out by Onsager in 1927, and is of the same form as an empirical equation proposed by Kohlrausch in 1907. In very dilute solutions of uni-univalent salts (up to about M/1000) the agreement between the experimentally determined values of the conductivity with those calculated from Onsager's equation, using the theoretical values of the constants, is good. At higher concentrations, there are substantial discrepancies.

It is implicit in the derivation of equation 4.11, however, that a term involving the ionic radius, a, should be included, and this term, as in the Debye-Hückel equation, becomes important unless the value of $\kappa.a$ is very small compared with 1. As a first approximation, we may write $\sqrt{I}/(1 + \kappa.a)$ in equation 4.11 in place of $\sqrt{I}$, and in this form the equation gives quite good results with uni-univalent electrolytes in concentrations up to 0·1 M. The values of a which give the best agreement with experiment are the same, for a given electrolyte, at all temperatures, and are sensibly the same as those inserted in the Debye-Hückel equation (equation 4.8). Mathematical simplicity, however, is only obtained by means of inserting approximations, and in still higher concentration more elaborate expressions must be used, and a correction introduced for the increase in viscosity of the solution. Good agreement with experiment is then obtained in solutions of some uni-univalent electrolytes at concentrations up to several times Normal.

Ion Association

If two oppositely charged ions come sufficiently close together, the electrical energy necessary to pull them apart becomes large compared with the energy of thermal agitation. (It is implicit in the Debye-Hückel analysis that the thermal energy is large compared with the electrical energy.) They will then become associated as an "ion-pair", and there will, in effect, no longer be complete electrolytic dissociation. It is reasonable to expect that this will be more likely to occur with large ions than with small, since they are less hydrated; and with multivalent ions than with univalent ions, since the electrical force is larger. In solutions of such electrolytes, the mean ionic activity coefficients are substantially smaller than those calculated from theory, even after allowing for the effects of solvation. Such solutions, also, are found to have electrical conductivities which are much lower than those predicted, even by the most complicated theory. It seems certain that electrolytic dissociation is, effectively, incomplete in these solutions, owing to the formation of ion-pairs. In solutions of potassium nitrate, for example, up to $0 \cdot 1$ M concentration, it is estimated that less than 3 per cent. of the ions are associated, and it may be that none are associated at all; in solutions of bivalent metal sulphates, on the other hand, a considerable fraction of the ions are associated, even in quite dilute solutions.

Such an admission of the possibility of incomplete dissociation does not in any way invalidate the calculations of ionic activities and activity coefficients by methods which measure the partial free energy, such as vapour pressure lowering, or the electrode potentials which will be discussed later. We choose, for simplicity, to consider the dissociation to be complete; if it is not, the fact will be reflected in the magnitude of the activity coefficient. We have no means of distinguishing between a reduction in ionic activity due to incomplete dissociation, and that due to, say, interionic electrical forces, except in terms of a discrepancy between theory and practice.

It may be well, at this point, to stress the fact that with strong electrolytes, the quantity which used to be (and is still, sometimes) referred to as the "degree of dissociation" may have any one of three different meanings. There is, first, a value which may be derived from van't Hoff's isotonic coefficient, and which is more properly called the "osmotic coefficient"; this defines, as we have seen in the previous chapter, the effect of the electrolyte in reducing the activity of the *solvent*, and is only indirectly related to the properties of the electrolyte itself. Secondly, there is a value which may be deduced from electrical conductivity, and which largely, and in some cases entirely, is a measure of the reduction in the *mobility* of the ions, and not of their concentration. Lastly, there is the activity coefficient, which is a true measure of the change in chemical potential of the ions, and thus of their "effective" concentration, or "active mass" as physico-chemical entities. It so happens that in relatively low concentration (say up to about $0 \cdot 2$ M) the values deduced from electrical conductivity agree reasonably well with those deduced from the osmotic coefficients. These, however, differ quite considerably from the activity

E*

coefficients, as may be seen by comparing the values given in Fig. 4.2 with those given in Fig. 3.2, p. 104.

THE SALTING-OUT OF NON-ELECTROLYTES

The extremely powerful electric fields in the solution in the neighbourhood of the ions will have the effect that, in general, polarisable molecules will tend to be held in these fields to the exclusion of non-polarisable molecules. In aqueous solutions, the solvent, water, is more polarisable than most non-electrolytes, particularly organic compounds. The latter are thus driven out ("salted-out") from the neighbourhood of the ions, and concentrated in the remainder of the solution; their activities will thus be greater than would be expected from the overall concentration, by an amount which is roughly proportional to the concentration of the ions. This rough proportionality is confirmed experimentally. As a corollary to this, we should expect that if the solute were *more* polarisable than water, it would congregate in the electric field round the ions. This occurs in the case of hydrocyanic acid, which is "salted-in".

There are many examples of this effect of an electrolyte in raising the activity of a non-electrolyte in aqueous solution, of which we can give only a few. The solubility of gases is less in salt solutions than in pure water: the gas in solution must be in equilibrium with that in the gas phase, so that if the addition of salt displaces some of the gas from solution, the partial free energy of that which remains must be increased. Again, the partial vapour pressure of ethanol, and other volatile solutes, in dilute solution is increased by the addition of neutral salts. And lastly, the depression of the freezing point by a mixture of an electrolyte and a non-electrolyte is greater than the sum of the depressions produced by each component alone.

DIFFUSION POTENTIALS AND
CONCENTRATION CELLS

The presence of electric charges on the constituent ions of an electrolyte in solution leads to the important consequence that even a very slight separation of the ions of opposite sign will result in the production of electromotive forces. Since, as we have seen, different kinds of ion move at different speeds, this means that electrical potential differences will be developed, in appropriate conditions, when two electrolyte solutions of different composition are brought into contact. These can be measured, by means of suitable electrical instruments, with great accuracy, and provide us with the most important method for determining ionic activities. The nature and magnitudes of these potential differences, also, are of great importance in physiology, not so much for the purpose of measuring ionic activities, as for studying the behaviour of electrolytes in living cells.

DIFFUSION POTENTIALS

Let us consider the general case of a solution of one electrolyte in contact with a solution of another electrolyte in the same, or a different, concentration. The ions of each solution will diffuse into the other, but they will, initially, not necessarily move at the same rate. The faster ions will outstrip the slower, until a "double layer" is developed, and the electrostatic forces will then have the effect of speeding up the slower ions, and slowing down the faster ones, until the whole double layer diffuses together. A potential difference is thus set up between the two solutions.

The virtual impossibility of achieving any substantial separation of the ions of opposite sign—i.e. one that might be detected by chemical methods—can be shown by performing a simple calculation. Suppose we have 10 litres of a 0·1 M solution of a uni-univalent electrolyte enclosed in a spherical vessel. Suppose, also, that by some means we were able to remove from this solution all the ions of one sign, leaving those of the opposite sign. Since we have 1 gram-ion present in the vessel, the charge would be 1 Faraday, or, say 10^5 coulombs: since the vessel would have a radius of 13 centimetres, its capacity would be 14×10^{-12} farads. The potential on it would thus be $10^5/14 \times 10^{-12}$ or 7×10^{15} volts. We shall see in this and later chapters that in some circumstances there is a slight separation of the ions of opposite sign, but the potential differences involved are usually of the order of a fraction of a volt: the deficit of ions of one sign, relative to those of the opposite sign would thus be about 1 part in 10^{15}.

There will be no state of equilibrium in such conditions of free diffusion; but there will be a steady state at the boundary between the two solutions in which the concentration of the ions, and the electrical potential of the solution, will change in a complex fashion as we pass from the bulk of one solution to the bulk of the other. Consider a small distance dx in the direction in which the diffusion is occurring, and let the potential difference between one end and the other be dE. We will limit ourselves, for simplicity, to the case of a uni-univalent electrolyte. The electrical work done in transporting 1 gram-ion over this distance is thus $F.dE$, where F is the Faraday constant and the electrical force acting on the gram-ion must be $F.dE/dx$. This force may be regarded as acting against a "friction", as in the general case of diffusion considered in the previous chapter, producing a certain velocity of movement. But in the case of the ions, this velocity can be measured in terms of the electrical conductivity in very dilute solution, the current flowing being directly proportional to the velocity of the ions, to the charge carried per ion, and to the number of ions present. In unit potential gradient, this velocity is known as the mobility, u_+ for cations and u_- for anions. If, therefore, the potential gradient is dE/dx, the velocity of the cations, for example, will be $u_+ . dE/dx$ and this velocity will be equal to the force acting, $F.dE/dx$, divided by the frictional resistance to its movement, f_c. Hence we deduce that $f_c = F/u_+$.

Moreover, the force on a gram-ion of cations due to diffusion can be written:

$$\frac{d\bar{G}_+}{dx} = -RT \cdot \frac{d(\ln a_+)}{dx} \qquad . \qquad . \qquad . \quad 4.12$$

(compare equation 3.29, p. 106). The velocity of the cations due to diffusion will thus be given by this force divided by the "friction", which will be the same whether the force is electrical or osmotic. The total velocity of the cations will be the sum of that due to electrical and that due to osmotic forces and becomes, therefore:

$$-u_+ \frac{dE}{dx} - \frac{u_+}{F} RT \frac{d(\ln a_+)}{dx} \qquad . \qquad . \qquad . \quad 4.13$$

By exactly similar reasoning, we deduce that the velocity of the anions will be:

$$+u_- \frac{dE}{dx} - \frac{u_-}{F} RT \frac{d(\ln a_-)}{dx} \qquad . \qquad . \qquad . \quad 4.13a$$

Now if there is no externally applied electromotive force between the two solutions there will be no net flow of current, and, in the steady state the total number of cations crossing any imaginary plane in unit time must be the same as the total number of anions crossing this plane in the same time. If the plane considered has unit area, the number of ions crossing it in unit time will be given by the product of their concentration and their velocity. Thus from the above expressions for the velocities, we can write in general:

$$-\Sigma \left[u_+ m_+ \left(\frac{dE}{dx} + \frac{RT}{F} \cdot \frac{d(\ln a_+)}{dx} \right) \right] = \Sigma \left[u_- m_- \left(\frac{dE}{dx} - \frac{RT}{F} \cdot \frac{d(\ln a_-)}{dx} \right) \right] \quad 4.14$$

the summation signs indicating that we evaluate the expressions for each kind of cation and for each kind of anion, and add together with due regard to sign, all those for cations on the one hand, and all those for anions, on the other hand. This expression, however, is of little value as it stands. First, we cannot deduce both cation and anion activities from a single equation, and we must assume arbitrarily that

$$\ln a_+ = \ln a_- = \ln a_\pm = \ln \gamma_\pm m$$

where $a_\pm$ is the mean ionic activity, $\gamma_\pm$ is the mean ionic activity coefficient, and m is the concentration of any particular cation or anion. These expressions, however, cannot be solved without making assumptions as to the way in which the electrical and chemical potentials change as we pass from one solution to the other. The most general assumptions, such as those made by Planck in 1930, lead to expressions which require elaborate mathematical treatment for their solution. Simpler ones were made originally by Planck in 1890 and by Henderson in 1909, who first studied the problem; and one of the simplest, for our present purpose, is that the electrical potential gradient is uniform throughout the boundary region. This is certainly not generally true, but in some simple cases, which we will consider here, all the assumptions give the same answer.

Suppose that we have a solution of a uni-univalent electrolyte in contact with a solution of the same electrolyte at a lower concentration. Equation 4.14 then reduces to:

$$\frac{(u_+ + u_-)}{(u_+ - u_-)} \cdot \frac{dE}{dx} = -\frac{RT}{F} \cdot \frac{d(\ln a_\pm)}{dx} \qquad . \qquad . \qquad . \qquad 4.15$$

We now integrate from $x=0$ to $x=d$ where d is the thickness of the boundary region; from $E=0$ to $E=\Delta E$, where ΔE is the potential difference between the two solutions; and from $a_\pm=(a_\pm)_c$ to $a_\pm=(a_\pm)_d$ where $(a_\pm)_c$ and $(a_\pm)_d$ are the activities in the more concentrated and the more dilute solutions respectively. We thus get:

$$\Delta E = \frac{RT}{F} \cdot \frac{(u_+ - u_-)}{(u_+ + u_-)}\left[\ln \frac{(a_\pm)_c}{(a_\pm)_d}\right] \qquad . \qquad . \qquad . \qquad 4.16$$

which can be written alternatively as

$$\Delta E = \frac{RT}{F} \cdot \frac{(u_+ - u_-)}{(u_+ + u_-)}\left[\ln \frac{m_c}{m_d} + \ln \frac{(\gamma_\pm)_c}{(\gamma_\pm)_d}\right] \qquad . \qquad . \qquad 4.16a$$

If the variation in the activity coefficient is neglected, equation 4.16a becomes the normal equation for the diffusion potential, or "liquid junction potential" between two electrolyte solutions of the same composition, but of different concentration. As a further approximation, we could insert the Debye-Hückel expression for the variation of the activity coefficient with concentration.

The other simple case, which is of somewhat greater interest in biological problems, arises when the two solutions in contact with one another contain, say, different cations but the same anion, the total electrolyte concentration being the same in both. Thus we might have 0·1 M. solutions of potassium chloride and sodium chloride diffusing into one another. Suppose that at any point within the boundary region, the concentration of one of the cations is $q.m$, the concentration of the other is $(1-q)m$, and the concentration of the anion (uniform throughout) is m.

If we neglect the activity coefficients, and remember that dm/dx is zero, the general equation 4.14 may be reduced to:

$$\frac{dE}{dx} = -\frac{RT}{F} \cdot \left[\frac{(u_+)_1 + (u_+)_2}{q((u_+)_1 + (u_+)_2) + (u_+)_2 + u_-} \right] \frac{dq}{dx}$$

This, on integrating over the whole boundary region, from $E = 0$ to $E = \Delta E$, and from $q = q_c$ to $q = q_d$ gives:

$$\Delta E = \frac{RT}{F} \cdot \ln \left[\frac{q_c(u_+)_1 + (1 - q_c)(u_+)_2 + u_-}{q_d(u_+)_1 + (1 - q_d)(u_+)_2 + u_-} \right] \qquad . \qquad . \quad 4.17$$

In the limiting case, when $q_c = 1$ and $q_d = 0$, this reduces to:

$$\Delta E = \frac{RT}{F} \ln \left[\frac{(u_+)_1 + u_-}{(u_+)_2 + u_-} \right] \qquad . \qquad . \qquad . \quad 4.17a$$

We have assumed that the ionic mobilities are independent of the concentration, which is by no means true. A rather better expression for the liquid junction potential is given by writing equation 4.17a in the form:

$$\Delta E = \frac{RT}{F} \ln \frac{\Lambda_1}{\Lambda_2} \qquad . \qquad . \qquad . \qquad . \quad 4.17b$$

where Λ_1 and Λ_2 are the electrical conductivities of the two solutions concerned.

In the general case, when the two solutions are different both in composition and concentration, the use of different assumptions as to conditions within the boundary region leads to different final equations. None of them agrees with experimental observation in all cases, although all agree reasonably well in some cases. Experimentally, it is found that the liquid junction potential depends quite markedly on the manner in which the junction is made, and changes with time thereafter, so that precise comparison with theory is impossible.

It is clear from these expressions that the diffusion potential developed at the junction between two solutions of different concentration depends upon the difference between the mobilities of the various ions concerned. An important consequence of this is that if the mobility of one of them is specifically reduced by the presence of some structure or membrane, the potential developed may be considerably increased, or less usually diminished. We shall find in Chapter 10 that most membranes encountered in living material, and many "dead" membranes, are more readily permeable to ions of one sign than to those of the other. We should thus expect to observe, and indeed do observe, potential differences associated with the presence of these membranes. They are of great importance in the physiology of the excitation of such structures as nerves and muscles, and also in the phenomenon of secretion.

CONCENTRATION CELLS

A very important special case arises when the mobility of either the cations or the anions is reduced to zero. In this case, either u_+ or u_- becomes zero, and we have, for example, from equation 4.16:

$$\Delta E = \frac{RT}{F} \ln \frac{(a_+)_c}{(a_+)_d} \qquad . \qquad . \qquad . \qquad 4.18$$

if the mobility of the anions is taken to be zero. Since the ions of one sign are now indiffusible, the salt as a whole is indiffusible, owing to the electrostatic attraction between the ions of opposite sign. The system will no longer become steadily more "run down" or "mixed up" by the diffusion of one solution into the other; a true thermodynamic equilibrium is now possible at the junction between the two solutions. The membrane or other structure, which is responsible for stopping, say the anions, is then said to be *reversible* towards the cations.

The existence of a true equilibrium in these conditions allows us to deduce the relation between the electromotive force and the activity ratio more directly. If we imagine an ion passing through the reversible membrane from one solution to the other, work (positive or negative) will be done on it against both the chemical potential difference and the electrical potential difference. The condition for equilibrium is that the total work should be zero. Thus, for one gram-molecule of a cation, for example, we write:

$$\Delta \bar{G}_+ - z_+ F \Delta E = 0 \qquad . \qquad . \qquad . \qquad 4.19$$

where $\Delta \bar{G}_+$ is the change in partial free energy, z_+ is the valency of the ions, and F is the Faraday constant. For ions, therefore, the condition for equilibrium is that the change in the *electrochemical potential* should be zero, this term being applied to the sum of the changes in chemical potential and electrical potential. It should be noted, however, that since we consider unit mass of the ions, and not unit electric charge, we have to add to the chemical potential a term in which the electrical potential difference is multiplied by the charge on the ions. Further, we have by definition:

$$\Delta \bar{G}_+ = RT \ln \frac{(a_+)_c}{(a_+)_d} \qquad . \qquad . \qquad . \qquad 3.7$$

assuming, still, that we are considering the cations. From these two expressions, equation 4.18 follows directly.

The most important example of a membrane reversible towards cations, is a metal in contact with solutions of one of its salts. A metal atom may dissolve on one face, going into solution as a cation and liberating an electron, while simultaneously a cation may be deposited on the other face as a metal atom, and taking up an electron. The electrons can move freely through the metal, since it is a good conductor of electricity. Clearly, if we had two solutions of different activity separated by a metal sheet, we might in imagination split this sheet into two, and insert a suitable instrument for measuring the potential difference between the two solutions. We cannot, however, by this simple device determine the ratio of the cation activities in the two solutions, since the circuit must be completed by making a second junction between the two solutions. From the definition of free energy, we cannot measure the free energy changes unless the system is capable of running down, although, of course, in an extremely slow and reversible manner. It must be possible for the solute activity to become the same in both solutions. We have already provided a mechanism whereby the cations can pass reversibly from one solution to the other, and we must therefore, complete the circuit by providing a mechanism whereby the anions can do so as well. An electrode system which is reversible towards anions may be constructed by using as an electrode a metal which has a relatively insoluble salt with the anion in question. The solution is kept saturated with this salt, so that if current is passed into or out of the solution, the metal of the electrode either goes into solution, reacts with the anion and precipitates out; or else is removed from the solution, releases the anion and more salt goes into solution.

By making up our circuit with two solutions of different activity, joined by two electrode systems, one reversible towards cations, and the other reversible towards anions, we have constructed a *concentration cell without liquid junction*. At the electrode reversible to cations, we have a potential given by equation 4.18 above; and at the electrode reversible to anions, we have a potential of the same form, but of opposite sign, as may be seen from equation 4.16 if u_+ is taken to be zero, instead of u_-. The combined potential difference is thus:

$$E = \frac{2RT}{F} \ln \frac{(a_\pm)_c}{(a_\pm)_d} \qquad . \qquad . \qquad . \qquad . \qquad 4.20$$

In practice, only a limited number of these cells can be constructed, owing to the lack of suitable electrode systems. One of the most important is that containing a hydrogen electrode and a chloride electrode. The hydrogen electrode, to which we shall refer again later, is made by saturating a platinum electrode with hydrogen; the chloride electrode may be either silver in contact with a solution saturated with silver chloride, or mercury in contact with a solution saturated with calomel. We can represent this cell in the following way (in all such diagrams, a full line represents the junction between a metal and a solution, and a broken line the junction between two solutions):

$$
\text{HCl} \atop (a_\pm)_c \left|
\begin{matrix}
\text{Pt} \\
(\text{H}_2)
\end{matrix}
\text{—Electrometer—}
\begin{matrix}
\text{Pt} \\
(\text{H}_2)
\end{matrix}
\right|
\begin{matrix}
\text{AgCl} \\
\text{satd.}
\end{matrix}
\; \text{Ag——Ag} \;
\begin{matrix}
\text{AgCl} \\
\text{satd.}
\end{matrix}
\right| \text{HCl} \atop (a_\pm)_a
$$

The connections to the electrometer, for measuring the E.M.F. developed, are shown as being taken from the hydrogen electrodes; the electrode in the more concentrated solution will then be electrically positive to that in the more dilute solution. Alternatively, the two hydrogen electrodes could be joined together, and the E.M.F. measured between the two silver electrodes. Such concentration cells without liquid junction provide the most reliable method for determining ionic activities.

In the above analysis, we have not considered the potential which exists between a solution and the metal of an electrode immersed in it. This does not enter explicitly into the total potential which is measured, and it is, in fact, impossible to measure this electrode potential by direct methods. We shall consider this from a different standpoint in Chapter 5.

The concentration cell without liquid junction is, as already remarked, only of very limited value, and, more usually, we have to adopt a less precise method of completing the circuit between the two solutions of different activity. If we merely allow the two solutions to come into contact, ions of either sign will be able to pass from one to the other without difficulty, but a diffusion potential will be set up which is likely to be uncertain in magnitude, and variable with time. But if we refer back to the approximate equation for the diffusion potential (equation 4.16), we see that at the junction between two solutions of a salt whose ions both have the same mobility (i.e. if $u_+ = u_-$), there would be no diffusion potential, however large the concentration difference. Referring back, again, to the Table of Mobilities on p. 122, we see that potassium and chloride ions have very nearly the same mobility. We can thus eliminate the diffusion potential to a very great extent by introducing between the two solutions forming the liquid junction, a highly concentrated, often saturated, solution of potassium chloride; ammonium nitrate may also be used, and must be used when the other components of the cell have insoluble chlorides. A very concentrated solution is used so that the contribution to the total diffusion potential of the other ions present is negligible. The system is not, now, strictly in an equilibrium state, and will run down "irreversibly" if given time; if properly set up, however, the rate at which it does so is so small as to be negligible for all practical purposes. The liquid-liquid junction potential is never completely eliminated, and the residue, although small enough to be neglected for most purposes, is usually uncertain in magnitude. We may represent such a *concentration cell with liquid junction*, as in the following example:

$$
\begin{array}{c}
\text{————————Electrometer————————}\\[4pt]
\text{Pt(H}_2\text{)}\quad\Big|\quad \dfrac{\text{HCl}}{(a_{\pm})_c}\ \vdots\ \dfrac{\text{KCl}}{\text{satd.}}\ \vdots\ \dfrac{\text{HCl}}{a_{\pm})_d}\quad\Big|\quad\text{Pt(H}_2\text{)}
\end{array}
$$

When great accuracy is required, determinations are made of the total E.M.F. of the cell when potassium chloride solutions of different concentration are interposed. From the data so obtained, the true value, if the diffusion potential were entirely eliminated, can be determined by extrapolation. In this system, there is only one pair of reversible electrodes, and the potential recorded will be given by:

$$E=\frac{RT}{zF}\ln\frac{(a_{\pm})_c}{(a_{\pm})_d} \qquad . \qquad . \qquad . \qquad . \qquad 4.21$$

where z is the valency of the ion for which the electrodes are reversible.

We can regard the E.M.F. developed by such a cell as being the sum of each of two E.M.F's developed by the two *half-cells*; and if we choose a certain half-cell as a fundamental standard, we can express the E.M.F.'s of all other half-cells in terms of this standard. Moreover, it is clear from the discussion in the previous paragraphs, that any reversible electrode system in a solution of constant composition and concentration, will give a reproducible and constant potential; it may thus be used as a standard half-cell whose E.M.F. can be determined in terms of the fundamental standard; subject, of course, to the uncertainty which may be introduced by the necessity for the interposition of liquid junctions. In practice, the reference cell for all half-cell potentials is the hydrogen electrode immersed in a solution of unit hydrogen ion activity (from the curve in Fig. 4.2, we can see that this might be 1·18 M. HCl, since the activity coefficient of HCl at this concentration is 0·85). This cell may be, and usually is, replaced by the calomel cell:

$$
\text{Hg}\quad\Big|\quad \dfrac{\text{HgCl}}{\text{satd.}}\ \vdots\ \text{KCl}
$$

The KCl solution may be 0·1 M. or 1 M., or 3·5 M. or saturated; with the two latter, no extra saturated KCl bridge need be added, although the potentials are not so accurately reproducible as with the 0·1 M. or 1 M. solutions.

A calomel cell is constructed by taking a suitable vessel (a small bottle can be used) and placing a layer of pure mercury at the bottom; electrical connection to the mercury is made by a platinum wire, either sealed through the wall of the vessel, or carried down from the top in a glass tube. The mercury is covered with a paste made of pure calomel rubbed up in a solution of potassium chloride of the desired concentration, and the vessel is filled with the potassium chloride solution; a tube, preferably sealed to the side of the vessel, is also filled with the KCl solution, and serves to make contact with the saturated KCl bridge and the other half-cell. Some of the many designs of vessel which have been used will be found in the books by Mansfield Clark (1928) and by Bates (1954).

The actual determination of activity coefficients is made in the following manner. If a concentration cell *without* liquid junction can be used, we put equation 4.20 in the form:

$$E = \frac{2RT}{F}\left(\ln\frac{m_c}{m_d} + \ln\frac{(\gamma_\pm)_c}{(\gamma_\pm)_d}\right) \quad . \quad . \quad . \quad 4.20a$$

Measurements are made of the E.M.F. between the most dilute solution of the electrolyte that can be easily handled—usually about 0·001 M.—and a series of solutions of increasing concentration. The activity coefficient of the most dilute solution is temporarily taken as 1, and the values for the more concentrated solutions are calculated from the E.M.F. measurements. These are then plotted against the square root of the concentration, as in Fig. 4.2, and extrapolated to zero concentration. At this point, the activity coefficient is strictly unity, so that all the other values must be multiplied by such a factor as will bring the extrapolated line to the value 1 at zero concentration. If a cell *with* liquid junction must be used, we put equation 4.21 in the form:

$$E = E_0 - \frac{RT}{F}(\ln m + \ln \gamma_\pm) \quad . \quad . \quad . \quad 4.21a$$

or

$$E + \frac{RT}{F}.\ln m = E_0 - \frac{RT}{F}.\ln \gamma_\pm$$

where E_0 is the E.M.F. of the auxiliary half-cell in use (ordinarily a calomel cell) with respect to the normal hydrogen electrode, and m and $\gamma_\pm$ are the concentration and activity coefficient, respectively, of the solution under investigation. By plotting the quantity $(E + \frac{RT}{F}.\ln m)$ against $\sqrt{m}$, and extrapolating to $m = 0$, we have $\ln \gamma_\pm = 0$, and thus $E_{(m=0)} = E_0$. We can then calculate the value of $\gamma_\pm$ for any other value of m.

If two similar half-cells are used to make connection from an electrolyte solution to an external electrical circuit, they will themselves develop no external E.M.F., since their potentials will be equal and opposite. Any E.M.F. that is observed, therefore, must be due to the presence, for example, of a diffusion potential or membrane potential of some kind. We shall see later that such measurements are of great importance in many aspects of physiology. It is convenient, in these circumstances, to make up the calomel, or silver chloride, cells in Ringer's solution, rather than in potassium chloride solution.

The accurate *measurement of the E.M.F.* developed by any kind of concentration cell involves the use of a *potentiometer*. There are two reasons for this. The first is that an accurate measure of the E.M.F. will not be obtained if, at the moment of measurement, any current is passing through the cell. Although the resistance of the connecting wires may be made very small, that of the solutions cannot, so that if any current passes, an appreciable "back E.M.F." will be generated. In addition, the passage of any considerable current may cause polarisation at the electrodes, and destroy their reversibility. When using a potentiometer, the E.M.F. developed by the cell is balanced against an appropriate fraction of that developed by an auxiliary battery. The existence of a balance is indicated by the absence of any deflection, one way or the other, of the galvanometer or electrometer used as the "null-point" instrument; current flows through the system only during the period before balance has been obtained, and not when the actual measurement is made. The second reason for using a potentiometer is that the accuracy of measurement will, in the last analysis, be limited by the length of the scale on which the readings are made. There are, in fact, circuits involving special thermionic valves, which satisfy the requirement of drawing a negligible current from the concentration cell, and which indicate the E.M.F. directly by means of a pointer moving over a scale; they are available commercially. The permissible length of such a scale, however, is limited by mechanical considerations. The simplest type of potentiometer consists only of a wire, of uniform cross section, with which contact can be made at any desired point. The auxiliary battery is connected across the ends of the wire, and the fraction of its E.M.F. which is present between the sliding contact and one end of the wire—and thus, when the system is balanced, the E.M.F. of the concentration cell—is measured by the fraction of the total length of the wire included between these points. In theory, there is no limit to the total length of wire that may be used, and thus to the accuracy with which the balance point may be measured. In practice, for convenience, the whole wire is divided into a number of sections of equal length (actually, of equal electrical resistance, which is the important factor), as indicated in the circuit diagram given in Fig. 4.3; all but one of these sections are wound on bobbins and tapped, as required, by means of a selector switch. The accuracy with which the E.M.F. may be estimated with a good potentiometer is, in many cases, limited by the accuracy with which the balance point can be established; this depends on the voltage sensitivity of the null-point instrument.

In the previous discussion, we have made use of the E.M.F. developed by a concentration cell in order to discover the activity of some particular kind of ion in a given solution. We may also use electrometric methods in

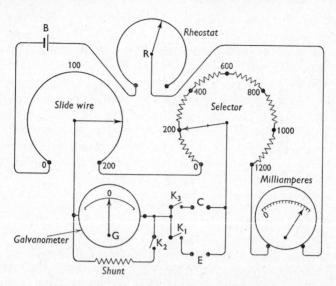

FIG. 4.3. CIRCUIT DIAGRAM OF A POTENTIOMETER

The source of E.M.F. to be measured is connected to the terminals E, and balanced against an appropriate fraction of the E.M.F. of the battery B; the condition of balance being identified by the absence of any deflection in the galvanometer, or electrometer, G. The required fraction of the E.M.F. of B is selected, approximately, to the nearest 100 or 200 mV. (according to the design of the particular instrument) by adjusting the position of the *Selector* switch; and then accurately, by adjusting the moving contact along the *Slide Wire*, the position of which is recorded on a scale graduated from 0 to 100 (or 0 to 200 as the case may be). The galvanometer is put into circuit by closing key K_1; even if balance has not been obtained, current flows through the external circuit only when this key is closed. It is almost essential that the galvanometer should be provided with a *Shunt*, as shown, which is only removed, by opening key K_2, when an approximate setting has been obtained. If a galvanometer is used, it should have a large internal resistance, and the sensitivity should, as a minimum, be sufficient for it to give an easily read deflection when supplied with 1 mV. through several thousand ohms.

The potentiometer is adjusted so that the scales read accurately in millivolts by connecting a "standard cell", either to terminals E, or better, to a separate pair of terminals C, put into circuit by the key K_3. The potentiometer dials are set to read the E.M.F. of the standard cell (1·0185 V. at 18° C.) and the rheostat R is adjusted until a balance is obtained. If extreme precision is not required, the instrument may be set up by adjusting the rheostat until the required current flows through the potentiometer, as indicated by the milli-ammeter; the value of this current may be discovered by a preliminary calibration by a standard cell, or in some instruments, is marked on the meter by the makers.

order to discover the end-point in a titration—i.e. to indicate when the concentration of some component of the solution titrated has reached some predetermined value. In principle, this component may be any ion whose concentration can be estimated by a titrimetric method, and for which a reversible electrode is available; but in practice, the number of applications is not very large. We shall discuss the application to acid-base titration in the next section, and that to oxidation-reduction reactions in Chapter 8. At this point, we may appropriately consider briefly the *electrometric titration of chlorides*, an analytical method of some value in physiological investigations. Suppose we have a solution containing chloride ions, and add a small quantity of silver nitrate—i.e. begin to titrate it with a silver nitrate solution of known concentration. The solution almost immediately becomes saturated with silver chloride; a silver electrode placed in the solution will behave as a chloride electrode, as already discussed, and develop an E.M.F., with respect to some standard half-cell, which depends only on the chloride ion concentration of the solution. Let the initial chloride concentration of the solution be m, and suppose that we have added enough silver nitrate to reduce the concentration to $(m - \Delta m)$. Then the E.M.F. between the silver electrode and the standard electrode will change from E to $(E - \Delta E)$, and we shall have:

$$E - (E - \Delta E) = \Delta E = RT \cdot \ln (m - \Delta m)/m.$$

Clearly, for a given value of Δm, ΔE becomes greater as m becomes smaller. If more silver nitrate is added than is sufficient to combine with the chloride ions present, we shall have a silver nitrate solution (saturated with AgCl) in contact with the silver electrode. The electrode will develop an E.M.F. which depends on the concentration of silver ions, and, as with the chloride electrode, the change in the E.M.F. which results from a given change in the silver ion concentration will decrease as more silver nitrate is added, and the silver ion concentration becomes greater. Thus the end-point of the titration is indicated by the fact that the ratio $\Delta E/\Delta m$ —say the change in the E.M.F. consequent on the addition of one drop of silver nitrate solution—reaches a maximum value and then begins to decline.

With this method, the end-point indication is precise and stable; it is unaffected by the presence of solutes other than chlorides, provided that their silver salts are soluble in the solution titrated (it is thus best to make the solution acid, but even then halides other than chlorides will be included with the chlorides); if proteins are present, they should be precipitated, but need not be filtered off; and finally, the electrodes may be made very small, and only small volumes of solution need be used. Indeed, for a given quantity of chloride, the end point of the titration becomes sharper as the volume of solution becomes smaller; for a given degree of precision, the lower limit to the quantity of chloride which can be estimated is set by the precision with which very small quantities of silver ions can be added to the solution. It is not necessary to use a potentiometer, but the instrument used to measure the E.M.F. should have a high internal resistance (an electrometer valve, or a cathode follower circuit may be used) and sufficiently sensitive to indicate changes of E.M.F. of a few millivolts. It is thus advisable to arrange that the E.M.F. applied to the instrument from the electrode system is small at the end-point of the titration, either by using a suitable kind of auxiliary half-cell, or by inserting a simple potentiometer.

THE ACTIVITIES OF THE HYDROGEN
AND HYDROXYL IONS

Water itself dissociates electrolytically, and hydrogen and hydroxyl ions are inevitably present in all aqueous solutions, whether or not other kinds of ion are present as well. The fact that, strictly, we should refer to oxonium ions in aqueous solution, not hydrogen ions, is commonly disregarded; no serious error results from this. The solutions met with in living organisms commonly contain weak acids and alkalies; these also will dissociate electrolytically, giving rise to hydrogen and hydroxyl ions. The degree of dissociation of each of these acids and alkalies, as we shall see below, is likely to be determined by the hydrogen ion activity of the solution; the dissociation of each may thus affect that of all the others, and the dissociation of all of them will be altered by any other factors which affect the hydrogen ion activity. The degree of dissociation of some of these acids and alkalies, as will be discussed in the next chapter, may affect the electric charge at an interface between two different phases, and the electrical potential difference across it. Hydrogen and hydroxyl ions, again, may be strongly adsorbed at interfaces, and so affect the electric charge. The properties of colloidal systems, accordingly, are likely to depend markedly on the hydrogen ion activity of the solution; and living cells contain many colloidal constituents. Of the greatest importance, perhaps, are the enzymes, whose catalytic activity is greatly affected by hydrogen ions (Chapter 7). Finally, all living systems depend for their continued activity on the supply of energy which is released when oxygen is reduced by hydrogen. Such an oxidation-reduction process, as we shall see in Chapter 9, is bound to affect, and to be affected by, the hydrogen and hydroxyl ion activities of the solution. Knowledge of the activities of these ions is thus of especial importance in a great many systems, not least in those of physiological interest.

It is a matter of common experience that the properties associated with acids and alkalies are much more strongly marked in some than in others. Some acids will turn out others from combination; their solutions, in equal concentration, taste much more sour, and invert solutions of cane-sugar more rapidly than do the others. It is here that the electrolytic dissociation theory showed itself to be of especial value, in that it was able to give precise numerical values to express the acid or alkaline properties of a solution. According to this theory, for example, hydrochloric and acetic acids in solution are dissociated into hydrogen and chloride ions, and into hydrogen and acetate ions, respectively; the only substance common to both are the hydrogen ions. That hydrochloric acid is the stronger of the two is due to the fact that it is more highly dissociated, and contains a higher concentration of hydrogen ions for a given concentration of the acid as a whole, as may be shown, for example, by measurement of the electrical conductivity. Here we have, then, a numerical value for the acidity, namely the concentration of hydrogen ions. Similar considerations apply to alkalies, say sodium or ammonium hydroxides, and here it is the concentration of hydroxyl ions which gives a measure of the alkalinity. As will be shown later, the product of the hydrogen and hydroxyl ion activities in solutions in water is constant; so that any given hydroxyl ion activity is associated with a definite hydrogen ion activity. For the sake of uniformity it is the custom to express both acidity and alkalinity in terms of hydrogen ion activity. Thus neutrality means the activities of the two ions as they are present in pure water, i.e. 1×10^{-7} at 25° C., and any activity of hydrogen ions less than this means alkalinity, and any greater means acidity.

The pH Notation. In most solutions that are ordinarily dealt with, the hydrogen ion activity (or concentration) is very small, and would have to be expressed by some such number as 3.4×10^{-8}. Sørensen, accordingly, suggested in 1909 that it would be less cumbersome to use the negative logarithm of the hydrogen ion concentration, and to denote it by the symbol P_H, indicating hydrogen ion potential (now changed to pH for the convenience of the printers). Thus a solution with a hydrogen ion concentration of 3.4×10^{-8} would have a pH of $-(0.53-8)=7.47$.

This method, although convenient in practice, has certain disadvantages for the beginner. The pH values *diminish* as the acidity *increases*. Moreover, while it is easy to see that a hydrogen ion concentration of 4×10^{-6} is double that of 2×10^{-6}, it is not at once obvious that a pH of 5.398 means double the acidity of one of 5.699. One has to get accustomed to thinking in negative logarithms. One is apt, also, to get a false impression as to the magnitude of the effects produced by small changes in hydrogen ion concentration. Thus serious disturbances are likely to be produced if the pH of a man's blood falls below 7.2 or rises above 7.6; the range of variation seems small, but it corresponds, in fact, to a 2.5-fold change in hydrogen ion concentration. A similar change in the concentration of several other kinds of ion would have an equally profound effect.

Methods of Measurement. It may be remarked at the outset that all the methods ordinarily used measure the mean ionic activity of HCl in the solution under investigation, whatever may be the actual anion present; they are all calibrated, in the last analysis, in terms of the E.M.F. set up by a concentration cell without liquid junction, as described above on p. 144. For routine purposes, however, it is usual to include a liquid junction, and to replace one of the hydrogen half-cells, shown on p. 145 by a standard calomel half-cell. The actual *concentration* of hydrogen ions, of course, is never measured at all. This has very little significance, however, since it is the activity which is of importance, in most cases, and not the concentration. In practice the term "hydrogen ion concentration", and the abbreviation "pH" are still generally retained when the difference between concentration and activity is not regarded as of great significance.

A few words may be said about the hydrogen electrode itself. At the electrode, the following reactions occur:

$$H_2 \longrightarrow 2H$$
$$H \longrightarrow H^+ + e$$

where e is an electron. The function of the platinum is thus not only to act as a conducting support for the hydrogen gas, but also to catalyse the formation of hydrogen atoms. Some current must be passed through the electrode during the course of making the E.M.F. measurements, even though it may be very small, and the electrode will only remain strictly reversible with respect to hydrogen ions so long as: (a) it is saturated with hydrogen gas; and (b) there is an adequate rate of formation of hydrogen atoms. The first criterion is satisfied by ensuring that the solution in the vicinity of the electrode remains saturated with hydrogen and the second by ensuring that the electrode surface is sufficiently active catalytically. For this purpose, a layer of platinum black (finely divided platinum deposited by electrolysis of a solution of platinum chloride) is laid down on the surface of the electrode. This surface, however, is easily "poisoned" by substances which are readily adsorbed, such as sulphur compounds, either present in the hydrogen gas as impurity, or in the solution; proteins, also, and other surface active compounds present in the solution have a deleterious action. Traces of oxygen in the hydrogen gas are to be avoided, moreover, since oxygen reacts with hydrogen on the platinum black surface, and so reduces the supply of available hydrogen atoms. It will thus be realised that the hydrogen electrode is only suitable for use with "clean" solutions, which are not often met with in physiology. The necessity of saturating the solution with hydrogen, also, makes its use almost impossible in solutions which contain dissolved gases, such as carbon dioxide, whose removal would seriously affect the hydrogen ion activity.

For some purposes, the *quinhydrone electrode* has its advantages. This is, strictly, an oxidation-reduction electrode, and a more complete treatment will be given in Chapter 8. There are many ways of regarding the behaviour of this electrode, and we may give here a brief consideration of one point of view. If an electrode in any solution is to acquire a potential which depends only on the hydrogen ion activity in that solution, the following reaction must occur at its surface, as we have already seen:

$$H^+ + e \rightleftharpoons H$$

Now in the hydrogen electrode, the catalytic action of the platinum black provides hydrogen atoms from the hydrogen molecules supplied for that purpose. Similarly, when quinone and quinol (hydroquinone) are present together in solution, an equilibrium will be reached between them, which can be represented as:

$$C_6H_4O_2 + 2H \rightleftharpoons C_6H_4(OH)_2$$

a supply of hydrogen atoms being thus provided. Consequently, in the presence of an electrode of a noble metal, such as platinum or gold, which does not react with any constituent of the solution, the hydrogen atoms will react reversibly with electrons in the metal and develop a potential difference. Now quinhydrone is an equimolecular mixture of quinone and quinol, which happens to be almost insoluble in water. It will, therefore, be present in excess in the solid phase and ensure that the concentrations both of quinone and quinol are constant: the concentration of hydrogen atoms will also be constant, just as with the hydrogen electrode in the presence of a constant partial pressure of hydrogen.

There is, however, one important limitation to the use of the quinhydrone electrode. Quinol is itself a weak acid, and dissociates appreciably into hydrogen ions and quinol ions if the pH of the solution becomes greater than about 8·5. The equilibrium between quinone and quinol then begins to involve hydrogen ions instead of hydrogen atoms, and the above considerations become invalid. Similarly, oxidising or reducing substances will react with the quinol-quinone system and the hypothetical concentration of hydrogen atoms cannot be maintained constant.

Possibly the most generally useful method of determining the hydrogen ion activity of solutions of physiological interest is that of the *glass electrode*. The surface of a suitable kind of glass behaves as if it were reversible towards hydrogen ions; it is not exactly clear why this should be, but it is suggested that there may be a specific adsorption of hydrogen ions, or an acidic dissociation of the surface layers, or both. But since glass has a very high electrical resistance, it cannot be used in the same way as an ordinary hydrogen electrode. Instead, we set up a cell similar in principle to a concentration cell without liquid junction, a very thin glass membrane being interposed between the two solutions whose hydrogen activity is to be compared, and the circuit completed by any convenient pair of half-cells. Strictly, we should use, for this, electrodes which are reversible towards the anions in the two solutions, as described above, on p. 144, but it is more generally useful to use saturated potassium chloride bridges and calomel electrodes. The arrangement of the cell is thus:

$$\text{Hg} \mid \text{HgCl} \mid \begin{matrix} \text{KCl} \\ \text{satd.} \end{matrix} \mid \text{Solution A} \parallel \text{Solution B} \mid \begin{matrix} \text{KCl} \\ \text{satd.} \end{matrix} \mid \text{HgCl} \mid \text{Hg}$$

(glass)

Since the glass membrane permits the passage of hydrogen ions only, the potential difference between Solution A and Solution B depends only on the ratio of their hydrogen ion activities, and is not affected by variations in the activities of other components. The E.M.F. of this arrangement is then given by:

$$E = \frac{RT}{F}(pH_A - pH_B) + k$$

where k is the residual potential across the glass when the same solution is put on both sides; the calomel electrode in the more concentrated solution (with respect to hydrogen ions) being electrically negative to that in the more dilute solution. (If we were able to use two glass electrodes as hydrogen electrodes, in the way already described, the one in the more concentrated solution would be positive. The two electrodes, however, are in effect joined together and are at the same potential, so that the more concentrated *solution* becomes electrically negative to the more dilute *solution*; it is the potential between the solutions that we measure by means of the "saturated" calomel electrodes.) It is usual to have a solution of constant, though not necessarily known, hydrogen ion activity on one side of the glass membrane, and to standardise the whole system by measuring the E.M.F. developed when solutions of accurately known hydrogen ion activity are placed on the other side.

It is highly desirable to standardise the whole arrangement with at least two solutions of accurately known hydrogen ion activity, since not only does this eliminate the residual E.M.F. across the membrane, k in the equation above, but it also determines the constant of proportionality in this equation; this should, of course, be equal to RT/F, or 0·058 at 18° C. Not infrequently this constant is appreciably smaller than the theoretical value; if it is considerably smaller, either the wrong type of glass is being used, or there is an insulation leakage in the electrical circuit which is causing an appreciable current to pass through the glass membrane.

The resistance of even a very thin glass membrane is very large, so that, in order to balance the E.M.F. developed against that provided by the potentiometer, an electrometer must be used, not a galvanometer. The Lindemann pattern was used in the early days, but a special thermionic valve (electrometer valve) is now universal. Complete equipments are available commercially. The calomel-saturated KCl half-cell in the solution of constant hydrogen ion concentration may be replaced by a quinhydrone electrode if desired, or both calomel half-cells may be replaced by silver-silver chloride half-cells. Many different patterns of glass electrode have been designed, to suit different purposes, and descriptions will be found in the appropriate monographs, such as that by Bates (1954).

Indicators. These are certain dyes which have a particular colour at a certain value of hydrogen ion concentration and another colour at another value, which may differ only slightly from the first. Since different indicator dyes change colour at different values of the hydrogen ion concentration, it will be clear that the acidity of any given solution may be determined by making an appropriate choice out of the whole series that is available.

The whole question of the theory of indicators cannot be entered into here, but may be found in Mansfield Clark's book (1928) for example, or in that by Kolthoff and Laitenen (1941). Generally speaking, they are salts of either a very weak acid or a very weak base, sometimes the free acid or base itself. The change in colour is due to the electrolytic dissociation of the salt with the production of an ion which has a different colour from that of the free undissociated acid or base. The degree of dissociation will vary with the hydrogen ion concentration, as shown in the next section. The theory, however, is complicated by the existence of "pseudo-acids" which have a different chemical structure in the free state to that in their electrolytically dissociated salts.

In the use of indicators, there are several precautions to be observed. In the first place, the hydrogen ion concentration at which certain of them change colour is not the same in solutions of pure acids or alkalies as in the presence of salts or proteins. The magnitudes of the "salt errors" and "protein errors", which differ from one indicator to another, will be found in the appropriate books, already referred to. In the second place, it will be obvious that the total amount of indicator present must not be so great as appreciably to neutralise, or react with, the hydrogen ions or other constituents of the solution under examination. Care must be taken, therefore, if the solution is only very lightly "buffered" (see below, p. 160).

THE DISSOCIATION OF WEAK ACIDS AND ALKALIES— BUFFERS

We have seen that application of the law of mass action to the dissociation of weak electrolytes leads to the Ostwald Dilution Law:

$$\frac{a^2 m}{(1-a)} = K \qquad . \qquad . \qquad . \qquad . \qquad 4.1$$

relating the degree of dissociation, a, to the total stoichiometrical concentration, m. This equation agrees reasonably well with experimental observations in dilute solutions, when a is determined by measurements of the electrical conductivity, but from what has been said in the foregoing sections, the agreement could only be expected to be approximate.

In the first place, the equation should have been derived by the use of activities instead of concentrations. In other words the concentration terms should all be multiplied by the appropriate activity coefficients. The mass action equation then becomes:

$$\frac{a^2 m}{(1-a)} \cdot \frac{(\gamma_\pm)^2}{\gamma_u} = K \qquad . \qquad . \qquad . \qquad . \qquad 4.1a$$

where $\gamma_\pm$ is the mean ionic activity coefficient, and γ_u is the activity coefficient of the undissociated electrolyte.

In the second place, the ratio Λ_c/Λ_0 from which the degree of dissociation is calculated, does not give the true degree of dissociation, since no account is taken of the change in mobility of the ions with concentration. We must use, instead of the equivalent conductivity at zero concentration, Λ_0, the equivalent conductivity at concentration am; this may be calculated from the Onsager equation. But, of course, since the application of this equation necessitates a knowledge of the true value of a, it is necessary to proceed by successive approximation, using first the uncorrected value of a, then a preliminary corrected value, and so on. The successive values of a so obtained rapidly become more and more nearly the same, so that a close approximation to the true value is soon obtained. The actual magnitude of these two corrections to be applied to the Ostwald dilution law is not usually very great, but they are important in principle.

The only weak electrolytes that we shall be concerned with are the weak acids and alkalies (the ampholytes behave as either one or the other according to circumstances). The accurate determination of the constant K in the dilution law as applied to these is of importance, since it is a measure of the hydrogen ion activity for a given stoichiometrical concentration—i.e. it is a measure of the *strength* as an acid or alkali. This can be determined from measurements of electrical conductivity, with the necessary corrections as just indicated, or more directly by measuring the hydrogen ion activities.

In principle, we have to determine the activities of the hydrogen ion and the acid anion in a solution of known stoichiometrical concentration. In the case of acetic acid, for example, we may use the cell:

$$\text{H}_2 \ \left| \ \begin{array}{c} \text{HAc} \\ m \end{array} \ \text{NaCl} \ \begin{array}{c} \text{AgCl} \\ \text{satd.} \end{array} \ \right| \ \text{Ag}$$

a hydrogen electrode being inserted into a solution containing acetic acid in known concentration, m, and sodium chloride in any suitable concentration; and the second connection to the solution being made through a silver-silver chloride electrode. Ideally, the second connection should be made through an electrode reversible with respect to the anion of the acid concerned, but this is rarely practicable. The potential of the silver-silver chloride half-cell with respect to the normal hydrogen electrode is determined in a separate experiment. Alternatively, a cell with liquid junction may be used, with some sacrifice of precision. The mean ionic activity coefficient may be calculated from the Debye-Hückel equation in one of its forms, and, if the solution is dilute, the activity coefficient of the undissociated acid may be put equal to 1. But it is preferable to make measurements on a series of cells of decreasing concentration, so that by plotting the relation of the constant K in the mass action equation, to the acetic acid concentration, we can extrapolate to zero concentration and so eliminate the whole activity coefficient factor of equation 4.1a. For acetic acid, the value of K so found is 1.754×10^{-5}: from the corrected conductivity measurements, a value of 1.753×10^{-5} is obtained, which is good evidence for the accuracy of the assumptions underlying the corrections.

Consider now the titration of a weak acid, HA, by a strong alkali, MOH. If we assume that both the strong alkali and its salt with the weak acid are completely dissociated, the essential reaction is a combination of hydrogen ions from the acid with hydroxyl ions from the alkali, so:

$$H^+ + A^- + M^+ + OH^- \longrightarrow HOH + M^+ + A^-$$

At this point, it is desirable to introduce the term "base", which has been avoided hitherto since some confusion is possible as to its exact meaning. G. N. Lewis, in 1923, defined a base as a substance which neutralises an acid, and an acid as a substance which neutralises a base; the "neutralisation" referred to consisting in the transfer of a pair of electrons from the base to the acid, so as to form a covalent bond. In the above example, this reaction occurs between the hydrogen of the acid and the hydroxyl of the alkali, the remainder of the acid and the alkali—i.e. the anion and cation, respectively, playing no part. In the same year, Lowry and Brönsted, independently, defined an acid as a substance which gives rise to hydrogen ions, and a base as a substance which combines with them. In general, therefore, we can write the reversible reaction:

$$\text{acid} \rightleftharpoons H^+ + \text{base}$$

As applied to the dissociation of water, we get:

$$H_2O \rightleftharpoons H^+ + OH^-$$

water being now the acid and the hydroxyl ion the base, so that in this case, the definitions are very similar to those of G. N. Lewis, but not quite the same. As applied to the dissociation of a strong acid, such as hydrochloric acid:

$$HCl \rightleftharpoons H^+ + Cl^-$$

the definitions lead to the conclusion that the chloride ion is now the "base"; it is, however, a very weak one, the equilibrium position being far over to the right unless the hydrogen ion activity is very large. On the other hand, for the alkaline substance ammonia, we write:

$$NH_4^+ \rightleftharpoons H^+ + NH_3$$

the base, NH_3, being relatively strong, the equilibrium position is well over to the left unless the hydrogen ion activity is very small. In a similar way, we can write:

$$H_3O^+ \rightleftharpoons H^+ + H_2O$$

water now appearing as a base, and the oxonium ion as the corresponding acid.

If we consider a substance which can give rise to, or combine with, more than one hydrogen ion, we shall have several successive reactions analogous to those just given. For carbonic acid, for example, we write:

$$H_2CO_3 \rightleftharpoons H^+ + HCO_3^-$$
$$HCO_3^- \rightleftharpoons H^+ + CO_3^{2-}$$

The bicarbonate ion is thus a base in the first reaction, and an acid in the second; whether it is to be regarded as the one or the other depends on the hydrogen ion activity of the solution. The behaviour of water is thus analogous to that of the bicarbonate ion.

The term "base", however, is also used, particularly in connection with solutions of physiological interest, with a somewhat different meaning. These solutions commonly contain organic acids whose concentration cannot easily be estimated, and whose identity may not be fully known. These acids are "neutralised" chiefly by substances such as sodium, potassium, and calcium, which are more easily estimated quantitatively, and the sum of their concentrations is often referred to as the concentration of "total base". The term "base" is thus applied to cations, or substances which, at least, may be cations—the salts concerned may not, in fact, be electrolytically dissociated; whereas according to the previous definition, the bases were anions, or uncharged substances. The difference, however, is more apparent than real. In the above equation for the neutralisation of an acid by an alkali, the concentrations of M and A must be identical at the end-point, whether the salt MA is electrolytically dissociated or not. In the remainder of this section, we shall use the term "base" in G. N. Lewis' sense, as a substance which neutralises an acid; although it may be more correct to apply the term to the anionic component of the salt formed, it is often more convenient to direct attention to the cationic component.

Returning now to the neutralisation reaction, it is clear that as far as the acid is concerned, the mass action equation:

$$\frac{a_{H^+} \cdot a_{A^-}}{a_{HA}} = K$$

must apply through the titration. Moreover, until the titration is completed, the whole of the added alkali is present as the salt of the acid titrated; the activity of the acid anion may thus be equated to the concentration of the added base, which we will now denote $[B]$, multiplied by the activity coefficient of the salt—i.e. $a_{A^-} = \gamma_{\pm}[B]$. We need not suppose that the base B is fully dissociated electrolytically. If $[C]$ is the initial concentration of the acid before titration, then after such a quantity of base has been added as to have a concentration [B], the concentration of the acid remaining is [C] − [B]. (This assumes that the base is added in a relatively highly concentrated solution, so that the total volume of the system is not altered.) The ratio [B]/[C] is the fraction of the acid which has been neutralised. We can thus write: $a_{HA} = ([C] − [B])\gamma_a$, where γ_a is the activity coefficient of the unneutralised acid. Re-writing the mass action equation, we thus get:

$$\frac{a_{H^+} \cdot [B]}{([C] − [B])} = K \cdot \frac{\gamma_a}{\gamma_{\pm}} = K' \qquad . \qquad . \qquad . \qquad 4.22$$

K' is often referred to as the "apparent acid dissociation constant". Its negative logarithm is often written pK'.

It has been assumed in this analysis, for the purpose of illustration, that the acid is originally un-ionised. This, of course, is not necessarily so, as has been made clear in the examples given above; in all cases, however, equation 4.22 may be applied. The shape of the curve relating pH to the ratio [B]/[C] may be seen in Fig. 4.4. It is to be noted, in this connection, that during the course of titration of a weak acid, the concentration of ions in the solution changes. There will thus be a progressive change in the ionic strength of the solution, and we may, in general, expect that the activity coefficient factor $\gamma_a/\gamma_{\pm}$ will also change; the value of the "constant" K' will thus depend to some extent on the fraction of the acid which has been neutralised.

It is clear, from equation 4.22, that if [C] = 2[B], we shall have $a_{H^+} = K'$; thus, if we know the value of the activity coefficient factor $\gamma_a/\gamma_{\pm}$, or can neglect it, we can deduce the value of the acid dissociation constant from the value of the hydrogen ion activity when the acid is exactly half titrated. Values of the dissociation constants of some acids will be found in Table 4.3.

Buffers. Let us consider, now, how rapidly the hydrogen ion concentration changes as we add base during the course of the titration. The reciprocal of this rate of change (in terms of pH rather than a_{H^+}) is termed the *Buffer Value* of the system; it is a measure of the extent to which small changes of total acid or base concentration may be made in the system without sensible changes in the hydrogen ion concentration. The action of the weak acid in stabilising the hydrogen ion concentration results from the presence of the undissociated acid, which acts as a reservoir of hydrogen ions; removal of hydrogen ions from the solution results in an increased supply from the undissociated acid; addition of extra hydrogen ions results in their partial absorption as undissociated acid.

This "soaking up", as it were, of hydrogen and hydroxyl ions was compared by Fernbach and Hubert, in 1900, to that of "tampons", the French word meaning "stoppers" or "plugs", and in this connection particularly, the absorbent plugs or pads used by surgeons. The same word, however, is also

TABLE 4.3

Acid Dissociation Constants

Substance	K_a	pK_a	Temp.
Acetic acid	$1 \cdot 75 \times 10^{-5}$	4·76	25
*β-hydroxy-butyric acid	$3 \cdot 03 \times 10^{-5}$	4·52	—
n-butyric acid	$1 \cdot 52 \times 10^{-5}$	4·82	—
Carbonic acid 1	$4 \cdot 5 \times 10^{-7}$	6·35	25
Carbonic acid 2	$5 \cdot 6 \times 10^{-11}$	10·25	25
Fumaric acid 1	$9 \cdot 5 \times 10^{-4}$	3·02	25
Fumaric acid 2	3×10^{-5}	4·52	25
*Iodoacetic acid	$7 \cdot 5 \times 10^{-4}$	3·13	25
*Lactic acid	$1 \cdot 33 \times 10^{-4}$	3·88	20
Malic acid 1	$3 \cdot 9 \times 10^{-4}$	3·41	25
Malic acid 2	9×10^{-6}	5·1	25
Phosphoric acid 1	$7 \cdot 5 \times 10^{-3}$	2·13	25
Phosphoric acid 2	$6 \cdot 23 \times 10^{-8}$	7·21	25
Phosphoric acid 3	$1 \cdot 3 \times 10^{-12}$	11·9	25
Proprionic acid	$1 \cdot 34 \times 10^{-5}$	4·07	25
*Pyruvic acid	$3 \cdot 2 \times 10^{-3}$	2·49	25
Succinic acid 1	$8 \cdot 7 \times 10^{-5}$	4·06	25
Succinic acid 2	$4 \cdot 8 \times 10^{-6}$	5·32	25
Tartaric acid 1	$9 \cdot 5 \times 10^{-4}$	3·02	25
Tartaric acid 2	$4 \cdot 55 \times 10^{-5}$	4·34	25
*Uric acid	$3 \cdot 2 \times 10^{-6}$	5·50	—
DL-alanine 1	$4 \cdot 57 \times 10^{-3}$	2·34	25
DL-alanine 2	$1 \cdot 35 \times 10^{-10}$	9·87	25
Adenosine triphosphoric acid 1	$1 \cdot 6 \times 10^{-4}$	3·8	—
Adenosine triphosphoric acid 2	$6 \cdot 4 \times 10^{-7}$	6·2	—
Anserine 1	$2 \cdot 29 \times 10^{-3}$	2·64	22
Anserine 2	$8 \cdot 32 \times 10^{-8}$	7·08	22
Anserine 3	$2 \cdot 95 \times 10^{-10}$	9·53	22
Carnosine 1	$2 \cdot 29 \times 10^{-3}$	2·64	22
Carnosine 2	$1 \cdot 32 \times 10^{-7}$	6·88	22
Carnosine 3	$2 \cdot 88 \times 10^{-10}$	9·54	22
Glycine 1	$4 \cdot 47 \times 10^{-3}$	2·35	25
Glycine 2	$1 \cdot 67 \times 10^{-10}$	9·78	25
Water	$1 \cdot 01 \times 10^{-14}$	13·996	25
Ammonium ions	$5 \cdot 5 \times 10^{-10}$	9·26	25

All figures are derived from titration except those marked* which are from conductivity measurements.

F

used for shock-absorbing systems of springs, rubber etc., such as the buffers of railway trains. Sørensen, in 1909, adopted the word and, in the translation of his paper into German, it was rendered "Puffer" and thence into English as "Buffer". A railway buffer does not absorb the train itself, but only its energy. The buffer systems at present under consideration do, in fact, absorb the ions themselves, although they may be regarded as absorbing, or releasing the partial free energy, or activity, of the hydrogen ions. A word more suggestive of a sponge would perhaps be preferable, but is not easy to find.

More precisely, the buffer value of a system is defined as $dB/d(pH)$, or the amount of base that must be added or removed in order to produce a small, unit, change in pH. Re-arranging equation 4.22 and differentiating, we get:

$$\beta = \frac{dB}{d(pH)} = -\frac{dB}{d(\log_{10} a_{H+})} = \frac{2 \cdot 303}{a_{H+}} \cdot \frac{dB}{d(a_{H+})} = 2 \cdot 303 a_{H+} \frac{K'[C]}{(K' + a_{H+})^2} \cdot \qquad 4.23$$

($2 \cdot 303$ is inserted in order to convert from logarithms to the base 10 to natural logarithms).

Moreover,
$$\frac{d\beta}{da_{H+}} = 2 \cdot 303 \frac{(K' - a_{H+})}{(K' + a_{H+})^3}$$

This becomes zero when $K' = a_{H+}$. The buffer value is thus a maximum at such a stage of the titration that the hydrogen ion concentration is equal to the apparent dissociation constant of the acid as is illustrated in Fig. 4.4. At this stage,

$$\beta_{max} = 2 \cdot 303 \frac{(K')^2}{4(K')^2} [C] = 0 \cdot 575 [C] . \qquad . \qquad . \qquad 4.24$$

The maximum buffering power of all substances to which the dilution law can be applied (i.e. those with apparent dissociation constants lying between about 10^{-4} and 10^{-10}) is the same at the same concentration. Moreover, by inserting the value of β_{max} in place of $[C]$ in equation 4.24, we see that:

$$\beta = a_{H+} \frac{4K'}{(K' + a_{H+})^2} \cdot \beta_{max} \cdot \qquad . \qquad . \qquad . \qquad 4.23a$$

so that if $a_{H+} = 1000 K'$,

we shall have: $\beta \fallingdotseq \frac{4}{1000} \beta_{max}$

The buffering power of all substances thus sensibly disappears at values of the pH which are more than 3 units greater or smaller than the value of pK', i.e. in symbols

$$\beta \fallingdotseq 0 \text{ if } pH - pK' \fallingdotseq \pm 3$$

It is important to remember, however, that pK' involves the activity coefficient of the salt of the weak acid, and so will depend to some extent on the concentration of the buffer system, and on the concentration and valency of any other electrolyte that may be present. This factor must often be taken into account when dealing with the dissociation of weak acids, and the buffering properties of systems of physiological interest.

If a solution contains two or more weak acids, their dissociation constants can be separately evaluated if they differ sufficiently in magnitude.

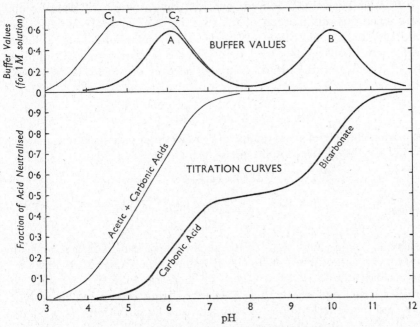

FIG. 4.4. TITRATION CURVES AND BUFFER VALUES

The heavy line, in the lower part, shows the titration curve of a dibasic acid with pK' values of 6·1 and 10·0 (approximately those of the first and second dissociation of carbonic acid in 0·1 M solution). The corresponding curve of buffer value against pH is shown at the top; the two peaks A and B are clearly separated, and occur at values of the pH which equal those of the pK'. The two parts of the curve have the same shape, and each part is symmetrical on each side of the peak; a curve of this form will be given by any monobasic weak acid, and its peak will be at a value of pH equal to the value of pK'.

The thin line, in the lower part, shows the titration curve of an equimolecular mixture of an acid with $pK'=6·1$ (say carbonic) with an acid with $pK'=4·65$ (say acetic). The corresponding curve of buffer values, C_1C_2, is flattened and spread out; the two acid dissociation constants cannot be accurately determined from the curve.

There are then two or more maxima in the curve of buffer value against pH, but unless these are at least 3 pH units apart, there will be some mutual interaction and distortion of the curves. The true values of the apparent dissociation constants can then be arrived at only by a process of successive approximation. The same considerations apply, of course, to the successive dissociations of a weak polybasic acid; the titration curve will have exactly the same form as that of two, or more, chemically different weak acids. Two such titration curves are shown in Fig. 4.4. If the dissociation constant of one of the acids present in the mixture is known, its titration curve will also be known and can be subtracted from that of the mixture; estimation of the dissociation constants of the other acids present may then be simple. A particular case of this type of correction occurs whenever the weak acid under investigation has a very small dissociation constant. The hydrogen ion concentration will then become very small towards the end of the titration, and an appreciable fraction of the hydrogen ions present will be derived from the water of the solution. Since water behaves as a weak acid with a dissociation constant of about 10^{-14}, its effect on the titration curve of another weak acid can be allowed for.

WATER AS AN ELECTROLYTE

Applying the law of mass action to the electrolytic dissociation of water, which may be written, for simplicity, as:

$$H_2O \rightleftharpoons H^+ + OH^-$$

we get: $$K = \frac{a_{H^+} \cdot a_{OH^-}}{a_{H_2O}}$$

where a_{H^+}, a_{OH^-}, and a_{H_2O} are the activities of the hydrogen ions, the hydroxyl ions and the undissociated water, respectively. Now water is a poor conductor of electricity, and the more carefully it is purified, the smaller is the conductivity; it must be very slightly dissociated electrolytic-ally, and the concentrations of hydrogen and hydroxyl ions must be very small. The activity of the undissociated water will thus be affected to a negligible extent by the electrolytic dissociation, and may be regarded as constant. We can thus write:

$$K_W = a_{H^+} \cdot a_{OH^-} = c_{H^+} \cdot c_{OH^-} \cdot \gamma_{H^+} \cdot \gamma_{OH^-}$$

From the conductivity of the purest water that can be prepared, we find

that at   25° C. $K_W = 1.05 \times 10^{-14}$ or $pK_W = 13.98$

and at   18° C. $K_W = 0.60 \times 10^{-14}$ or $pK_W = 14.22$

Since water can be regarded as a weak acid, its dissociation constant can be determined from the E.M.F. of a concentration cell without liquid junction similar to that described on p. 157 for use with acetic acid. The cell actually used is:

$$H_2 \mid HOH \quad KOH \quad KCl \quad AgCl \mid Ag$$

As before, by extrapolation of the observed potentials to zero electrolyte concentration, the dissociation constant can be derived. Its value is found to be $1 \cdot 008 \pm \cdot 001 \times 10^{-14}$ at 25° C.; this value is somewhat smaller than that derived from the measurements of electrical conductivity, and is more reliable since the conductivity measurements are very considerably affected by traces of conducting impurities. The most reliable values of K_W at a number of different temperatures, will be found collected together in the *International Critical Tables*, vol. 6, p. 152.

THE EFFECT OF TEMPERATURE ON HYDROGEN ION ACTIVITY

The dissociation of water is increased very considerably by a rise in temperature, as is seen from the figures for the dissociation constant given above; at 37° C. it has a value of $2 \cdot 45 \times 10^{-14}$, or $pK_W = 13 \cdot 61$. Since a neutral solution is defined as one in which the concentrations (or more strictly the activities) of the hydrogen and hydroxyl ions are equal, this occurs at a hydrogen ion concentration of $0 \cdot 78 \times 10^{-7}$ or a pH of 7·11 at 18° C., and at a hydrogen ion concentration of $1 \cdot 57 \times 10^{-7}$ or a pH of 6·805 at 37° C.

The dissociation of many weak acids, on the other hand, is much less affected by temperature. Thus, if we consider a buffer mixture of carbonic acid and bicarbonate which has a hydrogen ion concentration of $0 \cdot 30 \times 10^{-7}$ or a pH of 7·52 at 18° C., it will have a hydrogen ion concentration of $0 \cdot 40 \times 10^{-7}$ or a pH of 7·40 at 37° C. A solution containing $H_2PO_4^-$ and HPO_4^{2-} ions as a buffer mixture maintains an almost constant hydrogen ion concentration over quite a wide range of temperature. Thus while a buffer solution will not suffer any very considerable change in its actual hydrogen ion concentration as the temperature rises, it will become steadily more alkaline with respect to pure water, or to an unbuffered salt solution. Expressed in another way, if the hydrogen ion concentration of a solution is less affected by temperature than is that of pure water, the hydroxyl ion concentration will be more affected. This circumstance may be of importance in connection with the effects of temperature on the behaviour of living organisms.

AMPHOTERIC ELECTROLYTES

There is an important class of substances which can act either as acids or bases; that is, they can dissociate in such a way as to leave themselves with either a positive or a negative charge. The most important of such substances for our purposes are the amino-acids. These owe their nature as both acids and bases to the fact that they contain one or more —NH_2 groups, together with one or more —COOH groups.

We will consider the case of an amino-acid with one NH_2 group and one COOH group, and we will represent it as

$$NH_2—R—COOH$$

where R may be any organic residue; the simplest residue would, of course, be the $—CH_2—$ group, and our amino-acid would then be glycine. It was formerly supposed that in solution, this molecule took up a molecule of water and became $NH_3OH—R—COOH$. In acid solution, it lost an OH^- ion and became the cation $^+NH_3—R—COOH$, while in alkaline solution, it lost an H^+ ion, and became the anion $NH_3OH—R—COO^-$. In the same way, water may be regarded as losing an OH^- in acid solution, and an H^+ in alkaline solution; water is, indeed, an amphoteric electrolyte. Evidence has accumulated, however, that the supposed hydrated molecule hardly ever exists in the completely unionised condition, but that in more or less neutral solutions, it exists as an ion with both positive and negative charges simultaneously. It is accordingly known as an "hermaphrodite ion," or more usually, "zwitterion". There is, also, no need to postulate an initial hydration, followed by a loss of an OH^- ion or a H^+ ion: we can suppose that except in alkaline solutions, the $—NH_2$ group takes up a H^+ ion, and except in acid solutions, the $—COOH$ group loses one, the three states of the molecule being represented as:

$$\overset{acid}{^+NH_3—R—COOH} \rightleftharpoons \overset{neutral}{^+NH_3—R—COO^-} + H^+ \rightleftharpoons H^+ + \overset{alkaline}{NH_2—R—COO^-} + H^+$$

It is unnecessary to remark that an ion with two opposite charges moves to neither electrode, so that it can take no part in the conduction of an electric current. In this aspect, it is not, strictly, entitled to the name of an ion, in Faraday's sense. The dissociation is thus analogous to that of water, if this is written in the form:

$$H_3O^+ \rightleftharpoons H_2O + H^+ \rightleftharpoons H^+ + OH^- + H^+$$

This dissociation, as already discussed, is not essentially different from that of a dibasic acid, two hydrogen ions being given off successively, as we pass from acid to neutral and then to alkaline solutions. If we start with a neutral solution, and titrate with an acid, we shall determine the first dissociation constant, k_1; if we titrate with a base, we shall determine the second dissociation constant, k_2, according to the following equations:

$$^+NH_3—R—COO^- + H^+ \rightleftharpoons NH_3—R—COOH$$

$$^+NH_3—R—COO^- + OH^- \rightleftharpoons NH_2—R—COO^- + HOH$$

or $\qquad ^+NH_3—R—COO^- \rightleftharpoons NH_2—R—COO^- + H^+$

Note that according to the conception of an uncharged neutral molecule, titration with acid determined the *basic* dissociation, and titration with alkali determined the *acidic* dissociation, just as in the case of a weak base or weak acid respectively. On the zwitterion hypothesis, the addition of acid or alkali *suppresses* the dissociation of the ampholyte as an acid or base, respectively.

Applying the law of mass action to the reactions expressed in the equations above, and calling the ampholyte $^+HA^-$ for simplicity, we get

$$k_1' = \frac{[^+HA^-] \cdot [H^+]}{[^+H_2A]} \text{ or } [^+H_2A] = \frac{[^+HA^-][H^+]}{k_1'}$$

$$k_2' = \frac{[^+HA^-]}{[A^-][H^+]} \text{ or } [A^-] = \frac{[^+HA^-]}{k_2'[H^+]}$$

the dissociation constants being given superscripts to show that the activity coefficients are neglected.

THE ISO-IONIC POINT

An important consequence of the capability of amphoteric electrolytes to possess either a positive or a negative charge is that at some hydrogen ion concentration the average positive charge must be equal to the average negative charge. This hydrogen ion concentration is known as the *Iso-ionic point*, and is readily discovered, in terms of the two dissociation constants from the mass action equations. Since by definition, at this point

$$[^+H_2A] = [A^-]$$

we have

$$\frac{[^+HA^-]}{k_1'}[H^+] = \frac{[^+HA^-]}{k_2'[H^+]}$$

or

$$[H^+] = \sqrt{k_1'k_2'} \quad . \quad . \quad . \quad . \quad 4.25$$

According to the conception of an undissociated neutral molecule, the equation for the hydrogen ion concentration corresponding to the iso-ionic point is

$$[H^+] = \sqrt{\frac{k_a'}{k_b'} \cdot K_w} \quad . \quad . \quad . \quad 4.25a$$

where k_a' and k_b' are the apparent dissociation constants of the ampholyte as acid and base respectively, and K_w is the dissociation constant of water.

The value of the iso-ionic point may be discovered by measuring the acidic and basic dissociation constants of the ampholyte by titration, and inserting them in the above expression. It is also given by the pH of a solution of the pure substance, provided that the solution is not so dilute that the dissociation of the water will affect the pH appreciably. With proteins, the solution should have a concentration of at least 1 per cent.

LITERATURE

Historical.   Faraday (1834, 1839); Arrhenius (1887).

General—Theory and Methods of Measurement.   Robinson and Stokes (1955).

Strong Electrolytes.   Lewis and Randall (1923).

Measurement of E.M.F. and Conductivity.   Lingane (1953).

Hydrogen Ion Activity.   Mansfield Clark (1928); Kolthoff and Laitenen (1941); Bates (1954).

Activity and Osmotic Coefficients (Data).   B. E. Conway (1952); Robinson and Stokes (1955).

5

SURFACE PHENOMENA

If we have a system in which there are two or more parts differing from one another in physical state or chemical composition, and separated by a sharp boundary, we refer to these parts as *"phases"*, a term introduced by Willard Gibbs. At each boundary, there is a surface, or *interface*. Ideally, we suppose that at each interface there is a definite discontinuity in the physical and chemical properties of the components; but in fact, electrons, atoms and molecules are continually passing to and fro between one component and another, so that the more closely we look at the interface—the more highly we magnify it—the less sharp will it appear. This difficulty of defining precisely the nature of an interface is brought out by the following example. If we carefully place two solutions of different composition in contact with one another, there will initially be an interface between them; but this will eventually disappear owing to the mutual diffusion of the two solutions, and the exact moment at which it vanishes cannot be specified.

It is understood, also, that two parts of a system are divided into separate phases only if the interface has an appreciable size; but again, the critical size cannot be specified exactly. When we are dealing with molecules of "ordinary" size, it is not difficult to understand that a single molecule cannot form a separate phase from the medium surrounding it; there must be a close aggregate of molecules, which, it is usually considered, must be large enough to be detected by microscopic, or at least ultramicroscopic, vision. When we consider the colloidal state in the next chapter, however, we shall see that many substances are known whose molecules are themselves of this size; they form separate phases from some points of view, but not from others. Such difficulties of precise definition are, of course, common in all branches of science; they do not seriously interfere with the usefulness of the concepts of phases and interfaces.

SURFACE ENERGY

From this discussion it is obvious that surfaces, or interfaces, cannot exist between two substances in the gaseous state, where the separate molecules

F*

can move about freely. They only occur when the molecules of one or more of the substances concerned are solid or liquid, in which the molecules are held together, more or less closely, by the secondary valence, or van der Waals, forces. Now in the bulk of a solid or liquid, every molecule is surrounded on all sides by others of the same nature, and so is pulled equally in every direction. At an interface, on the other hand, a given molecule is pulled on one side into the bulk of the material by molecules of its own kind, whereas on the other side it may have only gaseous molecules, which exert little pull, or molecules of some quite different liquid or solid material, exerting quite a different pull. The molecules at the interface, then, are continually being pulled towards the interior. If the material is liquid, the interface will accordingly shrink to a minimum consistent with the incompressibility of the bulk of the material.

Since the molecules in the interface must be brought there against the attraction of the molecules in the bulk of the material, and will return to the bulk if allowed to, they must possess free energy in excess of that possessed by the molecules in the interior. This is the *Surface Energy* and the tendency of all surfaces to contract is in accordance with the second law of energetics—i.e. that free energy tends to diminish.

The Vapour Pressure of Drops.—One consequence of the existence of surface energy is that the vapour pressure of a liquid depends on the curvature of the surface. If a small volume of water evaporates from a very small drop with a highly curved surface, the surface will be appreciably diminished, and the work gained thereby will assist in the evaporation. With a very large drop, of course, the loss of the same amount of water will not affect the surface appreciably. This increase of vapour pressure becomes noticeable in drops of about 10^{-5} cm. (0.1μ) diameter. It accounts for the difficulty with which water condenses in a dust- and ion-free atmosphere. In order to make a drop 0.01μ diameter, the air would have to be 4 per cent. supersaturated and then about 140,000 molecules would have to collide simultaneously. For smaller drops, fewer molecules would be needed, of course, but the degree of supersaturation would have to be very much greater. In practice, condensation always begins on a particle of dust, or on a gas ion; in this case, the electrical charge reduces the surface energy, and so makes the formation of a new surface easier.

SURFACE TENSION

There is no force on a molecule in the surface which is tangential to that surface, since the distribution of the other molecules around it is symmetrical in this plane. The molecules in the surface, as can easily be observed, are perfectly free to move about in the surface. The tendency of the surface to diminish, however, makes it behave rather as if it were a stretched skin, or as if it were in a state of tension. This hypothetical surface tension is convenient since it can be regarded as the intensity factor in the surface energy, the area of the surface being the capacity factor.

One of the simplest ways to demonstrate this is due to van der Mensbrugghe in 1866. A loop of fine silk is taken and tied to a wire ring. If the whole be dipped into soap solution, so as to produce a film, the loop floats in the film; the silk thread forming its boundary is quite loose, and can be readily moved into any shape by means of a fine needle wetted with the soap solution (see Fig. 5.1). The film inside the loop is now broken by touching it with a bit of filter paper cut to a fine point. The loop is immediately drawn to a circular form by the tension of the film surrounding it, and can be felt to

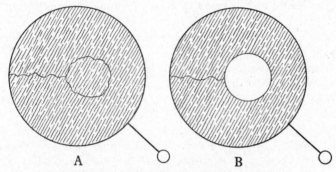

A   B

FIG. 5.1. RING OF IRON WIRE, ENCLOSING A SOAP FILM

In *A* there is a loop of fine silk floating in the film.
In *B* the portion of the film inside the loop has been broken by touching it with a pointed bit of filter paper. The result is that the tension of the film between the ring and the loop causes this film to contract as much as possible, thus drawing the loop into a circle, the figure of maximum area.   (Van der Mensbrugghe, 1866.)

resist attempts to change its shape by the needle. The soap solution is best prepared by the method of Boys from pure sodium oleate, with the addition of about 25 per cent. of glycerol.

The best way of showing that the form taken by a liquid when free from constraints is that with a minimum surface/volume ratio—i.e. a sphere—is to suspend a drop of one liquid in a large bulk of another with the same density but with which it does not mix. A mixture of carbon tetrachloride and toluol or xylol can easily be made, by trial and error, to have the same density as water at all ordinary room temperatures. Drops of this mixture are run into a jar, preferably flat-sided, containing water.

It is interesting to note that the phenomena shown by such suspended spheres of liquid were chiefly investigated by Plateau, the physicist of Ghent, after he became blind owing to gazing at the midday sun for experiments on vision. His researches were published in 1873. In his work he was assisted by his son-in-law, van der Mensbrugghe.

The methods used for determining the surface tension of liquids are described in many text-books of physical chemistry. Briefly these involve one of the following measurements.

(1) The height to which the liquid rises in a capillary tube. This is inversely proportional to the radius of the tube and directly proportional to the surface tension and to the cosine of the angle of contact between the liquid and air, i.e. to $\cos \theta_A$ or $\cos \theta_B$ in Fig. 5.2; for aqueous solutions in contact with *clean* glass, this has a value of 1.

(2a) The pressure required just to detach a bubble of air from a tube inserted in the liquid: or (2b) the maximum size of a drop of liquid which will just hang on the end of a tube. These values vary directly with the surface tension and inversely with the radius of the tube. The latter method (2b) is convenient for measuring the interfacial tension between two immiscible liquids.

(3) The height and diameter of a drop of liquid resting freely on a flat surface.

(4) The force required to detach a plate or ring of known dimensions from the surface of the liquid.

(5) The wave-length of ripples on the surface of the liquid, or on the interface between two liquids.

(6) The frequency of oscillation of a spherical drop after an initial deformation.

(7) The distance between successive swellings or constrictions as seen when a jet of fluid, emerging from a non-circular orifice, is viewed from one side.

In the last three types of measurement, the surface tension acts as the restoring force which maintains the oscillations. A critical review of the various methods, and the corrections that should be applied to the elementary theories, will be found in the book by N. K. Adam (1941). We may, however, add that the measurement of the surface tension at the interface between a living cell and its surrounding medium needs rather special technique, although the basic theories are the same. Details will be found in the review by Newton Harvey and Danielli (1938).

We have already identified the origin of the surface tension with the van der Waals forces between the molecules. We might expect, therefore, that since the average distance of one molecule from another becomes larger as the temperature rises, the magnitude of the surface tension should fall. This actually occurs, and surface tension has a negative temperature coefficient. Clearly, at the critical temperature, where the distinction between liquid and vapour disappears, the interface disappears also, and the surface tension of a liquid in contact with its vapour falls to zero.

Quantitatively, this phenomenon is expressed by Macleod's empirical equation; the surface tension of any liquid in contact with air (γ) is proportional to the fourth power of its density, i.e. the surface tension varies with temperature in the same manner as does the fourth power of its density.

Sugden, in 1924, put the equation into a slightly different form:

$$\frac{M}{D}\gamma^{1/4}=[P]$$

where M is the molecular weight of the substance and D is its density, so that M/D is the molecular volume, or volume occupied by one gram-molecule; this, multiplied by the fourth power of the surface tension gives a constant, called the "parachor". This parachor is useful in that it is a physical property of chemical compounds which is an additive property of the chemical composition. That is to say, by studying the parachors of a number of compounds of known composition, we can construct a table of the parachors of the elements and of certain typical structures, such as double bonds, and rings of various numbers of atoms. By adding these together in suitable proportions, we can derive the parachor of any compound of known structure. Conversely, and more usefully, the parachor of an incompletely known compound may be used to settle the details of its structure.

THE SURFACES OF SOLIDS

The molecules in solids are fixed relatively to each other, and, in consequence, various parts of solid surfaces may differ very considerably from each other. To begin with, the surface is very rarely perfectly smooth, so that the true surface area is usually greater than the apparent surface area. Polishing a crystalline surface destroys the crystal structure and creates a very hard amorphous layer—the "Beilby" layer, first described by Beilby in 1921. The polishing process appears to melt the surface layer momentarily, and no time is available for the atoms to take up the proper relative positions before solidification occurs. We cannot, therefore, reduce the uncertainty as to the magnitude of the true surface area of a solid by polishing its surface, without at the same time altering the structure of that surface very considerably.

Attempts have been made to evaluate the surface tension at the interface between a crystal and its saturated solution from the relative solubilities of small and large crystals. The argument is exactly analogous to that used in discussing the vapour pressure of small drops. It can easily be observed that in a saturated solution, large crystals grow at the expense of small ones, but, unfortunately, it is not possible to provide ourselves with crystals of different sizes, but with exactly the same chemical and physical structure. Breaking up large crystals by grinding will produce a "Beilby" layer, and sublimation or rapid crystallisation from solution results in particles which are incompletely crystallised, since the atoms do not have time to take up their proper positions before the whole mass is solidified. Since these amorphous, and semi-crystalline, structures crystallise spontaneously if given time, they must possess greater free energy than true crystals, and the calculated surface energy will be larger than that which would be present at a true crystal interface. The actual values of the surface tension so obtained are in the neighbourhood of 130 to 3000 dynes per centimetre, very much larger than that present at an air-water interface (73 dynes/cm.), but the significance of these figures is doubtful.

Knowledge of the arrangement and distance apart of the ions in certain crystals of salts with cubic lattices, makes it possible to calculate the surface free energies. The calculation is too complicated to be given here, but it is interesting that the free energies in the two planes of the lattice are very different from each other; the number of ions per square centimetre, and the arrangement of the ions are both different in the two planes. We shall remark later, that such crystals may adsorb substances differently on different faces.

We may appropriately refer here to the phenomenon of *Supercooling*. The formation of an ice crystal involves the creation of an interface, bounded on the solid side by an organised arrangement of water molecules. Work must be done in order to create the interface, and a considerable number of molecules must simultaneously take up the appropriate orientations. The formation of the first ice crystal thus involves an improbable process, but as soon as one crystal has formed, its field of force will assist in the orientation of further water molecules. A solution, consequently, will not begin to freeze until the temperature has fallen appreciably below the true freezing point, whereupon considerable quantities of ice will appear suddenly. Colloidal solutions, including the protoplasm of living cells, show this effect particularly well, in part, presumably, as a result of so many water molecules being orientated in the fields of force of the colloidal particles—in the lyospheres, which we shall discuss in the next chapter—and so being more unlikely to become re-orientated into ice crystals. This phenomenon plays an important part in the survival of living organisms, for short periods at least, at temperatures below their freezing points.

THE SPREADING OF A LIQUID AT AN INTERFACE

Consider a drop of liquid B resting on the surface of a solid, or another liquid A, as represented in Fig. 5.2. Along the line of contact, three surface tensions will be operating, that between B and the air γ_B, that between A and the air, γ_A, and that between B and A, γ_{AB}. Let the angles between the tangents to the surface at the line of contact be θ_A, θ_B and θ_{AB} as shown in the Figure. Then, if the drop is in equilibrium, it can easily be shown that the surface tensions and the angles must be related according to the equation

$$\frac{\gamma_A}{\sin \theta_B} = \frac{\gamma_B}{\sin \theta_A} = \frac{\gamma_{AB}}{\sin \theta_{AB}} \qquad . \qquad . \qquad . \qquad 5.1$$

Now if γ_A is larger than either γ_B or γ_{AB}, then $\sin \theta_B$ must also be larger than $\sin \theta_A$ or $\sin \theta_{AB}$ and θ_B must be smaller than either θ_A or θ_{AB}. In the limit θ_B becomes zero, and all the surface tensions act along the surface of A. In these conditions,

$$\gamma_A = \gamma_B + \gamma_{AB} \qquad . \qquad . \qquad . \qquad . \qquad 5.2$$

Any further increase of γ_A will be incompatible with a state of equilibrium, and the drop of B will spread over the whole surface of A. The condition for spreading is thus that

$$\gamma_A \geqslant \gamma_B + \gamma_{AB} \qquad . \qquad . \qquad . \qquad . \qquad 5.3$$

We can also look at the problem from a slightly different point of view. If we imagine the area of contact between the drop B and the surface A to be reduced by 1 sq. cm., the surface energy is reduced by an amount γ_{AB}. But, at the same time we have increased the surface areas of A and B

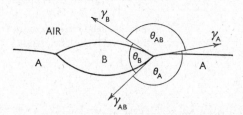

FIG. 5.2. DIAGRAM TO ILLUSTRATE THE FORCES TENDING TO PRODUCE SPREADING
OF ONE LIQUID ON ANOTHER

A drop of liquid B rests on the surface of another liquid A with which it does not mix. γ_A and γ_B represent the surface tensions between liquids A and B, respectively, and air; γ_{AB} represents the interfacial tension between liquid A and liquid B. The drop will spread over the surface of A if $\gamma_{AB} \geqslant \gamma_B + \gamma_A$.

by 1 sq. cm., and so increased the surface energy by an amount $(\gamma_A + \gamma_B)$. The net change in surface energy is thus given by:

$$W_{AB} = \gamma_A + \gamma_B - \gamma_{AB} \qquad . \qquad . \qquad . \qquad . \qquad 5.4$$

The quantity W_{AB} is called the "adhesional work" between A and B. If the drop is just on the point of spreading, comparison of equations 5.4 and 5.2 shows that $W_{AB} = 2\gamma_B$. Now $2\gamma_B$ is the decrease in surface energy when two surfaces of B, each 1 sq. cm. in area, come into contact so that the free surfaces are annihilated. It is the "cohesional work" of B. Thus the condition of spreading can be regarded as being the condition that the adhesional work between A and B should be equal to or greater than the cohesional work of B. We have, here, another instance of the second law of energetics; if the total surface energy is decreased by spreading, spreading will occur.

The magnitude of the energy change when spreading occurs, i.e. $W_{AB} - 2\gamma_B$, has been called by Harkins the "spreading coefficient".

Although theory predicts that spreading should occur whenever the spreading coefficient has a positive value, in practice, this applies only to perfectly clean surfaces. If the spreading coefficient is small, as is the case for octane on water, a very small amount of contamination will prevent spreading; if it is large, as for propyl alcohol on water, the spreading substance will displace a considerable amount of contamination.

TABLE 5.1

Spreading Coefficients of Organic Liquids on Water
(ergs per square centimetre)

Spreading Liquids.		Non-spreading Liquids.	
n-propyl alcohol	49·0	Monobrombenzene	−3·3
n-butyl alcohol	48·3	Carbon disulphide	−6·9
n-octyl alcohol	36·7	Mono-iodobenzene	−8·8
Aniline	24·4	Medicinal paraffin (average)	−13·5
Benzene	8·9	Methylene iodide	−26·5
Toluene	6·8		
Hexane	3·1		
Octane	0·2		

Mercury has a very large surface tension against air, so that it would be expected that all liquids, even water, would spread on it (in this case, γ_A is very large, so that, as seen from equation 5.3, very large values of $(\gamma_B + \gamma_{AB})$ would be needed to prevent spreading). This does, indeed, occur, but only if the mercury surface is perfectly clean, a condition which is extremely difficult to ensure owing to the ease with which adsorption takes place, with a consequent lowering of the surface tension.

On water surfaces, the ease of spreading of organic liquids is related to the solubility, as Harkins has shown. If the substance considered is soluble in water, the adhesional work is, presumably, very much greater than the cohesional. A large adhesion to water is conferred by the presence of "polar" groups such as —OH, —COOH, —CHO, and —NH₂. Hydro-carbon chains are non-polar and are not attracted to water. Thus all the hydrocarbons are insoluble in water and either will not spread at all on water, or do so with difficulty. Addition of a —COOH group makes the molecule soluble in water if the hydrocarbon chain is short (such as in acetic acid), but is incapable of making the whole of a long-chain molecule soluble; such molecules, however, readily spread at an air-water surface.

The conditions that regulate the spreading of a drop on the surface of a liquid, also account for the fact that solid particles will often float in the surface of water even though they sink once they have traversed it. Re-ferring back to Fig. 5.3 we see that, just as the drop will spread on the surface if θ_B becomes zero, so also will the surface flow over the drop if θ_A becomes zero. The drop, or if we like, the particle, will be wetted, and will sink through the surface. On the contrary, if the contact angle, θ_A, has a finite value, the particle will not be wetted, and so will not pass through the surface; flotation is possible. Thus a slightly greasy needle can be floated on water, while a perfectly clean one cannot.

This property of the surface is utilised by the small insects known as "water boatmen", or "pond skaters" (Gerridae), which can be seen running about over the surfaces of ponds. The flotation is here considerably assisted by the presence of large numbers of hairs, which increase the surface of contact with the water. The larvae of gnats and mosquitoes, also, hang from the surface by their breathing tubes. If the surface is covered by even a very thin layer of oil, the tubes are wetted by the oil, and the larvae drop away from the surface and are drowned.

MONOMOLECULAR LAYERS

The properties of the films that are formed by the spreading of organic substances on an air-water interface have been very thoroughly studied by Langmuir and by Adam. Most of the work has been done on long-chain hydrocarbon molecules with a polar group at one end, although other substances, such as proteins, carbohydrates and sterols have also been studied.

Such films are only one molecule thick (hence the term "monomolecular layer", sometimes contracted into "monolayer"). If allowed to spread over a large water surface, the molecules are all free to move independently of one another, and they lie flat on the surface. Their thermal agitation gives rise to a "surface pressure" which increases as the area occupied by the film is reduced, in just the same way as does the pressure of a gas when the volume is reduced. Consequently, such films are known as "gaseous films". (Curve I, Fig. 5.3.)

The surface pressure is measured by having a movable barrier in the water surface. The film is spread on one side only of the barrier, which is held in position against the surface pressure by means of a torsion wire. Further details will be found in the book by N. K. Adam (1941).

Considerable compression of a suitable gaseous film will result in a change of its properties. The surface pressure first becomes independent of the area occupied by the film, and then, with further compression, increases extremely rapidly. The film has, in fact, "condensed" to a liquid or solid state, the level portion of the curve, where the surface pressure is independent of the area, corresponding to the constant vapour pressure which persists so long as both liquid and gas are present together. (Curve III, Fig. 5.3.) Many substances, however, if allowed to expand indefinitely at room temperature, do not give gaseous films, but break up into islands of condensed film with "vapour" between them. In three-dimensional systems, also, many substances remain liquid or solid, as the case may be, at room temperatures, even *in vacuo*.

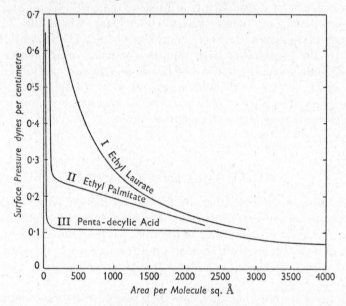

FIG. 5.3.   SURFACE PRESSURE

Surface Area Curves for Monolayers of: I, ethyl laurate; II, ethyl palmitate (both on water); and III, pentadecyclic acid (on N/50 HCl).

Curve I is continuous, and the film is gaseous over the whole range of measurement. It is not behaving as a "perfect" gas, however, since the product of pressure × area decreases as the pressure becomes greater.

In Curve III, there is a sharp discontinuity at an area a little less than 2500 sq. Å. per molecule. At areas less than this the surface pressure remains sensibly constant; the gaseous film is condensing to the liquid form. At an area of about 25 sq. Å. per molecule, the whole film is liquid, and the pressure rises very rapidly with further decrease in area.

In Curve II, there is no such discontinuity, nor does the surface pressure remain constant over a range of diminishing areas; but the film is clearly different from a true gaseous one (Curve I). It is described as "vapour expanded" down to the area at which it becomes liquid.   (Re-drawn from Adam, 1941.)

If one extrapolates the very steep portion of the force-area curve to zero force, as is shown in the larger scale figure (Curve I, Fig. 5.4), one derives the area which would be occupied by each molecule of the film when closely packed, but not compressed. If a series of long-chain aliphatic compounds is studied, it is found that the area occupied by each molecule (20·5 sq. Å.) is independent not only of the number of carbon atoms in the chain, but also, in many compounds, of the nature of the head group which is anchored to the water. It is inferred, therefore, that the chains in such condensed films, are packed tightly and standing on end, with the polar groups in the water surface. The area occupied by each molecule is decided by the size of the —CH_2 groups in the chain. With other compounds, the steep part of the force-area curve extrapolates to much larger areas (22-50 sq. Å.). These are, in some cases determined by the size of the end groups, but in others, possibly by kinks in the main chain. As is indicated in Curve II, Fig. 5.4, the compression curve of a straight chain compound may sometimes consist of two parts, the upper extrapolating to 20·5 sq. Å.

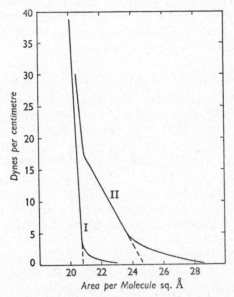

FIG. 5.4. CURVES OF SURFACE PRESSURE AGAINST AREA PER MOLECULE FOR FATTY
ACIDS (14 to 18 carbon atoms per molecule)

Curve I on distilled water. Curve II on dilute hydrochloric acid.
Note that Curve I extrapolates to zero pressure at an area of 20·5 sq. Å. per molecule, while Curve II extrapolates to zero pressure at an area of about 25 sq. Å. per molecule.
(Re-drawn from Adam, 1941.)

and the lower to a much larger value. It seems probable that the larger value is that of the large head group, and that by sufficient compression, every alternate molecule can be driven further into the water, and so able to tuck away its neighbours' heads into recesses in its main chain.

It will be noted that the two curves I and II in Fig. 5.4 both refer to the same substance, but that in curve I it has been spread on distilled water, and in curve II on dilute acid. Suppose we imagine a film to be spread on distilled water and adjusted to an area of 21 sq. Å. per molecule. The surface pressure will be about 2 dynes per cm. If we now imagine the distilled water to be replaced by dilute acid, the surface pressure would rise to about 16 dynes/cm., a very considerable change. Effects of this kind may be of importance in proto-plasm; we have reason to suppose that monolayers occur at all the interfaces that we can see (and possibly also on those that we cannot), and we know that the acidity is capable of quite considerable local variations. It is clear, also, that relatively small chemical re-arrangements at the head of the molecule may completely alter the nature of the film.

Certain substances, such as oleic acid, which have a double bond in the middle of the chain, form coherent films when spread at room temperature. The double bond, however, can be oxidised to two —OH groups by the action of permanganate in the water beneath the film. The middle of the chain thus becomes strongly polar, and is pulled into the water. The whole molecule thus lies flat on the surface, and the film becomes gaseous in nature. If the film is held at a suitable area per molecule, considerable changes in surface pressure would occur as a result of this oxidation.

If the molecular chains do not greatly attract each other, the condensed film is liquid, and the molecules can move about the surface freely, as is shown by the fact that dust particles can be blown about. If, on the other hand, the chains attract each other strongly, the film is solid, and dust particles become fixed. Extreme compression of a liquid or solid film brings about a collapse of the whole film, and the molecules are crowded on top of each other.

In addition to these three states, which correspond exactly with the three states of three-dimensional matter, the two-dimensional monolayers, particularly of long-chain aliphatic substances, can exist in "expanded" states, either "liquid-expanded" or "vapour-expanded". They are then intermediate in their properties between liquid and gaseous films. A liquid-expanded film has a force-area curve which is not very nearly horizontal in any part, as is that of a condensed vapour film where liquid and vapour are both present (Curve III, Fig. 5.3), nor rises steeply as in a pure liquid film; but slopes gradually, and fairly uniformly from a discontinuity indicating the loss of the gaseous state, and curves gradually into a line characteristic of the liquid state. The force-area curve for the vapour-expanded film is generally similar, but there is a continuous transition between the gaseous state and the expanded state (Curve II, Fig. 5.3). In both types of film, one end of each molecular chain is supposed to be more or less attached to the corresponding ends of its neighbouring chains, thus being "liquid"; while the other end is undergoing thermal agitation of considerable amplitude, thus being "gaseous". This is possible, since the chains of carbon atoms are in the nature of zig-zags, and free rotation is possible at each junction. It does not appear to be generally agreed whether the polar groups are attached to each other at the water surface, or whether the non-polar ends are attached to each other, and the polar groups in movement.

POLYMOLECULAR LAYERS

Langmuir and his co-workers have shown that it is possible to transfer many of the monomolecular films formed at an air-water interface, to the surface of a solid plate of glass or polished metal. All that is necessary is to dip the plate into the water on which the film has been formed and to withdraw it slowly. If we take, for example, a clean glass plate which is easily wetted by water—i.e. the surface is hydrophilic—there is no transfer of the film on the down stroke, when the plate is being pushed into the water, since it is the upper surface of the film which comes into contact with the plate, and this surface is hydrophobic. On the upstroke, however, when the plate is withdrawn from the water, the glass plate comes into contact with the lower, hydrophilic surface of the film, and the film is quantitatively transferred to the glass plate.

If a monolayer of stearic acid is formed on a solution containing a low concentration of salts with bivalent cations, and is kept under a steady surface pressure of some 10 to 30 dynes/cm., repeated dippings of a glass or metal plate result in repeated depositions of the monolayer. After the first layer has been deposited, the surface of the plate is hydrophobic, and a second layer will be deposited, hydrophobic side downwards, on the second downstroke. A third will then be deposited on the now hydrophilic surface, on the second upstroke, and so on. In this way layers containing many hundreds or thousands of monolayers can be deposited, and the total thickness easily measured by optical means (interference colours) or even by a screw micrometer. The results leave no doubt whatever, but that the primary layers are only one molecule thick.

One of the most remarkable properties of these multilayers is that the outermost layer is capable of being turned upside down. By suitable treatment, therefore, the coated plate can be made either hydrophobic or hydrophilic as desired. For further details, the reader should consult the review by Langmuir (1939).

ADSORPTION

Most substances dissolved in water lower the surface tension at the interface between the solution and a solid, or immiscible liquid. With the exception of certain inorganic salts, this is also the case at the interface between the solution and a gas. Further, at these interfaces there is free surface energy, which can be altered in amount by the deposition of substances at the interface. It follows, then, from the second law of energetics, that dissolved substances which lower surface tension will be concentrated at the interface, since free energy will be reduced.

This result is of fundamental importance, and was arrived at by Willard Gibbs from thermodynamic considerations in 1878, and by J. J. Thomson in 1888, from the dynamical point of view. It will be referred to in subsequent pages as the "Gibbs" or "Gibbs-Thomson" principle. It is really a particular application of the general doctrine of decrease of free energy, as shown by the headlines chosen by Gibbs himself for his work on "Heterogeneous Equilibrium", i.e., the formulation by Clausius of the two laws of energetics, as given in Chapter 1 (p. 9). As applied to surface *energy*, the Gibbs principle has a wider application than may appear from the above statement of it as referring to surface tension. It may be expressed thus: Any process that diminishes the free energy at an interface will tend to take place, whatever be the nature of the energy concerned, whether mechanical, electrical, chemical, or other. If the surface has an electric charge, a process diminishing it will be favoured. If it possesses chemical energy, a reaction reducing this energy will take place, if possible; and so on.

Accordingly, any substance in solution in a liquid, in contact with the surface of another phase, will be concentrated on that surface, if, by doing so, the free energy present there is decreased. This process is called "*adsorption*". Its characteristic is the relation to *surfaces* of contact. Whatever further process may follow it, chemical reaction, or diffusion into the body of the other phase, the first thing to take place is the local concentration. The rate at which subsequent events happen will naturally depend on the amount of this condensation.

As an example, the well-known effect of charcoal in decolorising or clarifying a solution may be given. If a dilute solution of a dye, such as "night-blue", be mixed with charcoal, it can be almost completely decolorised. That the dye is not destroyed, or chemically combined with the carbon, can easily be shown by filtering off the latter, and extracting it with alcohol, which will be found to become of a deep blue colour. The process is, in fact, reversible.

Clearly, if a substance *increases* surface energy, its concentration at an interface will be *lowered*, giving rise to negative adsorption. When sodium chloride solutions are shaken with charcoal, the concentration is raised, owing to the salt being displaced from the interface and sent into the bulk of the solution. At the interface between a salt solution and air, calculation shows that there is a layer which is free from salt, approximately one molecule thick. The magnitude of the negative adsorption depends somewhat on the degree of hydration of the ions. In order of decreasing effect, we have: $Cl > Br > I$; and: $Li > Na > K$. Bivalent ions have a greater effect per ion than univalent ions. It is, perhaps, only reasonable that the more an ion is hydrated, the more it is pulled away from the interface by the water molecules. The interfacial tension between hexane and water is affected in the same way by the presence of ions as is that between water and air.

From general energetic considerations, it is reasonable to expect that there should be a direct relation between the amount of a substance adsorbed per unit area of surface, or its surface excess (Γ), the surface tension (γ) and the chemical potential, or partial molar free energy of the substance in the bulk solution ($\bar{G}$). Such a relation has been derived by Gibbs; its rigid derivation cannot be given here, but will be found, for example, in the monograph by Adam (1941). The general equation is:

$$dy + \Gamma_1.d\bar{G}_1 + \Gamma_2.d\bar{G}_2 + \text{etc.} = 0$$

where the subscripts $_1$, $_2$, etc. refer to all the various components of the solution. It has the same general form, and may be deduced in the same way, as the equation given in Chapter 3 (equation 3.16, p. 87) relating the partial free energies and mole fractions of the solvent and the solute. If, as is usual, we are concerned with the adsorption of one solute only, we have:

$$dy = -\Gamma_2.d\bar{G}_2 ;$$

From equation 3.12, p. 85, we can write:

$$d\bar{G}_2 = RT.d(\ln a_2)$$

where a_2 is the activity of the solute, T is the absolute temperature and R the gas constant. If the solution may be regarded as very dilute and "ideal", the activity may be replaced by the concentration, so that:

$$dy = -\Gamma_2.RT.d(\ln c) = -\Gamma_2.RT.dc/c$$

or
$$-\Gamma_2 = \frac{c}{RT} \cdot \frac{dy}{dc} \quad . \quad \quad . \quad \quad . \quad \quad . \quad \quad 5.5$$

This formula has been tested experimentally by many workers. The majority have passed bubbles of air, or drops of mercury, through the solutions, collected and "broken" the bubbles or drops, and analysed the solution so formed. The agreement between theory and experiment has not always been very good. In some cases, the quantities adsorbed have been of the right order of magnitude, but in others they have been very much too large. Possibly electrical forces have been operating in addition to the pure surface forces postulated. McBain has attacked the problem by slicing off the surface of a watery solution with a special microtome knife; in these experiments, the excess concentration in the surface layer agreed with that expected theoretically within the limits of experimental error.

THE ADSORPTION ISOTHERM

In very dilute solutions, the lowering of the surface tension by many substances is found to be nearly proportional to the concentration, so that we can write:

$$\gamma_0 - \gamma = B.c \text{ and } d\gamma/dc = -B$$

The Gibbs equation is then transformed to the simple relation:

$$\Gamma = \frac{B.c}{RT} \qquad . \qquad . \qquad . \qquad . \qquad . \qquad 5.6$$

One of the characteristic properties of most adsorption processes, however, when the solutions are not extremely dilute, is that the amount taken up is *not* in direct linear relation to the concentration, as is implied by this equation. It is found, on the contrary, that the more dilute is the solution, the greater is the proportion of its contents that is adsorbed. An equation describing this relation was first given by Freundlich in the following form:

$$x/m = a.c^{1/n} \qquad . \qquad . \qquad . \qquad . \qquad 5.7$$

where x is the amount adsorbed by the surface m, from a solution whose final concentration is c, a and $1/n$ being constants for a particular surface and solution. A table of values for a number of typical cases will be found in Freundlich's book (1922). The temperature is supposed constant, so that the expression is that of the *adsorption isotherm*.

This equation may easily be derived from the fundamental Gibbs equation (equation 5.5 above). If we assume that the surface tension falls, not in direct proportion to the concentration of the solute, but in proportion to the $(1/n)$th power of the concentration, i.e. if we put:

$$\gamma_0 - \gamma = A.c^{1/n}$$

then

$$-c . \frac{d\gamma}{dc} = \frac{A}{n} c^{1/n}$$

Substitution in the Gibbs equation gives:

$$\Gamma = \frac{A}{n.RT} c^{1/n}$$

which is identical with the Freundlich isotherm if $a = A/nRT$.

The Freundlich equation has the same general form as the equation which expresses the partition of a solute between two solvents which do not mix with each other. If the solute is present in both solvents as single molecules, as is succinic acid in ether and water, for example, the concentration in one solvent is directly proportional to that in the other. If the solute is associated in one of the solvents, so that the number of molecules is halved, or otherwise diminished, as in the case of benzoic acid, for example, which is bimolecular in benzene, the relation is no longer linear, but parabolic; the concentration of benzoic acid in the water is proportional to the square root of the concentration in the benzene. The concentration of a substance in one phase may thus vary as a power of that in the other phase. If, then, the value of n in the Freundlich formula happens, in a particular case, to be a whole number, say 2, it might be a simple case of partition between two solvents, in one of which the substance is bimolecular. The Freundlich exponent, however, is often not a whole number, and is consequently an impossible one from the point of view of simple partition between two solvents, since it would imply the existence of fractions of molecules in one of the solvents. Again, in the case of the adsorption of arsenious acid by freshly precipitated ferric hydroxide, the exponent has the value 1/5. If this were a case of partition between solvents, arsenious acid must have a molecular weight in ferric hydroxide which is one-fifth of that which it has in water; but in water, it is already in single molecules. The concentration of carbon dioxide on charcoal increases in proportion to the cube root of the pressure. If this were a case of solution in charcoal, the carbon dioxide must have a molecular weight in charcoal which is one-third of that in the gaseous state, which is not possible.

The Kinetics of Adsorption

Langmuir, in 1916, considered the processes whereby a gas is condensed in a monomolecular layer on a smooth homogeneous solid surface. He imagined that of all the gas molecules that struck the surface in the course of their random motions, some would bounce off again immediately, and only a fraction, a, would become attached. If μ molecules strike the surface per second, $a\mu$ will remain. The molecules that are attached to the surface will slowly evaporate, the rate of evaporation being proportional to the total number of molecules present. If a fraction, θ, of the surface is covered with gas molecules, then the rate of evaporation may be written $\nu\theta$. It is supposed that only those gas molecules that strike the bare surface can become attached, so that the rate of condensation is $a\mu(1-\theta)$. If equilibrium has been reached, the rate of condensation is equal to the rate of evaporation, so that:

$$a\mu(1-\theta)=\nu\theta \qquad . \qquad . \qquad . \qquad . \qquad 5.8$$

Now $a\mu$ is proportional to the pressure of the gas (or to the concentration of the solution, if this is small) and may be written kp. Also, θ may be written as N/N_0, where N is the number of molecules adsorbed per unit surface area at the pressure p, and N_0 is the number adsorbed when the surface is completely covered. Substituting in equation 5.8, we get:

$$kp(1-N/N_0)=\nu.N/N_0$$

or
$$N/N_0=\frac{(k/\nu)p}{1+(k/\nu)p} \qquad . \qquad . \qquad . \qquad . \qquad 5.8a$$

Langmuir's expression can only be used with confidence in cases of adsorption by smooth homogeneous surfaces. In practice, solid surfaces are rarely homogeneous, and are only made smooth with the greatest difficulty. Heterogeneous surfaces would need an expression with a number of different values of a and v, since the rates of condensation and of evaporation will depend on the nature of the surface. The presence of cracks and crevices will further disturb the results, since the gas will not readily penetrate into them, and when adsorbed, will only evaporate slowly.

SATURATION

In Langmuir's treatment of the adsorption process, it is assumed that only one layer of molecules is attached to the adsorbing surface. The properties of such an adsorbed monolayer will be essentially similar to those of a monolayer formed by spreading, as already considered in an earlier section. If the surface pressure of a monolayer is F, then we can write:

$$F = \gamma_0 - \gamma$$

If, as in the simplest case of very dilute solutions, we put $\gamma_0 - \gamma = B.c$, then the Gibbs equation takes the form: $\Gamma = F/RT$. Now Γ is the number of molecules per unit area in the surface phase, so that $1/\Gamma$ is the area, A, occupied by each molecule. Hence we see that: $F.A = RT$. The surface layer thus obeys the simple gas laws, as has been observed for gaseous monolayers at large areas per molecule (compare Fig. 5.4). It will be clear, however, that there must be a limit to the density with which the molecules can be packed, as we have already seen when discussing the monolayers formed by spreading at an interface. Compression of gaseous monolayers leads to a departure from the perfect gas law relation, as it does in three-dimensional gases. If we make use of a more complex equation of state for the surface layer, corresponding to the van der Waals equation for the three-dimensional system, we can deduce more complex relations between the concentration of the solution and the amount adsorbed on the surface. Allowing, first, only for the space taken up by the molecules themselves, we may write: $F(A - b) = RT$. Remembering that $A = 1/\Gamma$, and assuming still that $F = \gamma_0 - \gamma = B.c$, we deduce that:

$$\Gamma = \frac{B.c}{RT + B.b.c} \qquad . \qquad . \qquad . \qquad . \qquad 5.9$$

The amount adsorbed thus increases with concentration in the solution less rapidly than it does in very dilute solutions, and approaches a constant value when $B.b.c \gg RT$; this implies that the amount adsorbed at the interface will approach a saturation value and become independent of the concentration—an occurrence which is, in fact, quite common in adsorption processes. This equation, it will be noted, has precisely the same form as that deduced by Langmuir (equation 5.8a), which also explicitly admits the existence of saturation conditions. But here they arise from the fact that it is supposed that the adsorbed substance can only be attached to certain special atoms, molecules, or groups, in the surface, saturation being reached when all these are occupied. The molecules are not necessarily tightly packed.

If, on the other hand, we allow only for the attractive force between the molecules and write: $(F + a.F^2)A = RT$, we find that the amount adsorbed increases *more* rapidly than it does in very dilute solutions. It is clear, therefore, that when both factors are operating, the relation may become very complex, even without introducing any more complex relation between the lowering of the surface tension and the concentration, or introducing activity coefficients.

We may approach the problem, also, by considering how the surface tension is likely to vary with concentration when the solution is not very dilute. It would seem not unreasonable to suppose that as the surface becomes increasingly covered by adsorbed molecules, each successive addition would cause a smaller change in surface tension; some kind of law of "diminishing returns", or "compound interest" law with a negative exponent (compare Chapter 1, p. 23) will operate. Moreover, the adsorbed substance may be able to form successive layers on the surface, and it is reasonable to suppose that the first one will cause a greater diminution of surface energy than succeeding ones, and each of these less than its predecessor. Each successive layer occurs on a surface whose energy is already reduced by the previous layer. These considerations, are, indeed, expressed in the relation between the depression of the surface tension and the concentration of the solute from which Freundlich's adsorption isotherm is deduced, provided, of course, that the value of the exponent $1/n$ is less than unity. They may, however, be expressed rather more clearly by writing the relation between surface tension and solute concentration in the form:

$$\frac{d\gamma}{dc} = -\frac{B'}{a+c}$$

Substituting in the Gibbs equation (5.5) we get:

$$\Gamma = \frac{B'}{RT} \cdot \frac{c}{a+c} \qquad . \qquad . \qquad . \qquad . \qquad 5.10$$

This equation, again, is identical in form with the Langmuir equation and with equation 5.9 deduced by means of different assumptions.

If the above equation for dy/dc is integrated, we get:

$$\gamma_0 - \gamma = C \cdot \gamma_0 \log \left(1 + \frac{c}{a} \right)$$

C being a fresh constant. Now for relatively concentrated solutions of fatty acids, for example, it is found that the reduction in surface tension is, indeed, a function of the logarithm of the concentration. And, further, the values of the constants in equation 5.10 for the various fatty acids are consistent with there being a close-packed monolayer of adsorbed molecules when saturation is reached.

Chemical and Physical Forces in Adsorption

Although the second law of energetics shows that adsorption must take place if the free energy is lowered thereby, we have, as yet, made no reference to the *forces* which produce this surface action. It has long been known that charcoal adsorbs gases that are easily liquefied, such as carbon dioxide and ammonia, to a much greater degree than it adsorbs the so-called "permanent" gases, such as nitrogen and hydrogen. Now gases liquefy because the attractive forces between the molecules become so large that the energy of thermal agitation is insufficient to lift them over the potential barrier, and so pull them apart. It is reasonable to suppose, therefore, that the forces holding the adsorbed molecules to the charcoal are of the same nature. They may be regarded as "physical" forces, and adsorption of this type is known as "molecular" or "van der Waals" adsorption, since the forces concerned are those that necessitate the introduction of the term a/v^2 in the van der Waals equation of state. We have already discussed the nature of those forces in Chapter 2. Just as liquids can be evaporated by raising the temperature and by reducing the pressure of the vapour in contact with them, so can the gases adsorbed by van der Waals forces be removed by heating the adsorbent, such as charcoal, and by exposing it to a vacuum.

The adsorption of gases by solids makes itself apparent to all who work with high vacua. The gases adsorbed by the walls of the apparatus must be removed by heating *in vacuo*, before a high vacuum can be maintained. Thermionic valves, for example, must be very carefully baked out during the course of manufacture, and before being sealed off, otherwise they would very soon cease to function. The adsorption of water vapour, also, on the surfaces of vessels which have been dried in a vacuum desiccator is a well-known source of trial to the chemist.

It is interesting to note the clear conception of surface condensation which Faraday had formed. On p. 181 of his *Experimental Researches on Electricity* (1839) he refers to "the attraction between glass and air, well known to barometer makers", and to the fact that they have no power of combination with each other. On p. 181, again, mention is made of the power of water vapour to condense *upon*, although not to combine with clay, charcoal, and turf, "assisted a little, perhaps, by a very slight solvent action" in the latter case.

The adsorption of *oxygen* by charcoal, however, introduces a new phenomenon. We find that a large part of the adsorbed gas can only be removed with the greatest difficulty, and then it comes off, not as oxygen, but as oxides of carbon. The forces that attach the oxygen to the charcoal are evidently extremely powerful, and are of the same order of magnitude as the covalent forces which unite the atoms in a compound. Adsorption of this type is known as "chemisorption" since the adsorbed material is attached to the adsorbent by "chemical" forces, involving the sharing of electrons. Chemisorption, then, may be regarded as essentially a chemical reaction with the material of the adsorbent. The difference between such a surface phenomenon and a reaction in true solution is that in the latter, the law of mass action is obeyed, the active mass present being equivalent to the number of molecules of the solute; whereas, in the former, the extent of surface, or the number of molecules situated there, is the controlling factor, corresponding to the active mass. The surface of the same quantity of matter may vary enormously, according to the degree of subdivision; if this is carried out in imagination so far that molecular dimensions are reached, ordinary chemical action is being dealt with.

Chemisorption, as might be expected, is more specific than van der Waals adsorption. Whereas the latter will always occur so long as the surface free energy is lowered, the former will only occur if the electronic configurations of the atoms of the adsorbed material and of the adsorbent are appropriate, and, probably, if an adequate activation energy has been acquired. It is supposed that van der Waals adsorption occurs first, and subsequently, by chance, some of the adsorbed atoms or molecules acquire enough energy of thermal motion to surmount the potential barrier and become chemisorbed.

Adsorbed atoms and molecules usually appear to be free to move about the surface on which they are adsorbed. This may, in some cases, be merely the natural result of the gaseous state of the adsorbed layer. We have already remarked that the molecules of a spread monolayer in the gaseous state are perfectly free to move about over the surface. In other cases, however, particularly those of chemisorbed substances, the surface mobility may occur through "activated" diffusion. An atom held to the surface at a particular spot may be regarded as being in an energy "hole". In this hole, however, it is undergoing thermal agitation, its energy of oscillation varying in random fashion about a mean which is determined by its temperature. If this is high enough, the atom may, sooner or later, acquire enough energy to lift it out of the hole. The extra energy will soon be lost to other atoms either of the adsorbed substance or of the adsorbent, and the atom that we are considering will again drop into an energy "hole". But this need not be the same hole that it had previously left, and it might, by chance collisions, travel along the energy "ridges" for quite a long distance before coming to rest again.

The distinction that is drawn between chemisorption and van der Waals adsorption does not mean that the latter is necessarily entirely unspecific. Indeed, it is probably impossible to draw a hard and fast line between the two types of adsorption. If there is some kind of "fit" between the fields of force of the surface and those of the adsorbed substance, adsorption will be more complete than it would be in the absence of such a fit. The relation of the van der Waals forces to the electronic configurations of the molecules is highly complex, and cannot be considered here. It involves the consideration of the mutual attraction between two dipoles permanent or induced, and of the effects of sympathetic fluctuations in the clouds of electrons. There is clearly plenty of opportunity for unexpected specificities, even among atoms that are not, in the restricted sense, chemically related.

Some examples of these specificities may be given. It appears that adsorption will only take place on the face of a crystal if the spacing of the atoms of the adsorbing crystal corresponds to that in the crystal of the adsorbed substance. Since the spacings are different on the different faces of the crystal, this means that a substance may be adsorbed on one face, but not on another. Thus urea is only adsorbed on one face of a crystal of ammonium chloride, and not on another. For a similar reason, probably, a lead nitrate crystal adsorbs methylene blue on one face, and picric acid on another. The specificities among non-crystalline material may be indicated by the following examples. Carbon and red oxide of iron adsorb benzoic acid ten times as strongly as they do acetic acid; chromium oxide adsorbs both acids equally; while platinum black adsorbs acetic acid slightly more than benzoic acid, but neither to any great extent.

The Effect of Temperature on Adsorption

Surface energy decreases with rise in temperature, and, accordingly, the amount of a substance adsorbed at a surface also decreases.

For example, the surface tension of lactic acid in 44 per cent. solution at 18° C. is 50·5 dynes/cm. and at 67° C. is 47 dynes/cm. Correspondingly, 2 grams of charcoal adsorbed 51 per cent. of the lactic acid from 20 c.c. of 0·71 per cent. solution at 0° C., but only 42 per cent. from the same solution at 40° C. At the temperature of liquid air, moreover, charcoal adsorbs gases to such a degree that it may be used to produce a high vacuum.

In some cases, however, complications arise. There is reason to believe that chemisorption has frequently quite a large energy of activation. At low temperatures, none of the atoms, either of the adsorbed substance or of the adsorbent, possess this energy. As the temperature rises, the proportion of atoms with the necessary energy also rises, and chemisorption begins to take place. Over a certain range of temperature, therefore, there is a pseudo-equilibrium only, and over this range of temperature the amount of substance adsorbed increases with rise of temperature. At still higher temperatures, the amount adsorbed once more falls with rise of temperature, as would be expected of an exothermic process.

The existence of an energy of activation has been inferred chiefly from the observations of Taylor and his co-workers on the adsorption of hydrogen by various metallic oxides. How far these conceptions can be more generally applied is still uncertain. In particular, there seems to be no good evidence for or against the existence of an activation energy in chemisorption from solutions. It seems probable, however, that we should be justified in postulating its existence, as is suggested by the following experiment (W. M. Bayliss, 1906). The amount of Congo-red taken up by filter paper is inversely proportional to the temperature, as would be expected of a simple adsorption process. If the temperature is raised to 100° C., however, the dye becomes fixed in the paper, and cannot be removed by washing. It would appear that chemisorption takes place when the temperature is raised sufficiently for the molecules to acquire the necessary activation energy.

THE VELOCITY OF ADSORPTION

In general, when a substance reaches the surface at which it is adsorbed, the actual process of attachment is very rapid. When a substance is being adsorbed from solution, the velocity of the process is generally limited by the rate of diffusion of the substance to the adsorbing surface. If there is chemisorption, however, with a large activation energy, and at a temperature at which there is only a pseudo-equilibrium, the process may be relatively slow; only a small fraction of all the molecules present at any moment will have the necessary activation energy.

The existence of adsorption at an interface between a solution and air, and the slowness with which the interface comes into equilibrium with the bulk of the solution, can be seen by blowing a bubble with a 1 per cent. solution of saponin. If the bubble is then allowed to collapse, it will fall into wrinkles and folds. The concentration of the saponin at the interfaces between the solution and the air was previously so great that any reduction of the surface area results in saponin being precipitated out, and the film becoming rigid.

The adsorption of gases by charcoal is often a very slow process, taking many hours for completion. To a great extent this is probably due to a slow diffusion of the gas into the pores of the charcoal, but an activation process may be concerned as well.

The fact that an appreciable time may be necessary for the formation of an adsorbed film is of importance in the measurement of surface, or interfacial, tension; and the fact, conversely, is demonstrated by these measurements. When they are made by means of *dynamic* methods, such as by observations on the vibration of drops initially deformed from a spherical shape, the surface is being continually renewed; whereas in the *static* methods, such as the rise in a capillary tube and the maximum weight of a drop, time is allowed for surface adsorption to reach equilibrium. With pure liquids, the same values are obtained by both methods. With solutions of surface active substances, which are concentrated in the surface layer, on the other hand, the two methods will not give identical values unless the adsorption occurs sufficiently rapidly. To take a well marked instance: a 0·025 per cent. solution of sodium oleate has a static surface tension of 26 dynes/cm., but a dynamic one of 79 dynes/cm., practically the same as that of water, so that little or no adsorption takes place in the time allowed before a new surface is formed.

It should be noted that measurement of the surface tension by measuring the wave-length of ripples on the surface of a solution, often classed as a "dynamic" method, does, in fact, give the "static" value; it appears that the surface is not changed by the passage of a ripple. The "drop weight method", however, can be made to approximate to a dynamic one, by rapidly delivering a drop of known size from a micrometer syringe, and finding the maximum size that can exist for a very small, but measurable, time.

The Influence of Adsorption on Chemical Reaction

The presence of an interface in a system in which chemical reactions are taking place may modify these reactions very considerably. Thus, when an electrolyte, such as acetic acid, is adsorbed on charcoal, a certain proportion is taken out of solution and cannot contribute to the electrical conductivity or osmotic pressure of the system. Salts, moreover, when adsorbed, cease to exist as free ions, and so give none of their characteristic reactions.

If a reaction mixture in equilibrium is placed in contact with an adsorbing surface, one of the components may be adsorbed to a greater extent than the others. It may thus be virtually removed from the system, and the equilibrium conditions of the reaction may be altered, as a result of the mass action effect. Thus, if we have the reaction:

$$A + B \rightleftharpoons Y + Z$$

preferential adsorption of Z may lead to a shift of the equilibrium in the direction of the disappearance of A and B. Free energy would obviously have to be supplied by the adsorption process, so that an appreciable shift of the equilibrium conditions is only likely to occur when the reaction is associated with but a small change in free energy. Many reactions of biological interest, however, such as hydrolyses, involve little or no change in free energy, and some change in the position of equilibrium can be expected in the presence of an adsorbent. We shall refer to this again in Chapter 7. Adsorption, also, may have an important action on the *velocity of reaction*, as distinct from its effects on the equilibrium position. This is an aspect of catalysis, and will be considered in Chapter 7.

Adsorption from Mixtures—Chromatography

When adsorption takes place from a mixture, all the solutes may be taken up in definite relative proportions. In addition, the solvent itself is condensed on the surface, and this leads to a very complex state of affairs. Moreover, if a surface which has adsorbed a particular substance be exposed to a solution of another one which has a greater power of lowering surface energy than the first, the less powerful one is more or less completely displaced by the other.

When rennet is shaken up in solution, it is more or less inactivated by adsorption on the surface of the froth produced. This inactivation is completely absent if a little saponin is added, although the foam is even greater than before. Saponin, in fact, lowers surface energy more than does rennet, and hence obtains possession of the surface.

This faculty of preferential adsorption of certain substances by certain surfaces is not, however, solely a matter of lowering surface energy. As we have seen, the atomic and molecular structures of the surface and the substance adsorbed are also important. From this has been developed a powerful tool for the analysis of complex solutions of organic and inorganic solutes, even when only very small quantities are available; and for the separation and isolation of the constituents, even when they are unstable or closely related chemically. The method was first used systematically by the botanist Tswett, in 1903, in order to separate the pigments and other constituents of plant extracts. The solution was allowed to percolate through a column of finely divided solid material; the most strongly adsorbed substances were retained at the top of the column, those less adsorbed penetrated further down, and those hardly adsorbed at all came out with the solvent. The different pigments thus formed bands of different colour in different parts of the column, and this gave rise to the term *"chromatography"*.

The column of adsorbent in such cases can subsequently be divided into parts, each containing one of the coloured substances. If the substances to be

G

separated are colourless, the solution emerging from the column can be collected in successive small portions, and each analysed separately. Further, the adsorbed substance can be "eluted" by running through solvents of different nature, first one which only removes the least strongly adsorbed substances, and then with progressively more powerful ones. A very wide variety of substances may be used as adsorbents, according to the nature of the substances to be adsorbed, such as alumina, charcoal, magnesia, calcium carbonate, talc, and starch, to name only a few. An equally wide variety of solvents may be used for elution, and almost every organic liquid (as well as water) has been used.

It is not ordinarily possible to discover any simple relationship between the chemical nature of the adsorbent and those of the substances adsorbed. But if the adsorbent is electrolytically dissociated, behaving either as an anion or a cation, it will take part in a process of *ion exchange*, and some generalisations can be made about its behaviour. Various silicates and alumino-silicates were originally used for this purpose, but now there is a whole range of synthetic resins, formed by the polymerisation of phenolic and other organic substances, each with its own particular properties. The anionic resins will take up cations from the solution, and the cationic resins will take up anions; and roughly, the higher the valency and the larger the ion, the stronger is the combination, although there are irregularities and exceptions. The ion exchange resins are thus of great value in separating various acidic and basic substances and salts, both organic and inorganic. A substance which has been taken up by the resin may be eluted, and replaced by another ion, even though this is less strongly combined, provided that it is present in sufficiently high concentration.

In 1941, Martin and Synge introduced *partition chromatography* in which the separation of the various constituents depends upon their relative solubilities (partition coefficients) in two different solvents. It was found that the separation was more effective if one of the solvents (water) was held on a column of solid material (silica gel was used) and the other (an organic solvent) was allowed to flow over it. In 1944, Consden, Gordon and Martin used filter paper for holding the water, and from this came *paper chromatography*. The paper, however, is not soaked with water, but only allowed to come into equilibrium with an atmosphere which is saturated with water vapour. The water itself is probably adsorbed on the paper and rather tightly bound, as will be discussed in the next chapter; and the separation of the various constituents in the solution which moves through the paper probably takes place by adsorption on, and ion exchange with, the cellulose, as well as by partition with the water.

In paper chromatography, a very small spot of the solution under test (0·002 to 0·02 ml. in volume, containing possibly only a few micrograms of solute) is placed at one end of a strip of filter paper. This end is then placed in the "developing" solvent (an organic liquid, usually, but not necessarily, more or less insoluble in water) and the whole placed in a closed atmosphere saturated with water vapour. The developing solvent soaks along the paper, carrying with it the solutes from the spot. These, however, lag behind the solvent by an amount which depends on their partition coefficients between the solvent and the water, and on the extent to which they are adsorbed on the paper. Each substance thus takes up a characteristic position, and in suitable circumstances may be identified from this position, suitable reagents being applied to the paper so as to produce coloured products with the substances under examination. An estimate of the quantity present can be obtained from the size of the spot and the intensity of the colour produced. A greater degree of selective separation may be achieved, if necessary, by applying the solution to one corner of a square of paper, by developing in one direction with one solvent and then in a direction at right angles to this by another solvent.

Precise technical details as to the conduct of chromatographic analysis cannot be given here. Descriptions of the nature of the adsorbent, and the nature of the paper to be used, the types of solvent and the kinds of substance which can be separated will be found in appropriate monographs, such as that by E. and M. Lederer (1957); many others are also available.

ELECTRICAL PHENOMENA AT INTERFACES

In the presence of water, the boundary between two phases is, almost without exception, the seat of an electric charge, and there is usually a potential difference across the boundary. At the boundary are two sheets of oppositely charged ions—the *Double Layer*. Helmholtz considered the sheets to be only one ion thick, but Gouy later pointed out that the ions of either or both may be subject to thermal motion; the sheets thus become diffuse and without distinct boundaries, as is indicated in Fig. 5.5. The evidence at present seems to be in favour of there being both a Helmholtz single layer, and a Gouy diffuse layer at most interfaces. One of the two layers may be on each side of the material interface, or both may be on the same side. The behaviour of the system is the same in either case.

The potential difference across a single interface can never be measured, since it is impossible to complete a circuit through any kind of measuring instrument without introducing at least one other interface. The best that can be done is to assume that all the interfaces except one remain constant in their properties; the changes that take place at that one when various alterations are produced in the system can thus be studied. It is instructive, however, to study the possible molecular arrangements that may be present at a single interface.

There are certain thermodynamic restrictions as to the magnitude of the interfacial potential under equilibrium conditions. Thermodynamically, the condition for equilibrium is that the algebraic sum of the chemical work and the electrical work done when an ion passes from one side of the interface to the other should be zero—i.e. that the *electrochemical potential*, as defined in the previous chapter (p. 143), should be the same on both sides. This implies that the interfacial potential *in equilibrium conditions* depends on the composition of the bulk phases, and not on any pheno-

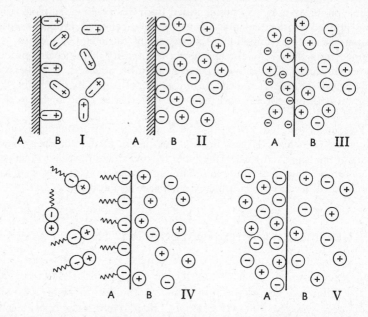

FIG. 5.5. DIAGRAMS TO ILLUSTRATE THE FORMATION OF ELECTRICAL DOUBLE LAYERS

    I. By orientation of polar molecules in Phase A or adsorbed from Phase B.

    II. By preferential adsorption on Phase A of ions of one sign in solution in Phase B.

    III. At a metal surface. Within the metal (Phase A) there are ions and free electrons. Some of the ions enter the solution (Phase B) giving it a positive charge, and leaving the metal with a negative charge.

    IV. Some of the molecules constituting Phase A undergo electrolytic dissociation, the cations entering Phase B in solution.

    V. At an interface between two electrolyte solutions of different concentration. The mobility of the ions of one sign is greater than that of the ions of the opposite sign: these, therefore, lead slightly as the electrolyte diffuses out from the more concentrated solution.

    Phase A has been shown as being negative in sign with respect to Phase B, but of course, apart from the metal surface, it may equally well be positive.

menon which occurs solely at the interface; although, of course, it is the properties of the interface which are responsible for any difference that there may be in this composition. An effect at the interface alone may, however, give rise to transient changes in the interfacial potential.

    There are several possible origins for electrical double layers and the interfacial potentials which accompany them.

(1) As we have seen, the molecules actually forming the interface are frequently orientated. At the contact of a block of a fatty acid, say, with water, the fatty acid molecules are orientated with the —COOH groups towards the water. Such molecules possess a dipole moment, and the orientation will result in, say, the negative ends of the molecules pointing outwards, and the positive ends pointing inwards (Fig. 5.5, I). Potentials arising from such orientation of dipoles have been called "*phase boundary potentials*", and by Freundlich "lyoelectric potentials". At an air-water interface, there is a potential difference which can be modified by the presence of a monolayer, and the potential difference due to the monolayer can thus be calculated. With both spread and adsorbed monolayers of most organic substances, the air surface is positive and the water surface negative, in conformity with the known dipole moments. The magnitude of the potential, however, is usually considerably less than that expected from the magnitude of the dipole moment. If we consider the double layer as a parallel plate condenser, we should expect the surface potential, ΔV to be given by

$$\Delta V = \frac{4\pi n \bar{\mu} \cos \theta}{\epsilon} \qquad . \qquad . \qquad . \qquad . \qquad 5.11$$

where n is the number of molecules adsorbed on each unit surface, $\bar{\mu}$ is the dipole moment, ϵ is the dielectric constant of the monolayer, and θ is the angle of tilt of the dipole with the surface. However the value of the dielectric constant is not known exactly, nor is the angle of tilt, which refers to the resultant dipole, and not necessarily to the molecule as a whole. The individual dipoles which contribute to the resultant, moreover, may be distorted in the film, and so give a net dipole moment to the molecules which is different both in magnitude and direction to that possessed by the molecules in bulk. In expanded films, under conditions where the tilt of the molecules would be expected to be relatively constant, the value of $\Delta V/4\pi n (= \bar{\mu} \cos \theta/\epsilon)$ is independent of the area occupied by the film, but depends on its chemical composition.

Water itself possesses a considerable dipole moment, as already mentioned in Chapter 2 (p. 39). As vapour, it is known to be strongly adsorbed by most solid surfaces, probably as a result of hydrogen bonds and of residual valencies, on the oxygen atoms. It is therefore highly probable that the water molecules will be orientated at most interfaces between solids and aqueous solutions, and would hence give rise to a potential difference at these interfaces. This is in accordance with the known fact that the vast majority of solid substances when in contact with water, behave in an electric field as if they were negatively charged. We shall return to this question later.

(2) If one or both of the phases in contact with each other contains

ions in solution, there may be a preferential adsorption of ions of one kind (Fig. 5.5, II). One sheet of the double layer will be a layer of, say, negative ions adsorbed at the interface, and the other will be the rather diffuse cloud of positive ions, in continuous thermal agitation, but unable to depart entirely from the region of the interface owing to the electrostatic forces. Interfacial potentials of this kind are known as "*adsorption potentials*". We have already seen that large organic molecules are very readily adsorbed at most surfaces. If these happen also to be electrolytes, such as the soaps, tetra-alkyl ammonium salts and many dyes, considerable adsorption potentials may be developed. The sign of the potential will depend, of course, on the sign of the large organic ion.

In pure water, most inert solids and immiscible liquids take up a negative charge. While this may be due in part to the orientation of the water dipoles, as already suggested, it is also possible that there is a preferential adsorption of hydroxyl ions. In alkaline solutions the charge is nearly always greater than in pure water, and in acid solution the charge is less, and in some cases, the sign may even be reversed. It would appear that, while the hydroxyl ion is adsorbed with greater ease than the hydrogen ion from solutions in which they are both present in equal concentrations, the hydroxyl ions in the surface can be replaced by hydrogen ions if the concentration of these in the solution is sufficiently great.

(3) The interface may be such that only one kind of ion can penetrate from one side to the other. The standard example of this is the interface between a metal and a solution of one of its salts (Fig. 5.5, III). The sign of such an "*electrode potential*" depends on the relative tendency of the ions in the solution to be deposited on the metal, and of the ions in the metal to pass out into the solution. In the metal, the ions form a crystal lattice, and are held in position by a kind of cement of free electrons. (The presence of these free electrons makes the metal a conductor of electricity.) For an ion to leave the metal and enter the solution, therefore, it has to free itself from the electrostatic and other forces which previously kept it in place, and then to take up water molecules so as to become an hydrated ion in solution. In his original treatment, in 1889, Nernst imagined an "electrolytic solution pressure", which represented a kind of diffusion pressure tending to drive the metallic ions into the solution, just as the osmotic pressure of the ions in solution tended to drive them back into the metal. The actual values calculated for the solution pressure, from measurements of the electrode potentials, vary from 10^{19} atmospheres for zinc, through $1 \cdot 3$ atmospheres for nickel, down to $1 \cdot 5 \times 10^{-36}$ atmospheres for palladium. Clearly these figures cannot represent any true pressures. The problem, however, can also be considered from a kinetic standpoint, as was done by Butler in 1924. We suppose that both the cation in the solution, and the metal ion in the electrode, have to surmount a potential

energy barrier before they can pass out of, or into, the solution respect-ively. We then find that the "electrolytic solution pressure" is an expression of the ratio of the probability that a cation should acquire the activation energy necessary for it to leave the solution, to the probability that a metal ion should acquire the activation energy necessary for it to enter the solution. (Compare Chapter 2, p. 54.) The observed very large variation in magnitude is thus quite reasonable.

(4) One of the phases, though not metallic, may be able to release ions which are sufficiently mobile to pass across the interface into the other phase (Fig. 5.5, IV). The ion-exchange resins, already referred to (p. 194) are excellent examples of this. There are also many electrolytes which exist in the colloidal state, either because many molecules become closely attached to one another, forming "micelles", or because the molecules are themselves "giant" (see Chapter 6, p. 234); in either event, they may be regarded as separate phases. Substances which can exist in true solution, also, may be present as solid particles of appreciable size, either because the solution is already saturated, or transiently, in the process of going into solution. In all such cases, diffusible cations or anions are detached from the ionisable groups and form the outer sheet of the double layer. Silicic acid, for example, takes up a negative charge, presumably because the hydrogen ions are more free to move than are the larger silicate ions; aluminium hydroxide, on the other hand, is positively charged, the hydroxyl ions being more mobile than the aluminium ions, which are probably held together by residual valencies. The matter is complicated, however, by the possibility of preferential adsorption of one or other of the ions. Multivalent ions, in general, are readily adsorbed, and the nega-tive charge on an inert substance, already mentioned, can be replaced by a positive charge if the solution contains, for example, aluminium ions. This effect doubtless contributes to the positive charge on particles of aluminium hydroxide.

(5) A very similar situation arises, on a larger scale, if two electrolyte solutions are separated by a barrier, or membrane, through which one kind of ion cannot pass. The most usual example is that of a solution con-taining a colloidal electrolyte separated from one containing only crystal-loidal electrolytes, by a membrane which is impermeable to colloids. This is the classical case of the "Gibbs-Donnan equilibrium", which will be considered in more detail later. It is clear, however, that formally, the state of affairs is similar to that at the surface of a metal, or at the surfaces of the colloidal electrolytes themselves.

(6) Finally, if an interface exists between two solutions of electrolytes, not necessarily in the same solvent, we may have *diffusion potentials* (Fig. 5.5, V). These have been considered in the previous chapter; and, of course, they must be transient unless the system is maintained by the

activity of some external agent, which must be capable of doing chemical or electrical work.

Diffusion potentials are probably concerned in the production of interfacial potentials between two immiscible liquids, such as an oil and water. The potentials set up in a system such as:

$$\text{Hg} \mid \text{HgCl} \mid \text{KCl} \mid \text{Oil} \mid \text{X aq.} \mid \text{KCl} \mid \text{HgCl} \mid \text{Hg}$$

where X may be an inorganic salt or a soluble organic compound, have been studied by Baur, Beutner and others, as being possibly related to the potential differences found in living systems. The precise origin of these potentials, however, is not at all obvious. The "phase-boundary" potentials due to orientation of one or more of the components at the interface, and those due to preferential adsorption of some of the ions present in X, are likely to develop quite rapidly, and, as already pointed out, thus cannot give rise to anything but a transient potential; whereas those observed are sensibly constant for many hours. It seems likely that there is a slow diffusion of some or all of the components from the watery solution to the oil, or *vice versa*. If X contains large organic anions or cations, together with small inorganic cations or anions, respectively, the organic ions will enter the oil first, being more soluble in it than are the inorganic ions, and a diffuse double layer will be set up. The sign and magnitude of the diffusion potential at such interfaces will thus depend not only on the relative mobilities of the ions, but also on their relative solubilities in the two phases.

Polarisation Potentials. Suppose we immerse two electrodes, say of platinum or some other noble metal, in an electrolyte solution, and connect them to an external source of electromotive force. As soon as any current passes, the metal ion in solution will be deposited on one of the electrodes, and a back electromotive force will develop, whose magnitude will depend on the standard electrode potential of the metal concerned. Unless the external source of E.M.F. is greater than this back E.M.F., the current will immediately cease; and the deposited metal will re-dissolve if the circuit remains closed and current can pass in the reverse direction. As soon as it has all been removed from the electrode, it will, of course, at once begin to be deposited again, the net result being that no appreciable current flows in either direction. In theory, as we increase the value of the applied E.M.F., it should be impossible to pass any current through the system until a critical value is reached: but usually, a small current passes when the applied E.M.F. is just below the critical value, and the current rises very rapidly as soon as the applied E.M.F. just exceeds this value. If the two electrodes are immersed in water, or if the ions in solution combine with water when discharged at an electrode (e.g. sodium ions), hydrogen and oxygen are released during the electrolysis, and the back

E.M.F. will be just over 2 volts. Such *polarisation potentials* will appear whenever a current is passed through an electrolyte by means of electrodes which are not reversible (non-polarisable); their magnitude depends on the nature of the solution, the nature of the electrodes, and the amount of current passing, and they are usually erratic and uncertain in magnitude.

The applied E.M.F. necessary to pass current through a solution may be used to identify the nature of the ions in solution, provided that certain precautions are taken. This is the basis of the method of analysis introduced in 1925 by Heyrovsky, and known as *Polarography*. The polarisable electrode usually consists of an arrangement whereby very small drops of mercury are allowed to form on the end of a fine tube and to drop off at intervals of a few seconds. The surface of the electrode is thus repeatedly renewed and does not become permanently contaminated. The second electrode is usually some non-polarisable system with a reliable value of electrode potential, such as the calomel half-cell (see Chapter 4, p. 146). The great value of observing the polarisation potentials at very small electrodes, such as the mercury drop, is that during the passage of the current the solution in the immediate neighbourhood of the electrode becomes denuded of the ions which are being deposited: the rate of deposition then depends upon the rate at which ions can diffuse through this denuded region. This rate depends primarily on the concentration of the ions in the bulk of the solution (see the sections on Diffusion in Chapters 3 and 4), and hardly at all on the applied E.M.F. As this is increased, therefore, the current flowing reaches a maximum value, and this value can be used as a measure of the concentration of the ions being discharged. For accurate results, of course, the conditions must be properly controlled, and details will be found in the appropriate monographs, such as that of Kolthoff and Lingane (1941), in which will be found, also, references to the original papers of Heyrovsky. If more than one species of ion is present, there will be a series of steps in the curve relating applied E.M.F. to current passing; the value of the E.M.F. at which the current is one-half the maximum for that step defines the nature of the ion concerned, and the height of the step defines its concentration. Since the discharge of an ion at an electrode is essentially the reaction of an electron with the ion, the same general considerations can be applied to any reaction involving an oxidation or a reduction; these are also electron reactions, as we shall see in later chapters. Polarography can thus be used for the quantitative analysis of many oxidisable and reducible substances in solution, including molecular oxygen. It is of great value in many types of work in that it is capable of giving accurate results with very dilute solutions (in many cases, small fractions of millimolar).

ELECTROCHEMICAL EQUILIBRIA AT INTERFACES— THE GIBBS-DONNAN RELATION

The presence of electric potential differences across interfaces may lead to an unequal distribution of freely mobile ions, even in conditions of

G*

thermodynamic equilibrium, which is of great importance. The problem was first considered in connection with the presence of colloidal ions within a membrane which was impermeable to them, and with particular reference to the measurement of colloidal osmotic pressures. But it is to be emphasised that the presence of a material membrane is unnecessary; nor is it essential that the indiffusible ion should be colloidal, the important factor being its immobility. The conditions that we have to consider may be represented thus:

$$
\begin{array}{c|c}
R^- & \\
Na^+ & \\
Na^+ & Na^+ \\
Cl^- & Cl^- \\
\text{Solution } i & \text{Solution } o
\end{array}
$$

Interface

We have a solution of a colloid (or other solute) which is acting as an anion, together with its associated sodium ions (or other cations) and a certain concentration of sodium chloride (or other diffusible electrolyte) inside a semi-permeable membrane (or on one side of an interface which it cannot penetrate) forming Solution i; outside the membrane (or on the other side of the interface) we have a solution of sodium chloride. To simplify the argument, we suppose that initially the concentration of sodium chloride is the same on both sides of the membrane. To begin with, therefore, the concentration of sodium ions in Solution i must be greater than that in Solution o; sodium ions must be present in sufficient number to neutralise not only the chloride ions, but also the colloid anions. Sodium ions will, therefore, tend to diffuse out from Solution i, but since they cannot be accompanied by colloid ions, a potential difference will be generated, which will stop further diffusion. Solution o will now be electrically positive to Solution i, and the potential difference will draw chloride ions out of Solution i and into Solution o until an activity gradient is developed which is large enough to return them at the same rate. No further change will then occur, and the system will have come into electrochemical equilibrium with a greater concentration of sodium ions in Solution i than in Solution o, and a smaller concentration of chloride ions. If the initial concentration of sodium chloride were not the same on both sides of the membrane, the same argument can be applied. We can imagine that both sodium and chloride ions first diffuse together, one way or the other, until equality of concentration had been reached. The unequal distribution of ions would then establish itself as before.

Since the system is in equilibrium, the electrochemical potential (equation 4.19, p. 143) must be the same on both sides of the membrane (or interface), and the electrical potential difference must be given by equation 4.18. Since the electrical potential difference due to the unequal distribution of cations must obviously be identical with that due to the unequal distribution of anions (there can only be *one* electrical potential difference), we have, for univalent ions:

$$\Delta E = \frac{RT}{F} \ln \cdot \frac{(a_{Na})_i}{(a_{Na})_o} = -\frac{RT}{F} \ln \cdot \frac{(a_{Cl})_i}{(a_{Cl})_o} \qquad . \qquad 5.12$$

and thus
$$\frac{(a_{Na})_i}{(a_{Na})_o} = \frac{(a_{Cl})_o}{(a_{Cl})_i}$$

This is the equation derived by Donnan in 1911, but it was also given essentially by Gibbs in 1874-78. The distribution of ions described by this equation is often known as the "Donnan (or Gibbs-Donnan) equilibrium", or the "Membrane equilibrium".

The membrane equilibrium equation can be extended to apply to all freely diffusible ionic species that are present in the solutions. But since the electrical force on a multivalent ion is z times that on a univalent ion (where z is the valency), it can be seen from equation 4.19, after inserting equation 3.29, that in equation 5.12 we must put zF in place of F; and thus the activities of the multivalent ions must be raised to a power equal to the inverse of the valency. In general, therefore,

$$\frac{(a_+)_i^{1/z_+}}{(a_+)_o^{1/z_+}} = \frac{(a_-)_o^{1/z_-}}{(a_-)_i^{1/z_-}} = r \qquad . \qquad . \qquad . \qquad 5.13$$

where r is a constant.

We may also reach the same conclusion by considering the actual rates of movement, or fluxes, of the ions through the membrane. Although the system is in equilibrium, there will continue to be an exchange of cations and anions across the membrane, although there will be no net transfer of either; the average velocities of both kinds of ions must be zero. From equations 4.13 and 4.13a (p. 140), we can thus write:

$$-F.u_+(dE/dx) - RT.u_+(d \ln a_+/dx) = 0$$
$$= +F.u_-(dE/dx) - RT.u_-(d \ln a_-/dx)$$

From this, equation 5.12 is easily deduced. This approach is valuable, since in certain conditions, to be considered in Chapter 10, the system may not be in equilibrium; but so long as there is no net ionic flux, and provided that certain assumptions as to the way in which the electrical and chemical potentials change across the interface are justified, equation 5.12 will still hold.

We may now proceed a stage further, and inquire how the actual value of the ionic distribution ratio, r, and thus the value of the electrical potential difference across the membrane, may be discovered. It is not difficult to see, in a general way, that the potential difference and the distribution ratio will rise as the concentration of the indiffusible salt, NaR, is increased, since the activity gradient of sodium ions will also be increased. Conversely, a rise in the concentration of sodium chloride will reduce the potential and distribution ratio, since although the activity gradient (da_{Na}/dx), will not be changed, the function $d(\ln a_{Na})/dx$, or $(1/a_{Na}) \cdot (da_{Na}/dx)$ which determines the chemical potential gradient, will fall. But in order to deduce the quantitative relations between the various factors, we must make use of two further properties of the system: (a) the solutions, both inside and outside the membrane, must be electrically neutral; (b) the solvent must be in equilibrium on the two sides of the membrane, implying, in some circumstances that a hydrostatic pressure (osmotic pressure) must be applied to one of the solutions.

For *electrical neutrality*, in Solution i and Solution o, respectively, we must write:

$$\Sigma(zm)_i + \Sigma(z^*m^*)_i = 0 = \Sigma(zm)_o + \Sigma(z^*m^*)_o . \qquad . \quad 5.14$$

where m represents the molar concentration of each of the diffusible constituents, m^* that of each of the indiffusible constituents; the molar concentration of each being multiplied by the appropriate valency z or z^*, with due regard to the sign of the charge, before the summation is made; and the subscripts i and o refer to the two solutions concerned. In general, of course, the concentrations and valencies of the diffusible ions are known, or can be discovered by analysis. The whole quantity $\Sigma(z^*m^*)$ can be discovered from the titration curve of the colloid (or other indiffusible electrolyte) with acid and base, since it represents the degree of ionisation at the hydrogen ion concentration of the solution considered.

For the *solvent* (*osmotic*) *equilibrium*, we should write merely, that the activity of the water is the same both inside and outside the membrane. This, however, is not of much practical use, and there is no simple method of deducing the activity of the water from the activities or concentrations of the solutes (Chapter 3, p. 88). We must make approximations, and assume that the reduction in the activity of the water is directly proportional to the sum of the molar concentrations of the solutes—the ordinary approximation for an "ideal" solution—introducing the osmotic coefficients if desired. We thus have:

$$RT[\Sigma(\phi m)_i + \Sigma(\phi^* m^*)_i] = RT[\Sigma(\phi m)_o + \Sigma(\phi^* m^*)_o] - \Pi \quad . \quad 5.15$$

where Π is the hydrostatic pressure, if any, necessary for the maintenance of equilibrium. It is thus clear that a complete and exact calculation of the value of the distribution ratio from the concentrations and degrees of ionisation of the crystalloidal and colloidal salts is not generally possible. We have to combine an equation involving ionic activities (5.13) with one involving stoichiometric concentrations, degrees of ionisation and valencies (5.14), and both with one strictly involving solvent activities (5.15). A number of assumptions and approximations must obviously be made, and the problem can usually be solved only if the number of different electrolytes present is small. In certain circumstances, however, the calculation can be made for the distribution of electrolytes between the interior of living cells and the external solution; the results agree reasonably well with experimental observations, and are of value in indicating which kinds of ion are freely diffusible into and out of the cells.

THE ELECTROKINETIC POTENTIAL

If the interface between two phases is placed in an electrical field, the two sheets of the double layer will tend to move in opposite directions. If the electrical field has a component parallel to the interface, and the two phases can move relatively to each other, they will do so. Thus, if we have water in a fine capillary, the walls, as we have seen, will be charged negatively, and the layers of water in contact with them will be charged positively. If we place an electrode at each end of the capillary, and apply an electromotive force, the surface layers of water will move through the capillary. This phenomenon is known as *Electro-osmosis*, or *Electro-endosmose*. It is best seen by using a pot of porous clay, or a collodion or cellophane sac, filled with, and standing in, a dilute acid solution.

The direction of the flow of water, for a given applied potential, will, of course, depend on the sign of the charge on the walls of the pot or sac. If we use a collodion sac which has been soaked in a solution of gelatin, or other protein, the sign of the charge on the walls is easily reversed by changing the hydrogen ion concentration of the solution, since the protein will dissociate as a base in acid solution, and as an acid in alkaline solutions.

The converse phenomenon to that of electro-osmosis is known as *Electrophoresis*. If we have a number of particles suspended in a fluid, and apply an electric field, the particles will move relatively to the suspending fluid. Each particle is surrounded by a double layer, and so, together with its shell of water, is electrically neutral. In an electric field, however, the diffuse outer shell can be sheared off one particle, and handed on to the next. The particles thus move in one direction and the outer ionic shells in the other. The direction of the movement, will, of course, depend on the sign of the charge on the particles.

A word may be said here, also, on *Streaming Potentials*. If a fluid is forced to flow through a capillary tube, a potential difference is set up across its ends. One may imagine that part of the diffuse half of the double layer is driven along the tube by the flow of fluid. Similarly, if charged particles fall through the suspending fluid, there is a certain amount of separation between the halves of the double layer, and a potential difference is set up in the direction of motion of the particles. The existence of such streaming potentials is to be inferred, of course, from the flow of the fluid in electro-osmosis, and the movement of the particles in electrophoresis, and all are essentially expressions of the same general phenomenon. The streaming potentials are mostly small, but may conceivably sometimes contribute to the potentials observed in living cells.

Measurement of the Electrokinetic Potential

From the velocity of electro-osmosis or electrophoresis under a known potential gradient, or the magnitude of the streaming potential under a known rate of flow, it is possible to calculate the apparent potential difference between the water or suspending fluid, and the walls of the tube or the particles. It must be emphasised that this is not the same as the true interfacial potential, which, as we have seen, cannot be directly measured. Adsorbed and orientated water molecules, for example, may be contributing to the interfacial potential, but they will remain attached to the solid at the interface, and will move with it in the electric field; the two parts of a dipole cannot be separated from each other. The diffuse Gouy layer can easily slip relatively to the remainder of the double layer, but it is generally supposed that the compact Helmholtz part of the double layer moves as a whole.

We will suppose for simplicity that the two halves of the double layer are single sheets, and together make up a parallel plate condenser. These plates have the *electrokinetic potential* usually designated ζ, across them, are distant d from each other, and the material between them has a dielectric constant, ϵ. Then the charge per unit area on the condenser is given by

$$\sigma = \frac{\epsilon \zeta}{4\pi d}.$$

If the external electric field has a potential gradient X volts per cm., the force bringing about the relative movement of the two halves of the double layer is

$$X\sigma = \frac{X\epsilon \zeta}{4\pi d}.$$

If the relative velocity is v, the viscous resistance to the motion of unit area is $\eta.(v/d)$, where η is the viscosity of the material between the two sheets of the double layer. Thus when a steady motion has been reached, we have

$$\eta \frac{v}{d} = X\sigma = \frac{X\epsilon\zeta}{4\pi d}$$

or

$$\zeta = \frac{4\pi\eta}{X\epsilon} \cdot v \qquad . \qquad . \qquad . \qquad . \qquad 5.16$$

It is usual to assume that the values to be taken for ϵ and η are the same as those of the water, or solution, in bulk. Since the layers are only a few molecules apart, it would seem to be somewhat surprising that this is justified.

In the development of equation 5.16, it was assumed that the interface was a plane. v. Smoluchowski, however, has shown that the same expression can be applied to the flow over a surface of any form. It can thus be applied to the flow past a spherical particle, for example, or, conversely, to the velocity of movement of the particle in a stationary fluid. The value of the electrokinetic potential can thus be derived by the same equation from the rate of electro-osmotic flow, the rate of electrophoresis, or the streaming potential. It is usually considered advisable, however, to indicate the type of measurement from which the electrokinetic potential has been calculated, since the theoretical basis for equation 5.16 is by no means absolutely secure.

It can be shown that even if we do not suppose that both halves of the double layer are single sheets, the same expression is obtained. This is because both the velocity of movement and the potential at any point in the double layer depends on the charge at that point. Let the charge vary with the distance from the interface according to some undetermined function. An elementary layer distant r from the interface will contribute a charge $\delta\sigma$. Hence the potential at this layer will be

$$\delta\zeta = \frac{4\pi d}{\epsilon} \cdot \delta\sigma$$

and the velocity will be

$$\delta v = \frac{Xd}{\eta} \delta\sigma.$$

Hence

$$\delta\zeta = \frac{4\pi\eta}{X\epsilon} \cdot \delta v.$$

By integration, the total potential is found to be related to the total velocity by the expression

$$\zeta = \frac{4\pi\eta}{X\epsilon} \cdot v$$

which is the same as we obtained previously.

The double layer, of course, does not actually consist of a single sheet of ions a precise distance from the charged interface, but is a diffuse cloud of ions of both signs; it is, in fact, essentially the same as the ionic cloud which surrounds each ion of a strong electrolyte, and which was postulated by Debye and Hückel in their calculation of the activity coefficient of a strong electrolyte (Chapter 4, p. 129). The electrokinetic potential, in fact, bears the same relation to the electric charge on the surface as the potential of a crystalloidal ion (i.e. its partial free energy) does to its charge (this, of course, is constant, whereas the charge at an interface is not); the one can be calculated from the other by using the same method of approach in both cases. If we consider a spherical particle of radius r, the electrokinetic potential will be defined by an equation of the same form as equation 4.6 (p. 130). It is convenient, now, to approximate the term $\exp(-\kappa r)$ somewhat differently, to $1/(1+\kappa r)$, and we get:

$$\zeta = \frac{ze}{\epsilon r} \cdot \frac{1}{1+\kappa r} \qquad . \qquad . \qquad . \qquad . \qquad 5.17$$

ze being the total charge on the particle, of radius r, and ϵ and $1/\kappa$, as in Chapter 4, being the dielectric constant and the equivalent radius of the ionic atmosphere. The value of κ, it will be remembered, is directly proportional to the square root of the ionic strength of the solution; it is also directly proportional to the charge on the particle, and inversely proportional to the absolute temperature. Values for a uni-univalent electrolyte (in which the ionic strength is identical with the concentration) in aqueous solution at 25° C. are given in Table 5.2. For particles with more than a single electronic charge, the figures should be divided by the number of such charges ("valency"). When the particles are of colloidal size, of course, the ionic strength will be determined chiefly by the other electrolytes present in the solution. The diffuse double layer will thus behave as if it were a single sheet, the distance from the interface (d in the development of equation 5.16) being given by the quantity $1/\kappa$.

TABLE 5.2

Values of the Equivalent Radius of the Ionic Atmosphere in a Uni-univalent Electrolyte at 25° C.

Concentration (molar)	0·1	0·01	0·001	0·0001	0·00001	(pure water)
$1/\kappa$ (μ)	0·00095	0·003	0·0095	0·03	0·095	1·0

If we now combine equation 5.17 with equation 5.16, and re-arrange slightly, we get:

$$v = \frac{Xze}{4\pi\eta} \cdot \frac{1}{r(1+\kappa r)} \qquad . \qquad . \qquad . \qquad . \qquad 5.18$$

We are usually interested, however, not so much in the total charge on the particle, which would probably depend on its size, as on the *surface density* of the charge, which might well be expected to be a property of the material of which the particle is composed. The charge density, σ, is, of course, given by the value of the total charge, ze, divided by the surface area, $4\pi r^2$. We thus get:

$$v = \frac{X\sigma}{\eta} \cdot \frac{r}{1+\kappa r} = \frac{X\sigma}{\eta\kappa} \cdot \frac{\kappa r}{1+\kappa r} \qquad . \qquad . \qquad 5.19$$

It must be remembered that a number of approximations have been made in the derivation of this expression, and it can be expected to be applicable only in certain conditions. The conductivity of the particle, for example, should be taken into account, as well as the time taken for the ionic cloud to form in front of the particle and to disappear behind it (compare the discussion on electrical conductivity, Chapter 4, p. 135). In particular, for very small particles, more elaborate expressions must be used, and the electrophoretic mobility is not independent of the size and shape of the particles. A full treatment of the subject will be found in the monograph by Abramson (1934).

We see from equation 5.19 that if κr is very much greater than 1, the mobility of the particle is independent of its size. Calculation shows that this criterion is satisfied for microscopic particles in dilute solutions of electrolytes, but not for ultra-microscopic particles. In more concentrated solutions, since κ becomes greater, the criterion is satisfied even for ultra-microscopic particles. This is an important conclusion, and is fully confirmed by experiment. It means that the electrophoretic mobility of particles of widely different sizes and shapes, in a given electrolyte solution, depends only on the charge density on the surface. This, it is reasonable to suppose, will depend only on the nature of the surface, i.e. on the composition of the particle, so that particles of the same material will all move at the same velocity, whereas particles of different materials will probably move at different velocities. Clearly, we have here a method of analysis which has proved to be of great value in the study of colloidal solutions, and particularly in the separation and identification of proteins.

The behaviour of the proteins, indeed, illustrates very clearly the effect of electrolytes on the electrokinetic potential. The charge on a protein-water interface arises chiefly as a result of electrolytic dissociation of the protein molecules at the interface. At a given hydrogen ion concentration, therefore, the charge density should be constant, and the effects of variations in the electrolyte concentration on the electrokinetic velocity of the molecules, or micelles, may be calculated by an expression of the form given in equation 5.19. Actually, however, accurate measurements have shown that the valency of most protein ions increases somewhat with increase in the ionic strength of the egg solution. In Fig. 5.6, the upper, nearly straight line, indicates the change in mobility of egg albumin with change in the ionic strength of the solution that would be expected from the change in valency, if there were no ionic clouds present to reduce the electrokinetic potential. The lower, curved, line represents the change in

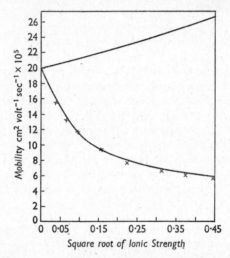

FIG. 5.6. THE EFFECT OF THE IONIC STRENGTH OF THE SOLUTION ON THE MOBILITY OF EGG ALBUMIN

Upper curve: mobility calculated on the assumption of free ionic migration. The rise in the calculated mobility is due to the change in the valency of the protein ions.

Lower curve: mobility calculated from the Debye-Hückel equation, as modified by Henry. The crosses represent the observed values. Temperature $0.5°$, pH 7.10.

(Tiselius and Svensson, 1940.)

mobility calculated from equation 5.19, and indicates the effect of the ionic cloud, the value of κ being determined from the Debye-Hückel equation, and that of r from the known molecular weight of egg albumin. The crosses, lying closely about this line, represent the experimentally determined values.

The concentration of protein ions, and thus the valency, at any given value of protein concentration and ionic strength, can be determined by measuring the membrane potential—i.e. the potential difference across a membrane impermeable to the protein but permeable to the crystalloidal ions, as discussed in an earlier section (p. 202). The concentrations of the ions in the external solution are measured by chemical analysis; the ionic distribution ratio is calculated from the membrane potential (equation 5.12), and thus the concentrations of the diffusible ions in the protein solution are known. The difference between the concentration of cations and that of anions must be equal to the concentration of protein ions (equation 5.14). This tacitly assumes, unjustifiably, that the ionic activity coefficients are the same in the protein solution as in the external solution. The effect of the protein on the ionic activity coefficients may be allowed for, however, in the following way. The membrane potential is measured, at a given value of the ionic strength, with various concentrations of the protein, and the values of the ratio (membrane potential)/(protein concentration) are extrapolated to very small values of the protein concentration; the ionic activity coefficients are then identical in both solutions. The observed value of the membrane potential at any particular value of the protein concentration can then be adjusted in such a way that the (membrane potential)/(protein concentration) ratio has its extrapolated value.

For more complete accounts of the theory of the electrokinetic potential, electro-osmosis and the streaming current, the reader is referred to the monographs by Abramson, Gorin and Moyer (1942) and by Alexander and Johnson (1949); the article by Booth (1953) gives a more advanced treatment of the ionic double layer and its importance in surface phenomena.

Experimental Methods. The electrophoretic mobility of the particles in a suspension may, in general, be measured either (*a*) by microscopic observation of the movement of individual particles, or (*b*) by the moving boundary method, which is, in essentials, the same as the method by which the transport numbers of crystalloidal ions are measured. The latter is the more useful for colloidal solutions, the particles of which cannot easily be seen under the microscope.

(*a*) In the microscopic method, the electrophoresis is made to occur in a drop of fluid placed between small electrodes on a microscopic slide, and the motion of individual particles is observed with an eye-piece micrometer. A complication arises in that, owing to the charge on the walls of the cell, the suspending fluid will take up an electro-osmotic flow. The movement of the particles will thus be the algebraic sum of their own motion in the electric field, and that of the fluid surrounding them. Now the cell is a closed system, so that the flow of the suspending fluid near the walls towards, say, the cathode, must be countered by an opposite flow, towards the anode, in the centre of the cell. If this were not so, there would be an accumulation of fluid round the cathode, which, in a closed rigid system, is impossible. At some region in the cell, therefore, the suspending fluid will be stationary, and in this region, the observed movement of the particles is a true measure of their electrophoretic velocity. The position of this stationary layer can be calculated from theoretical considerations, or, alternatively, the true electrophoretic velocity can be determined by measuring the apparent velocity at a number of different distances from the walls of the cell, and by finding the true average (see Fig. 5.7).

(*b*) In the moving boundary method, a U-tube (Fig. 5.8) is half filled with water (or the solution which forms the continuous phase of the colloidal system to be examined). The colloidal solution is run in slowly from below, so as to fill the lower half of the U-tube, maintaining a sharp boundary where it meets the supernatant water. A potential difference of 100 to 200 volts is applied by means of two electrodes immersed in the upper liquid, and the movement of the boundaries is noted. To obtain quantitative measurements, non-polarisable electrodes should be used, and it is convenient to have a large bore tap in each limb of the U-tube; this greatly facilitates the formation of

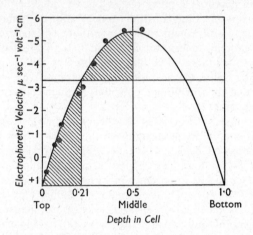

FIG. 5.7. THE VARIATION IN THE OBSERVED ELECTROPHORETIC VELOCITIES OF OIL DROPLETS AT DIFFERENT LEVELS IN A FLAT ELECTROPHORESIS CELL

The ordinates are the velocities of the particles in μ/sec. corrected to a potential gradient of 1 volt/cm.

The abscissae give the distances from the top of the cell as fractions of its total depth.

The plotted points are the experimentally observed values: the smooth curve is that predicted by theory.

In the upper half of the cell, the suspending fluid flows in the opposite direction to the movement of the particles at levels between 0 and 0·21, and in the same direction at levels between 0·21 and 0·5: the lower half of the cell is symmetrical with the upper. The true electrophoretic velocity of the particles is observed at a level of 0·21 from the top— i.e. −3·25 μ/sec. The figure 0·21 is obtained from the consideration that the total volume of suspending fluid flowing in one direction must be equal to the total volume flowing in the opposite direction, the cell being closed: thus the two areas shaded in the figure should be equal.

The electro-osmotic flow of the suspending fluid is given by the observed velocity of the particles at the top of the cell *minus* the true electrophoretic velocity—i.e. +1·2 −(−3·25)=+4·25 μ/sec.   (From data of Ellis, 1912.)

sharp boundaries. The movements of the colloid may be observed visually, if it is coloured, or otherwise easily distinguishable, or it may be photographed by ultra-violet light. Alternatively, use may be made of the change in refractive index at the junction between the colloidal solution and the water or dialysate; this is now the most usual procedure, and the methods used will be described in the next chapter, in connection with the measurements of rates of diffusion and sedimentation (p. 281). It must be remembered that there are always other ions present besides those of the colloid, and that unless precautions are taken, the migration of these ions will influence that of the colloid.

Details of these precautions, as well as of the general methods to be employed will be found in the monographs by Abramson (1934) and Alexander and Johnson (1949).

One of the difficulties encountered in this type of measurement is the distortion of the boundaries between the colloid and the solution above it, due to diffusion, and above all, convection; the passage of the current necessarily generates heat. This can be avoided by using a strip of filter paper, soaked with the solution under test, in place of the U-tube shown in Fig. 5.8, and dipping at each end into a vessel containing a suitable electrolyte solution; the electrodes communicate with these vessels. The heat can be dissipated

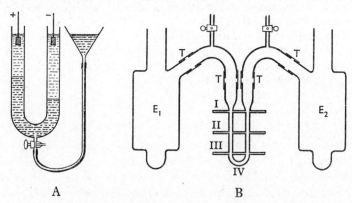

A   B

FIG. 5.8. APPARATUS FOR DETERMINING THE ELECTRICAL CHARGE ON COLLOIDAL PARTICLES AND FOR SEPARATION OF COLLOIDS BY ELECTROPHORESIS

A. On the left is Hardy's modification of Whetham's method of measuring the migration of coloured ions. The lower part of the U-tube contains the colloidal solution, which is run in below the buffer solution, in the upper part, through the tap. The position of the boundaries, as shown, is such as would be found after electrophoresis of a negatively charged colloid for two hours or so.

B. On the right is the Tiselius apparatus. E_1 and E_2 are large vessels, up to 2 litres capacity, containing buffer solution. AgCl electrodes are inserted into the cups at the bottom, which contain concentrated KCl solution. The U-tube, containing the colloid, is made in four sections, I, II, III and IV. Sections II and III can be moved sideways by pneumatic devices (not shown) so as to close the U-tube for filling, and for withdrawal of portions of the solution for analysis, after electrophoresis is completed. A "counter-current" (see p. 259) can be set up through the taps at the top.   (Tiselius, 1937.)

readily owing to the large surface/volume ratio, and the paper itself greatly slows down any movement of the solution as a whole due to convection. In such *paper electrophoresis*, however, other complications appear. First, the paper itself is electrically charged, and, as in the microscopic method, the suspending fluid will move in the potential gradient, and so affect the movement of the substance under examination. Secondly, this substance may be adsorbed on the paper, and the procedure then becomes a combination of electrophoresis with adsorption chromatography. As a rule, however, the chief object of the procedure is to separate the different constituents of the solution, and these effects do not interfere with this—indeed, in some conditions they may actually contribute. The various substances, having moved in a direction

determined by the sign of their charges, and by an amount determined by
their mobilities and the extent of their adsorption, remain on the paper as
spots which may be brought out by the use of suitable colouring reagents, as
in paper chromatography. More detailed information may be obtained from
the monographs on the subject, such as that by Block, Durrum and Zweig
(1955).

Although we have treated electrophoresis in relation to particles of microscopic, or ultra-microscopic, size, it is not in fact limited to these; as already
remarked, the principle is the same as that used for measuring the mobilities
of crystalloidal ions. Paper electrophoresis is particularly suitable for use with
crystalloidal substances, and it has been greatly used, for example, in the
separation of amino-acids.

Considerably less attention has been devoted to the measurement of
electro-osmosis and streaming potentials. Descriptions of the methods which
have been used, and references to the original papers, will be found in the
monograph by Abramson (1934).

SURFACE TENSION AND SURFACE CHARGE

Since electric charges of similar sign repel each other, it would naturally
be expected that a charged surface would tend to spread itself as far as
possible. Since the surface tension is a measure of the tendency of the surface to contract, we should predict, therefore, that the surface tension of a
charged surface would be less than that of the same surface when uncharged. This is, indeed, the case, and the phenomenon can best be
observed at the interface between mercury and an aqueous solution. The
surface tension can easily be measured by the method of capillary rise (or
rather fall, in the case of mercury): the charge can easily be altered either
by imposing a potential difference across the interface from an external
source, or by adjusting the concentration of mercury ions in the aqueous
solution.

The relation between the surface tension at such an interface, and the
applied potential is of the form shown in the curves of Fig. 5.9. If the
applied potential is such as to make the mercury more positive, the surface
tension falls. On reversing the sign of the applied potential, the surface
tension rises to a maximum, and then, as the mercury becomes progressively more negative, with respect to the solution, falls once more. It
is reasonable to suppose that at the maximum of the curve, the mercury
surface is uncharged, and that in the absence of an applied potential
difference, it naturally takes up a potential which is positive with respect
to the solution.

This *electrocapillary effect* is made use of in the instrument known as the
capillary electrometer, which was extensively used in the early days for recording the action potentials of nerves, muscles and plants. A column of mercury

in a capillary tube is in contact with an acid solution which contains no mercury ions; there is thus no way in which current can pass across the mercury-solution interface unless the potential applied is sufficiently large to cause a release of hydrogen or oxygen (compare p. 200 above). The instrument thus draws extremely little current from the circuitn uder test, but has the drawback of having rather a large capacitance; there may thus be quite large transient currents when a potential is suddenly applied. It is now completely discarded in favour of amplifiers and oscillographs as far as the recording of action potentials is concerned, and is only very rarely used for any other purpose.

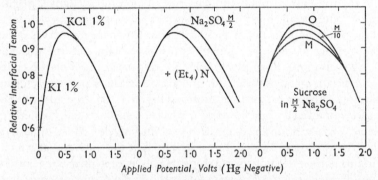

FIG. 5.9. ELECTROCAPILLARY CURVES FOR MERCURY IN VARIOUS SOLUTIONS

The ordinates represent the interfacial tension relative to the maximum value observed (at about 0·5 volts applied potential).

I shows the effect of the adsorption of iodide ions, which occurs when the mercury surface has a positive charge.

II shows the effect of the adsorption of tetra-ethyl ammonium ions, which occurs when the mercury surface has a negative charge.

III shows the effect of the adsorption of sucrose, which occurs whether the mercury surface is charged or not.   (Data of Gouy—after Adam, 1941.)

Direct measurements of the changes in surface tension produced by changes in the surface charge can only be made with liquids, but no observations have apparently been made on, say, oil-water interfaces, similar to those made on mercury-water interfaces, probably because of the technical difficulties. Indirect estimations of the surface tension between solid surfaces and aqueous solutions can be made by studying the contact angle between a bubble of air, or droplet of paraffin oil or toluene, and the solid surface. On applying potential differences, curves are obtained which are very similar in shape to those obtained with the mercury-solution interfaces.

ADSORPTION AND THE SURFACE CHARGE

The presence of an electric charge on a surface would be expected to affect the adsorption of electrolytes, since there would be an electrostatic repulsion for ions of the same sign as the surface charge and an attraction for ions of the opposite sign. The existence of such an effect is well shown by the electrocapillary curves of mercury. If we compare the curves obtained from a mercury surface in contact with solutions of (a) potassium chloride and (b) potassium iodide (Fig. 5.9, I), we find that the two curves are identical on the right-hand side of the maximum (applied voltage greater than about $0.5V$), where the mercury surface is negatively charged, but that on the left-hand side, where the mercury is positively charged, the surface tension is always lower in the presence of potassium iodide than it is in the presence of potassium chloride. The capillary active, negatively charged, iodide ion is most highly adsorbed when the mercury surface has a charge of the opposite sign. Similarly, if we compare the curves obtained in the presence of sodium sulphate with those obtained in the presence of tetra-ethyl ammonium sulphate (Fig. 5.9, II), adsorption of the capillary active cation is greatest when the mercury surface is negatively charged. Un-ionised substances, such as sucrose (Fig. 5.9, III) are adsorbed more or less symmetrically and lower the surface tension equally whether the mercury surface is charged positively or negatively. Most organic sub-stances, however, even though un-ionised, shift the potential at which the maximum surface tension is developed. This is presumably because they possess dipoles which are orientated at the surface, and so contribute to the interfacial potential.

It is not to be supposed that since the curves for potassium chloride and sodium sulphate are nearly symmetrical, there is no adsorption. With these salts, and with some others, it may be that cations and anions are adsorbed about equally, or that even when adsorbed, they have little effect on the surface tension. In such cases, when there is little or no surface activity, the concentration of an ion at the interface—in the "*surface phase*", as it has been called—will be determined solely by the electrical forces; the electrical attraction for anions, for example, and repulsion for cations, will produce an increase, or decrease, in the activity of the ions in the surface phase, such that an electrochemical equilibrium is attained. We can then apply the equations of the Gibbs-Donnan equilibrium; and thus, for example, the activities of hydrogen, sodium, chloride, calcium and alum-inium ions in the surface phase will be related to those in the bulk of the solution by the equation:

$$\frac{(a_H)_s}{(a_H)_b} = \frac{(a_{Na})_s}{(a_{Na})_b} = \frac{(a_{Cl})_b}{(a_{Cl})_s} = \sqrt{\frac{(a_{Ca})_s}{(a_{Ca})_b}} = \sqrt[3]{\frac{(a_{Al})_s}{(a_{Al})_b}} = r . \qquad . \quad 5.13$$

where a denotes activity and the subscripts s and b refer to the surface phase and the bulk solution, respectively.

Moreover, since the surface phase must be electrically neutral, equation

5.14 may be applied, with the simplification that there is only one kind of indiffusible ion. As an example of the magnitude of the ionic concentrations in the surface phase, we may consider the case of egg albumin in solution in the presence of a uni-univalent electrolyte at a concentration of $N/100$, as studied by Danielli in 1941. The valency of the protein ions is assumed to be that deduced from the titration curve; the volume of the surface phase is known from its thickness, as given by the Debye-Hückel theory (Table 5.2, p. 208), and the radius of the egg albumin molecule, as given by osmotic pressure and diffusion studies. The concentration of indiffusible ions is thus known. The approximation is made that concentrations may be used in place of activities, and equations 5.13 and 5.14 are simultaneously solved by a process of successive approximation. The conclusion is reached that the difference between the hydrogen ion concentration on the surface of the egg albumin molecules and that in the bulk of the solution, under the conditions considered, reaches 0·5 pH unit, or more, when the hydrogen ion concentration of the bulk solution is well removed (2 pH units) from the iso-ionic point. The value of r in equation 5.13 may thus reach 3 or more.

Alternatively, use can be made of the fact that the potential difference between the surface phase and the bulk solution is, in fact, the electrokinetic potential. This, as may be seen by combining equations 5.12 and 5.13, is thus given by:

$$E = \frac{RT}{F} \ln r$$

Knowing the electrokinetic potential, therefore, and the activity of any particular ion in the bulk solution, we can calculate its activity in the surface phase. Values of the pH difference calculated in this way agree well with those calculated from the valency of the protein and the volume of the surface phase.

These considerations show, at least partly, why it is that multivalent ions of the appropriate sign are taken up by charged interfaces, such as those of the ion exchange resins, for example, so much more completely than univalent ions. As is demonstrated by equation 5.13, the concentration ratio of any given kind of ion between the surface phase and the bulk of the solution, in equilibrium conditions, must be raised to the inverse power of its valency. If the value of r is, say, 10—and it may well be greater than this—the concentration ratio of sodium ions will be 10, that of calcium ions will be 100 and that of aluminium ions will be 1000.

It is, perhaps, a matter of terminology whether such a concentration of ions at an interface as a result of electrical forces, should be called "adsorption". As ordinarily defined, adsorption is considered to be brought about in consequence of a reduction of surface energy. If this occurs, as well as the reduction of electrical energy, the above considerations cannot be applied, since they presume a condition of electrochemical equilibrium.

On the other hand, it must not be forgotten that ions may be genuinely adsorbed by reason of their action in lowering the surface tension, and quite apart from the effects of the electrical attraction, as may be seen in Fig. 5.9, I and II; both the iodide ion and the tetra-ethyl ammonium ion are clearly adsorbed, even at the peak of the electrocapillary curve, when the mercury surface has no charge. The ions will then affect considerably the surface charge, and may, indeed, be responsible for creating it, as has already been mentioned earlier in this chapter. In such conditions, the effects of varying the nature and concentration of the electrolytes in contact with the surface are likely to be complicated. Suppose first, as the simpler case, that the adsorption of a preferentially adsorbed ion increases steadily with increase in its concentration, following, more or less, the Langmuir adsorption equation (equation 5.9, p. 186). The surface charge rises accordingly, and at first the electrokinetic potential rises with it (Fig. 5.10, A). Later, however, owing to the influence of the increasing density of the ionic atmosphere, the electrokinetic potential reaches a maximum, and then falls. After the charge has reached its maximum, or saturation, value the potential falls in proportion to the square root of the concentration, as would be expected theoretically. On the other hand, suppose that in addition to a preferentially adsorbed univalent ion, there is also a multivalent ion of the opposite sign. At first, the preferential adsorption increases the charge, as in A, but as the electrolyte concentration rises, the multivalent ion of opposite sign also becomes adsorbed, and the charge is reduced to zero and eventually reversed in sign (Fig. 5.10, B). The electrokinetic potential may show a small initial rise, as the charge rises, but almost immediately it begins to fall again. At the point where the charge is zero, the electrokinetic potential must, of course, also be zero. Beyond this, both charge and potential behave, with reversed signs, in the same general way as they did in the first case.

The Iso-electric Point. The effects of varying the hydrogen ion concentration on the magnitude and sign of the charge at an interface is a special case of the effects just discussed. When the charge is due to the electrolytic dissociation of the material on one side of the interface, such an effect is to be expected, unless the material behaves as a strong acid or base. But it is also to be expected when the charge is due to preferential adsorption, since hydrogen and hydroxyl ions are usually adsorbed quite strongly. At most kinds of interface, there is some hydrogen ion concentration at which the interface is uncharged, and the suspended particles, for example, will not move towards either electrode when subjected to electrophoresis. This is called the *iso-electric point*, and is usually given in the

pH notation. If the surface adsorbs ions of one sign very strongly, or does not dissociate amphoterically, the iso-electric point will lie in extremely acid or alkaline regions, and will be of no practical importance.

It is important to remember that the iso-electric point is not necessarily or indeed usually, identical with the iso-ionic point, as defined in Chapter 4 (p. 167), although the terms are sometimes used rather indiscriminately. The term "iso-electric point" was originally applied to the hydrogen ion concentration at which a *colloidal* ampholyte possesses no net charge. The term "iso-ionic point" is defined as the hydrogen ion concentration at which amphoteric ions neither lose nor gain hydrogen ions; we have no information from the

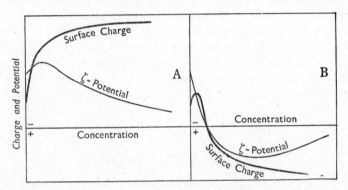

FIG. 5.10. TYPICAL CURVES SHOWING THE RELATION OF THE SURFACE CHARGE (THICK LINES) AND OF THE ELECTROKINETIC POTENTIAL (THIN LINES), ON AN "INDIFFERENT" SURFACE, TO THE ELECTROLYTE CONCENTRATION.

The surface takes up a negative charge even at zero concentration of the electrolyte, and then takes up additional charge (negative or positive) as the concentration is increased.

The electrokinetic potential (ζ-potential) becomes smaller as the electrolyte concentration increases, except in so far as this general effect is opposed by the more specific effect on the magnitude of the surface charge.

On the left, in A, are shown curves for the condition in which the sign of the charge is not reversed by the presence of the electrolyte: the increase in the ζ-potential when the electrolyte concentration is small may not occur.

On the right, in B, the sign of the charge becomes reversed when the electrolyte concentration exceeds a certain value: the initial increase in negative charge may not be present. (After Abramson, 1934.)

titration curves as to whether there is, or is not, a charge on the molecule or particle as a result of the uptake or loss of ions of other kinds.

The iso-electric point of a given surface may be measured in several ways, some of which are only suitable for special purposes. In the first place, the electrokinetic potential may be measured at various values of the hydrogen ion concentration, in any of the ways already described. By interpolation, the hydrogen ion concentration is found at which this potential is zero. Experiments of this kind were originally responsible for the conception of the iso-electric point. Secondly, in suitable cases, the hydrogen ion concentration corresponding to the maximum of the electrocapillary curve may be found; this is clearly only applicable to very special cases. Thirdly, when the surface dissociates as an ampholyte, we may measure the membrane potential, which, of course, becomes zero at the iso-electric point.

The presence of neutral salts has been shown to affect the position of the iso-electric point quite considerably. If one ion of the salt combines with the material of the surface, or is readily adsorbed by it, the charge will be affected, and a different concentration of hydrogen and hydroxyl ions will be needed to neutralise it. Where the surface charge results from the ionisation of an amphoteric electrolyte, the effect of the presence of uni-univalent inorganic electrolytes is usually small, though not negligible; the presence of multivalent ions, however, may have a considerable effect. In the complete absence of electrolytes, it would appear from extrapolation that, in the proteins at least, the iso-electric point becomes identical with the iso-ionic point. Thus for egg albumin, the iso-ionic point is at pH 4·86, whereas the iso-electric point rises from pH 4·585 in solutions of ionic strength 0·10, to pH 4·71 in solutions of ionic strength 0·01. The iso-electric point of haemoglobin has been found to behave similarly.

DYEING AND STAINING

These processes are clearly heterogeneous in character, and adsorption processes must play an important part. The frequent specificity of certain dyes for certain types of surface suggests, however, that the final process is probably one of chemisorption. With one or two exceptions, all dyes are neutral salts; the distinction is that the so-called "basic" dyes are salts of an organic coloured base with an inorganic acid, usually hydrochloric, while the "acid" dyes, on the other hand, are salts of an organic acid with an inorganic base, usually sodium. Moreover, when the dye salts are electrolytically dissociated, as in most cases, the positive ion is the coloured one in the "basic" dyes, and will be taken up by negatively charged surfaces, whereas the coloured negative ion of the "acid" dyes will be taken up by positively charged surfaces. The "basic" dyes are frequently hydrolytically dissociated, with the formation of electropositive free bases in the colloidal state. Thus, for example, filter-paper, an electronegative surface, will take up large quantities of an electropositive substance such as night-blue, but only a trace of a negative dye such as Congo-red. Further, when neutral salts, having no action on the material concerned, such as sodium chloride, are added, the effect is to *increase* the adsorption of *negative* dyes and to *diminish* that of *positive* dyes. The explanation is probably that the neutral salt diminishes the electrokinetic potential of the surface, as might be expected from the Gibbs-Donnan relation; the adsorption of a similarly charged body is thus facilitated, while that of an oppositely charged one is diminished. The adsorption by filter-paper of colloidal arsenious sulphide (electronegative) is affected in the same way as that of Congo-red.

Since most of the staining bodies in preparations of living cells are colloids with negative charges, it is easy to understand why electropositive dyes, such as many of the "basic" ones are, should be adsorbed. It is also suggestive that haemoglobin, one of the few colloids which may be electropositive in faintly acid solution (as in most histological preparations) takes up "acid" dyes, such as eosin and acid fuchsin.

LITERATURE

Surface Action in General. Boys (1912); Freundlich (1922); Adam (1941).

Surface Films and Monolayers. Adam (1941—Chapter 2); Langmuir (1939).

Adsorption. Langmuir (1939); Adam (1941—Chapters 3 and 7).

Chromatography. Lederer and Lederer (1957); Block, Durrum and Zweig (1955).

Electrical Phenomena at Surfaces. Adam (1941—Chapter 8).

Electrophoresis, Streaming Potentials etc. Abramson (1934); Abramson, Gorin and Moyer (1942); Alexander and Johnson (1949—Chapter 12); Booth (1953); Block, Durrum and Zweig (1955).

Polarisation Potentials, Polarography. Kolthoff and Lingane (1941).

Concentrations of Ions in Surface Phase. Danielli (1944).

6

THE COLLOIDAL STATE

If we take a piece of metallic gold, immerse it in water, and divide it up into smaller and smaller parts, it is obvious that in the end, supposing that our powers of manipulation were adequate, we should arrive at the molecular condition. But, before this state is reached, we should have passed through a state in which the particles were so fine as to be invisible, as such, by ordinary means of illumination; and they would remain in permanent suspension, so as to simulate very closely a true solution, in which the substance dissolved is in the molecular, or even ionic state. In the course of this process of division, the larger fragments of gold of the early stages sink at once, after being stirred up, but as smaller and smaller particles are formed, the time taken to fall becomes longer and longer, until, when less than a certain size, they do not appear to sink at all. They are now in what is called the *"colloidal state"*. Their dimensions at this stage are enormously greater than those of molecules of gold, but it is clear that we can draw no definite lines of demarcation between the visible solid lump, from which we started, the colloidal state and the final molecular state.

We cannot, of course, actually perform the operation in the manner described. In an indirect way, however, it was done by Faraday in 1858, who found that, by acting on solutions of gold salts by reducing agents, beautiful red or purple solutions were obtained. He also showed that these solutions, although permanent, were, in reality, suspensions of minute particles of metallic gold. It is interesting to note that some of Faraday's gold preparations are still preserved in the Royal Institution.

Since these gold solutions have served as the foundation for much subsequent work the method of preparing them is worth description. The ruby-red solution is made thus, in the words of Faraday himself: "If a pint or two of the weak solution of gold before described" (i.e., about 2 grains of gold chloride in two or three pints of water) "be put into a *very clean* glass bottle, a drop of the solution of phosphorus in sulphide of carbon added, and the whole well shaken together, it immediately changes in appearance, becomes red, and being left for six to twelve hours, forms the ruby fluid required; too much sulphide and phosphorus should not be added, for the reduced gold then tends to clot about the portions which sink to the bottom." The method is improved by the addition of potassium carbonate, in order to neutralise the free acid produced in the reaction; the absence of colloidal matter from the water used appears to be especially necessary if uniform results are to be obtained. The necessity of cleanliness was well known to Faraday himself, although at that time the properties of colloids were unknown. A beautiful deep blue solution of gold can be made by reduction with hydrazine hydrate. Gold chloride 0·1 per cent. is neutralised by sodium carbonate and very dilute hydrazine hydrate (one part in 4000 of water) added drop by drop, carefully avoiding excess.

How do we know that we have to do with suspended solid particles in these preparations? They are quite transparent to light of ordinary intensity, although this does not apply to all colloidal solutions; where the particles are larger the solutions are turbid, and their appearance suggests their nature. Even the most transparent gold preparations, however, were found by Faraday to show turbidity in the track of a powerful beam of light. It is a matter of common observation that dust particles, completely invisible under ordinary light, become clearly visible in a beam of sunlight; the phenomenon observed by Faraday in a colloidal solution is similar to that of the motes in a sunbeam. It is frequently called the "Tyndall-phenomenon", but its discovery was really made by Faraday. Tyndall pointed out that the light reflected, or rather diffracted, from the path of the beam is polarised, a fact which proves that the particles are of the same order of dimensions as the mean wave-length of the light used.

Most of our knowledge of the fundamental properties of the colloidal state is due to Thomas Graham, who started from a different point of view from that of Faraday. He noticed in 1861 that certain substances are extremely slow to diffuse, and devoid of the power to crystallise. They are also unable to pass through a membrane of similar nature to themselves, such as sized paper or parchment paper (unsized paper treated with sulphuric acid). Amongst these substances are hydrated silicic acid, starch, albumin, gelatin, etc. He says: "As gelatine (κόλλη = glue) appears to be its type, it is proposed to designate substances of the class as *colloids*, and to speak of their peculiar form of aggregation as the *colloidal condition of matter*. Opposed to the colloidal is the crystalline condition. Substances affecting the latter form will be classed as *crystalloids*. The distinction is no doubt one of intimate molecular constitution." It will be noted that, although Graham speaks here of the "colloidal condition" of matter, he appears to regard the class of colloids as quite distinct from that of crystalloids. "They appear like different worlds of matter". At the same time he is aware that the same substance, silica for example, may be obtained in either state, while on the page following that on which the above statement is found, he suggests that the colloid molecule may be "constituted by the grouping together of a number of smaller crystalloid molecules." Perhaps stress is intended to be laid rather on the word "appear". In any case, it is better to speak of the "colloidal state" and not of "colloids" as a class. This is especially true since it has been shown that many substances, especially proteins, which form undoubtedly colloidal solutions, are also capable of forming true crystals. Many substances, on the other hand, which readily form "crystalloidal" solutions, can only be made to crystallise with the greatest difficulty.

The common property of both Faraday's and Graham's colloids is the large size of the particles compared with that of the water molecules amongst which they are suspended. In the one case they are capable of diffracting even visible light, and in the other, they are incapable of passing through pores which are fully large enough for the water molecules to pass through. The colloidal state, then, is of the nature of a heterogeneous system, or a system of more than one separate phase. It differs from a coarsely heterogeneous system, such as a mass of gold immersed in water, in that it is, to ordinary observation, homogeneous, and only shows its micro-heterogeneous character by special methods of investigation. On the other hand, it is distinguished from true solutions of small molecules or ions by the fact that there are different phases, separated by surfaces of contact, with corresponding special properties. These properties, indeed, are likely to be especially marked, owing to the minute state of subdivision, and the large ratio of surface area to mass.

The large increase in the surface of a given mass of material on dispersion as a colloidal suspension is shown by the following calculations. The particles of gold in some preparations of colloidal gold have a radius of about 10^{-6} cm., or 1 $m\mu$. A sphere of gold of 0·1 cm. radius has a surface of 0·126 cm.^{2}; while the surface of the same mass, if subdivided into these colloidal dimensions would have a surface of 1·26 m.^{2}—i.e. 100,000 times greater. If this mass of gold were dispersed in a million litres of water, each cubic millimetre would contain 1000 particles. There would be about 250,000 atoms of gold in each particle, of which about 16,000 would be on the surface. Again, 1 c.c. of viscose, if extruded into a rod 1 μ diameter, would be 800 miles long.

It is convenient to have names for the two phases of which a colloidal system usually consists. Most commonly used nowadays are "continuous" phase, corresponding to the solvent in a true solution, and "disperse" phase, corresponding to the solute. A substance, accordingly, is said to be "dispersed" when it forms a colloidal solution, and not "dissolved". Some workers use the terms "internal" phase for the disperse phase, and "external" phase for the continuous phase; the names will be used here indifferently.

The two phases of which a colloidal solution consists may obviously be of many various kinds, as is illustrated in Table 6.1. The most important systems for the physiologist are those consisting of solids and liquids, Nos.

3, 4 and 6 in the Table. The names "*sol*" and "*gel*" were introduced by Graham to denote the presence or absence of obvious fluidity in a colloidal system. Roughly, it may be said that in a sol the continuous phase is liquid, and in a gel, it is solid, as may be seen by comparing systems 4 and 6. In some kinds of gel, however, it would be more correct to say that both phases, one solid and the other liquid, are continuous; neither can be described as being either internal or external. Systems possessing rigidity, also, and thus in a sense "gels", may be formed when both phases are liquid. The two types of system form freely from one another, as is well known in gelatin; a colloidal solution of silicic acid, also, at first liquid, or a sol, becomes a gel in process of time.

TABLE 6.1

Various Types of Colloidal System

Internal or Dispersed Phase.	External or Continuous Phase.	Example.
1. Gas .	Liquid . . .	Foam.
2. Liquid .	Gas	Fog.
3. „ .	Another immiscible liquid	Emulsion or emulsoid ; milk.
4. „ .	Solid	Jelly, as gelatin in some forms.
5. Solid .	Gas	Tobacco smoke.
6. „ .	Liquid . . .	Ordinary colloidal solution, such as those of gold, arsenious sulphide, etc.
7. „ .	Another solid . .	Ruby glass.

Perrin divided colloidal solutions into "hydrophile" and "hydrophobe", according to the affinity of the dispersed phase for water; "*lyophile*" and "*lyophobe*" would be better, as Freundlich pointed out, since water may be replaced by other solvents. Typical instances of the lyophile class are gelatin and gum, and of the lyophobe class, gold and arsenious sulphide. This classification is almost coterminous with that of Hardy into "reversible" and "irreversible" colloids, according to whether, after evaporation to dryness, they will go into solution again, or remain as a solid film. Silicic acid, however, is lyophile, but after evaporation to dryness does not go into solution on addition of water, as gum does. Perrin's division also corresponds, though less completely, with the classification proposed by Wo. Ostwald, who grouped colloidal systems into "*emulsoids*" or "*suspensoids*" according as the dispersed phase is liquid or solid. This last system is in many ways a useful one, although it does not direct

H

attention to what is perhaps the most important distinction between different classes, that is the affinity of the dispersed phase for water. The word "emulsoid" is intended to indicate the liquid nature of the dispersed phase, the particles, unlike those of *emulsions*, being necessarily of colloidal dimensions. But if the dispersed phase consists of a lyophilic solid, it may contain a greater or less proportion of water, or other solvent, as in the proteins, and it may thus possess any degree of solidity. On the other hand, if the dispersed phase consists of an immiscible liquid, such as petroleum, the system has properties more like those of the lyophobe class, such as a comparatively high sensitivity to electrolytes. When, moreover, the internal phase, though liquid, is in extremely minute droplets, its mechanical properties closely resemble those of a solid, the great pressure due to the surface forces conferring rigidity on them; the fact that they are retained by a membrane of the kind used by Graham, even when subjected to high pressures, shows that they cannot be sufficiently distorted to pass through apertures less than a certain size, which is large compared with molecular dimensions. It will be found, however, that whatever method of distinction is employed, it will be necessary to admit the existence of intermediate forms, that is systems which have some of the properties of each class.

The characteristic which carries with it most of the other differences in the general behaviour of a colloidal system is the affinity of the internal phase for water, or other solvent, constituting the external phase. It will be clear that the more water the internal phase contains—and it may contain as much as 90 per cent.—the less will be the difference between the properties of the two components at the interface of contact, and consequently the less will be the surface energy. It is not uncommon, now, to use the term "emulsoid" chiefly for the systems with lyophilic particles, and to use the term "emulsion" for those with liquid, but lyophobic, particles, even if they are colloidal. It is the class of colloidal solutions variously called emulsoid, lyophile, stable, or reversible that are of most importance to the physiologist. These four names, as we have seen, are not synonymous, but are, in general, applicable to the majority of the systems in which we are interested.

One important characteristic of the colloidal state, that of *instability* was clearly recognised by Graham. After referring to the fact that colloidal solutions of silica sooner or later become gelatinous and finally crystallise, he says: "The colloidal is, in fact, a dynamical state of matter; the crystalloidal being the statical condition. The colloid possesses ENERGIA. It may be looked upon as the probable primary source of the force appearing in the phenomena of vitality. To the gradual manner in which colloidal changes take place (for they always demand time as an element), may the characteristic protraction of chemico-organic changes be referred".

Thermodynamically, Graham's colloids, most of which come into the category of lyophile colloids, and Faraday's colloids, which are lyophobes, are unstable for different reasons. When a quantity of a substance in relatively large units is broken up and dispersed or dissolved in another substance, work has to be done against the cohesive forces of the substance which is broken up. On the other hand, work is done *by* the adhesive forces between the substance dispersed and the dispersing medium. If these are greater than the cohesive forces, the dispersion will proceed spontaneously and will be reversible. Such is the case with substances which go into true solution, and with the lyophile colloids (hence the name). With these, we can take a portion of the dry solid and disperse it in water, for example, just as if we were preparing a true solution.

The lyophobe colloids, on the other hand, are essentially insoluble in water. They are prepared either by precipitation from soluble substances, or by disintegration of larger masses of liquid or solid substances, chemical or mechanical work being done on them in the process; they are metastable, and only remain in suspension, as we shall see, by virtue of the fact that the individual particles are kept from settling out by reason of their thermal agitation (Brownian movement), and from coalescing into larger particles by reason of their electric charges.

Arsenious sulphide sols are formed by passing hydrogen sulphide through a solution of arsenious acid. Metallic hydrosols can, in many cases, be prepared by reducing their salts with various reagents, such as phosphorus or form-aldehyde in the case of gold. In traces, certain metals such as lead and copper pass into what seem to be colloidal hydroxides by mere contact with water; the water may then become toxic to living tissues. When a metallic salt be-comes hydrolytically dissociated in water, prolonged dialysis removes the free acid, leaving the hydroxide in a colloidal state; this occurs, for example, with ferric and thorium salts. In all these preparations, the colloidal particles appear to consist of adsorption compounds between the precipitated substances and the soluble salts from which they were formed. Ferric chloride, for example, on dialysis gives a series of colloids containing less and less chloride in relation to iron, from 3 of Cl to 1 of Fe, to 1 of Cl to 400 or 500 of Fe, in no stoichio-metrical proportion. If dialysis is continued until nearly all the chloride is removed, the colloid tends to deposit rapidly; it seems to be stable only when in adsorption combination with a certain amount of the chloride.

Sols of various metals may also be prepared by disintegration with an electric arc (Bredig) or a spark (Svedberg) in the water or other liquid. Com-mercially, many colloidal suspensions and emulsions are manufactured by mechanical disintegration. A coarse suspension, for example, is made to pass through a fine gap between a rotating and a stationary plate; the particles are broken up into an extremely fine state partly by the actual grinding action of the mill, but more by the enormous hydraulic shear to which they are sub-jected. In the case of emulsions, the suspended droplets may be brought to the necessary state of fineness by forcing a coarse emulsion through fine holes or slits under pressure. The domestic machine for converting a coarse suspension of butter in warm milk into cream makes use of this process. Another method which works on essentially the same principle is the use of supersonic vibrations. These are high frequency sound waves and when the amplitude is made large, the localised compressions and rarefactions produced in the emulsion result in an extremely violent agitation.

Even the lyophile colloids, however, are not truly stable, owing to the fact that the particles are so large. It may be that the individual molecules are very large, as in the proteins, starch, and many modern polymers. In these, only parts of the molecule, as a rule, show great affinity for water, or other dispersion medium, so that a small change in the physical or chemical structure of the molecule may result in a loss of this affinity and consequent coagulation of the system. In other cases, the solution is colloidal as a result of the particles consisting of groups or aggregates of molecules, as for example, in dyes such as Congo-red. The attraction of the dispersion medium is not sufficient to bring about a complete disruption of the solid material into individual molecules. Again, quite a small change in the properties of the colloid, or the dispersion medium, may well be sufficient to produce coagulation.

Obviously, a hard and fast line cannot be drawn between the two types of lyophile colloids just considered, any more than there can between the lyophile and lyophobe colloids. If all the particles are of the same size, and of a size which corresponds to the minimum molecular weight as calculated from the chemical composition (i.e. the weight of the molecule which contains at least one gram-atom of every component) then the molecules are clearly not aggregated in the solution. If, on the other hand, the size of the particles varies over a wide range, but is always very much greater than would correspond to the minimum molecular weight, then the solution is colloidal as a result of aggregation. But there are many colloidal solutions in which the situation is not so clear cut. The lyophobe colloids are all colloidal as a result of aggregation.

As a result of the large particle size, properties such as the velocity of chemical reaction and osmotic pressure, which depend on the number of particles in a given volume of solution, have small values in colloidal solutions. On the other hand, in solutions of the relatively stable, lyophile colloids, those properties such as refractive index and viscosity, which depend on the volume or mass of the disperse phase in relation to that of the continuous phase, characteristically have large values.

In practice, it is found that Graham's criterion of not passing through membranes of parchment paper, collodion or cellophane is the most satisfactory one for deciding whether a particular solution is a colloidal one. This property goes together with the various other properties dependent on surface development, although it must be admitted that it would appear to be somewhat arbitrary to fix the point at a definite dimension. Parchment paper membranes, however, do not all have pores of the same size, and collodion membranes can be prepared with pores of any desired size, within limits. This makes it possible to determine the diameter of the largest and smallest particles in any given solution; but it makes the use of such membranes as the criterion of what is and what is not a colloidal solution, somewhat ambiguous. A similarly arbitrary distinction would have to be made if we used Faraday's criterion of showing turbidity when strongly illuminated. The size of particle which just shows perceptible scattering will depend on the intensity and wave-length of the light used. But all this is really of little consequence, since it is, in any case, impossible to define a certain particle diameter as being the upper limit of a true solution, and the lower limit of a colloidal solution. On the contrary, there is a range of increasing particle size over which the properties which are recognised as being peculiar to colloidal solutions are gradually developed, and those which are recognised as being peculiar to true solutions gradually disappear.

DIALYSIS

The separation of colloids from crystalloids, and their purification when separated, is often very conveniently performed by the method used by Graham himself in 1861, and called by him "dialysis". Substances in the colloidal state do not pass through membranes such as parchment paper, while crystalloidal substances do so very readily. Graham showed, for example, that 96 per cent. of the salt content of a 2 per cent. solution of sodium chloride passed through a parchment paper membrane in 24 hours, when the volume of the water outside was 10 times that of the solution, and was changed once. Dilute hydrochloric acid applied to one side of the paper reddened litmus paper on the opposite side in 5·7 seconds.

The simple forms of dialyser which were used by Graham are in practice very effective. A sheet of parchment paper is placed across a wooden hoop, or glass bell-jar, so as to form a flat diaphragm; the free edges are turned up and folded, and tied with thread round the hoop or jar. The liquid to be dialysed is placed within the hoop or jar, and the whole is immersed in a vessel of water. It is better not to allow the level of the liquid inside to rise above the upper edge of the paper, since it is difficult to make a tight joint with the hoop or glass bell. A continuous current of water may be caused to flow through the outer vessel, but a given volume of distilled water is more effective if used in several changes of the whole volume of liquid in the outer vessel.

A very simple and effective form of dialyser can also be made from the cellophane tubing used commercially as sausage skins. The tubing is sold in long lengths, and a suitable piece is cut off, tied with string at one end, filled with the solution to be dialysed and tied at the other end. The whole is then immersed in water. It is best to leave an air space at one end, since at first, water is often absorbed into the colloid solution as a result of the transient osmotic effects, and considerable pressures may be developed. Cellophane, however, is remarkably strong mechanically, so long as there is no tendency for it to tear, and a sac made from this sausage skin will usually stand a pressure of several hundred millimetres of mercury without bursting.

J. J. Abel, in 1913, applied the process of dialysis to the investigation of chemical changes occurring in the higher animals or in their constituent organs. The blood, issuing from an artery or vein is made non-coagulable (Abel used an extract of the heads of leeches, but other substances are now available), and is made to pass through a series of collodion tubes, immersed in warm Ringer's solution. Collodion, like parchment, is impermeable to colloids. After passing these tubes, the blood is returned to the animal and thus is kept in continuous circulation through the dialyser. In its passage, it gives up the diffusible substances which it contains to the outer fluid, in so far as they are not already present in equal concentration. The substances that were identified as diffusing out from the blood were sugar, urea, phosphates, amylase and amino-acids. Abel succeeded, by this means, in obtaining considerable quantities of amino-acids.

The same principle has also been used for constructing an "artificial kidney". By using a sufficiently long cellophane tube, kept moving in a large bath of 0·9 per cent. sodium chloride solution, dogs and even human subjects have been kept alive for some days after both kidneys have ceased to function. Clinically, a more convenient procedure is to use the walls of the blood vessels running to the intestines, as the dialysing membranes; by maintaining a slow flow of saline solution through the abdominal cavity, by means of tubes inserted through the walls, patients can be kept alive for some days during temporary failure of their kidneys.

BROWNIAN MOVEMENT

In 1828, the botanist Robert Brown noticed particles in microscopic preparations which were in a continuous state of rapid oscillatory motion; the smaller the particles, the greater the amplitude of the movement. Various suggestions were made from time to time to explain this "*Brownian*" *movement*, such as convection currents due to inequalities of temperature, the effect of the illumination necessary to make the particles visible, mechanical vibrations and electrical charge, but none were found to stand the test of experimental investigation. It was first suggested by Ramsay in 1879, and again, independently by Gouy in 1888, that the Brownian movement resulted from the bombardment of the particles by the molecules of the suspending fluid; but it was the work of Perrin in 1908, that definitely showed that this was so, and that Brownian movement is essentially identical with the random movement of thermal origin postulated by the kinetic theory of gases.

Perrin's evidence is based on the following considerations. If we assume that the movements of the particles in a colloidal suspension are due only to thermal agitation, the average kinetic energy of the particles will be identical with that of the molecules of the suspending fluid, or of any other molecules in solution. If, therefore, we could measure the average kinetic energy of the colloidal particles, or some quantity related to it in a known way, we could apply the equations deduced from the kinetic theory of gases (Chapter 1, p. 17), and derive a value of the number of molecules in a gram-molecule, N, the Avogadro number. If there is indeed equipartition of energy between molecules and colloidal particles, this value of N should be the same as that deduced from observations on molecular systems. Perrin measured three different quantities, all of which could be related to the kinetic energy of the particles; all three gave sensibly the same value of N, within the limits of experimental error, and Perrin considered that the best mean value of N from his measurements was $6 \cdot 85 \times 10^{23}$ in general agreement with the other estimates of its value available at the time. The most accurate measurements of N, based on quite different assumptions, made by Millikan some 10 years later, lead to the value $6 \cdot 062 \times 10^{23}$. The agreement between the two figures is as close as could be expected, and there seems no doubt that Brownian movement is the same thing as the molecular movement of the kinetic theory. Perrin's experiments thus demonstrate that the conception of the equipartition of kinetic energy is valid for particles differing in diameter by a factor of some 60,000; the conception would thus seem to be fully justified.

Perrin's experimental methods consisted, in effect, in measuring the diffusion constant of the colloidal particles. The tendency of the molecules in a gas or liquid, to become equally distributed, by diffusion from regions of high concentration to regions of low, is an expression of their kinetic energy of random movement. (In Chapter 3, it was assumed that the driving force in diffusion was the partial molar free energy gradient; but this is only a more general way of regarding the phenomenon.) According to the assumption under examination, this applies also to the particles of a colloidal suspension.

Perrin's first method took account of the fact that molecules, and colloidal particles, have mass, and will tend to sink under the action of gravity. They were allowed to come into equilibrium, the tendency to sink just balanced by the tendency to become uniformly distributed by diffusion, with the result that there was a concentration gradient in the suspension; this was measured by observing the particles under a microscope, and measuring the number in a given small volume at different depths of the suspension. This concentration gradient is analogous to the fall in atmospheric pressure with height above sea level. The rate of sinking of a particle will be determined by its volume and density relative to that of the suspending fluid—which can be measured—the acceleration of gravity, and a "frictional coefficient". The compensating rate of diffusion will be determined by the concentration gradient and the diffusion constant, which, from equations 3.30 and 3.31, will be given by $RT/N.f_D$, where f_D is the "frictional coefficient". This last is thus eliminated, and a value of N can be derived. We shall return to this again later, when considering the determination of molecular weights by sedimentation in the ultra-centrifuge.

In Perrin's second method, the diffusion constant was estimated by direct observation of the movement of the particles. According to an equation derived by Einstein, the diffusion constant is simply related to the average value of the square of the distance travelled by a particle in any one co-ordinate of space in a given time. This distance can be measured by observing the

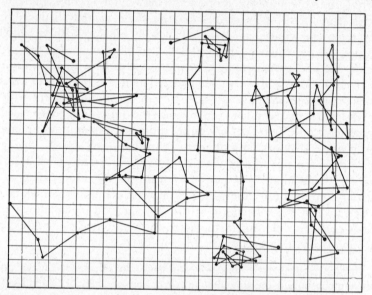

FIG. 6.1. BROWNIAN MOVEMENT

Paths obtained by joining the consecutive positions of three particles of mastic at intervals of thirty seconds. They only give a feeble idea of the complexity of the real trajectories. If the positions were indicated from second to second, each of the rectilinear segments of the figure would be replaced by a polygonal contour of thirty sides, as complicated as the drawing given here.   (Perrin, 1909.)

position of a given particle at stated intervals of time, over a long period, as indicated in Fig. 6.1. It is necessary, however, to know the value of the frictional coefficient; this, for the particles used by Perrin, is given with good accuracy by the equation derived by Stokes, $f_D = 6\pi\eta a$, where η is the viscosity of the suspending fluid, and a is the radius of the particle.

The third method depends on the fact that when the dimensions of the particles are sufficiently large, many of the impacts of the water molecules will be directed more or less tangentially, and so cause rotation of the particles; this can be observed when they contain some distinguishing mark, as an inclusion in course of their formation. From these observations, by the use of an equation, also developed by Einstein, a value of N can be derived, although with less precision than by the first two methods.

For these observations, it was obviously necessary to prepare suspensions of particles of a uniform size and sufficiently large for observation to be made in the depth of a cell on the stage of a microscope. Gamboge, mastic and resin were the substances used, and preparations containing particles of a uniform size were made by the use of fractional centrifugation. The mass and volume of each particle were measured in the following way. All the particles in a given small volume were precipitated in the bottom of the chamber under the microscope, and the number counted; the number of living cells, such as red blood cells, or egg cells, in a given volume is commonly measured in the same way. The total mass of suspension, and its density, in a known large volume was then determined by evaporation to dryness. Alternatively, the rate of fall of the particles, under gravity, was measured in a capillary tube, standing vertically, and the radius calculated from the Stokes equation (compare the measurement of sedimentation velocity, p. 278 below).

Perrin's observations were described by W. C. McC. Lewis as the first really conclusive evidence for the existence of molecules (*A System of Physical Chemistry*, 1916); we are not compelled to be content only with equations derived from energetics, since the visible particles in colloidal suspensions behave precisely like the molecules postulated in the atomic theory. At the time that they were performed, they provided the most accurate estimates of the value of the Avogadro number, N. Justification for the conclusions reached lay in the consistency of the results obtained by the three methods, as much as in their agreement with the earlier estimates, based on measurements of the viscosity, and dielectric constant, of gases, and on the constant b in the van der Waals equation of state, for example; these indicated only that the value of N lay between the limits of 4×10^{23} and 20×10^{23}.

The later, more accurate measurements of Millikan were derived indirectly from the measurements of the elementary electric charge—the charge on the electron. If this is denoted e, then the charge on a gram-ion of a univalent electrolyte, the faraday, F, must be equal to $N.e$. The value of F is known accurately from measurements of electrolysis; the value of e was measured by subjecting electrically charged droplets of water—or better, oil— in air to a known electric field, and so opposing their tendency to fall under gravity. The droplets became charged by taking up an ionised molecule of the gas in which they were suspended, the ionisation being produced by X-rays or a radium salt. The charge on the oil droplets could be observed to change discontinuously, upwards and downwards, by a constant quantity, as positive and negative ions were taken up in succession. Other, even more accurate, methods have since been developed, and Millikan's value is, in fact, 0·6 per cent. too large.

THE CONSTITUTION OF COLLOIDAL PARTICLES

In the inorganic sols, such as those of the metals, the particles are merely very small crystals, and their structure, as revealed, for example, by X-ray analysis, does not differ essentially from that of macroscopic crystals.

H*

Similarly, the emulsions, such as milk, contain small globules of oil, and, except at the interfaces, where, as we have seen in the previous chapter, the molecules are probably orientated, they have the same structure as has the oil in bulk. When we come to the colloidal solutions of chief biological interest, however, we meet with particles whose constitution and structure are important as determining, very largely, the behaviour of the solution.

GIANT MOLECULES

There are certain relatively small molecules which, by virtue of the configurations of their two ends, readily unite so as to form long chains. In the living world, two classes of such molecules are of prime importance, the monosaccharides on the one hand, and the amino-acids on the other.

If we take glucose as an example of the first class, we see that by writing down the formulae of two molecules, we can by abstraction of a molecule of water, bring about a union between them, as shown below, the two molecules being united through an atom of oxygen.

Moreover, at each end of the double molecule, there is a group which can join on to another glucose molecule in the same way. There is thus, in theory, no limit to the number of glucose units that can be joined up together. When some thousands have been so united, a macro-molecule of starch or cellulose is formed. The cellulose chain, built up of β-glucose residues, remains more or less straight and unbranched, and long fibres are formed: whereas, if α-glucose residues join up, forming starch, the chain turns back on itself, or a number of shorter chains, of 24-30 residues, join up side to side, or in a branching chain, and granules are formed. The hydrophobic groups can thus bunch themselves together in the interior of the macro-molecule, leaving the hydrophilic groups on the surface. Starch can be made to dissolve in water; cellulose cannot.

Again, if we write the formulae of two amino-acid molecules in the form:

we can, again by abstracting a molecule of water, bring about a union
between them. At the ends of this double molecule are again groups
capable of uniting with further amino-acid molecules. In this way we
build up first polypeptides, and then, as the chain grows longer, proteins,
so:

These two types of polymerisation into macro-molecules, however, are
not mutually exclusive. Some of the most important colloidal and structural constituents of living organisms contain both carbohydrates and
proteins, and, indeed, possibly lipids as well. Thus, for example, the *mucus*
which is common as a protective secretion on the linings of the alimentary
canals of all animals, and on the skins of those which live in the water, are
glycoproteins, the repeating units consisting of hexosamines of various
kinds. In *chitin*, again, from which is constructed the exoskeletons of
arthropods, the repeating units consist of acetylglucosamine, and the
molecules have much the same general structure as cellulose. The amino-
acetyl group which forms one of the side-chains permits the formation of
—CO—NH— bonds with proteins; the exoskeleton is, in fact, made up
of alternate layers of chitin fibres running in one direction and protein
fibres running at right angles to them, the two sets of fibres being bonded
at the points where they cross. Lastly, mention must be made of the
nucleic acids. They are of rather a different nature, each unit consisting of
a purine or pyrimidine base, a pentose sugar (ribose or de-oxyribose) and
phosphoric acid. They unite with one another through the phosphoric acid
group, the rings of the purine and the pentose being flat and parallel with
one another. Astbury has likened the structure to a pile of pennies.

There are many other examples of colloidal systems which are composed of giant molecules and are of great importance in everyday life, but
of less importance to the physiologist than are the celluloses and proteins.
As a natural product, there is rubber, and as synthetic products, there are
the various artificial rubbers and "plastics" such as bakelite, polythene and
numerous similar substances which are now produced commercially in
such large quantities.

Such long chains, the units of which are held together as a result of
definite chemical combination, are known as *primary valence chains*. They
are not necessarily straight. The protein chain, as indicated by the formula
above, has a zig-zag backbone, even when it is as straight as possible: but
it may also be bent back on itself to such an extent that a globular molecule
may be formed. Each amino-acid residue can rotate freely about the links

between itself and its neighbours. But since there is only one position in which the whole chain is straight, while there is an enormous number in which it is bent, the bent form is by far the most probable: thermal agitation will tend to make the chain fold up in an irregular way, with a gain in entropy, and free energy will be needed to straighten it out. Moreover, in aqueous solution, the hydrophilic groups will tend to be on the outside, as far as possible, while the hydrophobic groups will tend to bunch together, as far removed from the water as possible. Soluble proteins thus almost universally have molecules of a globular form; the insoluble proteins are fibrous in nature and the molecules are usually in the form of more or less helical or zig-zag chains. They are found in skeletal and supporting structures, such as hairs, connective tissue, muscles etc.; while the soluble proteins are found in the tissue fluids and cell contents of animals and plants.

The molecular configuration of the fibrous proteins and polysaccharides, and the manner in which the molecules are packed together, has been elucidated chiefly by the method of studying their X-ray diffraction patterns; the work of Astbury and his colleagues has been fundamental in this field, and general accounts will be found in Astbury's Croonian Lecture (1947) and in the article by Rudall (1950). X-ray analysis is not capable of giving much information about the globular macro-molecules, since there is not sufficient regularity in the arrangement of the chains. But in the fibrous proteins, in particular, the average spacing between the regularly recurring side-chains can be accurately measured, and hence the space occupied by each amino-acid residue.

Although not strictly relevant to a discussion on the colloidal state, we may perhaps indicate briefly some of the main conclusions reached from these studies. The fibrous proteins may be divided into two chief classes: the keratin-myosin-epidermis-fibrin group; and the collagen group. In the former are included the fibrous proteins of the epidermis of mammals, amphibians, and certain fishes; fibrous structures such as hair, horn, nails etc.; and the chief protein of muscle fibres, myosin. In the second group are included the white connective tissue fibres, tendons, cartilage, elastoidin of the scale of fishes, and certa n other similar proteins; and lastly, the degradation product of all these proteiins, gelatin.

The keratin-myosin group of proteins can exist in two different states. Normally, the length of chain occupied by each amino-acid residue is 5·1 Å., considerably less than would be expected from stoichiometrical considerations —i.e. from the space occupied by each atom, and the angles between the valency bonds. In this condition, known as the α-form, the chain must be folded on itself in a fairly regular manner, each fold containing two or three amino-acid residues. Stretching such fibres results in an unfolding of the chains, and the mean side-chain spacing, now 6·8 Å., corresponds to that expected from stoichiometrical considerations. This condition is known as the β-form. On releasing the fibres, they return spontaneously to the α-form. Very few proteins exist naturally in the β-form, the commonest being, perhaps, the fibroin secreted by silk glands.

The fibres of the collagen group have a spacing intermediate between that of the α-form and that of the β-form. This probably results from the relatively high proportion of proline and oxyproline in the molecules; the iminazole rings in these amino-acids pull the chains together, and they cannot be extended by stretching.

An interesting point is that in the nucleic acid chains the main pattern repeats at intervals of 3·3 to 3·4 Å., so that it would fit neatly on to a protein chain in the β-form. Combinations of nucleic acids and proteins—the nucleo-proteins—turn up repeatedly as important constituents of living cells, mostly with highly specialised functions.

COLLOIDAL MICELLES

The name "micelle" is given to a colloidal particle which is made up of a number of molecules held together by the ordinary forces of cohesion, or secondary valence forces. As a rule, the constituent molecules themselves consist of primary valence chains, and the association into a micelle is orderly, the chains all lying parallel to each other and linked at intervals by bonds of varying degrees of rigidity. The orderliness, however, is not so complete as it is in a true crystal, since the chains, although all parallel to one another, are set at random distances from each other, and are not all the same way up. Such partial orderliness is known as the *paracrystalline* or *mesomorphic* condition. Micelles of this kind are found typically in soap solutions; but some form of orientation takes place whenever a fibrous or laminar structure is formed, as we have seen with carbohydrates and proteins. The orientation, is not always spontaneous but may be the result of stretching or shearing forces while the structure is being formed. Molecules with a polar group at one end, such as those of fatty acids and soaps, will often form micelles with radial symmetry: all the polar groups, being attracted to the water, are on the surface, and the non-polar groups, being attracted to each other, will pack into the interior.

Such substances in which there are atoms, molecules or very small particles arranged in an orderly fashion (as seen most perfectly in crystals, for example), but in which the spacing or general arrangement is different in different directions in space, are known as *anisotropic*. They have the property that the velocity with which light is transmitted through them, as indicated by the refractive index, depends upon the relation between the direction of vibration of the light waves—i.e. the plane of polarisation —and the axes of the orderly arrangements. When there are only two different axes of orderliness, as in a fibre or flat sheet, the substance is said to be *birefringent*. Birefringence can be readily detected by the use of polarised light, and is a most useful method of detecting the existence of orientation of colloidal particles.

In most micelles, a certain number of water molecules are incorporated among the giant molecules which are the main constituent. But in some colloidal solutions, the amount of water in the disperse phase is quite large. The micelles then consist of a more concentrated sample of the continuous phase, and are known as *coacervates*. They form spontaneously in many colloidal systems, both inorganic and organic; and in spite of the relatively

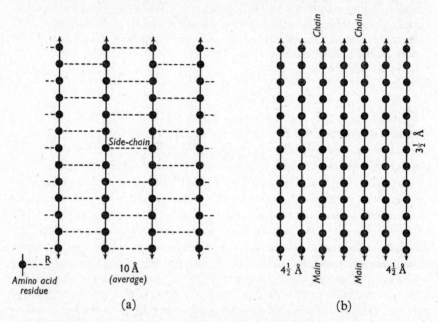

FIG. 6.2. DIAGRAMMATIC REPRESENTATION OF PROTEIN CHAINS

The chains are in the α-form: in (a) they are shown united into a grid by covalent and salt linkages between the side-chains; (b) represents a side view of a number of the grids shown in (a) superimposed on each other, and united into an aggregate or micelle by "backbone" linkages (hydrogen bonds).   (Astbury, 1940.)

large amount of water within them, are often birefringent and thus well orientated. They are known as "tactoids". On the other hand coacervation may only occur when the colloidal system is treated mildly in a manner which might lead to coagulation if the treatment were stronger.

The fibrous proteins normally exist as micelles, in which the main chains are packed alongside each other into sheets, and these sheets are then piled on one another, as indicated in Fig. 6.2. They are held in position by relatively loose unions (mainly hydrogen bonds) between the actual "backbones" themselves, and by stronger unions between appropriate side-chains (—S—S— linkages and salt bonds). The chains thus remain relatively extended, in spite of the thermal agitation which tends to make them fold up. But if these couplings are broken, say by alkaline hydrolysis, or in some cases merely by the application of hot water, the main chains can slip over each other, and may unite in a new configuration; in this way a permanent bend can be put in a hair, or other similar structure.

Alternatively, the main chains may collapse on themselves, and take up the "supercontracted" form. The X-ray diffraction pattern may then change in such a way as to indicate the presence of β-form chains at right angles to the main fibre direction. It is suggested that this may result from an extreme degree of folding; instead of having, say, three residues along the fibre direction, followed by three across, and so on, as in the α-form chain, we have, say three residues along the fibre direction followed by nine across, these being in the β-form. Rather more drastic treatment with reagents such as might be expected to block the reactive groups on the side-chains which form the cross-linkages, reduces the whole system to an amorphous condition and no definite X-ray diffraction pattern is obtained.

A more detailed discussion of the properties of macro-molecular systems will be found in the chapter by Bateman in Höber's text-book (1945).

THE STABILITY OF COLLOIDAL PARTICLES

If sand is shaken with water, and the mixture then allowed to stand, the sand rapidly falls to the bottom, leaving the water clear and free from grains. Why, then, do the particles of gold in Faraday's colloidal preparation, whose density is greater than that of sand, remain suspended for an indefinite time? It would seem that this is undoubtedly connected with their size. As has already been discussed, the particles of colloidal systems are sufficiently small for the velocity of thermal agitation to be at least comparable with the rate of sedimentation under gravity; Brownian movement is thus the chief cause of the permanence of the colloidal state. In addition, the *density* and *viscosity* of the medium in which the particles are suspended will clearly be of importance: the greater is the density, the less the effective weight of the particles, and the less the tendency to sink under gravity; the larger is the viscosity, the more slowly will the particles fall.

We are now faced with the problem, however, as to the nature of the forces which prevent the particles from sticking together and forming grains large enough to fall rapidly. The larger the number of particles into which a given mass is divided, the greater is the surface energy; consequently, by the principle of Carnot and Clausius, the system, if allowed, will change in such a way as to diminish this free energy. The presence of *electric charges* is one of the most important factors concerned in this. The surfaces of colloidal particles, like other interfaces, will be expected to possess electric charges; if they are all of the same sign, the particles will repel each other, and aggregation will be opposed. On the other hand, if by any means some are given charges of opposite sign to those of the rest, aggregation will occur as a result of their mutual attraction. That the electric charge is not the sole cause of permanent suspension, however, is shown by the fact that it can be reduced to zero without affecting the stability. The simple electrostatic repulsion, moreover, cannot, by itself, prevent two colloidal particles from coming into contact with each other, since it can be calculated that the kinetic energy may reach a value sufficient to overcome the repulsion that results from the observed value of the electrokinetic potential. On the other hand, the extremely large electrostatic fields that exist within the electric double layer will have the effect of holding the water dipoles firmly in position. It is calculated that by this means a skin of water might be held round each colloidal particle at a pressure of more than 18 atmospheres, and it is probable that these skins— called by some authors, the *lyospheres*—are incapable of penetrating each other. The effective thickness of these electrostatic fields can be calculated, and may well be of the order of size of the colloidal particles themselves. It is of note that Constantin and Perrin found that the diameter of the "repulsion spheres" between gamboge particles $0.66 \ \mu$ diameter was about $1.1 \ \mu$.

The Action of Electrolytes

The action of electrolytes on the stability of substances in the colloidal state is of considerable interest in view of what has been said in the previous chapter as to their profound and often complex action on the electric charge and potential at an interface. The fact that salts precipitated gold hydrosols was known to Faraday in 1858, and it was this action of salts which first attracted the attention of investigators. Schultze, in 1882, noticed that the power of various electrolytes increased with their valency much more than in simple proportion to the increased number of electric charges. Hardy, in 1900, by more quantitative methods, formulated a law according to which, if we call the precipitating power of a univalent ion x, that of a bivalent ion will be x^2, and that of a trivalent one x^3. The active ion is that one whose charge is of the opposite sign to that of the colloid precipitated. In Hardy's words: "The coagulative power of a salt is determined by the valency of one if its ions. This prepotent ion is either the negative or the positive according to whether the colloidal particles move down or up the potential gradient. The coagulating ion is always of the opposite electrical sign to the particle." This is known as "*Hardy's rule*".

Since we cannot add one ion without the other, we must discover which is the active one by taking a series of salts with the same anion or the same cation, respectively. We find, for example, that potassium chloride, sulphate and phosphate of the same concentration in potassium ions, have approximately the same effect on a negative colloid, say arsenious sulphide, although the valency of the anions is respectively one, two and three. On the other hand, the chlorides of potassium, calcium and lanthanum differ widely in their actions. On a positive colloid, the members of the latter series are equal, whereas the chloride, sulphate and phosphate of the same metal are of increasing potency, in that order.

Both Hardy's generalisations are now known to be approximate only. The ion whose charge is of the same sign as that of the colloid is not entirely without effect, but exerts a stabilising influence which increases with its valency. Furthermore, the relative coagulating power of different ions varies with the concentration of the colloid, so that no law so simple as the valency rule can be generally true.

Before proceeding further, it is necessary to remark that the two great classes of colloid, the lyophobe and the lyophile, differ widely in their sensitivity to the precipitating action of electrolytes, the former being very sensitive, and the latter comparatively insensitive. Egg-white, for example, a typical lyophile emulsoid, is precipitated by lanthanum ions in a concentration of about $0 \cdot 002$ M, whereas arsenious sulphide, a lyophobe suspensoid, is precipitated by the same ions in a concentration of $0 \cdot 00005$ M. It is not surprising, therefore, in view of Hardy's rule, that univalent ions, as far as their effects purely as charged ions are concerned, are practically inactive on lyophile colloids.

It is a difficulty in chemical analysis that precipitates will not deposit because of the absence of electrolytes to cause their aggression. Sometimes it is possible to add a trace of an appropriate positive or negative trivalent ion, which will produce immediate clearing.

In the preparation of sols of lyophobic substances by precipitation or disintegration, it is essential that no appreciable amounts of electrolyte should be present; otherwise, the sols are not permanent. On the other hand, it appears that stable sols cannot be formed when extreme precautions are taken to exclude all electrolytes other than those resulting from the dissociation of water. The sol particles apparently gain the electric charges necessary for stability very largely by adsorption of ions from the solution, and this cannot take place to a sufficient extent if the solution is exceedingly dilute.

The mechanism of the action of electrolytes must clearly be related to the neutralisation of the electric charge on the colloidal particles by the opposite charge on the precipitating ion. If the charge on the particles is neutralised, or reversed, by the adsorption of ions, it follows that these ions must be carried down with the precipitate. It was indeed found by Linder and Picton that when arsenious sulphide is precipitated by barium chloride, the barium ions go down with the precipitate, while the liquid becomes

acid from the hydrochloric acid set free. The barium ions are held fast to
the precipitate, and cannot be removed by mere washing with water,
although they can be replaced by other cations, when washed with solutions of their salts.

A difficulty which is sometimes felt with regard to the precipitation of
colloids by electrolytes should be mentioned. When one ion of the precipitating
salt is carried down with the coagulum, it must either be exchanged for an
equivalent amount of other kinds of ion which are displaced from the surface
of the particle; or the other ion, of opposite sign, must also be carried down
too, but in the outer sheets of the electric double layer. It is obvious that
one of the ions cannot be left in the solution uncompensated by ions of the
opposite sign.

Although this simple conception roughly describes the observed
phenomena, it is incomplete in many respects. In the first place, if precipitation occurs only when the charge is exactly neutralised, one would
expect that the quantity of the precipitating ion carried down with the
colloid would be inversely proportional to its valency; if a given charge is
neutralised by x trivalent ions, it should need $3x$ univalent ions. This,
however, has not been found to be true. As we saw in Chapter 5, the action
of electrolytes on the charge and potential at an interface may be complex,
and the effect on the charge is not necessarily identical with that on the
electrokinetic potential. As is shown in Fig. 6.3, suspensions of typhoid
bacilli which have been sensitised by treatment with "immune" serum
(serum from an animal which has been made immune to the action of the
bacteria) are agglutinated by the addition of various salts whenever the
concentration is such that the electrokinetic potential is reduced to less
than about 15 millivolts. If the addition of an electrolyte results in a
reversal of the sign of the charge, as with salts of aluminium, mercury and
copper, precipitation occurs over a range of concentrations when the
electrokinetic potential is within the critical value, positive or negative,
while at higher concentrations the suspension is again stable. At very high
concentrations again, when the electrokinetic potential falls once more,
precipitation occurs. Moreover, if the charge on the bacilli in the presence
of uni-univalent electrolytes is calculated by the methods discussed in
Chapter 5 (p. 209), it is found that it remains constant, or increases somewhat, as the concentration rises, even though the electrokinetic potential
falls. The potential decreases as a result of the increased density of the
diffuse double layer, while the increase of the charge is due, presumably,
to some specific adsorption (compare Fig. 5.10, p. 219). Results of the
same general nature may be observed in many different kinds of suspension.
It is reasonable to suppose, therefore, that the stability of colloidal particles
in general depends on the magnitude of the electrokinetic potential, rather

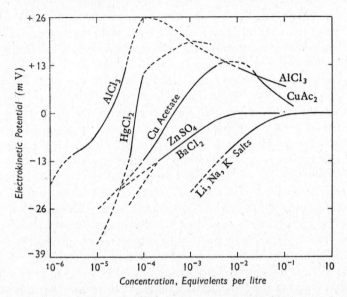

FIG. 6.3. EFFECT OF SALT CONCENTRATION ON THE ELECTROKINETIC POTENTIAL
AND AGGLUTINATION OF SENSITISED *Bacillus typhosus*

Ordinates: Electrokinetic potential, calculated from the electrophoretic mobility.

Abscissae: Concentration in equivalents per litre (logarithmic scale).

Over the range of concentration and potential where the lines are drawn in full, the bacteria were agglutinated; in other ranges, there was only partial or no agglutination. Note that agglutination occurred only when the electrokinetic potential was within the range ±13 millivolts, approximately.

Note also that the concentration necessary to reduce the potential to the limiting value depended on the valency of the cation, as is to be expected, since the bacteria are ordinarily negatively charged. All the salts of univalent cations used (LiBr, NaCl, Na acetate, NaNO$_3$, Na$_2$SO$_4$, and KCl) produced identical effects. Similarly the effects of ZnSO$_4$ and BaCl$_2$ were very nearly identical, but Cu acetate and HgCl$_2$ were not only more potent, but also reversed the sign of the charge, as did AlCl$_3$, probably owing to some specific adsorption. The actions of HCl and H$_2$SO$_4$ (not shown), also, were much greater than would be expected, the curves lying between those of Cu acetate and HgCl$_2$, and the charge was reversed; that of NaOH was small, and the critical potential was not reached.

(After Northrop and de Kruif, 1921.)

than on that of the charge; precipitation occurring when the electrokinetic potential has been reduced to a certain value.

The reversal of the sign of the charge, and restoration of stability, are illustrated, also, by an experiment of Mines in 1912. The blood corpuscles of the dog-fish *Scyllium* are agglutinated (aggregated) by cerium chloride in a concentration of 0·0008 M. In a concentration of 0·08 M. they remain in suspension. Tested by their direction of migration in an electric field, the corpuscles are found to have a negative charge when in a solution of sodium chloride corresponding to that of the blood plasma of the fish. In the strong cerium chloride solution, the charge is reversed, the corpuscles now being positively charged.

It must be admitted, however, that experimental observation makes it quite certain that the magnitude of the electrokinetic potential is not the only, or even in many circumstances, the most important, factor concerned in the maintenance of stability. In circumstances in which the charge remains reasonably constant, for example, we should expect the electrokinetic potential to vary more or less inversely as the square root of the ionic strength of the suspending fluid; the concentration of a given kind of ion, just necessary to produce a certain amount of aggregation, should thus vary inversely as its valency (compare equation 5.17, p. 208). In the rule of Hardy and Schulze, it is the logarithm of the aggregating power that is proportional to the valency. It seems that electrolytes, particularly those with multivalent ions, must affect the charge on the surface as well as the electrokinetic potential. The value of this potential, however, is probably of importance in deciding the minimum distance between two particles. We have already mentioned that it seems probable that the lyosphere of one particle cannot penetrate that of another. The coagulating action of neutral salts, on this hypothesis, would be due to their action in reducing the size of the lyospheres, thus permitting two particles to come into closer contact, and possibly within range of each other's cohesive, van der Waals, forces. That the lyospheres may be of quite considerable size in the absence of electrolytes, and very considerably reduced in their presence, is shown in the figures given in Table 5.2 (p. 208).

This point is further brought out by the fact that as the electrokinetic potential is reduced by increasing the electrolyte concentration, a value is first reached at which aggregation just begins, but proceeds very slowly. Further reduction in the electrokinetic potential results in an increase in the rate of aggregation, until a limit is reached, beyond which no further increase in rate is possible. Presumably at this point, at every collision, the particles come within the range of the cohesive forces, and the rate of aggregation depends only on the frequency of collisions. Indeed, the observed rate has been shown to agree well with the rate calculated by Smoluchowski on this hypothesis. When the electrokinetic potential is such that aggregation takes place very slowly, it is to be supposed that the thickness of the lyosphere is such that only those particles whose relative kinetic energy is abnormally large, can approach each other sufficiently closely to cohere.

Actually, it can be calculated that the energy required to bring two particles into contact is proportional to the quantity ζ^2/κ, where ζ is the electrokinetic potential and $1/\kappa$ is the mean radius of the ionic atmosphere. Increase in electrolyte concentration results both in a fall in ζ and a rise in κ. There will thus be a very sudden fall in the energy term as the electrolyte concentration increases.

In the last analysis, therefore, the criterion of whether a colloid will be precipitated by an electrolyte will be the magnitude of the cohesive forces between the particles. Lyophobe colloids, in which, as we have seen, the cohesion between the particles is large, will be easily precipitated; lyophile colloids, where the adhesion to the suspending fluid is greater than the cohesion between the particles, will not, in general, be precipitated even though the electrokinetic potential is reduced to zero. There is reason to suppose, however, that electrolytes may affect the cohesive forces, as well as the electrokinetic potential, possibly as a result of specific adsorption, or chemical reaction, at the surface of the particles. When Northrop and de Kruif, for example, used *Bacillus typhosus* which had not been specially sensitised by immune serum, they found that there was no agglutination even when the electrokinetic potential was reduced to zero, if the salt concentration needed to do so was greater than about 0·01 equivalents per litre. The relation between the electrokinetic potential and the concentration of the various electrolytes was very similar to that shown in Fig. 6.3 for sensitized bacteria. Tri- and quadrivalent ions, and copper ions, produced agglutination when the electrokinetic potential was reduced to less than about +15 mV, as in Fig. 6.3; but magnesium, calcium and sodium ions produced little or no agglutination in any concentration. This may be due to the relatively concentrated solutions of uni- and bivalent ions affecting the surface properties of the bacilli in some way, and Northrop and de Kruif have obtained some evidence for this; but copper ions and the tri- and quadrivalent ions certainly have other actions besides those of reducing the electrokinetic potential, since they reverse the sign of the charge.

The Hofmeister, or Lyotropic Series. It might reasonably be expected that the greater the hydration energy of an ion, or the greater the solvation, the more effective would it be in withdrawing the water molecules from the lyospheres of the colloidal particles, and so permitting two such particles to come into close contact. Such action would be altogether independent of any purely electrical action that the ion may have on the double layer. Multivalent ions do in fact, have greater hydration energies than the univalent ions (Chapter 4, p. 127), and this may account, in part, for some of the failures of the simple valency rule.

Hofmeister, in 1888, studied the relative effectiveness of a number of electrolyte solutions in salting out albumin, and arranged the anions in the following order of decreasing effectiveness:

Citrate > Tartrate > Sulphate > Acetate > Chloride > Nitrate > Chlorate

Cations could only be arranged in a rather indefinite order.

Studies of other colloidal properties, such as viscosity, osmotic pressure, precipitation of suspensoids, etc., give very similar, although not identical, series for the anions, and indicate a descending order of cations roughly as follows:

Th > Al > Ba > Sr > Ca > Mg > H > Cs > Rb > K > Na > Li

When we consider these series, there does not seem to be any very obvious reason for the different behaviour of the various salts, except for the general decrease of effectiveness with reduction in valency. A simple chemical effect seems to be excluded by the fact that the same series is found in the action on substances so different in constitution as albumin, gelatin, agar and starch. As Hatschek pointed out in 1912, the various phenomena all appear to be manifestations of a change in the distribution of water between the two phases; the salts of the Hofmeister series may be supposed to do this as a result of their hydration energies, and the cations, for example, appear in roughly, but by no means exactly, the same order in both series (compare Chapter 4, p. 127).

There can be no doubt that the actions of ions on colloidal systems are not due solely to their electrical charges, nor, as it would appear, simply to their hydration energies. We must take account, also, of their individual "chemical" properties.

Complex Colloidal Systems

When a solution of an electropositive colloid, such as ferric hydroxide, is added to one of an electronegative colloid, such as arsenious sulphide, if the proportion of the two is such that the charges will mutually annul each other, both colloids are precipitated as a complex, and the solution is left free from both. The precipitate will, in such a case, have no charge. If excess of either colloid is present, only partial precipitation will occur, and both colloids will be present in the precipitate and in the liquid above, although in different proportion in the two. In other words, we have an adsorption compound formed, whose composition depends on the relative concentration of its components in the solution, and whose electric charge has the sign of that colloid which is in excess.

The mutual precipitation of colloids of opposite sign may explain why the effect of a given amount of electrolyte in precipitating a colloid depends on the suddenness with which it is added. If a quantity, capable of precipitating when added all at once, is added in small portions at a time, a process of acclimatisation, or tolerance, is established, and no apparent effect is produced. Sudden addition of the electrolyte may reverse the sign of the charge on some of the particles, without affecting that on the others; mutual precipitation will then occur. Gradual addition will affect the electrokinetic potential of all the particles equally, and may not reduce it to the critical value for precipitation.

The distinction between the formation of an adsorption compound and a true chemical combination is well shown by the following experiment. If we take a (colloidal) solution of the free acid of the dye Congo-red, which has a blue colour, and add to it quickly a solution (also colloidal) of thorium hydroxide, a precipitate of a *blue* colour is formed. This precipitate can be filtered off, or better centrifuged off, and resuspended in water. On allowing it to stand at room temperature, it slowly becomes red and part of it goes into solution; this change can be produced quickly by boiling. Now the surfaces of the particles of the Congo-red acid have a negative charge, as can be shown by electrophoresis; the particles of the thorium hydroxide, on the other hand, have a positive charge. There will therefore be an attraction between them, and on coming into contact, the particles will adhere. But now we have free acid and free base in close apposition, although uncombined as shown by the blue colour. Chemical combination—or perhaps chemisorption—then takes place slowly (more rapidly on heating) and the red colour characteristic of the Congo-red salt appears. We have encountered similar phenomena in Chapter 5 in connection with adsorption on macroscopic surfaces.

In general, mutual aggregation does not take place when lyophilic colloids of opposite charge are mixed; solutions of different kinds of protein, for example, can be made without risk of mutual precipitation. The lyophilic particles, being surrounded by a firmly attached layer of water molecules, cannot come into contact with each other, even when subjected to mutual electrostatic attraction. In suitable conditions, however, complex coacervates may develop, containing several different components; some relatively specific chemical forces must be involved in this, such as hydrogen bonds, or salt linkages between atoms or groups of atoms, or the formation of chelates by atoms of multivalent metals. In such complexes, as in those between oppositely charged lyophobic colloids, there is no quantitative, stoichiometric, relation between the constituents; they may be present in any ratio, within limits. These peculiar types of compound are commonly met with wherever colloidal systems are present, not least in living organisms; of particular interest to the physiologist, as already remarked, are the coacervates which contain carbohydrates, proteins and lipids, in varying proportions.

PROTECTIVE ACTION AND SENSITISATION

It was known to Faraday in 1858 that the precipitating action of "salt" on gold solutions could be prevented by the addition of a trace of "jelly". Other lyophile colloids have this action, although in different degree, and the fact serves as the basis of the "gold number" introduced by Schulz and Zsigmondy as a means of characterising different proteins. It seems certain that this *protection* against the action of electrolytes is due to the deposition of a film of the lyophile colloid over the surface of the solid, lyophobic, particles.

The protective action is not necessarily complete. With arsenious sulphide and with Congo-red, for example, actual precipitation by calcium sulphate may be prevented by the addition of albumin, as with gold sols; but if such mixtures are carefully compared with the originals, it may be seen that they are somewhat more turbid. Under the ultra-microscope (p. 268 below), Congo-red in the absence of electrolytes cannot be resolved into particles. After the addition of serum albumin and calcium sulphate, although no precipitation occurs, as when salt is added alone, the solution is nevertheless seen to be full of very distinct, but not brilliant, particles.

In some cases, the lyophobic sol becomes more sensitive to electrolytes in the presence of a lyophilic colloid. It is then said to be "sensitised". A vanadium pentoxide sol, for example, is precipitated by gelatin in very low concentrations. Sensitisation probably occurs as a result of a single "protecting" molecule or micelle being simultaneously adsorbed on two or more particles, which are thereby held together; the aggregate so formed is too large to remain permanently in suspension.

It appears that sensitisation changes into protection when there is just enough of the lyophile colloid present to form a complete coating to the lyophobic particles. When this has occurred, a certain amount of aggregation does not necessarily result in precipitation, as was observed with Congo-red in the experiments just described.

Monomolecular Films of Proteins

The films of lyophilic colloid, and especially of proteins, which are responsible for "protection" and "sensitisation" are, for the most part, monomolecular; such "monolayers" may be more closely studied by the methods described in Chapter 5 (pp. 177-180). All soluble proteins can be spread at the interface between a watery solution and air or an oily fluid (bromobenzene has been used, for example). A small drop of a concentrated solution, or a small particle of solid protein, need only be placed on the surface of a suitable solution, which is best made acid, neutral or alkaline according to the particular protein that is used. In acid solutions spreading is facilitated by anions, and in alkaline solutions, by cations. The univalent ions increase in efficiency with decrease in the degree of hydration—i.e. the lyotropic series is followed; multivalent ions are considerably more effective than univalent ions.

Protein monolayers are highly compressible, but cannot be regarded as gaseous since there is a limiting area beyond which they will not spread. When occupying this limiting area, the thickness of the film is such that the main amino-acid chains must be lying flat at the surface, instead of being folded into a globular form, as they are when the molecule is in solution. According to Langmuir the chains are held at the interface by the hydrophobic groups in the molecule which place themselves in the air (or oil) side of the interface instead of being enclosed within the hydrophilic groups, as they are in the globular, soluble, form of the molecule. These hydrophobic groups are free to move about the surface except in so far as they are tied to each other by the hydrophilic chains. Such a structure would account for the great compressibility of the film. The existence of a limiting area indicates that all the protein molecules in the film are joined together, probably by means of the bonds that previously kept each molecule folded; instead of different parts of the same chain being united, junctions are made between one chain and another.

Compression of a protein monolayer results in an increase in the viscosity, until, with sufficient compression, a definite rigidity appears; the film has acquired the properties of a gel. It is probable that this occurs when the chains have been forced so close together that each becomes firmly united to its neighbours at several points. If the film is held for some time at this, or a somewhat greater, degree of compression, it will no longer expand when the compressing force is released; crystallisation, or coagulation, has taken place and the protein is "denatured". If the film has not been compressed, however, the molecules can, in some cases, be made to return to the globular form and to go into solution without any great change in their properties. Thus pepsin has been spread on an interface, and returned into solution without any great loss of proteolytic activity.

Protein monolayers, also, are readily formed on the surfaces of "inert" particles, such as quartz, glass or collodion, or those of suspensoid colloids as described above; the particles then become sensibly identical, as colloids, with particles of protein. Thus, for example, the sign of the charge on the particles of a gold sol cannot be changed by moderate changes in the acidity of the suspending fluid; when "protected" by a protein such as gelatin, the sign of the charge changes when the acidity is changed in such a way as to pass through the iso-electric point of the gelatin. The fine particles of fat present in the blood stream of the higher mammals, and known as "chylomicrons", also appear to possess such a protective film of protein, and they do not behave like droplets of oil. The red blood corpuscles, on the other hand, are not so "protected". It is noteworthy that the mobility and iso-electric point of such coated particles are the same as those of the protein in solution, so that the unfolding of the molecular chains of the surface seems to have no appreciable effect on the electrokinetic properties.

EMULSIONS

A considerable amount of study has been devoted to the conditions of stability of colloidal solutions in which both the continuous and the disperse phase are liquids. Such emulsions have the interesting and important property of being able to exist with either of the two liquid components in the continuous phase; thus if we consider the two components which have been most studied, watery solutions and oils, we can prepare either an oil-in-water, or a water-in-oil, emulsion.

The stability of the oil-in-water emulsions is determined both by the electric charge on the particles, and by the surface energy at the interface. While it is possible to prepare emulsions in which the stability is maintained only by the electric charge, the majority and those of greatest interest, are only stable by virtue of the presence at the interface of a "stabiliser" whose function is to convert the surface of the oil particles from lyophobic to lyophilic, and to reduce the interfacial tension to a very low value. Empirically, it has been found that when this is reduced to some 5-10 dynes/cm., emulsification can be produced by shaking; when it is reduced to less than 1 dyne/cm., emulsification takes place spontaneously.

The stabilisers are mainly salts of long-chain paraffins and soaps, which are strongly adsorbed at the oil-water interface; maximum stability is attained when the adsorbed molecules are close-packed. Proteins also act as stabilisers, their action being essentially the same as that of the "protection" of lyophobic colloids, as discussed in the previous section. They probably act partly by forming an elastic semi-solid film at the interface, and so hinder any change of form such as would be involved in the coalescence of several particles on collision. The most stable emulsions are formed by using two stabilisers, both of which consist of relatively large non-polar molecules with polar groups attached: one of these should be soluble in oil and the other in water. It is further necessary that the molecular configurations of the two stabilisers should be such that a complex can be formed at the interface; the non-polar parts within the particles, as well as the polar parts just outside the interface, must be such as to fit together neatly. In this way, an extremely condensed surface film is formed, and the interfacial tension is reduced to a very low value. The water soluble substance, in addition, should be ionisable, so that the oil particles may be electrically charged.

Schulman and Cockbain, for example, have obtained very stable emulsions of liquid paraffin ("nujol") in water by using cholesterol as the oil-soluble stabiliser and sodium cetyl sulphate or gelatin as the water-soluble stabiliser. They demonstrated the necessity for complex formation at the interface by using sodium cetyl sulphate and either oleyl alcohol, or elaidyl alcohol (which are cis-trans isomers) as the oil-soluble substances. Very poor emulsions were formed with the former, and good ones with the latter.

Phase Reversal. It was shown by Clowes in 1916 that if soaps are used as stabilisers, oil-in-water emulsions are formed in the presence of univalent cations, while water-in-oil emulsions are formed in the presence of bivalent cations. If both types of cation are present in a certain ratio, either the phase relations are variable, or no emulsion can be formed. Accordingly, if a calcium salt is added to an oil-in-water emulsion which has been stabilised by a sodium salt of a soap, the phases can be reversed, and a water-in-oil emulsion formed; the critical sodium/calcium ratio (in moles) lying between 50/1 and 100/1. This antagonism between, say, sodium and calcium in the formation of emulsions recalls the antagonism in their action on living cells. Now it is clear from the discussion in the previous chapter (pp. 216-218), that the concentrations of sodium and calcium ions in the surface phase of the emulsion may be quite different from those in the bulk of the solution (compare equation 5.13). As has been pointed out by Danielli, the ionic distribution ratio, r, in these circumstances may quite reasonably attain a value of 20; if we consider a bulk solution containing 0·1 M. NaCl, and the "critical" concentration of $CaCl_2$ is, say, 0·002 M., the surface phase will contain $20 \times 0·1 = 2$ M. NaCl, and $(20)^2 \times 0·002 = 0·8$ M. $CaCl_2$. The Na/Ca ratio in the surface phase is thus only 2·5, and the sodium and calcium ions are present in approximately equivalent concentrations. These considerations make it easier to understand why the phase reversal should occur when the Na/Ca ratio in the bulk solution is so large.

In general, it seems as if the phase relations of the emulsion are determined by the solubility of the stabiliser; if it is more soluble in water than in oil, then water is the continuous phase; if it is more soluble in oil than in water, oil is the continuous phase. It is, however, probably more correct to say that water-in-oil emulsions are only formed when the surface film possesses considerable rigidity, and consequently is not electrically charged; a charged film cannot be rigid, owing to the repulsion between the charges. The presence of multivalent cations will bring about this condition, since they will discharge the oil droplets which would otherwise be negatively charged by the anions of the long-chain stabiliser; and, moreover, they will combine with several of these univalent anions and so have the effect of linking them together and reducing their mobility. The discharged oil droplets will coalesce, and the intervening water molecules are squeezed out as a result of the affinity between the polar groups of the adsorbed stabilising molecules.

GELS

When a gelatin solution, which is a freely-flowing liquid at temperatures above 20°-25°, is cooled, it "sets" to a substance which has the property of preserving the shape into which it is trimmed. It has, also, elasticity of form, so that, within limits, it returns to its original form after distortion. Clearly, a form of coagulation has taken place, since the particles of gelatin, previously free to move relatively to one another, can now no longer do so. A gel, however, differs from an ordinary coagulum, in that it contains, and as it were immobilises, an enormous proportion of the dispersion medium; in some cases over 99 per cent. of the gel may be water.

It is noteworthy that these very dilute gels, which have considerable structural rigidity, although consisting so largely of a fluid medium, are derived from colloidal solutions whose particles are very long and thin. We picture these particles, therefore, cohering at their ends only, and so forming a felt-work amidst the solution. The structure might thus be compared with a three-dimensional wire netting, or barbed wire entanglement. Such structures have a considerable mechanical rigidity, although the actual amount of solid material present is quite small. Such end-to-end cohesion of the particles may easily result during the formation of micelles by long-chain giant molecules. Some of the molecules may take up positions with one end in one micelle, and the other in another; the two micelles will thus be firmly united. Such formations are believed to occur, for example, in the jellies formed by carbohydrate molecules, such as starch. On the other hand, the micelles may become joined by secondary valence forces, not side-by-side, in relatively close packing, but end-to-end. Such partial association might be expected to occur if the cohesive forces were not very large. Two micelles, for example, on colliding, remain attached to each other in whatever relative orientations they happen to be; strong cohesional forces would then pull them into a closely packed position. It is not unexpected, therefore, to find that many gel structures are unstable, and spontaneously change into coagulation; the closely packed condition is the stable one, and thermal agitation eventually brings the micelles into the appropriate orientations. During this process, to which the name "synaeresis" has been given, the whole gel structure shrinks, and part of the dispersion fluid, previously incorporated within it, is driven out, and appears as drops on the surface.

Continuous growth of a felt-work structure may easily lead to the formation of a honeycomb structure. In this, membranes of the dispersed material enclose spaces containing the dispersion medium and there is thus a phase reversal. What was previously a continuous phase is now dispersed within the framework formed by what was previously the disperse phase.

The two phases are not, in general, made up of the pure dispersion medium and the pure dispersed material respectively, as is seen from the following figures, given by Hardy for a ternary mixture of gelatin, alcohol and water. The numbers represent grams of gelatin per 100 c.c. of the gelatin solution at 15°.

Total Mixture.	Internal Phase.	External Phase.
6·7	17·0	2·0
13·5	18·0	5·5
36·5	8·5	40·0

Bachmann, moreover, observed that the intermicellar fluid in a gel of 1 per cent. sodium palmitate, contained 0·06 per cent. of the salt.

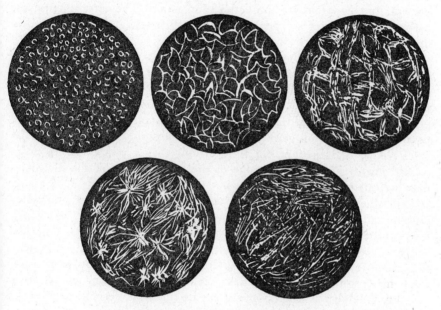

FIG. 6.4. THE FORMATION OF SOAP GELS, AS SEEN IN THE ULTRA-MICROSCOPE, MAGNIFIED ABOUT 200-300 FOLD

Upper row: successive stages in the gelation of a 5 per cent. solution of potassium stearate in water. The particles, seen on the left, elongate progressively into threads, and join up to form the felt-work seen on the right.

Lower row: sodium stearate solution, about 10 per cent. in water, freshly prepared and some time later. On the left are seen the threads, characteristic of the gel, growing out from a number of particles: on the right, the threads are beginning to break up again into separate crystals.   (Bachmann, 1912.)

The formation of gels by pure soaps, as observed in the ultra-microscope is illustrated in Fig. 6.4. It is well known that a fairly strong hot solution of sodium or potassium stearate or palmitate sets to a more or less transparent, tenacious jelly, when it cools. This usually changes later into an opaque, white, friable mass. The former corresponds to a fine felt-work, as seen under the ultra-microscope; while the latter is obviously crystalline. The structure of the gel, as first formed, shows a strongly polarised cone of light and is, therefore, of an extremely fine degree of heterogeneity. As cooling proceeds, the particles become larger and Brownian movement is easily seen. These particles continue to increase in number, obstruct one another in movements, and form threads, which result in the production of a felt-work. After a time, this felt-work changes into distinct separate crystals. Whether the first particles are to be regarded strictly as "micelles", that is, as aggregates with crystalline properties, is a matter for argument. It is clear, however, that the vectorial forces, which ultimately result in the formation of distinct crystals, must be always present, but apparently require time for action. The ultra-microscopic particles, probably of a crystalline form, at first separate out arranged in threads and networks.

It must not be thought, however, that gels are only formed from substances with long-chain molecules. Relatively simple inorganic molecules, such as ferric hydroxide and silica, readily form gels, and some of the most interesting, as containing the least amount of solid substance per unit volume, are formed by inorganic substances such as vanadium pentoxide and calcium germanate. It must be supposed that these molecules readily agglutinate in the form of long chains, rather than in close-packed heaps. Further knowledge of the configuration of the molecules may indicate why this should be so.

That the forces which attach the colloidal particles together, and maintain the gel structure, are relatively weak is shown by the ease with which they can be broken. In some cases, such as gelatin, the increased thermal agitation consequent on a relatively small rise in temperature can destroy the structure and the gel is converted into a sol. In nearly every case, mechanical agitation, more or less violent, has the same effect. This property is known as *Thixotropy*. It is particularly noticeable, in the very dilute gels formed by highly anisotropic particles. In these, simple shaking of the solution results in a complete breakdown of the gel structure and the formation of a sol with practically the fluidity of water. In the more concentrated gels, thixotropy is only observed as a result of more violent mechanical disturbance. Thus mere shaking has no effect, but repeated shearing, as by being forced through a narrow tube, will bring about a partial breakdown of the structure. This will be referred to again when dealing with the viscosity of colloidal solutions. The extremely violent mechanical agitation produced by supersonic sound waves will break down the structure of almost any gel. Clearly, then, a colloidal solution will be regarded as a gel or a sol according to the mechanical disturbance to which it is subjected. In practice, it is rather arbitrarily accepted that if the structure is sufficiently rigid to withstand the gravitational forces on it, it is a gel.

The behaviour of gels towards electrical forces, also, is peculiar. In spite of the fact that a gel is rigid, in the sense that its particles cannot move relative to one another under the influence of gravity, it presents unexpectedly little opposition to the movement by electrical forces of particles within it. Thus the mobility of an ion is not very much less in a gel than it is in a sol of the same total concentration. A small ion might be imagined as passing readily between the meshes of the felt-work, or other structure, but such an explanation cannot account for the fact that the mobility of relatively large particles, up to 50μ diameter is unaffected by the presence of the gel structure. The structure is sufficiently rigid to prevent them settling under the influence of the gravitational field, but appears to have little influence on their rate of movement under an electrical field. With relatively stiff gels, it is sometimes necessary to "work" the particle by moving it backwards and forwards several times before the mobility falls to a steady value. This suggests that the structure is broken down largely by the shearing action of the moving particle, just as it is when the gel is forced through a narrow tube. It is possible, also, that the electrical field has some action on the constituent particles of the gel; some degree of orientation may be produced, so that pathways as it were, are formed in a direction parallel to that of the field.

IMBIBITION

One of the most obvious characteristics of gels is the amount of dispersion medium—in most cases water—that they will take up, and the great pressures which have to be exerted before it can be removed. The pressures that can be exerted by a dry gel in the presence of water are enormous; starch, for example, is capable of exerting a pressure of over 2,000 atmospheres and the stalk of the sea-weed *Laminaria* has been found to take up 16 per cent. of water even when exposed to a pressure of 42 atmospheres.

The process of imbibition is usually, though not always, attended by an increase in the volume of the gel. The inorganic gels, such as silica, take up water without change in volume, whereas the organic gels such as gelatin, starch, agar (the colloid responsible for the swelling of sea-weed) all increase very considerably in volume. But even in this case, the combined volume of gel and water taken up is always less after imbibition than before. Pure water is very considerably compressed when incorporated in the gel.

This compression of water can be demonstrated in the following way. Pieces of the dried material, such as *Laminaria*, are attached to the submerged part of a hydrometer, and the scale adjusted to a convenient point by addition of weights. As the material swells, the hydrometer sinks, showing that the water which has become part of the imbibition system has increased in density. Of course, the temperature must be kept constant.

Since the volume of the water is reduced during imbibition, one would expect, from the principle of Le Chatelier that the temperature would rise. This is, indeed, the case, and the heat of imbibition is an easily measurable quantity, of the order of 0·2-1cal./g. of colloid.

The presence or absence of swelling during imbibition is, presumably, decided by the firmness of the attachments between the colloidal particles in the gel framework. It is probable, however, that it is not so much the primary valence links in the main chains that are of importance here, as the secondary valence links between one chain and another. Weak links here will allow the chains to slide over one another, and so allow the whole chain of micelles to lengthen. Primary valence chains of helical or zig-zag form also will be more easily stretched than straight ones. In the limit, if the linkages are weak enough, the thermal energy of the constituent molecules may be sufficient to break the connection altogether. In this case swelling will proceed indefinitely and the gel will be converted into a sol. This occurs if solid gelatin, for example, is placed in warm water; in cold water, the thermal energy is inadequate, the swelling reaches a limit, and the gel remains intact.

The swelling of gels is much affected by the presence of *electrolytes*, and especially of acids and alkalies. The action of the latter is especially pronounced on the swelling of protein gels, and is undoubtedly connected with their properties as amphoteric electrolytes: the amount of water taken up is a minimum at the iso-electric point, but is not zero. Imbibition, therefore, depends, to some extent, on the presence of an electric charge on the particles. The presence of neutral salts reduces the amount of water taken up by imbibition, in much the same way as they depress the electro-kinetic potential.

The exact nature of the process whereby the water is taken up into the gel has been the subject of some dispute. In some cases, notably the inorganic gels, it is possible to demonstrate the existence of microscopic pores and cracks. Water would be held in these by ordinary capillary forces, just as it is in a capillary tube, but it would not be subjected to very great compression, nor is there any reason why a detectable amount of heat should be evolved. Moreover, such capillary water should distend the structure as a whole.

It seems more probable that most of the water is held by an adsorption process. It is known that water can be adsorbed at an interface, the molecules being held by the Van der Waals, or secondary valence, forces. In addition, as already mentioned, it is highly probable that the water dipoles would be firmly held in the enormous electrostatic field that surrounds a charged particle. The water of imbibition is, in fact, largely to be identified with the water held in the lyospheres. Thus an electrically neutral gel would take up water by a process of molecular adsorption on the gel structure; if given an electric charge, more would be taken up as a result of the presence of the electric field. In addition, there may be some water taken into the interior of the micelles, in a form somewhat analogous to water of crystallisation. In this case, the micellar structure is disturbed, and the X-ray patterns may be destroyed; adsorption of water on the surface of the micelle leaves the X-ray pattern unaffected. The evolution of heat, the reduction in volume, and the action of electrolytes are all adequately accounted for on this hypothesis.

On the other hand Procter and Wilson, and later Loeb, showed that the swelling of proteins, especially gelatin, could be explained as an osmotic phenomenon. The gel, it is true, is not surrounded by a semi-permeable membrane, but the cohesion of the molecules restricts their movements just as effectively. Water, therefore, will be drawn into the gel in just the same way as it is drawn into an osmometer. This point of view will be discussed in rather more detail in a later section.

BOUND AND FREE WATER

The water molecules which are held in the lyospheres under considerable compression, and thus at least part of those which are taken up by gels during imbibition, do not behave as ordinary water molecules, or as components of the continuous phase. The three chief criteria that have been used to determine the presence of such "bound" water are: (1) some part of the total water present in the system cannot be frozen out as ice crystals, even at very low temperatures; (2) some part of the water cannot dissolve substances that are readily soluble in the "free" water; and (3) a certain amount of water is present in crystals or particles of the pure colloid which have been separated mechanically from the mother liquor and "dried" in air.

(1) The fraction of the total water that has been frozen may be estimated by determining the quantity of heat which is required to melt it, or the change in volume when it melts.

(2) A known, and rather large, amount of cane-sugar is added to the system under investigation, and the depression of the freezing point is measured. Alternatively, and better, only small quantities of some extra solute—usually sodium chloride—are added, and the change in vapour pressure is measured thermoelectrically (Chapter 3, p. 90).

(3) The amount of water bound in the crystals or particles may be discovered either by direct comparison of the water content of the crystals and the mother liquor, or may be inferred from the density of the crystals in comparison with that of the dry substance.

On the whole the determinations by all the methods are consistent with the existence of about 0·2-0·5 g. of bound water associated with each gram

I

of protein, the exact amount being different in different proteins. Determinations by the method involving freezing of the solution and measurement of the amount of ice formed by the heat required to melt it, and by the method involving the addition of relatively large concentrations of sugar, both give values considerably higher than those obtained by other methods. There are reasons for supposing, however, that these methods are less reliable than the others.

The distinction between "bound" and "free" water can never be an absolute one; there is almost certainly a gradation from the very tightly bound water within the colloidal micelles and which is part of the molecular structure, to the less tightly bound water of the lyospheres, and thus to the completely "free" water. The problem is thus complicated by the difficulty of measuring the total water content of a colloid. The more rigorous are the methods employed for drying it, the more "bound" water is removed, and the limit is only set, particularly in the case of the organic colloids, by the complete destruction of the colloidal material.

The water which is "bound" by colloids is not essentially different from the water of solvation taken up by ions (Chapter 4, p. 127), and its precise definition is equally uncertain. Owing to the relatively large size of the colloidal micelles, and the relatively large fraction of the total volume of the system which they occupy, it may, however, be quantitatively rather more significant in systems of interest to the physiologist. It may be concluded, nevertheless, that at least at the concentrations ordinarily found in living systems, the fraction of the total water present that is "bound" is not of very great significance; and, indeed, some authors are not convinced that it exists at all. We are, in any case, justified in expressing the concentrations of such solutions in terms of the total water content, without making correction for the amount that is "bound".

A discussion of the whole problem of bound water will be found in the article by J. B. Bateman in Höber's *Physical Chemistry of Cells and Tissues* (1945, Section 2, Chapter 7), including a Table giving the values found for a number of different proteins by the various methods that have been used.

PROTEINS

Proteins are probably the most important colloidal constituents of living organisms; they are thus of particular interest to the physiologist. As already described (p. 235 above), the giant protein molecules are built up by the union of a large number of amino-acid molecules. The end members of the main chain, and those attached to side chains, all retain their properties as amphoteric electrolytes, and proteins, therefore, are also amphoteric electrolytes. Their properties as colloids, will depend, as do those of

other colloids, on the electric charge of the particles, whether giant molecules or micelles; but unlike many other colloids, the charge is determined
chiefly by the electrolytic dissociation of the constituent amino-acids.
Proteins, therefore, will be positively charged and behave as bases, in acid
solutions, and will be negatively charged and behave as acids, in alkaline
solutions, the precise hydrogen ion concentration at which the reversal
occurs depending on the particular protein considered. The behaviour of
proteins in solution, like that of other colloidal systems, will depend on the
electrolyte composition of the solution, but the hydrogen ion concentration
will be particularly important, not so much the absolute value as the
amount by which it departs from the iso-ionic point of the protein
concerned.

Proteins are lyophilic, and are not coagulated even at the iso-electric
point, or in the presence of electrolytes in sufficiently high concentration
to reduce the electrokinetic potential to zero. Very high concentrations of
electrolytes, however, will have a "salting-out" effect, removing water
from the lyospheres and bringing about precipitation. Saturated solutions
of ammonium sulphate and sodium sulphate are frequently used for precipitating proteins, and many can be made to crystallise by this means,
notably egg albumin, as was first shown by Sørensen. Other proteins, such
as haemoglobin, can be made to crystallise by merely cooling a solution of
high concentration to low temperatures; these proteins, therefore, behave
as ordinary crystalloidal substances in this respect.

It is not at all easy to identify proteins, or to separate one from another
by purely chemical methods. The particular kinds of amino-acid contained in any particular protein can be identified, after complete hydrolysis,
most readily by paper chromatography. But its chemical and physical
properties depend more on the relative proportions of the amino-acids,
and on the order in which they are arranged, than on their chemical
identity. Some proteins, however, contain an unusually high proportion of
basic amino-acids, and many contain special "prosthetic" groups which
can be identified chemically. Proteins, in general, are identified largely by
the ease with which they may be salted-out, by their molecular weights,
and above all by their electrical properties, i.e. their electrophoretic
mobilities and iso-electric points.

Electrophoresis is a valuable method for separating into its components
a mixture of proteins in solution. For this purpose, the acidity of the solution
is adjusted, if possible, to be close to the iso-electric point of one of the components, and well removed from those of the others. When the iso-electric
points are such that this cannot readily be done, it is advantageous to oppose
the continuous movement of the proteins towards one or other of the electrodes, by a slow flow of the solvent solution. Very prolonged electrophoresis
can thus be carried out without the proteins coming into contact with the

electrodes; small differences in the mobilities will thus produce a considerable degree of separation. Somewhat similar arrangements can be made when using paper electrophoresis.

In Fig. 6.5 is shown, as an example, the results of electrophoresis of raw egg white, and of the solutions obtained in successive stages of purification; this was done both by electrophoresis in a counter-flow apparatus of the type designed by Tiselius (shown in Fig. 5.8, p. 213), and by chemical methods.

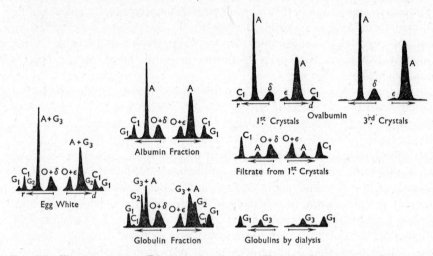

FIG. 6.5. ELECTROPHORETIC PATTERNS GIVEN IN THE TISELIUS APPARATUS BY SOLUTIONS OBTAINED IN SUCCESSIVE STAGES IN THE SEPARATION OF THE PROTEINS CONTAINED IN EGG WHITE

Raw egg white was separated into the albumin fraction and the globulin fraction by precipitation with ammonium sulphate: the albumin (A) was further purified by repeated crystallisation, the ovomucoid (O) and conalbumin (C_1) remaining in the filtrate; the globulins (G_1, G_2 and G_3) were purified by dialysis against water. The peaks marked δ and ϵ are not due to the presence of a separate protein, but are effects produced by the boundaries between the protein solution and the buffer solution.

The arrows show the direction of movement of the proteins in the electric field in the two limbs of the apparatus: "r" indicates rising away from the initial boundary, "d" indicates descending from it.   (Longworth, Cannan and MacInnes, 1940.)

Jacques Loeb, in a series of papers which he summarised in his monograph (1924) was responsible for calling attention to the mutual relations of a number of properties of protein solutions which vary with the acidity and electrolyte concentration of the solution. In the first place, there is the osmotic pressure, which will be discussed in detail later. Then there is the solubility, in water or alcohol-water mixtures, which falls to a minimum when the charge is reduced to zero, but rises on each side of the iso-electric point. Finally, there is the viscosity of some protein solutions, and the swelling of protein gels, both of which are, in effect, measures of the amount of water taken up by the protein micelles.

Starting from the assumption that the charge on the protein molecules resulted solely from electrolytic dissociation, he pointed out that the osmotic pressure must vary with hydrogen ion and electrolyte concentrations according to the laws of membrane equilibria (Chapter 5, pp. 201-205). Moreover, since the protein micelles would behave as small osmometers, the proteins being immobilised by the cohesional forces, the amount of water taken up, and hence the viscosity and swelling, would follow the osmotic pressure; viscosity and swelling would also be regulated by membrane equilibria. The solubility of gelatin and some other proteins in alcohol-water mixtures also might be expected to depend on the amount of water taken up by the micelles. The greater the osmotic pressure of the micelles, the greater must be the alcohol concentration outside them before the water is lost and precipitation occurs. On the basis of these considerations, Loeb concluded that the effect of electrolytes on the charge of the protein molecules, and on the properties related to it, depended only on the valency of the ions involved; the existence of the Hofmeister, or lyotropic, series was denied. Nevertheless, while Loeb was correct in assuming that the charge on the protein molecules is *primarily* determined by electrolytic dissociation, it is necessary to admit that preferential adsorption of ions may also occur. The effect of a neutral salt does not, in fact, depend only on the valencies of the ions: there are, in addition, specific effects depending on their hydration energies and chemical properties. The iso-electric point, for example, of many proteins is shifted in the presence of electrolytes, particularly those with multivalent or organic ions. The protein zwitterion appears to combine chemically with many anions, as well as with multivalent cations, according to the equation:

$$Na^+ + Cl^- + {}^+Pr^- = (ClPr)^- + Na^+$$

Or, alternatively, we can say that the protein molecule preferentially adsorbs anions and multivalent cations. In view of the continuous gradation between van der Waals adsorption, chemisorption and chemical combination, it is doubtful whether there is any significant difference between these descriptions. The existence of such combination does not, of course mean that Loeb's applications of the concepts of membrane equilibria are unsound; account must be taken, however, of the fact that the charge on the protein molecules or micelles is not determined solely by the hydrogen ion concentration.

DENATURATION

The soluble, lyophilic, proteins are all readily converted into a lyophobic form, in which they either become totally insoluble in water, or at least insoluble at the iso-electric point. Such "denaturation" is most easily brought about by heating the solution (the coagulation of egg white is a familiar example), by the action of ultra-violet radiation, or by shaking the solution violently, so as to form a froth. In the last case, a monolayer of protein is formed on the surface of each air bubble, with consequent unfolding of the protein chains; it is supposed that the compression of the film by the subsequent breaking of the bubbles is responsible for the denaturation, rather than the mere formation of the monolayer, which does not, in itself, cause denaturation.

The process whereby the solution within the silk gland of the silk worm is converted into the insoluble thread of silk fibroin is one of denaturation, and it appears that the change is very similar to a process of crystallisation. It is suggested that the solution is supersaturated with respect to the protein and that the stretching and shearing forces applied during the process of secretion bring about an orientation of the molecules and firm unions at several points. The process, in fact, is exactly similar to that by which denaturation is supposed to occur in a highly compressed monolayer. In heat denaturation, on the other hand, the particles which are thrown out of solution are not fully crystalline, although the water of hydration, according to Adair, is only a little less than that of the true crystals. The electrophoretic behaviour of the particles of heat denatured proteins appears to be similar to that of the protein before denaturation, except for a shift in the iso-electric point. The insolubility in water is thus not directly connected with any great change in the charge on the particles.

Altogether, it cannot be said that the process of denaturation is well understood. The close union of the protein chains with one another apparently prevents the hydrophilic groups from congregating at the surface, and so making the whole molecule soluble. On the other hand, this process must differ markedly from that of simple crystallisation since protein crystals are readily soluble in water.

THE VISCOSITY OF COLLOIDAL SYSTEMS

We saw in Chapter 3 that the specific viscosity of a dilute solution or suspension increases in direct proportion to the relative volume occupied by the solute or the dispersed phase (equation 3.37, p. 114). The relative volume of the dispersed phase in a suspensoid sol is usually small enough for this simple relation to hold; but in emulsoid and lyophilic systems, the relative volume may well be much larger. Even when relatively dilute, in terms of molarity, the dispersed phase may occupy a significant fraction of the whole volume, and the particles may interact with each other very markedly. Not only is the simple equation relating specific viscosity to the relative volume no longer applicable, but in many systems it becomes impossible to give a precise meaning to the term "viscosity". If we attempt to measure the viscosity of such a colloidal solution or suspension, by any of the ordinary methods, we find that the value obtained depends upon the conditions in which we make the measurement. In particular, we find that the solution behaves as if the force between two adjacent layers, moving at different speeds, is not directly proportional to the velocity gradient, as it should be; the value of the "apparent viscosity" (as it is called by Barr in these circumstances) falls as the velocity gradient (or rate of shear) rises. In a capillary tube viscometer, therefore, the apparent viscosity falls as the applied pressure and rate of flow, are increased. Or, if we plot the applied pressure against the rate of flow, we do not get a straight line passing through the origin, but a curved line, convex to the axis of pressure, which

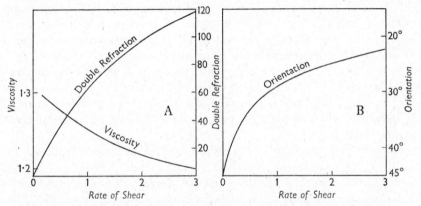

FIG. 6.6. VARIATION OF APPARENT VISCOSITY OF A SUSPENSION OF ANISOMETRIC PARTICLES AND OF ORIENTATION OF THE PARTICLES, WITH RATE OF SHEAR

Measurements made on 0·02 per cent. suspension of tobacco mosaic virus at 14·4° C.

Abscissae: Rate of shear in terms of angular velocity of outer cylinder of concentric cylinder viscometer.

Ordinates: A. Left-hand scale: relative viscosity. Right-hand scale: magnitude of double refraction in units of rotation of analysing Nicol prism.

B. Average angle between long axes of particles and direction of streamlines, as derived from double refraction observations (45° corresponds to random arrangement. 0° to perfect orientation).   (After Robinson, 1939.)

may become sensibly straight if the applied pressure and rate of flow are sufficiently large; this, however, does not pass through the origin on extrapolation.

This anomaly has several origins. First, if the suspension contains small asymmetric particles, there will be a tendency for them to become orientated in the planes of shear, and this will be opposed by the random rotations induced by the Brownian movement. The greater the rate of shear, however, the more nearly will the particles approach the condition of complete orientation, and so the smaller will be the apparent viscosity. This fact is illustrated in Fig. 6.6. The apparent viscosity of a suspension of tobacco mosaic virus (which has long rod-shaped particles) falls as the rate of shear increases, and at the same time, the average degree of orientation (as measured by the amount of birefringence (see p. 237 above)) increases.

Secondly, there may be a "coherence resistance" (the term used by Hess) or a "friction" (the term used by Bingham) between the particles of the colloidal system. This force, unlike the true "internal friction" is not simply proportional to the rate of shear. According to Bingham (see for example his monograph, 1922), who has mainly studied the viscosity of paints, the particles begin to coalesce when the concentration becomes sufficiently great, and eventually the aggregates become comparable in size with the diameter of the tube. At this point, true viscous flow ceases and "plastic" flow begins. The existence of such a friction or coherence resistance, will give rise to a pressure-flow diagram which rises gradually from the axis of pressure at zero rates of flow, and which approximates at high rates of flow to a straight line cutting the pressure axis at a finite value of the pressure. When only low pressures are applied, we get what Bingham calls "slippage". The suspension is sheared only at the periphery of the tube, and the central parts move as a solid rod: as we progressively increase the pressure, this rod becomes progressively thinner, as its outer layers become sheared off.

It is clearly necessary to postulate such a coherence between the colloidal particles of gels (compare p. 252): and, indeed, gels possess anomalous viscous properties to a marked degree. The breaking down of this coherence by shearing forces is the basis of thixotropy (p. 254). The thixotropic behaviour of suspensoids, such as blood and paint, however, is somewhat different from that of gels, in that the re-coherence of the particles, after the shear has ceased, appears to be almost instantaneous, whereas the thixotropic gels usually take some time to set again.

Thus a solution of gelatin of suitable concentration, and not freshly cooled from a temperature above the setting point, always shows thixotropy to a marked degree, i.e. the resistance to shear decreases with time as the shearing stress is maintained. By constructing a pressure-flow diagram starting from low rates of flow, increasing them progressively to high rates, and then decreasing them again, a loop is obtained—i.e. the apparent viscosity at any given rate of shear becomes smaller with time. Blood shows just as marked a curvature of the pressure-flow diagram, but there is no such loop, or hysteresis, and the apparent viscosity at a given rate of shear does not vary with time—at least over easily measurable intervals.

If the particles are asymmetric, as well as possessing coherence, it is to be expected that the degree of orientation will depend upon the rate of shear, whether they are in Brownian movement or not. Orientation will be opposed by the interactions between the particles, and will only occur if the rate of shear is sufficiently great to break up the aggregates. There is evidence that an effect of this kind occurs in mammalian blood.

Lastly, there is the rather obscure phenomenon of the accumulation of the suspended particles about the axis of a capillary tube through which the suspension is made to flow. This occurs, of course, only when the particles are too large to be in Brownian movement. The extent to which it occurs appears to increase with the rate of shear. Since the velocity gradient is greatest at the periphery of the tube and zero at the axis, this movement of the suspended particles means that the greater part of the shear takes place in fluid which has been partially depleted of the suspended particles, while the bulk of the suspension is practically unsheared. The apparent

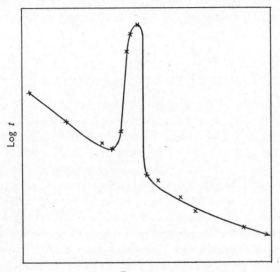

Temperature

FIG. 6.7. CHANGES IN VISCOSITY OF ALBUMIN IN THE PROCESS OF COAGULATION

Abscissae: temperature. *Ordinates:* logarithms of the time of flow through the capillary tube of the viscometer.

There is a large rise in viscosity at the temperature at which the albumin begins to become coagulated, possibly owing to the formation of some " structure". At higher temperatures, the relative viscosity of the suspension of coagulated albumin is sensibly the same that of the colloidal solution before coagulation.   (Wo. Ostwald, 1913.)

viscosity will thus be determined almost entirely by the thickness of the peripheral layer, falling as this increases with the rate of shear.

In certain cirumstances, the relative viscosity of a colloidal solution may change very rapidly over a small range of temperature; some marked change must occur in the relative volume of the disperse phase, or in the anomaly of flow, or in both. A particularly striking instance of large changes in viscosity produced by small changes in temperature is shown by such colloids as gelatin which form gels, and also by those which coagulate on heating. As an illustration, we may take the change in the viscosity of a dilute albumin sol when heated (Fig. 6.7). From 50° to 57° the absolute

I*

viscosity decreases regularly. At 57·5°, just before the appearance of turbidity, a large increase occurs, which, at 60° gives place to an equally steep decrease. After that, the curve forms practically a continuation of the direction of the first part below 57°, as if nothing had happened in the meantime. During the process of coagulation, it would appear that either the particles of albumin take up large quantities of water, and release them again when coagulation is complete, or, more probably, some form of structure is formed in the initial stages, which leads to a large increase in the coherence resistance; the viscosities were measured at a relatively small rate of shear. This structure subsequently breaks up when coagulation is complete, and a true sol has been formed.

DETERMINATION OF THE SIZE AND SHAPE OF COLLOIDAL PARTICLES

The size and weight of the particles, or molecules, in a colloidal solution may, as an upper limit, be such that they are just visible with a high-power microscope, or, as a lower limit, be such that they possess many of the properties of molecules in true solution. The methods which are available for measuring their sizes and weights are correspondingly diverse. Suspensoid and lyophobic colloids, which, as we have seen, show the Faraday-Tyndall phenomenon of scattering a beam of light, may be studied by optical methods. With emulsoid, and lyophilic colloids, on the other hand, Graham's criterion that the particles fail to pass through suitable membranes may be developed so as to give a measure of their size. In addition, Perrin's methods of demonstrating that colloidal particles are in kinetic equilibrium with the molecules of the solvent, have been developed, particularly by Svedberg, into methods for determining their sizes; these are, in theory, applicable to both lyophobic and lyophilic colloids, although in practice they are mainly used with the latter.

MICROSCOPIC OBSERVATION

Since light is a wave motion, it spreads, or is *diffracted*, round the edges of opaque objects, or of objects with different refractive indices from their surroundings, just as sound can be heard round the corners of a building. It can be shown, by the application of wave-theory, that in a microscope, for example, the objects will only be seen distinctly if *all* the diffracted light can be collected by the objective lens. Now the angle through which the light is diffracted falls as its wave-length (λ) is decreased; and the maximum angle at which light can enter and pass through the objective increases with increase in its "numerical aperture" (N.A.), a quantity which depends on the design of the lens, increasing in general as its focal length decreases, and which increases with increase in the refractive index of the material between the lens and the object viewed. In order to be able to see very small objects clearly, therefore, we must reduce the wave-length, and increase the numerical aperture, as far as possible. Abbé showed that the size of the smallest object that can be seen distinctly is given by: $0\cdot5\lambda/\text{N.A.}$ (an arbitrary definition must, of course, be given to the word "distinctly"). In practice, the value of N.A. cannot be made to exceed $1\cdot4$, and for visible light, $\lambda = 0\cdot5\,\mu$ (5000 Å.) approximately; no objects smaller than about $0\cdot2\,\mu$ (2000 Å.) in diameter can thus be seen sufficiently distinctly for their sizes to be measured. Few colloidal particles are as large as this, so that direct microscopic observation with visible light is not of very great value.

The *electron microscope*, however, enables us to make accurate images of particles which are at least an order of magnitude smaller than those which we can see by ordinary light. The equivalent wave-length of the stream of electrons used in the microscope may be as small as $0\cdot04$ Å. (as against 5000 Å. for visible light), but owing to practical limitations in the construction of the electron "lenses" (in which the electrons are deflected by magnetic fields) the smallest particles which can be detected have diameters of about 10–20 Å. The sizes of even quite small colloidal particles may thus be measured. Moreover, the technique of "shadowing" by a noble metal allows us to measure on the electron photomicrograph not only the length and width of the particles, but also the thickness.

An oblique beam of the free ions of a heavy metal (gold, tungsten and several others have been used) is projected in an electric field on to the preparation, the whole arrangement being in a high vacuum. The atoms of the heavy metal form a film which is thicker on the side of an elevation which faces towards the source of the beam of ions than on the side away from it. In the electron microscope, the electrons are absorbed in proportion to the thickness of the film on the preparation, and the electron photomicrograph has the appearance of a photograph of a rough object illuminated obliquely. The height of any part of the preparation can thus be estimated from the length of its "shadow", provided, of course, that we know the angle at which the ions were projected.

The electron microscope, however, has two serious limitations. In the first place, the absorption of electrons by an object depends on the atomic weight of its constituent atoms; colloidal particles of proteins and carbohydrates, for example, which contain only relatively light atoms, absorb electrons poorly. This can be overcome by "staining" the particles with some substance containing a heavy metal, such as osmium tetroxide or phosphotungstic acid, although it cannot then be certain that the particles remain unchanged in size and shape. Secondly, the object viewed must be in a high vacuum, since a stream of electrons is very rapidly absorbed by air. It must, therefore, be completely dry, and the particles of lyophilic colloids will not be in the state in which they were originally.

The Ultra-microscope. It occurred to Siedentopf and Zsigmondy in 1903 that if a colloidal solution is much diluted, illuminated by a powerful beam of light and examined by a microscope placed perpendicularly to the beam so as not to receive the direct light, the diffraction images of the separate particles would be visible.

In the form of ultra-microscope made for the examination of liquids, a very intense but small beam of light is projected horizontally, by means of a system of condensing lenses, into the liquid contained in a small cell with a flat side towards the light and an open top. The track of the beam is examined from above by means of a microscope provided with a water-immersion objective. If the solution contains particles, they are seen as bright discs with vigorous Brownian movement. The limit of visibility depends on the intensity of the illumination and on the difference in refractive index between the particles and the suspending fluid. The finest particles cannot be distinguished separately, but are indicated by a haze. Further details, and illustrations of the field seen by the observer, will be found in the book by Zsigmondy (1920).

Dark Ground Illumination.—Alternatively, one may use a specially constructed sub-stage condenser, as first introduced by Wenham in 1872. The central rays of the illuminating beam are cut out by means of a stop, and the peripheral rays are reflected by a paraboloid, or better cardioid, surface so as to meet at a point in the object under examination; they cross at such an angle as to pass outside the field of the objective in use, which picks up only the light refracted or diffracted from structures in the preparation. Dark ground illumination is a standard procedure in microscopy, and is described in many books on the subject.

The use of the ultra-microscope has been of great value in studying many problems of the colloidal state. Although it gives no direct information as to the size and shape of the particles, it is possible to count the number in a small, and known, volume of the solution. If the total content of colloidal matter in a much larger volume of the solution can be determined, say by some chemical or optical method, the average weight of each particle can be calculated. By this method, for example, the mass of each particle of the free acid of Congo-red was found to be approximately $2 \cdot 3 \times 10^{-14}$ grams. Taking the mass of the hydrogen atom to be $1 \cdot 6 \times 10^{-24}$ grams, that of the molecule of the acid (molecular weight 652) is $1 \cdot 04 \times 10^{-21}$ grams; there would thus be some 2×10^7 molecules in each particle.

A known area of the illuminated field can be defined by means of scales in the eye-piece of the microscope. The depth of the solution in which the particles are counted is restricted by the depth of the field illuminated. This can be measured by arranging the optical system so that an image of a slit is focused immediately below the observing microscope; by rotating this slit through 90°, what was previously the depth of the illuminated field now becomes its width, and this can be measured with an ocular micrometer.

If the colloidal particles under examination have the shape of thin rods,

they will not show up at all brilliantly if they happen to be orientated so as
to lie along the direction of the illuminating beam. Since, however, they
will be in Brownian motion, a twinkling effect will be produced as they
move about and present different angles to the incoming light. Such an
effect is a clear indication that the particles are far from spherical in shape.
No such twinkling is observed with the ordinary dark-ground illuminator,
since in this the light enters in a cone of wide angle and thus in all directions within this cone. This, however, may in some circumstances be an
advantage. If particles which are highly anisodiametric (whose shape is far
from spherical) are fixed in some particular orientation, as they may be in
a gel and in some living tissues, they may be invisible in the ultra-microscope, but will show up under dark ground illumination.

THE SCATTERING OF LIGHT

In addition to the use of the diffracted light for direct observation of the
colloidal particles under the ultra-microscope, estimates of their size, and
in suitable conditions, their shape, may be obtained by quantitative
observations on the Faraday-Tyndall phenomenon. The exact relation
between the size and shape of the particles, and the intensity of the
scattered light in different directions relative to that of the incident beam
may be derived theoretically from the fundamental properties of electromagnetic waves; this was first done by Lord Rayleigh in 1871. Two cases
must be considered.

If the dimensions of the particles are small compared with the wave-
length of the light, the intensity of the scattered light is symmetrical in the
forward and backward directions—i.e. about a plane at right angles to the
incident beam. And for particles of a given size, the fraction of the incident
light which is scattered is inversely proportional to the fourth power of
the wave-length of the light, the constant of proportionality being directly
related to the size of the particles. Correction factors are necessary if the
solution is not so dilute that the particles may be considered to be entirely
independent of one another. The shape of the particles does not come in.
This relation holds, if ordinary light is used, for particles up to 500 Å.
(0.05μ) in diameter—i.e. up to a molecular weight of the order of 50
million; but it cannot, in practice, be used for very small particles, since
the turbidity, at any given value of the wave-length, falls as the particles
become smaller. In solutions of the smaller proteins, for example, very
great care has to be taken to exclude particles of dust, aggregated protein
molecules, and any such particles which are substantially larger than the
molecules under examination; if only a few of these are present, they will
scatter as much light as a great many of the smaller molecules that we are
interested in.

If, on the other hand, the particles are about the same size as the wave-length of the light used, the situation becomes more complex. More light is scattered forwards than backwards, and the ratio, for a given angle on each side of the 90° plane, depends upon the shape of the particles. Again, corrections have to be made if the solution is not very dilute, and the particles do not behave independently. We cannot go into the details of the equations relating the size and shape of the particles to the wave-length of the light and the intensity scattered in various directions; they are very complex, and the article by Oster (1950) should be consulted by those interested. The essential point is that the size and shape (i.e. whether spherical, rod-shaped, or disc-shaped) can be determined by observation of the intensity of the light of known wave-length scattered in two directions which are symmetrical about the 90° plane, e.g. at 45° and 135° to the direction of the incident light.

The fact that the intensity of the scattered light increases as the wave-length decreases means that the particles of a colloidal solution will, in general, scatter blue light more than red, and the solution will appear yellow by transmitted light. If, however, the particles are large compared with the wave-length of the light, there is less differentiation between short waves and long, and the colour of the suspension tends to become grey, as is a fog. If such large particles have an intrinsic colour, they will affect the colour of the whole solution as a result of the preferential *reflection* (as distinct from diffraction) of certain wave-lengths. On the other hand, if the particles are very small indeed, and approximate in size to molecules or ions in solution, the effects of scattering will become small, and the colour of the solution will be determined by the specific absorption properties of the ions or molecules. This effect can be seen in gold and platinum sols; coarsely colloidal platinum, for example, is of a more or less violet colour, and as the degree of dispersion is increased, the colour becomes more and more like the orange colour of platinum salts in solution.

Dialysis and Ultra-filtration

Careful study of the factors involved in the formation of collodion membranes has made it possible to form membranes with pores of very uniform size, which, also, can be varied according to the precise method of formation. In principle, therefore, the size of the particles in a colloidal solution can readily be determined by finding a membrane whose pores will just not allow them to pass through. This would be long and tedious if the process of dialysis were used. But by the application of high pressures to the colloidal solution, it is possible to force the liquid phase through the membrane, and thus to separate the crystalloidal components from the colloidal, and to concentrate the latter.

This was first done by C. J. Martin in 1896. His filter consisted of a porous clay tube whose pores were filled with gelatin. This was fixed in a gun-metal case and was filled with the liquid to be filtered. A pressure of some 30 atmospheres or more was applied to the solution. Modifications made since this time have allowed flat sheets of various membranes to be used; a material with a suitable permeability may thus be selected, and it is often possible to work with very much lower pressures, in some cases of less than 1 atmosphere.

Unfortunately, however, it is found that the limiting pore size, as determined in this way, is considerably greater than the true diameter of the colloidal particles as determined by other methods. A correction factor must be introduced, but having once calibrated a series of membranes on particles of known size, they can then be used for determining the particle size in unknown colloidal solutions. In this way Elford and his co-workers were able to determine the sizes of the particles (giant protein molecules) in virus solutions.

The size of the pores may be measured in one of two ways. In the first, the membrane is covered with water on one side, and air is forced through from the other; the smaller the pores, the larger will be the surface forces exerted at the air-water interface within the pores, and the larger will be the pressure required to force air through them. In the second method, water is placed on both sides of the membrane, and is forced through from one side to the other; the pressure required to produce a given rate of flow is a measure of the viscous forces in the pores, and so is greater, the smaller the pores. It is, of course, necessary to know the average length of the pores; although usually assumed to be identical with the thickness of the membrane, it is not necessarily so. The first method gives the maximum size of the pores, and the second gives the average size; the relation between them is a measure of the uniformity of the membrane.

The necessity for the introduction of the empirical correction factor arises from three causes. (1) The actual structure of the membrane is not strictly that of a sieve, with pores of circular cross section running straight across from one side to the other, but approximates more to that of a sponge; the passages are irregular in size and take very irregular paths. (2) There is a considerable amount of adsorption on the walls of these passages, both of the colloid under investigation and of other substances which may happen to be present in the solution; there is, also, in most cases, a considerable layer of water of hydration. Apart from the actual reduction in size of the pores by the adsorbed molecules, there is the possibility of electrical forces hindering the colloidal particles from entering or leaving the pores of the membrane. (3) The presence of shells of water of hydration (the lyospheres) and the departure of the particles from a spherical shape, may affect the limiting pore size in an uncertain manner; thus it might be expected, for example, that a long thin rod would stick in a pore which would easily pass a spherical particle of the same volume. Further details on the construction and properties of the graded ultra-filtration membranes will be found in the article by Elford (1937).

THE OSMOTIC PRESSURE OF COLLOIDAL SOLUTIONS

The osmotic pressure of a solution, as we have seen in previous chapters, is determined by the total molecular concentration of the solute. If a molecule is dissociated in any way, electrolytically or hydrolytically, each fraction acts as a unit, equivalent osmotically to a molecule. Similarly, if there is association of molecules, the associated group behaves as a single molecule. The measurement of osmotic pressure is thus a most valuable means of determining the actual number of independent particles in unit volume; if we know the total mass of the disperse phase in a colloidal solution, measurement of the ósmotic pressure of the solution will enable us to calculate the mass of each particle.

A brief consideration will show, however, that the osmotic pressure is not likely to be very great, particularly in suspensoid systems. A true solution in 0·1 M concentration has an osmotic pressure of about 1700 mm. Hg at 0° C. (compare Chapter 3, p. 95). But if the molecules in a solution of this concentration were aggregated in groups of 500, say, then the solution, although containing the same amount of total solid in unit volume, will contain only 1/500 times the number of active elements, and the osmotic pressure will be reduced to 3·4 mm Hg. With those substances which are colloidal on account of the large size of their single molecules, as with haemoglobin, for example, no very great osmotic pressures can be observed, since it is impossible to obtain solutions of any great molar concentration. From its content in iron, the minimum molecular weight of haemoglobin is 16,700, so that a 0·01 M solution must contain at least 17 per cent. of solid. Colloidal solutions of such strength cannot often be obtained, and a 0·1 M solution would be solid.

The first clear proof that colloidal solutions have a measurable osmotic pressure was given by Starling in 1896. A sample of blood serum was filtered through a gelatin membrane by pressure, and the filtrate, containing the crystalloidal constituents of the serum only, was placed on the outside of an osmometer, with a gelatin membrane; within the membrane was placed a sample of the unfiltered serum. Any hydrostatic pressure developed across the membrane must have been due to the osmotic pressure of the colloidal constituents, since the crystalloidal ones were identical on both sides. A pressure of 30-40 mm. Hg was obtained. Since then, the osmotic pressures of protein solutions have been extensively studied, as have those of cellulose derivatives and other high polymers, mainly in organic solvents.

No very elaborate apparatus is needed in order to measure the osmotic pressure of a colloidal solution. Adair, for example, used simple collodion sacs fixed to capillary tubes, and many types of apparatus have been described in which flat sheets of parchment paper or cellophane can be used. Krogh (1939) has described some types of osmometer which can be used for very small quantities of solution. Owing to the instability of many colloidal solutions, particularly of proteins, it is advisable to work at 0° C.

Measurement of the osmotic pressure of colloidal solutions is often considerably complicated by the fact that they act as multivalent acids or bases, the valency depending on the hydrogen ion concentration, and reversing in sign at the iso-electric point. The presence of such a colloidal electrolyte within an osmometer will lead to an unequal distribution of crystalloidal ions between the inside and outside of the membrane (the Gibbs-Donnan equilibrium) and this must therefore be allowed for. Near the iso-electric point, the osmotic pressure will correspond to the true molecular weight; on either side of the iso-electric point, however, the apparent osmotic pressure will rise, owing to the fact that the colloidal electrolytes retain (by electrostatic pull) a number of oppositely charged ions, which are thereby rendered incapable of diffusion through the membrane. The presence of neutral salts, moreover, will affect the observed osmotic pressure, except at the iso-ionic point. The presence of non-electrolytes, on the other hand, which are freely permeable through the membrane used, will not affect the osmotic pressure, except by actually changing the properties of the colloid.

There is good reason for supposing, at least in protein solutions, that the two osmotic pressures, that due to the colloid itself, and that due to the ions associated with it, act independently of each other. The observed osmotic pressure is thus merely the sum of these two separate osmotic pressures. We may thus write, as our general equation:

$$\Pi_{obs} = \Pi_c + \Delta\Pi_i \qquad . \qquad . \qquad . \qquad 6.1$$

where Π_{obs} is the osmotic pressure actually observed in any colloidal solution, whether ionised or not, or in the presence or absence of other electrolytes, Π_c is the osmotic pressure due to the colloid—and this is the quantity that we wish to discover in order to find the molecular or particle weight of the colloid—and $\Delta\Pi_i$ is the difference between the osmotic pressure exerted by all the ions in the colloidal solution, and that exerted by all the ions in the solution outside the osmometer.

Let us assume, first, that the solutions are so dilute that activities can be replaced by concentrations, that electrolytic dissociation is complete, and that the van't Hoff equation for osmotic pressure (equation 3.19) can be applied. For simplicity, also, and to illustrate the argument, we will suppose that the only crystalloidal electrolyte present is sodium chloride. Thus:

$$\Pi_{obs} = RT[m_c + (m_{Na})_I + (m_{Cl})_I - (m_{Na})_o - (m_{Cl})_o]$$
$$= RT[m_c - (m_{Na})_o(1-r) - (m_{Cl})_o(1-1/r)] \qquad . \qquad . \qquad 6.2$$

where the subscripts refer to the colloid, the sodium ions and the chloride ions, inside the osmometer (I) and in the outside solution (O) respectively; r is the ionic distribution ratio, as defined in equation 5.13 (p. 203). All the quantities in this equation except m_c can be measured; $(m_{Na})_O$ and $(m_{Cl})_O$ by direct analysis of the external solution, r by measurement of the electrical potential difference across the membrane (equation 5.12), or by measurement of the hydrogen ion concentrations in the two solutions, and Π_{obs} by direct measurement in an osmometer. The molar concentration of the colloid can thus be determined, and if the mass concentration of the solution is known, the molecular weight can be calculated.

Loeb (1922) showed that the equations just derived describe with reasonable accuracy the variation of the osmotic pressure of gelatin and casein solutions with variations in hydrogen ion concentration and in total electrolyte concentration. Adair, however, has shown that if even reasonably accurate quantitative results are to be obtained, the solutions cannot be regarded as "ideal" unless the concentrations are less than 0·01 M.; the van't Hoff equation, consequently, cannot be applied. Thus, with haemoglobin, the direct proportionality between osmotic pressure and concentration breaks down when the haemoglobin concentration exceeds 1 per cent.; with such low concentrations, the osmotic pressure observed is very small, and so liable to considerable uncertainty. It is reasonable to assume, however, that the values of the osmotic pressure per unit concentration, obtained at very low concentrations, will be the true values, and it is thus necessary to extrapolate the observed values back to zero concentration. With some colloids, such as haemoglobin, we can make use of an equation corresponding to the van der Waals equation of state, but with most, empirical formulae must be used, or the extrapolation performed graphically. It is best, in this case, to plot osmotic pressure per unit concentration both against concentration and against the observed osmotic pressure, and to make use of the plot which best approximates to a straight line.

In the treatment developed by Adair, such a series of measurements at different colloid concentrations was used, also, to eliminate the effect of the unequal distribution of crystalloidal ions. We have seen in Chapter 3 that the osmotic pressure of a solution is, strictly, a measure of the activity of the *solvent* and not of that of the solute; and that we can relate the one to the other only by a differential equation (equation 3.17, p. 88), involving both activities and concentrations. In order to deduce the osmotic pressure set up by the unequal distribution of ions, we must know how the ionic activity ratio (inside/outside) varies with the net excess ionic concentration, from the values of unity and zero, respectively (when the colloid concentration is zero) up to the values occuring in the solution on which measurements are being made. The ionic activity ratio in any

particular solution is measured in terms of the electrical potential difference across the membrane (equation 5.12); and since the solution within
the osmometer must be electrically neutral, the excess ionic concentration
must be equal to the total charge on the colloid ions, per kilogram of water,
as determined from the titration curve (equation 5.14). It is not, in fact,

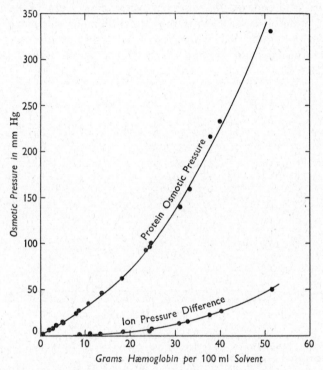

FIG. 6.8. THE OSMOTIC PRESSURE OF HAEMOGLOBIN SOLUTIONS

Temperature: 0° C. Equilibrated with a solution of 0·1 M KCl, 0·0613 M Na₂HPO₄
and 0·00533 M KH₂PO₄, pH 7·8.

The lower curve gives the partial pressure across the membrane that results from the
unequal distribution of crystalloid ions, and calculated from the observed membrane
potential.

The upper curve gives the partial pressure across the membrane that is due to the
haemoglobin itself, and derived by subtracting the ion pressure difference from the
observed osmotic pressure.   (Adair, 1929.)

necessary to know precisely what ions are present, or in what concentrations. For simplicity, the composition and concentration of the solution
outside the osmometer are kept unchanged throughout the series of
measurements, and Adair's final equation becomes:

$$\Pi_{obs} = \Pi_c + F\int m_c z_c \,.\, dE \qquad . \qquad . \qquad . \quad 6.3$$

where F is the faraday, E is the potential difference across the membrane,
and $m_c z_c$ is the equivalent concentration of the colloid ions. The second

term on the right-hand side of the equation can be evaluated by plotting the equivalent concentration of the colloid in each experiment, as discovered from the titration curve, against the membrane potential, as measured in that experiment, and finding the area beneath the curve from the origin up to any desired value.

Fig. 6.8 shows how the observed osmotic pressure of haemoglobin solutions, and the ionic osmotic pressure difference calculated from the membrane potential, vary with the concentration of haemoglobin. Fig. 6.9 shows the effect of varying the hydrogen ion concentration on the

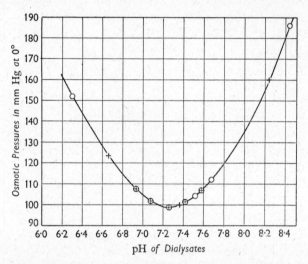

FIG. 6.9 OSMOTIC PRESSURE OF SHEEP CARBOXY-HAEMOGLOBIN, EQUILIBRATED WITH AMMONIUM PHOSPHATE BUFFERS, CONCENTRATION 0·01 M AND VARYING pH HAEMOGLOBIN CONCENTRATION 0·004 M.

The circles and crosses show the values observed on two different preparations of haemoglobin: the crosses within circles show the mean values obtained on both preparations.   (Adair and Adair, 1934.)

observed osmotic pressure. When the total electrolyte concentration is low, the effect is very marked, as shown; if the electrolyte concentration is made large, there is little effect, as would be predicted from theoretical considerations. The minimum osmotic pressure is observed at a value of the pH which is in the neighbourhood of the iso-ionic point, but not exactly at this point.

DIFFUSION, SEDIMENTATION AND VISCOSITY

In the development of the theory of diffusion, in Chapter 3, we saw that the rate of diffusion of a solute depended on the activity gradient (or for an "ideal" solution, on the concentration gradient) and on a "frictional coefficient" (f_D). By combining equations 3.32, 3.31 and 3.30, we may derive the equation:

$$\frac{dc}{dt} = D \cdot \frac{d^2c}{dx^2} = \frac{RT}{N.f_D} \cdot \frac{d^2c}{dx^2} \qquad . \qquad . \qquad . \qquad 6.4$$

where dc/dt is the rate of change of the concentration at any point x, measured from some reference point, in the direction in which the substance is diffusing; dc/dx is the concentration gradient at that point; and R, T and N are the gas constant, the absolute temperature and the Avogadro number, respectively. Weight concentrations (c) have been substituted for molar concentrations $(m = c/M)$, since the molecular weight, M, is, by hypothesis, unknown. If we assume that the molecules of the solute, or the particles of the suspension, are very large compared with those of the solvent, that they are spherical, and that they are so far apart that the movements of one do not affect the movement of any other—i.e. that the solution is very dilute—then we can relate the frictional coefficient per molecule to the radius of the molecules by the equation deduced by Stokes:

$$f_D = 6\pi.\eta.a \qquad . \qquad . \qquad . \qquad . \qquad 6.5$$

where η is the viscosity of the solvent, and a is the radius of the molecules. Combination of equation 6.4 with equation 6.5 leads to a relation between the rate of diffusion of a solute and the radius of its molecules, as was first deduced by Einstein in 1905. Moreover, the weight of each molecule is given by $(4/3).\pi a^3.\rho$, where ρ is its density, and the molecular weight, consequently, by $M = (4/3).\pi a^3.\rho.N$.

Measurement of the rate of diffusion may be made either at a free boundary between the solution and the pure solvent, or within the pores of, say, a sintered glass disc. The latter is technically the easier, since there is much less risk of errors due to convection currents and mechanical disturbances. But the exact measurement of the effective area and length of the pores presents some difficulty; it is usual to calibrate the disc by means of a standard solution of a substance of known molecular weight in known concentration, and to assume that the calibration holds for the test solution of unknown molecular weight and probably of different concentration. The free boundary method does not present these uncertainties, and with the apparatus designed by Svedberg, Lamm, Neurath and others, gives good results. The concentration at any point in the solution, its rate of change with time, and the concentration gradient at that point, are best measured by optical methods, as described below (p. 280). For more detailed information, the text-book of Alexander and Johnson (1949) should be consulted.

Some estimates have been made of the molecular weights of certain proteins on the basis of the above relations, but the assumption that the molecules are spherical is quite gratuitous, and is now known to be erroneous in most cases. Moreover, if the molecules are hydrated, their density will not be that of the solid material, and cannot be known with certainty unless their actual masses are known; and it is this which we are trying to measure. We must, therefore, devise a method whereby the frictional coefficient is eliminated, or measured independently.

The Ultra-centrifuge. One of the methods used by Perrin in order to discover the size of the particles in his suspensions was to measure the rate of settling under gravity, and to apply the Stokes equation (equation 6.5). In solutions of crystalloids, and even in those of the stable colloids, the amount of settling in a column of reasonable height is far too small to be useful; the gravitational force is small compared with the diffusional force of thermal agitation. The gravitational force, however, may be replaced by a larger force, which in practice, and for convenience, is made a centrifugal force; this, within limits, may be made as large as desired, and certainly large enough to produce measurable settling of colloidal particles.

If a sufficiently large centrifugal force is applied, the actual rate at which the particles are thrown down may be measured. Let the average weight of a particle of the colloidal solution be M/N (M being the mean molecular weight and N being Avogadro's number); let its density be ρ_p, its volume being $M/(N.\rho_p)$; let the density of the solvent, or suspending fluid, be ρ_s. Suppose the particle in question is at a distance x from the axis of the centrifuge, which is rotating with an angular velocity ω. Then the force acting on the particle is given by: $\omega^2 x(\rho_p - \rho_s).M/(N.\rho_p)$. If f_s is the frictional coefficient per molecule, then the rate at which the particle will move in the centrifugal field will be given by:

$$v = dx/dt = \omega^2 x(1 - \rho_s/\rho_p).M/(N.f_s) \qquad . \qquad . \qquad 6.6$$

which may be written in the form:

$$s = (1 - \rho_s/\rho_p).M/(N.f_s) \qquad . \qquad . \qquad . \qquad 6.6a$$

the ratio $v/\omega^2 x$ being defined as the "sedimentation constant", s, usually given a subscript to denote the temperature at which the measurements were made, e.g. s_{20}. A well defined concentration gradient is developed in a short time (provided the centrifuge is rotating sufficiently rapidly) and the rate at which this moves is observed by one of the optical methods to be described below. The rate of rotation of the centrifuge must, clearly, be known with some accuracy. The density of the suspending fluid is readily measured, but that of the particles, as already remarked, is less certain; this will be referred to again later. The Stokes equation may be used in order to derive a value for the frictional coefficient; but if we ensure that the conditions (concentration and temperature in particular) are similar in diffusion and sedimentation measurements, we can assume that the frictional coefficients are identical, and combine the results of separate observations on diffusion and rate of sedimentation. We may then insert in equation 6.6a, the relation $1/(N.f_D) = D/(RT)$, derived from equation 6.4, where D is the diffusion constant.

Alternatively, by using a relatively small centrifugal force, and continuing for long periods, a condition of equilibrium may be reached between the rate of sedimentation and the opposing rate of diffusion. When this condition is reached, there is no net movement of the particles, and so, on the average, no friction. From equation 3.29 (p. 106), neglecting activity coefficients, we may write, for the velocity of diffusion:

$$v = -\frac{RT}{N.f_D} \cdot \frac{1}{c} \cdot \frac{dc}{dx}$$

If we equate this with the velocity of sedimentation, as given above, and assumed that $f_D = f_s$, we get:

$$M = \frac{RT}{c} \cdot \frac{dc}{dx} \cdot \frac{1}{\omega^2 x (1 - \rho_s/\rho_p)} \qquad . \qquad . \qquad . \qquad 6.7$$

With this procedure, it is thus necessary to measure the concentration gradient at some known distance from the axis of rotation, and the actual concentration at this point, as with the measurements of the diffusion constant. There is a practical difficulty that the rate of rotation of the centrifuge must be kept very constant while equilibrium is being attained, possibly a matter of many hours.

Equation 6.7 is essentially that used by Perrin in his "first method" (p. 231 above), in which he implicitly eliminated the frictional coefficient by allowing the tendency of the particles to settle under gravity to be opposed by their tendency to diffuse uniformly throughout the solution. The centrifugal acceleration, w^2x is replaced by the gravitational acceleration, g, and M is replaced by $N.w$, where w is the average mass of the particles, and N is the Avogadro number.

When as in most cases, the particles under examination are electrically charged, the sedimentation and diffusion measurements must be made in the presence of a moderately high concentration of electrolytes—i.e. the electrokinetic potential must be reduced to a low value. Otherwise, during sedimentation and diffusion, the charged particles would tend to become separated from the ionic atmospheres surrounding them, and erroneous values of the sedimentation and diffusion constant would be obtained, as a result of the electrostatic forces introduced. With a 1 per cent. solution of a protein, for example, this charge effect is sensibly abolished in the presence of 0·2 M NaCl or KCl.

The development of the ultra-centrifugal method for determining the particle weights in solution is due almost entirely to the work of Svedberg and his co-workers. A very complete account of the methods and machines that are used will be found in their monograph (Svedberg *et al.* 1940), and a less detailed account in the book by Alexander and Johnson (1949).

The design of the apparatus is based on the considerations that not only is it necessary to subject the solutions to a very large centrifugal force, but it is necessary, also, to observe the solution and to measure the concentration at various levels, while the centrifuge is in action; and last, but not least, all possibility of disturbances within the solution as a result of convection currents must be eliminated. Accurate observation while the machine is running is made possible by very careful construction and balancing of the rotor; convection currents are eliminated (1) by enclosing the solution in cells which have the shape of a sector of the circle which is described during rotation, and (2) by enclosing the rotor in an atmosphere of hydrogen. The high thermal conductivity of hydrogen allows the heat generated in the bearings, and by the movement of the rotor, to be dissipated rapidly to the surroundings. For relatively low speed runs (up to 20,000 r.p.m.) the hydrogen is at atmospheric pressure; for high speed runs (up to 70,000 r.p.m.) the pressure is reduced to about 20 mm. Hg so as to reduce the amount of heat generated by the rotor. A complete vacuum would eliminate the heat generated by the friction of the rotor against the surrounding gas, but would prevent the heat generated in the bearings from being transferred from the rotor to the surroundings. In Svedberg's machines, the rotor is driven by two oil turbines, one at each end of the shaft: with oil pressures up to about 15 atmospheres, and with suitable rotors, speeds of up to 150,000 revolutions per minute, and centrifugal forces of over 1 million times gravity have been obtained. As an alternative to the use of an oil turbine to drive the rotor, compressed air may be used: this method has been developed chiefly by Beams and by Pickels. The advantage of this is that by a suitable design of turbine not only is the compressed air used to rotate the machine but also to carry the weight of the rotor, and thus to reduce greatly the frictional losses in the bearings. The rotor in which the observation cells are mounted is enclosed in a partially evacuated housing through the wall of which the driving shaft passes to the air turbine; an airtight seal being made by means of an oil gland. With this type of machine, speeds of about 90,000 revolutions per minute can be attained, and centrifugal forces of about 300,000 times gravity. The design of such an instrument is illustrated in the book by Alexander and Johnson (1949).

Observation of the Boundary between Solution and Solvent.—This is a problem which is common to the measurements of sedimentation equilibrium, sedimentation velocity, rate of diffusion and, as we saw in Chapter 5, electrophoretic velocity and the electrokinetic potential; an outline of the methods used may be conveniently given at this point. They may be divided into two chief classes, according as use is made of the light absorbing properties of the solute, or of the fact that usually the solution or suspension has a greater refractive index than the solvent or suspending fluid. In the former, the centrifuge cell is illuminated uniformly with light of a wave-length which is strongly absorbed by the sedimenting material (such as ultra-violet light when proteins are being studied). Photographs of the cell are taken at intervals during the sedimentation, and the density of each photographic record is measured at a number of points in the boundary region, a suitable photometer being used. Calibration records are also made on the same plate with the same exposure of solutions of the material under investigation in known concentration. In this way we discover how the concentration falls off with distance at the boundary, and it is then possible to discover whether the sedimenting substance is homogeneous, or contains particles of more than one size. Some records obtained in this way are shown in Fig. 6.10, which indicates, also, how non-homogeneity of the particles is brought out.

The refraction methods depend upon the fact that there will be a gradient of refractive index at the boundary between the suspension and the suspending fluid from which the particles have been removed. This will act as a prism, and a ray of light passing across the cell in this region will emerge in a direction which is not parallel to that in which it entered. The deflection

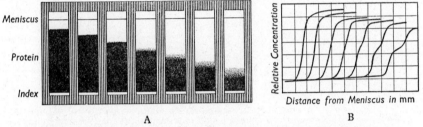

FIG. 6.10. THE SEDIMENTATION OF HAEMOCYANIN IN THE ULTRA-CENTRIFUGE

A: photographs by ultra-violet light of the solution during centrifugation.

B: photometer curves of the density of the photographic emulsion at different points in the solution.

Centrifugal force, 78,000 times gravity: time between exposures, 5 minutes.

The solution used was a mixture of *Sepia* blood and *Octopus* blood: both contain haemocyanin, but that of *Sepia* has a lower molecular weight than that of *Octopus*, and thus sediments more slowly, as shown by the development of two boundaries.

(Svedberg and Hedenius, 1934.)

produced, moreover, is an accurate measure of the rate of change of refractive index with distance along the cell at the point in the cell through which the ray passed: it is thus, also, an accurate measure of the rate of change of concentration, or of the first differential coefficient of the quantity given by the light absorption method. There are two main methods by which the magnitude of the deflection may be measured. (*a*) *The Scale Method.* An accurately graduated scale is viewed through the centrifuge cell. In the region of the boundary of the sedimenting material, the graduations of the scale will be shifted sideways in just the same way as distant objects appear to be shifted, or to shimmer, when viewed through currents of hot air ascending from ground heated by the sun. The distorted image of the scale is photographed, and the amount of shift of each graduation is measured. From this, and the dimensions of the optical system, the concentration gradient can be calculated. This method is considered to be the most precise, although the most laborious, of all the methods hitherto used. (*b*) *The Schlieren Method.* The general optical arrangement is shown in Fig. 6.11. Light from an illuminated slit, *S*, is collected by a condensing lens, *L*, passed through the centrifuge cell, *C*, and brought to a focus S' in front of the camera lens O; this latter being focused on the surface of the cell. The optical axis of the lens system is parallel to the axis of rotation of the centrifuge: the cell rotates in a plane perpendicular to the plane of the paper, and sedimentation is occurring towards the bottom of the diagram. If there is a region in the cell in which the refractive index is changing, the rays passing through this region will be deflected, and brought to a focus at some point S'': they can thus be made to fall on a diaphragm, D, which does not obstruct the passage of the undeflected rays. There will then be a black band across the image of the centrifuge cell on the photographic plate, P, at the position of the boundary of the sedimenting material. This method gives a simple and rapid means of following the boundary in a sedimentation velocity experiment. Clearly, the closer the diaphragm is placed to

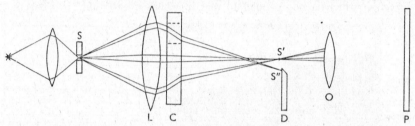

FIG. 6.11. DIAGRAM OF THE OPTICAL ARRANGEMENT FOR OBSERVATION OF A DIFFUSION CELL, AN ULTRA-CENTRIFUGE CELL, OR AN ELECTROPHORESIS CELL, BY THE SCHLIEREN METHOD

S, illuminated slit: L, condensing lens: C, cell containing sedimenting or diffusing material: D, diaphragm: O, object lens of camera: P, photographic plate.

The centrifuge cell is rotating in a plane perpendicular to the plane of the diagram, and sedimentation is occurring from above downwards. The boundary lies between the dotted lines. The paths of three pencils of light are shown: the lower and central ones pass through homogeneous parts of the fluid and form an image of the slit at S'; the upper one passes through the boundary regions, is deflected as a result of the refractive index gradient, forms an image of the slit at S'' and is interrupted by the diaphragm D. No light from this region of the cell reaches the photographic plate, and a dark band appears in the image of the centrifuge cell at the boundary region.

the undeflected image of the slit, the smaller will be the limiting value of the concentration gradient which is just detected. In the *diagonal schlieren* arrangement, the edge of the diaphragm is put closer to the image of the slit at one end than at the other. Provided that the slit is correctly orientated—i.e. is at right angles to the radius of the rotating cell at the point of observation—each end of its image will correspond to each side of the cell. The record on the photographic plate will then indicate the positions of small concentration gradients at one side of the cell, of intermediate values in the middle, and of only very large values at the other side. If the boundary region is uniform from side to side, we can interpret the record as a plot of the concentration gradient through the boundary region from the pure solvent to the homogeneous solution. This method is probably the one most used at present: a record obtained in an electrophoresis experiment has been given in Fig. 6.5.

Use of the Viscosity of the Solution. The frictional constant may also be derived, in certain circumstances, from the viscosity of the solution, and then inserted into the equations for diffusion or sedimentation as desired. If the dispersed phase consists of approximately spherical particles small enough to be in Brownian movement, such as the globular protein molecules, little difficulty arises, and the various extensions of the equation developed by Einstein (equation 3.37, p. 114) relating the specific viscosity to the relative volume of the dispersed phase, may be applied. Such measurements give a value of the total "effective" relative volume of the solute or suspended particles, and the frictional constant may then be calculated by means of the Stokes equation (equation 6.4). But if the particles are highly asymmetric in shape, such as are many of the long chain macro-molecules, or in any case if they are in sufficient concentration to interact with one another, the interpretation of the results becomes more difficult, and the equations that have been developed are of doubtful theoretical significance. Equations of a more or less empirical nature have been used successfully in the study of the various members of homologous series of macro-molecules, and these will be found in the monograph by Svedberg and his co-workers (1940) and in the text-book by Alexander and Johnson (1949).

The Shape of the Particles. When the method used for determining the average weight of the particles involves an independent estimate of the frictional constant, as when the diffusion velocity is combined with the sedimentation velocity or viscosity, or when the two latter are combined with each other, an estimate can be made of the shape of the particles. From the volume of each particle, as calculated from its weight and an assumed specific volume, a frictional constant can be calculated by means of the Stokes equation. If the observed frictional constant is greater than this, it can be assumed that the particles are not spherical, and a certain degree of asymmetry can be assigned to them. In doing this, however, we are tacitly assuming that the particles are not hydrated; if each particle contains, or is associated with, an appreciable quantity of water, its effective radius will be greater than that calculated from the weight and the specific volume of the solid material. Similarly, the specific viscosity will be greater than that calculated from the weight and specific volume of the particles if their "effective" relative volume is increased either by the presence of water of hydration or as a result of their being asymmetrical and sweeping out a volume determined by their long axes (Chapter 3, p. 114). There is no way of eliminating this uncertainty as to the origin of an unexpectedly large value of the frictional constant except by the use of independent evidence as to the degree of hydration, or asymmetry, of the particles.

The methods of determining the size and shape of colloidal particles and molecules which involve measurements of osmotic pressure, diffusion, sedimentation and viscosity—i.e. those which in effect measure physico-chemical properties of the solution—are most suitable for use with the smaller particles. Those involving the optical methods and ultra-filtration are better for the larger particles. But there is a range of colloidal solutions in which the particle size has been measured by direct microscopic observation, by light scattering and by ultra-filtration, on the one hand; and from the osmotic pressure of the solution and by diffusion and sedimentation, on the other hand. The agreement between the methods is, on the whole, satisfactory. It must be emphasised that when the particles are not all of precisely the same size or shape—as is very common in colloidal systems—all the methods give average values, and the averaging is not necessarily carried out in the same way. Measurement of the physico-chemical properties of the solution gives an average which is weighted in favour of the smaller particles; direct observation, light scattering and ultra-filtration give averages which are weighted in favour of the larger particles. Precise agreement between the methods in these circumstances can hardly be expected. Direct evidence as to the homogeneity of the particles in respect of their size and shape may be obtained from observations on the rate of sedimentation or diffusion. Two or more distinct boundaries may be observed, as in Fig. 6.10, or the rate of change of concentration in the boundary region may depart significantly from that expected in a system of uniform particles. It is to be expected, also, that inhomogeneity would be indicated by a departure of the measured molecular weight from a simple multiple of the minimum molecular weight as calculated from elementary chemical analysis of the substance concerned. The direct measurements of molecular weight, however, are rarely of sufficient precision to permit conclusions of value to be drawn from such a comparison. A critical survey of the methods of determining the sizes and shapes of particles will be found in the article by Sadron (1953 *b*).

LITERATURE

General. Faraday (1858); Graham (1861); Wo. Ostwald (1922); Alexander and Johnson (1949).

Brownian Movement and Kinetic Theory. Perrin (1923).

Giant Molecules. Astbury (1947); Rudall (1950); Bateman (1945).

Stability and Electric Charge. Abramson (1934).

Proteins. Loeb (1924); Adam (1941—Chapter 2); Abramson, Moyer and Gorin (1942).

Viscosity. Bingham (1922); L. E. Bayliss (1952).

Ultra-microscope and Dark-ground Illumination. Zsigmondy (1920).

Scattering of Light. Oster (1950).

Ultra-filtration. Elford (1937).

Osmotic Pressure. Loeb (1924); Adair (1929).

Diffusion, Sedimentation and Viscosity. Svedberg and others (1940); Alexander and Johnson (1949).

7

CATALYSIS

Systematic studies of the chemical changes that take place in living organisms began to be made as soon as the science of chemistry was sufficiently well developed. It very soon became plain that these changes are for the most part of a kind such as, in the laboratory, can only be brought about by powerful reagents and high temperatures. The hydrolysis of proteins to amino-acids, for example, is effected in the laboratory by boiling concentrated hydrochloric acid; but in the organism, it takes place, at an equal rate, at ordinary temperatures and in a medium which is neutral, or just faintly alkaline. Many other reactions take place which can be performed only by the most elaborate laboratory procedures. Blood is supplied to various organs of an animal, for example, and without the assistance of any other liquid, we obtain, saliva, milk, urine, and so on.

The nature of the processes concerned was first indicated by the great chemist Berzelius (1837), who directed attention to what he called a "force which differs from those hitherto known". A discovery had been made by Kirchhoff in 1812 which gave the first clue to an understanding of the vital processes; he found that starch could be converted into glucose by the action of dilute sulphuric acid, which was itself unchanged in the process, since it could be recovered at the end. Thénard, a few years later, had discovered hydrogen peroxide, and noticed that it was decomposed not only by soluble alkalies but also by many kinds of solid insoluble substances, such as manganese peroxide, silver, platinum, and the fibrin of blood. These do not take part themselves in the new compounds formed, but remain unaltered; they were stated to act by an "indwelling force, whose nature is still unknown". Shortly before Thénard's discovery, Humphry Davy had found that platinum, under certain conditions, had the power of causing the oxidation of alcohol vapour in air. Edmund Davy, his cousin, made a more active preparation, which was actually platinum in a very finely divided state, and Döbereiner made a spongy platinum which could cause even oxygen and hydrogen gases to combine. This property, as Berzelius pointed out, is not, however, confined to platinum, but in less degree, is possessed by other substances. Thus, while platinum is active even below 0° C., gold requires a higher temperature, silver still higher, and glass at least 300° C.

Berzelius then considered the phenomena of alcoholic fermentation, known since the earliest times, before written history, but not at that time known to be due to a living organism. He wrote: "We had made acquaintance with the fact that, for example, the change of sugar into carbonic acid and alcohol takes place in fermentation under the influence of an insoluble body, which we call 'ferment', and also that this ferment could be replaced, although less effectively, by animal fibrin, coagulated plant albumin, cheese and similar substances, as well as with the experience that the process could not be explained by chemical action between the sugar and the ferment analogous to double decomposition. Comparing it with known relations in the inorganic world, it was seen to be most like the decomposition of hydrogen peroxide under the influence of platinum, silver, or fibrin; it was, therefore, natural to suppose that the action of the ferment was an analogous one." What is common to all these observations is the manifestation of a "new force", different from chemical affinity in the ordinary meaning of the words, in that a substance may effect chemical changes without itself taking part in them. Berzelius was careful, however, to avoid any suggestion that this "force" is other than a special manifestation of known properties of matter. He gave the following definition: "I will call it the *catalytic* power of substances and the decomposition effected thereby, *catalysis*; just as we understand by *analysis* the separation of the constituents of substances by means of ordinary chemical affinity. Catalytic power appears to consist essentially in the fact that substances are able to set into activity affinities which are dormant at this particular temperature, and this, not by their own affinity, but by their presence alone."

Turning to living nature, it is pointed out that "we have justifiable reasons to suppose that, in living plants and animals, thousands of catalytic processes take place between the tissues and the liquids and result in the formation of the great number of dissimilar chemical compounds, for whose formation out of the common raw material, plant juice or blood, no probable cause could be assigned. The cause will perhaps in the future be discovered in the catalytic power of the organic tissues of which the organs of the living body consist."

With respect to the name itself, it must be admitted that "catalysis" suggests an opposite kind of process to that of "analysis"; so that, since this latter implies the separation of a process or compound into its constituents, catalysis might be taken to mean a synthetic process. The word has come into general use, however, to denote such processes as those referred to by Berzelius. It is also convenient to have a word for the agent itself: "catalyst" is most frequently used.

THE FUNDAMENTAL FACTS OF CATALYSIS

The nature of catalysis, and the essential properties of catalysts, become apparent if we consider some illustrative examples. If ethyl acetate and water are mixed in equal molecular proportions, and allowed to remain for some weeks, the ester is hydrolysed with the formation of ethanol and acetic acid; but, however long a time be allowed to elapse, only a certain part of the ester is decomposed, in spite of the fact that there is sufficient water to hydrolyse the whole of it. The rate of conversion becomes smaller and smaller until it ceases, and at this time it is found that the four components of the system are present in the proportion of one-third of a gram-molecule each of alcohol and acid, two-thirds of a gram-molecule each of ester and water. Further, suppose we commence with acetic acid and ethanol, also in equimolecular proportions, and allow the reaction to proceed until it stops, we find that we obtain the same proportion of the four components. Clearly we have here a case of equilibrium, or balance of opposing reactions.

These reactions obviously proceed extremely slowly. We can, however, increase the rate enormously by adding some mineral acid, the equilibrium condition then being reached in a few hours instead of many weeks. Three important facts may be derived from experiments of this kind. First, the velocity of the reaction depends on the amount of acid added; but the composition of the system, when equilibrium is reached, is independent of the amount of acid added, and, indeed, is the same in the presence of acid as it is when the reaction is allowed to proceed "spontaneously". Secondly, the acid added is still present, when the system has reached equilibrium, in the same state, and the same concentration, as it was originally. Lastly, the rate of the reaction is increased by the addition of acid, whether we start from ester and water, or from acid and alcohol; and, moreover, the two rates must be increased in the same proportion. This follows from the fact that the equilibrium position is not changed by the presence of the acid.

This may easily be seen from a rough analogy, which must not be followed in too great detail. Suppose that two people start to walk towards one another from two distant places. Where they meet will clearly depend on the relative rates at which they walk; if they walk at the same rate, they will meet half-way between the places from which they start. Now imagine that one of them is in a hurry, and is "catalysed", so that, instead of walking, he uses a bicycle. He will meet the other man before he has taken many steps from home. It is also obvious that if one man cycles, the only way by which the two could meet at the same place ("equilibrium position") is that the other man cycles also. It is necessary, moreover, that the two men should hurry in proportion to their original walking speeds; if they did not walk at the same speed, then they must not cycle at the same speed, or they would meet at a different equilibrium point. Both of them, in fact, must be "catalysed" to the same extent.

These points are further illustrated by the curves in Fig. 7.1. The system here is one of glucose, glycerol, glyceryl-glucoside and water, and the reaction is catalysed by a substance obtained from almonds, and known as "emulsin". Both glucose and the glucoside are optically active substances, glucose being dextro-rotatory and the glucoside laevo-rotatory. The course of the reaction is thus conveniently followed by measuring the

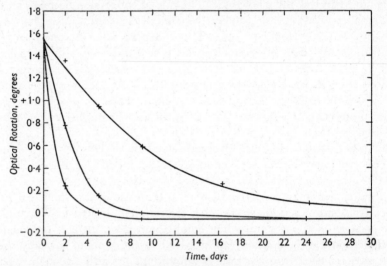

FIG. 7.1. THE SYNTHESIS OF GLYCERYL-GLUCOSIDE IN THE PRESENCE OF DIFFERENT CONCENTRATIONS OF A CATALYST

The three curves show the course of the reaction, as measured in terms of the optical activity of the solution, in the presence of the enzyme emulsin, the concentration of emulsin increasing in the ratio 1:4:12 from the top curve downwards. The velocity of the reaction increases with increase in the concentration of the catalyst, but the final position of equilibrium is unchanged.   (W. M. Bayliss, 1913.)

optical activity of the solution. The velocity of the reaction clearly increases with increase in the quantity of catalyst added, although the end-point is unchanged. In the absence of catalyst, this particular reaction is too slow for any change to be detected over the period of time considered.

Experiments of this kind, moreover, demonstrate that a catalyst does not actually set into action a new process, but merely hastens one that was already in progress. Ostwald, therefore, defined a catalyst as a substance that increases the rate at which equilibrium is reached; at the same time, however, he pointed out that the reaction, without the catalyst, may be so slow that it appears not to take place at all. The important point is that the reaction must be such that if it proceeds at all, it does so with a reduction in free energy, and is thus "spontaneous" in the thermodynamic sense. The catalyst also, cannot itself form part of the final chemical system in equilibrium, since it is still present at the end of the reaction in an unaltered state (there are exceptions to this, which will be considered later). It is characteristic of catalysts, therefore, that they exert a powerful action even when present in very minute amounts, in proportion to those of the components of the reaction catalysed. For instance, the reaction between hydrogen peroxide and hydriodic acid is appreciably accelerated by the presence of 1 gram-molecule of molybdic acid in 31 million litres of solution. This point is brought out even better in the reactions catalysed by enzymes, to be discussed in more detail below. Trypsin, for example, can readily be detected by its hydrolytic action when 1 gram-molecule is present in 1000 million litres of solution; one molecule of catalase will bring about the decomposition of 44,000 molecules of hydrogen peroxide per second.

A simple experiment will assist us in understanding the essential properties of a catalyst and avoid confusion with some other processes, which have a superficial resemblance to those of catalysis. Take a piece of carefully cleaned, polished plate-glass about a metre long and some 20 cm. broad. Rest one end on the table and raise the other end on an adjustable support. Now take a brass weight of about one kilogram, polish the bottom and place it on the top of the glass plate, which forms an inclined plane. By delicate adjustment of the angle of the plane, it will be possible to find such a position that the weight slides down very slowly. This is the most difficult part of the experiment, since a speck of gritty dust will stop the descent, so that it is well to polish the surface with a little talc and a chamois leather immediately before the weight is placed on it. This part of the experiment represents a reaction taking place of itself very slowly. Apply, next, a little oil to the bottom of the weight and again place it at the top of the plane. It will slide down with great rapidity. The oil represents the catalyst.

There are several instructive points about this scheme. Notice first that the energy available in the "reaction" is simply that due to the fall of the weight from the vertical height of the top of the plane to that of the lower end, and that this is unaffected by the addition of the catalyst, which therefore takes no part in the final state. A point of importance in relation to the catalytic reactions in the living organism is, however, that the form of the energy may be different in the two cases. Without the oil, the weight arrives at the bottom with very little kinetic energy, most of its potential energy having been lost as heat, due to friction along the glass. With oil, very little energy is lost as heat and the weight arrives at the bottom with considerable kinetic energy. This teaches us that the actual products of a catalysed reaction are not necessarily identical with those obtained in the absence of a catalyst.

The next point is that, within limits, we can vary the rate of fall by the application of much or little oil. Although the catalyst does not affect the position of the end-point, the rate at which this is reached depends on the

K

amount of catalyst present. Moreover, we note that a given small amount of oil has a large effect when applied to a weight which has not previously been oiled, but a negligible effect when considerable amounts of oil are present already. The catalytic action is not directly proportional to the quantity of catalyst present.

One more fact, the meaning of which will be appreciated later, is that in our model the oil partially disappears by sticking to the glass, so that the whole of it is not present on the weight at the bottom. In a certain sense we may say that it has "combined" with some other constituent of the system. In some catalytic reactions we meet with phenomena of this nature; for example, in the chamber process of sulphuric acid manufacture, the nitric acid, which acts as a catalyst, slowly disappears, being used up in subsidiary reactions.

CATALYSIS IN HETEROGENEOUS SYSTEMS

We shall find presently that the particular catalysts of especial interest to us are in the colloidal state. In the reactions illustrated in Fig. 7.1, for example, the emulsin can act as a catalyst even in liquids in which it is completely insoluble, and from which it can be filtered off, leaving no trace in solution. It is necessary, therefore, to consider briefly the mechanism of reactions in systems of more than one phase. The theory of these reactions is due chiefly to Nernst. They may be said to take place in four stages. Suppose the catalyst is present in the form of particles, and that the other components, which are to be made to react, are in true solution. In order that they may be affected by the catalyst, it is obviously necessary that they first diffuse to it. If, however, the catalyst is in colloidal solution —i.e. in very small particles which are uniformly distributed—the distance over which diffusion has to occur is likely to be small; the reactants will arrive at the catalyst (and the resultants will move away from it) as rapidly as they can be removed (or created) by the main chemical reaction. The reactants must next become attached in some way to the catalyst, either by adsorption, or perhaps by some form of chemical reaction. Adsorption, in general, is a rapid process, requiring little activation energy; but, as we shall see later, it would seem that in some catalysed reactions, more powerful and specific forces of attraction are involved, and the activation energy may be appreciable. The third stage is the main chemical reaction itself, whose rate, of course, will be determined by the effectiveness of the catalyst. And finally, the products of the reaction must evaporate, or become desorbed or dissociated, from the surface of the catalyst.

In all heterogeneous reactions, the rate of the reaction, as measured, is naturally that of the slowest member of the series. In a great many, and perhaps most cases, this will be the main chemical reaction itself. But there are also cases in which the controlling rate is that of the uptake of the reactants by the catalyst, or the removal of the resultants from it.

If the concentration of the reactants on the surface of the catalyst is greater than that in the solution, as a result of adsorption, for example, the velocity of the reaction would be increased by a simple mass action effect. This was, in fact, the explanation suggested by Faraday for the effect of platinum in causing combination of oxygen and hydrogen. He suggested that a condensation of the gases took place on the surface of the platinum, so that the molecules were brought into close contact, and on p. 180 of his *Experimental Researches on Electricity* (1839) he speaks of an "attractive force of bodies" causing association more or less close, without at the same time producing chemical combination, but "which occasionally leads, under very favourable circumstances, to the combination of bodies simultaneously subjected to this attraction".

But over and above any possible mass action effect, adsorbed substances may be more or less reactive than they are when in bulk solution. A long-chain molecule, for example, orientated at an interface, may be distorted, so that parts of it may be more accessible to reagents in one of the phases on each side of the interface at which it is adsorbed. Moreover, as discussed in Chapter 5, adsorption occurs most readily when the external fields of force of the adsorbed substance fit those of the adsorbent; if the fit is not quite exact, however, adsorption may take place, but the adsorbed molecules may be distorted, or strained, work being done on them in the process, by the fields of force of the adsorbent. Such molecules have acquired extra energy, and this may enable them to surmount energy barriers which would otherwise be practically impassible. Chemisorbed substances, also, by virtue of the attachment by covalent bonds, lose their chemical individuality to a greater or less extent. Thus oxygen adsorbed on tungsten will not combine with hydrogen even at high temperatures, whereas oxygen adsorbed on platinum will do so more readily than it does as a free gas: carbon monoxide adsorbed on platinum, however, will not readily combine with oxygen. Such chemisorption cannot really be distinguished from the formation of an intermediate compound. If the catalyst molecule is sufficiently small, we can often discover a simple stoichiometrical relation between the catalyst and the reacting substance, and we speak of an intermediate compound: if the catalyst has a large molecule, or is grossly heterogeneous, as is platinum black, there is usually no simple stoichiometrical relation, and we speak of an adsorption.

Faraday's views on the possibility of the close approximation of oxygen and hydrogen on the surface of platinum being sufficient to cause their molecules to enter into combination led to a long discussion with De la Rive, who held that there is an intermediate formation of some oxide of platinum. With our knowledge of Faraday's wonderful insight into the mechanism of natural phenomena, we may well be inclined to think that he was most likely on the right side in this case. Kohlrausch remarked, "Er riecht die Wahrheit", "he smells the truth" (see Tyndall's *Faraday as a Discoverer*, 1870, p. 55).

The question of whether the reactivity of two substances is increased or decreased by adsorption on a surface may be related to the activation energies involved (*a*) in releasing the substances in question from the surface, and (*b*) in bringing about the combination. On the one hand, if, say, an oxygen atom needs a very large amount of energy before it can break away from a tungsten surface (as would seem to be the case) there is little chance of its being able to do so; the frequency with which an oxygen atom leaves the surface, and then combines with a hydrogen molecule, may well be vanishingly small. On the other hand, if the activation energy is large, but not excessively large, it will, on the average, be acquired at appreciable, though rather large, intervals of time; we may imagine the catalytic action of platinum in the reaction of hydrogen and oxygen as being due, in part, at least, to the fact that atoms of both substances are held on the surface for considerable periods of time (as compared with the duration of an ordinary collision, less than 10^{-13} seconds) and closer together than they would ever be in the gas phase except actually during a collision. Thus whenever an atom happens to acquire the necessary activation energy, it has a high probability of encountering hydrogen atoms, and of reacting with them. In the gaseous state, a large fraction of the atoms with the necessary energy fail to collide with an atom of the other kind which also has the necessary energy. In addition, as already mentioned, the adsorbed atoms and molecules almost certainly acquire energy from atoms of the adsorbent, with which they are in close association.

An example of catalysis by an inorganic surface is given by the extensive work of Palmer and Constable during 1920 to 1923 on the dehydrogenation of alcohols. They found, to begin with, that the heat of activation is very much less when the alcohols are adsorbed on a copper surface, than when they are free; the molecules may, apparently, become activated by energy other than that of thermal agitation. The rate of the reaction, also, with the primary alcohols, is independent of the length of the carbon chain, or of the presence of branches in the chain; substitution of a secondary alcohol ($=CHOH$) end group, instead of the primary alcohol ($—CH_2OH$), however, results in a five-fold increase in the rate of reaction. It is presumed, therefore, that the alcohols are attached to the copper surface by their alcoholic end groups, and that these are strained in the process in such a way that two hydrogen atoms break away; the carbon chain is not attached to the surface, and so takes no part in the reaction.

Catalysis by adsorption of the reacting substances on a surface may also result from an action of rather a different kind, that is, by dissipating the energy released by the reaction. In the recombination of hydrogen atoms to form molecules, for example—the reaction most studied from this point of view—there is a very large release of energy, and the energy content of the hydrogen molecules is so large that, unless it is removed by "inactivating" collisions with the atoms of the surface, the molecules will immediately dissociate again into atoms. The surface on which the reacting substances are adsorbed thus, in general, ensures that the energy content of the molecules of the reaction product, when they are first formed, is not vastly greater than that of similar molecules which are in energy equilibrium with the system as a whole. Although the amount of energy released in reactions of biological interest is not usually very large, this function of the catalyst may be of importance, and it may serve as a mechanism for transferring the energy to some other process or reaction. We shall return to this point in a later section.

It is clear, therefore, that surface catalysis is likely to occur whenever the surface is capable of adsorbing the reactants; in most cases, however, it is more important that it should, also, be capable of activating them. If adsorption is too complete, it is likely that activation will not occur. Adam (1941), therefore, has extended Emil Fischer's lock and key analogy to the effect that the key must not only be able to enter the lock (adsorption must occur) but it must be able to shoot the bolt (activation must follow). If a third, heavily adsorbed substance is also present in the reaction mixture, it may occupy the surface, without undergoing chemical reaction, at the expense of the reactants, and so "poison" the catalyst.

There is good reason for supposing that inorganic surface catalysts, such as various metals, or charcoal, possess active patches, occupying quite a small fraction of the total area, at which all, or practically all, the reaction takes place. For instance, one and the same preparation can often catalyse several different reactions, each to a different extent. The catalytic activity, also, can be reduced to negligible proportions by the presence of a highly adsorbed "poison" in quantity quite insufficient to provide even a monomolecular layer over the whole surface. In such cases, one of the reactions catalysed may be poisoned very much more effectively than others. It has been found, again, that the activity of a given substance, such as copper, becomes considerably reduced whenever it is treated in such a way that the atoms become regularly arranged; for example, if they are deposited electrolytically, allowed to arrange themselves by heating the material to a suitable temperature, or formed by polishing into the very homogeneous "Beilby layer". Charcoal has particularly variable and complex patches, whose properties depend upon the presence of small quantities of other constituents, notably iron and nitrogen, and which catalyse different reactions.

Such an activating action of auxiliary materials is very common in all kinds of inorganic surface catalysts. The properties of these have been very extensively studied owing to their great importance in chemical engineering; indeed, it may be said that most of the important industrial chemical processes involve the use of catalysts. The catalysts used consist chiefly of metals which are capable of forming covalent and semi-polar bonds, such as platinum, iron, copper, nickel and molybdenum. These are, in nearly all cases, activated by the addition of small quantities of other substances, known as "promoters"; they consist of the oxides of silicon, aluminium, magnesium, thorium and many other metals, or merely of supports, of some refractory material, and appear to act by creating active patches, similar to those formed on charcoal by iron and nitrogen, already mentioned. In this respect, there may be some similarity—perhaps only superficial—between these inorganic catalysts and the organic ones, enzymes, which are of such importance to living organisms, as will appear in the next section.

ENZYMES

Berzelius, as we have seen, concluded that in living animals and plants, there must be "thousands of catalytic processes" at work. As various substances were extracted from organisms, and the similarity of their actions to that of alcoholic fermentation became obvious, it was natural to call them "ferments". And when Cagniard de Latour showed, in 1838, that alcoholic fermentation was due to a living organism, substances such as the "diastase" precipitated by Payen and Persoz in 1833 from extracts of malt, were called "soluble", "unorganised", or "unformed" ferments, and distinguished from "organised", or "formed" ferments. In process of time some confusion was caused by this double use of the word "ferment", and Kühne, in 1878, thought it well to introduce a new name for the soluble, or unorganised ferments. The passage in which this name was first introduced is sufficiently interesting to be translated here:

"The latter designations (formed and unformed ferments) have not gained general acceptance, since on the one hand it was objected that chemical bodies, like ptyalin, pepsin, etc., could not be called ferments, since the name was already given to yeast-cells and other *organisms* (Brücke); while, on the other hand, it was said that yeast-cells could not be called *ferment*, because then all organisms, including man, would have to be so designated (Hoppe-Seyler). Without stopping to inquire further why the name excited so much opposition, I have taken the opportunity to suggest a new one, and I give the name *enzymes* to some of the better-known substances, called by many 'unformed ferments'. This name is not intended to imply any particular hypothesis, it merely states that ἐν ζύμη (in yeast) something occurs that exerts this or that activity, which is supposed to belong to the class called fermentative. The name is not, however, intended to be limited to the invertin of yeast, but it *is* intended to imply that more complex organisms, from which the enzymes, pepsin, trypsin, etc., can be obtained, are not so fundamentally different from the unicellular organisms as some people would have us believe." The name "enzyme" has come into general use, although "ferment" is still to be met with as synonymous with it; while the application of this name "ferment" to living organisms has dropped out of use. Enzymes, therefore, may be shortly defined as the catalysts produced by living organisms.

To distinguish the different enzymes from one another, Duclaux suggested adding the termination "-ase" to the name of the substance on which the enzyme acts, now usually called the "substrate"; thus "lactase" is the enzyme which acts on lactose. Certain old names, such as "pepsin" and "trypsin" are, however, still in use. The termination "-lytic" has been used for a class of enzymes acting on a group of substances by splitting them into their component parts; a "proteolytic enzyme" is one that acts on the proteins in general, and includes pepsin and trypsin. Armstrong, however, justly pointed out that "proteolytic", by analogy with "electrolytic" should mean decomposition by means of protein, not decomposition of the protein itself. To avoid this misuse, the termination "-clastic" was suggested, and is now in common use.

The categorical statement that enzymes are catalysts, neither more nor less, now generally accepted, would not have gone unchallenged in the past. The essential property of a catalyst is that it changes the velocity of a chemical reaction, without itself being one of the reactants, or a constituent of the products of the reaction. It may initiate a reaction which does not appear to proceed of itself, but if so, the reaction will be exergonic; a catalyst cannot provide chemical energy.

There are certainly some reactions which proceed slowly by themselves, and are accelerated by enzymes; the hydrolysis of esters, already discussed, may be mentioned. There are also reactions which proceed rapidly in the presence of enzymes, but, in their absence, go too slowly, at ordinary temperatures, to be detected; many of them, however, can be made to go at measurable rates by raising the temperature. The hydrolysis of cane-sugar may be given as an example; glucose, also, is perfectly stable in air at ordinary temperatures, although its oxidation, in solution, is catalysed by enzymes; if placed in oxygen and heated to a suitable temperature, however, it will burn spontaneously. When a reaction can be made obvious by raising the temperature, it is justifiable to conclude that it is not entirely absent at ordinary temperatures.

A more important point of difficulty is the question of the relation of the enzyme to the final products of the reaction. In some cases, the enzyme has been recovered at the end of the reaction unchanged, as is the acid in the hydrolysis of esters; in other cases, it disappears, partially or entirely.

This disappearance, however, is due to the instability of the enzyme; that it does not form a component of the final equilibrium is shown by the numerous experiments in which it has been found that the nature and concentration of the products of the reaction are independent of the amount of enzyme added. If the enzyme formed a component of the re- action system, the position of the final equilibrium, and possibly even the nature of the products of the reaction, would be altered, by mass action, according to the amount of enzyme present. A series of curves illustrating this point will be found in the monograph by W. M. Bayliss (1925), and one such set has already been given in Fig. 7.1. Some apparent exceptions to this may result from the fact, as Haldane (1930) has pointed out, that a system may be able to react in more than one way; the spontaneous reaction may go most rapidly so as to form one set of resultants, while an enzyme may catalyse the reaction which forms a different set. In these circumstances, the enzyme will appear to change the nature of the re- action. It is quite certain, however, that no enzyme has been described which will lead to a reaction proceeding with a gain in free energy.

In certain circumstances, there may be a "false equilibrium" in which the final result depends upon the concentration of the enzyme. Careful examina- tion of the experimental observations, however, suggests that this is due to the enzyme becoming inactivated before it has had time to carry the reaction as far as the true equilibrium position. Naturally, the more enzyme is present at first, the faster will the reaction proceed; and, moreover, the longer will it be before the whole of the enzyme has disappeared.

It is sometimes found, nevertheless, that the position of the equilibrium is genuinely shifted, to some extent, when an obviously reversible reaction is catalysed by an enzyme. Such a shift, however, may also occur when the catalyst is an acid or other inorganic substance. This fact has caused some difficulty, which would, indeed, be more serious if the reactions concerned were associated with any considerable change in free energy; one would then have to suppose that energy was supplied by the catalysts, or from some other source. The fact that they are obviously reversible, however, shows that the free energy change must be small. The question arises chiefly in hydrolytic reactions, and these can easily be shown to be associ- ated with very little heat change—in the conversion of 1 mole of methyl acetate to 1 of methanol and 1 of acetic acid, for example, only -900 calories, or 0.38 per cent. of the heat of combustion of the ester. In all catalytic reactions, there is some kind of temporary combination between the catalysts and both the reactants and the products of the reaction, associated with a definite change in the energy of the system. If a large quantity of catalyst be added, the active masses of the reactants and pro- ducts will be affected by the withdrawl of some of them to form the various complexes or combinations with the catalyst. In general, the various complexes are not equally stable, so that the active mass of one of the reactants may be affected more than that of the others, and an apparent shift in the equilibrium results. In the system ethyl acetate, water, acetic acid, ethanol, the equilibrium constant (ester) (water)/(acid) (alcohol) has, as we have seen, the value 4; in the presence of large amounts of hydrochloric acid as a catalyst, the value may rise as high as 8. On the assumption, however, that the complex $HCl . 2H_2O$ is formed, the active mass of the water is so reduced that the equilibrium constant becomes 4. In some experiments of Dietz on the hydrolysis of amyl butyrate, the equilibrium was reached with 85·5 per cent. of ester when acid was the catalyst, and with 75 per cent. when lipase was used (lipase is an enzyme which can be extracted from the pancreas, a secreting gland associated with the alimentary canal in most kinds of animal). Presumably the complex acid-water is relatively more stable than the complex enzyme-water.

When we are dealing with catalysis in heterogeneous systems, as with enzymes, moreover, the preferential adsorption of one of the components of a reaction may lead to a change in the equilibrium position, as was discussed in Chapter 5 (p. 192). The presence of hydrophilic colloids, also, may have a similar action with regard to the equilibrium position in hydrolytic reactions. In high concentrations, they may have the effect of reducing the activity coefficient of the water, since they will take up water by imbibition, as discussed in Chapter 6 (p. 255).

THE CONSTITUTION OF ENZYMES

We cannot, as yet, describe completely the constitution of any enzyme in precise chemical terms. In practice, therefore, enzymes are characterised in terms of the components of the reactions which they catalyse. Many of these reactions do not proceed at measurable rates in the absence of the enzyme, and it is often convenient to describe an enzyme as being responsible for actually initiating, or bringing about, some particular reaction. While this avoids much cumbersome phraseology, it must always be borne in mind that an enzyme, by itself, cannot bring about a reaction which is not energetically "spontaneous"; there is always a reduction in the free energy of the system even when the reaction occurs only when the enzyme is present.

We may distinguish two main classes of enzyme: those which split molecules into two or more parts by adding the elements of water or phosphoric acid, and which may be called *hydrolysing* or *phosphorylising*; and those which activate oxygen or hydrogen—free or in combination— bringing about *oxidations* and *reductions* (oxidases, dehydrogenases, reductases). There are also two other groups of enzymes with rather more

K*

varied properties: those which split molecules into parts without the addition of water, or, of course, add the parts together again (decarboxy-lases, and many others); and those which transfer groups or radicals of various kinds, notably phosphoryl, acetyl, methyl and amino, from one molecule to another. All these classes may be further divided according to the type of molecule attacked. In addition, there are other enzymes which do not fall easily into any of these groups. More complete classifications will be found in the text-books of Biochemistry, such as that by Baldwin (1957); and the monographs by Sumner and Somers (1953) and by Tauber (1949) contain full "dictionaries" of the properties of all known enzymes.

Physical Properties of Enzymes. All enzymes are in the colloidal state in solution. They do not diffuse through thick parchment paper, but, as samples of this paper vary in the dimensions of their pores, and as the molecules of different enzymes differ in size, it may be found that some enzymes may diffuse slowly through some papers. They are destroyed by heat by a process similar to that by which proteins are denatured. As colloids, they have an electric charge, varying with the nature and con-centration of the electrolytes present with them. This charge appears to play some part in the mechanism of their action, as will be seen presently. There is indirect evidence that many, if not all, are optically active.

Chemical Nature of Enzymes. Precise chemical identification of an enzyme presents great difficulty. In the first place, as a rule, only minute quantities are available; enzymes are so intensely active, and present in such small concentration, that enormous quantities of material—yeast, plant tissues, animal secreting glands, for example—must be worked up in order to obtain only a few milligrams of the pure substance. In the second place, enzymes are proteins, and it has not yet been possible to ascribe a precise chemical structure to any protein molecule. It was thought originally that enzymes had the composition of proteins, but then, as preparations were made of greater purity, it was found that the protein reactions disappeared more and more, although the preparation gained in activity per unit weight. Advances in chemical technique, however, later made it possible to prove that all the enzymes that have been thoroughly studied are proteins, after all. This reversal of conclusions is due to the fact that most of the impurities in the preparations are proteins, and, as Northrop pointed out in 1937, to the fact that the chemical tests for pro-teins are very much less sensitive than the catalytic tests for enzymes by means of the reactions specifically associated with them; the chemical test for pepsin or trypsin, for example, is only 1/10 to 1/100 as sensitive as is the test of protein digestion.

The protein nature of enzymes was first clearly established in 1926 when Sumner succeeded in isolating and crystallising the hydrolysing enzyme urease. This was followed by the crystallisation, by Northrop and

his co-workers, of pepsin and trypsin in 1930 and 1931. The first crystallisation of an oxidation-reduction enzyme was that of the Warburg-
Christian "Yellow enzyme" by Teorell in 1934. Thereafter, purification
and crystallisation of one enzyme after another followed rapidly, and by
1943, 22 pure enzymes had been established as chemical individuals: the
isolation and identification of enzymes continues, and seems likely to do
so almost indefinitely.

Most of the oxidation-reduction enzymes, and some others, appear to
differ in one essential feature from the hydrolysing enzymes; they consist
of a protein in association with a substance of relatively small molecular
weight, known as a *prosthetic group*, and neither of these is active without
the other. The hydrolysing enzymes, in so far as is known, do not contain
any special prosthetic groups. These special groups may be tightly bound
to the protein, or may be very easily dissociable from it; they are then not
to be distinguished from the *co-enzymes* which have been known for many
years. Indeed, where Warburg refers to the prosthetic group and the
protein component of the enzyme, Neuberg and Euler refer to the *co-
enzyme* and the *apo-enzyme*, the two together forming the *holo-enzyme*.
The majority of the hydrolytic enzymes act on macro-molecules, while the
majority of those known to contain prosthetic groups, or to require co-
enzymes, act on molecules which are in true solution. We do not, at present,
know enough about the nature of enzyme action to be able to say whether
these facts have any significance. In general, prosthetic groups do not
split off from the protein part of the enzyme at all readily; they can be
made to do so, however, by suitable chemical treatments, and the two then
made to re-combine. Co-enzymes, on the other hand, will usually dissociate
more easily from the apo-enzyme, and the two only remain united in the
presence of free co-enzyme; in some cases, the equilibrium concentration
of free co-enzyme may be too small to be estimated.

It would appear that Bertrand's conceptions as to the nature of enzymes
had some foundations in fact. In an address to the French Association for the
Advancement of Science in 1909, he expressed them as follows. One of the
constituents of the system is capable, on its own account, of producing the
reaction studied to a slight degree, but requires the presence of another
substance, inactive in itself, before its activity becomes appreciable. The
former is some such substance as acid, alkali, calcium or manganese salt, etc.
The latter is a more complex substance, often similar to egg-white, and
colloidal in character. This view is similar to that stated by von Wittich in
1872, as regards pepsin, which was held merely to intensify the action of
hydrochloric acid. It is not quite clear, however, whether von Wittich intended
to make the general statement that all enzyme actions are of this nature,
although it seems implied; the example chosen, however, was an unfortunate
one, as it has turned out. This view received support also from the facts
connected with the "artificial laccase" prepared by Dony-Hénault in 1908, in

which the active agent is colloidal manganese hydroxide, protected from aggregation by the presence of a "stable" colloid, gum arabic.

In addition, there are many substances, of relatively simple and known constitution, which take part, in a catalytic manner, in the complex chains of reactions involved in metabolic processes. These are not ordinarily included among the co-enzymes, since, for the most part, their existence, and composition, were known before their significance, as components of definite enzyme reactions, was understood. In the presence of suitable enzymes, these substances will accept electrons, hydrogen atoms, or various kinds of organic group, or radical, such as amino, methyl, acetyl and phosphoryl groups, from one kind of substrate, and then donate them to another kind. They are often referred to as *"carriers"* of electrons, radicals, or organic groups, as the case may be. They may be regarded as substrates in certain kinds of enzyme reaction; but, on the other hand, they cannot, in fact, be rigidly distinguished from the co-enzymes. As we shall see below, there is very good reason for believing that enzymes undergo reversible combination (chemical, chemisorption or van der Waals adsorption) with their substrates; and when a substrate is itself a reversible link in a chain of reactions, its behaviour is not essentially different from that of a co-enzyme or a prosthetic group. The difference is a quantitative one, in the tightness of the union with the protein part of the enzyme, and is largely a matter of terminology. We shall have occasion to discuss some of these carriers in more detail in the next chapter.

Many of the prosthetic groups contain metals as essential constituents, in most cases in the form of metal chelates, united with special organic compounds by means of covalent or semi-polar (co-ordinate) bonds; iron and copper are perhaps the commonest of these metals. In many cases, also, although the prosthetic group is not known to contain a metal as part of its structure, the enzyme is active only in the presence of certain metals; magnesium, manganese and cobalt may be given as examples. All these metals must be supplied to the organism from the environment, and become essential constituents of the soil for plants, or of the food for animals. The special organic compounds, also, both in the prosthetic groups and those constituting the co-enzymes and radical-carriers, may have to be supplied from the environment. All can, apparently, be synthesised by plants; many by micro-organisms; but only a few by animals.

In a great many enzymes, or even the majority, the protein apo-enzyme is soluble in water, although, of course, the solution is colloidal. Other enzymes, however, remain insoluble—in the sense that they are thrown down by ordinary centrifugation except when treated so violently that they are destroyed, or at least lose their prosthetic groups. Such enzymes probably form part of the cell structure and cannot be detached from it without undergoing disintegration. Purification is obviously exceedingly difficult. These enzymes remind one of the inorganic surface catalysts with their "active patches".

More detailed accounts of the physico-chemical constitution of enzymes will be found in the monograph by Northrop and his colleagues (1948) and in the article by Moelwyn-Hughes (1950).

A few words may be said with regard to the *methods of purification* used for enzymes. They are, in general, those used for the purification of proteins, described in Chapter 6, but some special methods may be needed owing to the small quantities available, and particular care must be taken in view of the instability of most of the enzymes. First, fractional precipitation may be used, by means of protein precipitants such as acetone, ammonium sulphate, etc. Secondly, fractional adsorption ("chromatography", as described in Chapter 5), on such substances as calcium triphosphate, alumina, kaolin and various synthetic resins, at a suitable value of the acidity, followed by elution at some other acidity, will permit further separation. Thirdly, the solution may be electrodialysed through suitable membranes, the acidity being adjusted so that, for example, the wanted component is electrically neutral and remains in the central compartment, while the unwanted components are drawn into one or other of the electrode compartments; or, alternatively, the solution may be subjected to paper electrophoresis. Lastly, crystallisation may be attempted, usually after preliminary purification by the first three methods. The solubility of the enzyme is cautiously reduced by the addition of a protein precipitant, by cooling, or by dialysis to remove electrolytes. At the end, the purity of the product can be tested by ultra-centrifugation or by electrophoresis and its molecular weight determined, as described in Chapter 6.

Some pure enzymes, such as catalase, are relatively stable, even in solution, but many will become spontaneously inactivated, particularly when in dilute solution, in a matter of hours or perhaps days, at room temperature, and of days or perhaps weeks at $0°$ C.: by no means all are stable even when dried and kept in a desiccator. Micro-organisms, of course, must be kept out of the solutions, otherwise their enzymes will destroy the particular enzymes wanted.

The Catalytic Activity of Enzymes

The reactions in which enzymes are concerned are, for the most part, ordinary chemical reactions, and the velocity at any moment should therefore be proportional to the thermodynamic activities, or as a first approximation to the concentrations, of the reactants at that moment. And, as catalysed reactions, since the catalyst is not one of the reactants, the velocity *constant* should be proportional to some quantity which defines the catalytic activity, or effective concentration, of the enzyme. This, however, may not be even approximately the same as the actual concentration; and the activity of the enzyme may depend on factors other than its concentration. As will be seen, an enzyme can be *activated* or *inactivated* reversibly by temperature, pressure, and by the presence of many different kinds of substance in solution; or, in extreme cases, it may be irreversibly destroyed. An agent which will cause inactivation when in low concentration or intensity, is likely to cause destruction if its intensity, or duration of action, are increased. The concentrations of activating and inactivating substances may increase or decrease during the course of the reaction; the catalytic activity of the enzyme may thus rise or fall progressively and there will be a progressive change in the velocity of the reaction, over and above that due to the change in the concentrations of the reactants. This possibility raises a practical point of some importance. As Bredig pointed out, in comparing the results of the action of enzymes under different conditions, or concentrations, we ought to compare the velocities of the reactions *at the same stage*, since, in this way only, can we be certain of having the same proportion of substrate and products of the main, and perhaps subsidiary, reactions. Alternatively, we must compare the times taken to effect equal changes, not the changes produced in the same time.

We will first describe some of the experimental observations which have identified the agents affecting the catalytic activity of enzymes; and return to the theoretical treatment of the kinetics of enzyme action in a later section.

Concentration of Substrate. In all enzyme reactions, the law of mass action fails to apply when the concentration of the substrate exceeds a certain value; the velocity of the reaction then fails to increase in proportion to the increase in substrate concentration, and may become constant, or even decrease. The actual value of the concentration at which this occurs differs from one kind of reaction to another. It is this kind of behaviour which provides the clearest evidence for the conception that the first step in a catalysed reaction is the union, by chemical combination or by adsorption, of the substrate with the catalyst. At a certain concentration of substrate, the active surface available will be "saturated", so that further increase in concentration will not increase the amount on the enzyme at any moment, and therefore there will be no increase in the velocity of the reaction. We shall consider this in more detail in the next section.

This effect was known at a very early date in the history of the investigations into the nature of enzyme action. It may be illustrated by some experiments of E. F. Armstrong in 1904, in which a given small amount of the enzyme lactase catalysed the hydrolysis of lactose. When the concentration of lactose was 1 per cent. or less, the velocity *constant*, as estimated by the change produced in the first three hours, was sensibly independent of the substrate concentration, as is to be expected from the law of mass action. When the concentration of lactose was 10 per cent. or greater, the *velocity* of the reaction

—i.e. the actual quantity of lactose hydrolysed in a given time (46 hours)— was sensibly constant.

Again, in the case of the action of the enzyme trypsin on caseinogen, studied by W. M. Bayliss in the same year, the velocity of the reaction increases with increase in the caseinogen concentration, though not in direct proportion to it, up to a concentration of 5 per cent.; between 5 per cent. and 8 per cent. the velocity is independent of the substrate concentration; and on further increase, the velocity actually falls.

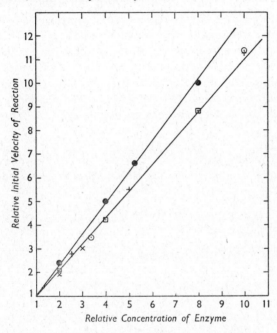

Fig. 7.2. The Relation between the Concentration of the Enzyme and the Initial
Velocity of the Reaction

The following reactions are represented:

⊙ : urease—urea
▫ : trypsin—casein
× : invertase—cane sugar
+ : amylase—starch
● : purified pepsin—egg albumin.

The first four are plotted from data of Marshall (1913), Northrop (1919), v. Euler (1921) and Nelson (1924), respectively, as given by Moelwyn-Hughes (1940); the last is from data of Northrop (1920).

Concentration of Enzyme. In the absence of complicating factors, it is to be expected that, if the initial concentration of the substrate is kept constant, the initial velocity of the reaction should be proportional to the enzyme concentration. This simple relation holds for some kinds of enzyme reaction, as is demonstrated by the experimental results plotted in Fig. 7.2; but it does not hold for many other kinds of enzyme reaction.

In these, the catalytic activity of the enzyme preparation is clearly not directly proportional to its concentration. This may be seen from the results given in Table 7.1, taken from an experiment on the hydrolysis of caseinogen, catalysed by trypsin (W. M. Bayliss, 1904). The course of the reaction was followed by measuring the electrical conductivity of the solution; this gives a measure of the increase in the concentration of free carboxyl groups. The "specific activity" of the enzyme, given in the fourth column of the Table, is obtained by dividing the relative mean rate of the reaction by the relative concentration of the enzyme, and represents the activity of equal amounts of enzyme when present in different concentrations. The catalytic activity of a given quantity of trypsin clearly falls as its concentration is increased. The mean rate, in fact, varies more nearly with the square root of the enzyme concentration (figures in brackets) than with the concentration itself. This square root relation is known as the "Schütz rule", which we shall refer to again later.

TABLE 7.1

Rate of Hydrolysis of Caseinogen, catalysed by Trypsin

Relative Concentration of Enzyme	Time taken for equal Change in Minutes	Relative Mean Rate	"Specific Activity"
8 (2·7)	41	3·4	3
5 (2·2)	48	3·0	4·2
4 (2·0)	55	2·6	4·6
2 (1·4)	81	1·8	6·2
1 (1·0)	144	1·0	7

Inactivation and Destruction of the Enzyme. The various agents which have been observed to cause inactivation fall naturally into two classes. There are those which act on all, or nearly all, enzymes, and which belong to the class of agents which have a precipitating or denaturing action on all proteins; and there are those which act only on certain types of enzyme.

Rise of Temperature accelerates very markedly the spontaneous tendency of all proteins, including enzymes, to become denatured. If an enzyme solution is heated to a temperature not greater than about 50° C. (although enzymes vary in their sensitivities), and is not kept at this temperature for too long a time, it becomes inactivated, but the inactivation is reversible. If heated to 80° C. or over, most enzymes become irreversibly destroyed with great rapidity. The destructive effect of a rise in temperature, however, is never sudden, so that the inactivation becomes more and more apparent the longer the duration of the exposure to a particular temperature. The velocity of the process which brings about inactivation rises very rapidly with rise in temperature, and, accordingly, the activation energy has a very large value—some 50,000 to 200,000 calories per mole, comparable, indeed, to that for the denaturation of a protein; it is thus not a catalysed process. At any given temperature, also, the rate of inactivation depends on the hydrogen ion concentration of the solution, and there is generally an optimum value for stability of the enzyme, at all temperatures. This is not, generally, identical with the optimum value of the hydrogen ion concentration for catalytic activity, to be discussed below; and this provides additional evidence that the spontaneous inactivation, which is accelerated by a rise in temperature, is not due to a self-destruction of the enzyme by its own catalytic action.

In common with all chemical reactions, the velocity of an enzyme reaction is increased by a rise in temperature. As the temperature is raised, however, it is found that above a certain particular temperature, the velocity begins to diminish, and on further rise in temperature, becomes zero. At these temperatures, the effect of rise in temperature in accelerating inactivation preponderates over its effect in accelerating the catalysed reaction. The temperature at which the velocity has a maximum value has been termed the *optimum temperature*.

Some of the early workers with enzymes seem to have regarded the existence of an optimum temperature for enzyme action as something mysterious, even indicating "vital action". We see that it is merely the expression of the sensitivity of the colloidal arrangements of the enzyme system to randomisation by thermal agitation; it is not confined to enzymes, but may be observed in inorganic colloids.

General protein precipitants which inactivate or destroy enzymes are salts of the heavy metals (particularly mercury, silver and copper); the acid protein precipitants, such as picric, phospho-tungstic, and tannic acids; and radiation such as *ultra-violet light* and β- and γ-rays. The action of silver ions on urease is of interest in this connection, since it has been shown that a reversible inactivation first occurs quite rapidly, and that this then slowly changes to an irreversible destruction. We are reminded very strongly of the change from van der Waals adsorption to chemisorption, which occurs at solid surfaces, and which we discussed in Chapter 5 (pp. 189, 191). Some of the protein precipitants, such as ammonium sulphate, alcohol, acetone and others, do not result in any considerable destruction, even though they throw the enzyme out of solution. We have already referred to their use in the purification of enzymes.

We may include under this heading, also, the action of proteoclastic enzymes. Pepsin and trypsin will attack the protein parts of most, if not all, enzymes (the apo-enzymes) and thus cause irreversible destruction.

Specific Inactivating Agents. Those enzymes in which the prosthetic groups contain metals are all inactivated by cyanides, sulphides and azides, presumably as a result of combination with the metal. Many enzymes, also, are known to contain sulphydryl (—SH) groups, and become inactivated if these groups are oxidised, or allowed to combine with certain organic compounds, such, for example, as iodoacetates, arsenoxides and mustard gas. A number of other enzymes, not known to contain —SH groups, are inactivated or destroyed by oxidising and reducing agents. Other substances which probably react with certain essential groups in the enzyme molecule are fluorides, and narcotic substances generally, such as urethane, although the exact point of attack is uncertain. Many other examples could be given of agents which inactivate certain particular enzymes only; these are of great value as evidence of the constitution of the enzyme in question.

We have already referred, in an earlier section, to the fact that many substances can be adsorbed on inorganic heterogeneous catalysts, without being subsequently activated and caused to take part in a chemical reaction. These substances will prevent the access of substances which can be activated; the key will enter the lock, but is not so constructed as to be able to actuate the mechanism. The same phenomenon is to be observed with enzymes, but owing to the greater specificity of most enzymes, only substances whose molecules are similar in structure to those of the normal substrate can be adsorbed. One of the "classical" examples is provided by the dehydrogenase which catalyses the oxidation of succinic acid. The reaction is inhibited by the presence of malonic acid, with a structure very similar to that of succinic acid; this, apparently, is taken up by the enzyme, although the appropriate hydrogen atoms are not thereby activated. Such *competitive inhibition* occurs also with enzymes which activate only one of two optically isomeric compounds: the isomer which is not activated may, nevertheless, occupy some of the enzyme and so reduce the rate of the reaction. Competitive inhibition can be definitely identified only by studying the kinetics of the reactions, as we shall see later.

Inactivation may also be caused by the *products of the reaction*. In catalysis in general, there is, as we have seen, combination, or adsorption, of some kind, between the catalyst and the substrate. The products of the reaction, therefore, must be released, or desorbed, at least as rapidly as they are formed, or else they will prevent the uptake of fresh substrate. With many enzymes, this blocking action by the products of the reaction has a marked effect in reducing the activity of the enzyme. This form of inactivation increases progressively during the course of the reaction, and, as the concentration of the products builds up, there is competition between substrate and products for the active group of enzyme. This will lead to a progressive slowing of the reaction over and above that to be expected from changes in the concentration of the substrate.

If an enzyme is inactivated sufficiently rapidly, by any of the processes just discussed, it may disappear, and the reaction cease, before the true equilibrium position has been reached. Such a position of "false equilibrium", as pointed out on a previous page, will be shifted by the addition of more enzyme, and it would appear as if the enzyme were taking part in the reaction. Many of the causes of inactivation, such as change of hydrogen ion concentration as a result of the production of acid or basic substances, can be eliminated without difficulty; but spontaneous inactivation, as at high temperatures, cannot be prevented.

Anti-enzymes. A number of substances are known which inactivate certain enzymes specifically; they appear, mostly, to be proteins. We may instance the trypsin inhibitor, isolated and crystallised by Northrop from pancreatic juice, and the similar substance, which has also been isolated, which inhibits pepsin: and various other anti-enzymes have been described as being present in normal animal tissues. An interesting anti-enzyme is that present in *intestinal worms*, protecting them from the action of trypsin in the lumen of the intestine. This anti-enzyme, however, does not protect the worms from the action of the proteinase, ficin, contained in the sap of fig trees; a fact which has been known in Central and South America for centuries, where the sap of certain fig trees is used as a cure for intestinal worms.

Of a somewhat different nature are the anti-enzymes which may be formed in consequence of the fact that enzymes are proteins. When a foreign protein is injected into an animal, some kind of neutralising substance is produced. This is known as the "antibody", while the injected substance which produces it is the "antigen". Most of the earlier work which apparently demonstrated the existence of corresponding specific "anti-enzymes" was not convincing, and the observations could be explained on other grounds. With the preparation of pure enzymes, however, unequivocal evidence has been obtained of the existence of anti-urease, anti-catalase and anti-papain; indeed, the first has been crystallised, and appears to be a glyco-protein.

The general problem of the inhibition of enzymes is discussed in the article by Massart (1950).

Activation. In the course of the development of our knowledge as to the nature of enzyme action, many substances have been described which increase the activity of enzyme preparations. Of these, certain metallic ions are now known to form part of the prosthetic group, while others may exchange with the natural metal with an increase in activity. It would appear that chloride ions, which activate amylase, and hydrocyanic acid, which activates papain, are involved in some way in the active groups of the enzymes, but beyond this nothing more can be said. Substances containing the —SH group, notably glutathione, have also been found to have an activating action, and these may act either by combining with, and removing, traces of heavy metals which are inactivating the enzyme, or by preventing the oxidation of the active groups in the enzyme by impurities in the solution. Similarly, the activation by certain hydrophile colloids, such as albumin and gum, may well result from their competing with the enzyme for the adsorption of surface active poisons or heavy metal ions, and so protecting it from inactivation. Many substances, however, which have been described as activators of enzymes have the effect of changing the optimum hydrogen ion concentration; the apparent activation can be removed if the hydrogen ion concentration is adjusted to the optimum value, both in their presence and in their absence.

The Hydrogen Ion Concentration. Variations in the hydrogen ion concentration of the solution have profound effects on the catalytic activity of enzymes. In extremely acid and extremely alkaline solutions (outside the range of pH 2 to pH 10), enzymes, in common with many other kinds of protein, are in general destroyed irreversibly. But within this range, each enzyme has a zone of hydrogen ion concentrations, sometimes quite narrow, over which its activity is maximum, as is indicated in Fig. 7.3. Such curves are very reminiscent of curves of electrolytic dissociation, and it would seem from their shapes and positions that it is only the *uncharged* enzyme molecules which are active. Where there is an optimum pH inside the region where irreversible destruction does not occur, as with saccharase and urease, for example, the enzyme is presumably an amphoteric electrolyte; and, indeed, it is possible to determine the iso-electric points of enzymes in the same ways as are used to determine those of other proteins. It turns out, however, that in general the optimum pH for catalytic action is *not* identical with the iso-electric point, and, moreover, the value of the former often varies with the nature of the salt used to buffer the solution at the required pH, and with the concentration of the substrate, while the value of the latter remains unchanged. This difficulty can be got over by the very reasonable assumption that it is the charge on certain specific groups that determines the catalytic activity, and that these may have no net charge at a value of the hydrogen ion concentration which is different from that at which the molecule as a whole is uncharged.

A further factor of importance is the variation of the charge on the substrate. This is of particular importance for the proteinases pepsin, trypsin and papain, and, as a rough approximation, it would appear that these act most effectively on protein molecules which possess positive, negative, and zero electric charge, respectively, as is indicated in Fig.

7.3, A and B. The pH at which the activity is a minimum, for both pepsin and trypsin, depends on the nature of the substrate, and is approximately that of its iso-ionic point. In addition, however, it has been found that trypsin is reversibly denatured and inactivated in solutions alkaline to pH 7, and that the activity depends upon an equilibrium between the active and the inactive forms; this equilibrium is shifted, with increase

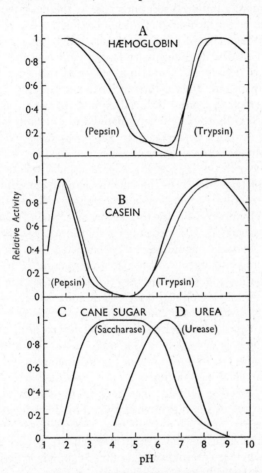

FIG. 7.3. THE RELATION BETWEEN THE HYDROGEN ION CONCENTRATION OF THE SOLUTION
AND THE ACTIVITY OF SOME ENZYMES

Thick lines: enzyme activity as a fraction of the maximum activity, plotted against pH.

Thin lines (in A and B): titration curves of substrates.

A. The action of pepsin and trypsin on haemoglobin (Northrop 1922).

B. The action of pepsin and trypsin on casein (Northrop, 1922).

C. The action of saccharase on cane sugar (Michaelis and Davidsohn, 1911).

D. The action of urease on urea in 2·5 per cent. solution in citrate buffer. The shape and position of the curve depends upon the concentration of the substrate and on the chemical nature of the buffer used.   (Howell and Sumner, 1934.)

in alkalinity, such that the proportion of inactive trypsin progressively increases.

It is to be noted that in quite a large number of enzyme reactions, there is a formation of acidic or basic groups. The hydrogen ion concentration will thus tend to shift during the course of the reaction, with the result that the activity of the enzyme will also shift. Failure to guard against this by the use of adequately buffered solutions has, in the past, led to erroneous views being held as to the course of these reactions.

Zymogens. When enzymes are synthesised by living cells, they will, presumably, pass through preliminary stages, and it seems that the substances known as "zymogens" constitute stages of this kind. The proteinases pepsin, trypsin and chymo-trypsin, that are secreted to the exterior of the cells in which they are produced, appear in such preliminary, and inactive, forms; and these have been isolated and crystallised.

The manner in which pepsinogen, trypsinogen and chymo-trypsinogen are converted into the active enzymes has been studied by Northrop and his co-workers (see Northrop, *et al.* 1948). The reactions are interesting in that the conversion of trypsinogen to the enzyme is performed by the enzyme itself, and the reaction is therefore auto-catalytic; chymo-trypsinogen is converted into chymo-trypsin by the action of trypsin, with which it is always closely associated. If a pepsinogen solution is brought to a pH of less than 6, it becomes spontaneously converted into pepsin and an inhibitor; these together form a dissociable compound. Pure trypsinogen solutions also change spontaneously into trypsin, but, as has already been remarked in a previous section, the pancreatic juice as secreted contains a trypsin inhibitor, so that under normal conditions, this reaction does not take place. The reaction, therefore, is started by an additional enzyme, enterokinase, which is secreted by the walls of the intestine. A similar enzyme is also to be found in moulds of the Penicillium type. In this process, there is, in alkaline solutions, a side reaction which leads to the formation of an inactive protein from trypsinogen, with the result that the conversion to trypsin is not quantitative. This fact, together with the auto-catalytic action of trypsin itself and the presence of the trypsin inhibitor, is responsible for the disputes which are to be found in the literature, as to whether enterokinase has a true catalytic action, or whether it reacts stoichiometrically with trypsinogen.

THE KINETICS OF ENZYME ACTION

We start by assuming that the basis of the catalytic action of enzymes is the reversible formation of a compound of some kind between the enzyme and its substrate. If the substrate is thereby "activated", the catalysed reaction occurs, the products dissociate off and the enzyme is left free to combine with more substrate; if the reaction does not occur, the compound dissociates into enzyme and substrate again. If we call the enzyme E, the substrate S and the product of the reaction P, we have the following reactions taking place:

$$E+S \underset{k_2}{\overset{k_1}{\rightleftharpoons}} ES \overset{k_3}{\longrightarrow} P+E \qquad . \qquad . \qquad . \qquad 7.(\mathrm{i})$$

THE MICHAELIS EQUATION

Denoting the molar concentration of the substrate by m_S, that of the enzyme, originally, by m_E, and that of the enzyme-substrate compound by m_{ES}, the concentration of the free enzyme at any moment will be $m_E - m_{ES}$. Then, since the compound ES is being formed at a rate depending on the concentrations of E and S, and is disappearing in two ways, into E and P and back into E and S again, we have, from the law of Mass Action:

$$dm_{ES}/dt = k_1 m_S(m_E - m_{ES}) - k_2 m_{ES} - k_3 m_{ES} \qquad . \qquad . \qquad 7.1$$

where k_1, k_2 and k_3 are the velocity constants of the three reactions taking place simultaneously.

The concentrations of the various components will adjust themselves until a "stationary state" is reached, in which $dm_{ES}/dt = 0$. Moreover, since the velocity of the main reaction, v, is by our hypothesis, determined by the concentration of the enzyme-substrate compound, we can write:

$$v = k_3 m_{ES} \qquad . \qquad . \qquad . \qquad . \qquad 7.2$$

Combining equations 7.1 and 7.2, we get:

$$v = \frac{k_3 m_E m_S}{K_m + m_S} \qquad . \qquad . \qquad . \qquad . \qquad 7.3$$

where K_m is written in place of $(k_2 + k_3)/k_1$. If m_S is made very large compared with K_m, this equation reduces to:

$$v = k_3 m_E = v_{\max}$$

and the velocity of the reaction becomes independent of the concentration of the substrate. The observed failure of the reaction velocity to increase indefinitely as the substrate concentration is increased, is thus to be expected. Inserting this limiting value of the reaction velocity into equation 7.3, we get as our final equation:

$$v = v_{\max} m_S/(K_m + m_S) \qquad . \qquad . \qquad . \qquad 7.4$$

This is the equation developed by Michaelis and Menten in 1913, and K_m is known as the *Michaelis constant*. It is a measure of the affinity of the

enzyme for its substrate, and as such is a very useful quantity, characteristic of each individual enzyme-substrate system.

The reader will note that the Michaelis equation is of the same form
as that of the electrolytic dissociation of a weak acid or base (Chapter 4,
p. 160). If plotted with the substrate concentration on a logarithmic scale,
the familiar S-shaped curve is obtained, as shown in Fig. 7.4. The value
of the Michaelis constant is readily obtained from such a plot as the value
of the substrate concentration at which the reaction proceeds with one-half
the maximum velocity. This diagram, also, indicates how well the equation
is obeyed by the saccharase-saccharose system, and this good agreement
between theory and experiment is observed in a great many enzyme

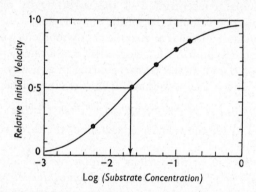

FIG. 7.4. CURVE ILLUSTRATING THE MICHAELIS-MENTEN EQUATION

Ordinates: initial velocity of the reaction as a fraction of the maximum velocity.

Abscissae: logarithm of the substrate concentration (molar).

The dots on the curve represent values obtained experimentally from the hydrolysis
of saccharose, catalysed by saccharase. They lie closely on the line, showing the agreement with the theory. In this case, $\log K_m$, as shown by the arrow, is found to be -1.70,
so that $K_m = 0.02$ M.   (Re-drawn from Kuhn, 1923.)

systems. An alternative, and somewhat preferable, method of testing the
applicability of the Michaelis equation to any particular reaction, and of
discovering the maximum velocity, is to turn equation 7.4 upside down.
We then get:

$$\frac{v_{\max}}{v} = \frac{K_m}{m_S} + 1 \qquad . \qquad . \qquad . \qquad 7.4a$$

Thus, if $1/v$ is plotted against $1/m_S$, a straight line should be obtained:
this line, if extrapolated to $1/m_S = 0$ cuts the axis of $1/v$ at the value of
$1/v_{\max}$.

Many authors have reported observations which show that the velocities
of certain enzyme reactions are not related to the substrate concentration in
the manner to be expected from the Michaelis equation. In some cases, for

example, the reaction will not proceed at all unless the substrate concentration exceeds a certain value; this might be due to the presence in the enzyme preparation of an impurity which competes with the substrate under investigation for the active groups on the enzyme, and is only displaced by fairly high concentrations of the substrate. In other cases, the reaction velocity does not approach its maximum value, at high substrate concentrations, so rapidly as would be expected. The curve relating velocity to substrate concentration approximates more to a parabola than to the expected hyperbola. As Haldane (1930) pointed out, this might be the result of the enzyme having several active groups, with different affinities for the substrate; the observed curve would then consist of a number of overlapping hyperbolae, with different parameters, and would approximate, in a general way, to the shape observed.

In the above derivation of the Michaelis equation, it is tacitly assumed that there is a chemical combination between enzyme and substrate, and that the law of mass action can be applied. It is not necessary, however, to make such an assumption. If we turn back to Chapter 5, p. 185, we see that Langmuir's conception of adsorption by a solid surface at certain specific spots, and re-evaporation of the adsorbed gas, or solute, from these spots, leads to an equation (5.8a) relating the amount adsorbed to the pressure of the gas (or concentration of the solute) of exactly the same form as equation 7.4. It is impossible, in fact, to distinguish between adsorption and chemical combination except in terms of the energy involved in the formation and dissociation of the compound. Since, also, the Langmuir expression can only be applied when the surface is smooth and homogeneous, it is not surprising, from this point of view, that the Michaelis expression is not always obeyed by such complex systems as enzymes.

It will be seen from Fig. 7.4 that the velocity of any enzyme reaction will be about 90 per cent. of its maximum (or "saturation") value when the substrate concentration is 10 times the value of the Michaelis constant for this reaction. Roughly speaking, the values of the Michaelis constants for reactions involving hydrolysis lie in the region of 10^{-1} M to 10^{-3} M; in solutions likely to occur in living systems, the substrate concentration will rarely be sufficiently large for enzymes of this type to become even approximately saturated. For reactions involving oxidation and reduction, however, the values of the Michaelis constants lie in the region of 10^{-4} M to 10^{-6} M, the enzymes thus having a greater affinity for their substrates than have the hydrolysing enzymes; in such reactions, even in living systems, it is quite likely that the enzymes may become saturated. It is possible that this may be of significance in regulating the complex sequences and cycles of oxidation and reduction which are characteristic of the oxidative metabolism of living systems.

Returning now to equation 7.3, and remembering that the velocity of the reaction, v, may be identified with the rate of change of the substrate concentration, dm_S/dt, we can perform the necessary integration, and derive an expression defining the time course of a reaction whose components obey the Michaelis requirements. We get, therefore,

$$k.m_E = \frac{K_m}{t} \cdot \log_e \frac{(m_S)_0}{(m_S)_t} + \frac{(m_S)_0 - (m_S)_t}{t} \qquad . \qquad . \qquad 7.5$$

where $(m_S)_0$ and $(m_S)_t$ are the concentrations of the substrate at the beginning of the reaction, and at time t, respectively. Two limiting cases are of interest. In the first place, if m_S is large compared with K_m—i.e. as we have already remarked, if the enzyme is saturated with substrate—then the whole logarithmic term becomes negligible, and the change in m_S per unit time is constant, and directly proportional to the enzyme concentration; the reaction then proceeds with uniform velocity. In the second place, if m_S is small compared with K_m, the logarithmic term is dominant, and the equation approximates to that for a unimolecular reaction (Chapter 2, p. 45), the velocity *constant* being directly proportional to the enzyme concentration. The generalised course of an enzyme reaction thus consists of an initial period during which the velocity is constant, and proportional to the enzyme concentration, followed by a period of progressively decreasing velocity; and a final period during which the velocity falls off at a rate to be expected of a unimolecular reaction. In any particular circumstances, of course, the first or last of these periods may be missing.

The Kinetics of Inhibition

Enzyme inhibitors act, presumably, by combining with the enzyme in such a way as to remove, or reduce, its catalytic activity. The kinetics of the partially inhibited reaction depend on the nature of the reaction between inhibitor and enzyme.

Irreversible Inactivation. The simplest case is that in which the reaction is, to all intents and purposes, irreversible, as, for example, is the action of most protein precipitants: the concentration of the enzyme, m_E, is then reduced to some value $m_E - f(m_I)$, where $f(m_I)$ is some function of m_I, the concentration of the inhibitor. If the combination between enzyme and inhibitor is stoichiometric, the quantity $f(m_I)$ will reduce to $a(m_I)$, where a is an integer. As may be seen from equation 7.3 the only effect on the kinetics of the reaction will be that the limiting velocity is reduced to a value $v_{max} \cdot m_E/[m_E - f(m_I)]$: the slope of the line relating $1/v$ to $1/m_S$ is unchanged. A more elaborate case is that in which, for example, the inhibition is brought about by a proteoclastic enzyme acting on the enzyme whose reaction kinetics are being studied. Here, the quantity $f(m_I)$ is itself a function of time, and the conditions become highly complicated.

Competitive Inhibition. If the reaction between enzyme and inhibitor is reversible, the concentration of the compound at any moment and thus the extent of inhibition, will depend on the concentration of the substrate; by combining with the enzyme, it will cause the enzyme-inhibitor compound to dissociate. In addition to the three main reactions, 7.(i), discussed above, we have the side reaction:

$$E + I \rightleftharpoons EI . \qquad . \qquad . \qquad . \qquad 7.(ii)$$

These reactions will reach equilibrium, and we can write:

$$m_{EI} = \frac{m_I(m_E - m_{ES})}{K_i + m_I} \qquad . \qquad . \qquad . \qquad 7.6$$

where K_i is the equilibrium constant. The concentration of the free enzyme thus becomes $(m_E - m_{ES} - m_{EI})$. Equation 7.3 still holds, however, and the velocity of the reaction in the presence of the inhibitor, v_{ci}, is given by this equation if we replace m_E by $(m_E - m_{EI})$. We thus get, after inserting equation 7.6:

$$v_{ci} = \frac{k_3 . m_E . m_S . K_i}{K_m(K_i + m_I) + m_S K_i} \qquad . \qquad . \qquad . \qquad 7.7$$

As before, if the substrate concentration, m_S, becomes very large, the velocity of the reaction reaches a limiting value. This, as can be seen, is identical with that reached in the absence of the inhibitor, as is to be expected, since the substrate then drives out the inhibitor from combination with the enzyme. Thus, we get, as the "inverted" equation:

$$\frac{v_{\max}}{v_{ci}} = \left(1 + \frac{m_I}{K_i}\right)\frac{K_m}{m_S} + 1 \qquad . \qquad . \qquad . \qquad 7.8$$

This is again the equation of a straight line, and, although the intercept of this line is the same as that of the line represented by equation 7.4a, the slope is increased by the factor $(1 + m_I/K_i)$. The equilibrium constant K_i can thus be determined.

Non-Competitive Inhibition. In this, the reaction between enzyme and inhibitor is still reversible, but the position of equilibrium is not affected by the concentration of the substrate. We can regard the reaction as occurring between the inhibitor and the enzyme-substrate compound:

$$ES + I \rightleftharpoons ESI . \qquad . \qquad . \qquad . \qquad 7.(iii)$$

Or we can consider that the substrate reacts with the enzyme-inhibitor compound:

$$EI + S \rightleftharpoons ESI \qquad . \qquad . \qquad . \qquad 7.(iii)a$$

In either case, the concentration of the free enzyme becomes $(m_E - m_{ES} - m_{EI} - m_{ESI})$. If K_i is now the equilibrium constant of either of the reactions in which the compound ESI is formed, suitable algebraic treatment leads to the equation:

$$v_{nci} = \frac{k_3 m_E m_S K_i}{K_m(K_i + m_I) + m_S(K_i + m_I)} = v'_{max}\left(\frac{m_S}{K_m + m_S}\right) \qquad . \qquad 7.9$$

where v'_{max} is the limiting velocity when the substrate concentration is very large. This, however, is not identical with the limiting value when there is no inhibition, or when the inhibition is competitive, but is given by:

$$v'_{max} = v_{max}\left(\frac{K_i}{K_i + m_I}\right) \qquad . \qquad . \qquad . \qquad 7.10$$

Thus in the "inverted" equation, both the slope and the intercept of the line relating $1/v$ to $1/m_S$ are increased by the factor $(1 + m_I)/K_i$.

The following illustration may assist the reader in understanding the facts in heterogeneous catalysis. I must apologise for its apparently trivial nature. Imagine a number of snails in the neighbourhood of strawberry plants bearing ripe fruit. A snail, in the course of its wanderings, eventually comes into contact with a strawberry; this is the preliminary process of diffusion, or molecular agitation (we neglect the fact that the snails are probably sensible of the presence of the food even when not in contact with it). The next stage, that of adsorption, or chemical combination, follows rapidly as the animal attaches itself to the fruit. If nothing more happens, there is no chemical reaction, and the snail will leave the strawberry again. The final chemical stage is the devouring of the fruit and its subsequent hydrolysis. The strawberry, it may be noted, will eventually disintegrate "spontaneously"; but the rate of this process is greatly increased by the presence of the snails. It is obvious that the rate will be proportional, not to the total number of snails, necessarily, but to the number "adsorbed"—i.e. to the quantity m_{ES} in the Michaelis equation. It is clear, also, that the rate of digestion of strawberries will depend on the number of strawberries present, since this will control the chance of a snail encountering a strawberry in its wanderings. On the other hand, if the number of strawberries becomes so great that all the available snails are continually occupied, further increase will not affect the rate of the reaction. A saturation value has been reached. Moreover, if some of the snails become surfeited by the strawberries, the enzyme may be said to be inactivated by the products of the reaction. If the gardener puts down a poisonous or narcotic substance on some alternative bait, comparable in attractiveness with the strawberries, the snails will suffer "competitive inhibition", or perhaps irreversible denaturation; if the poison is applied only to the strawberries, the inhibition is "non-competitive", since it affects only the "adsorbed" snails.

The Schütz Rule

We have already mentioned the empirical relation, found to hold under certain limited conditions, by which the amount of reaction products formed is proportional to the square root of the product of the enzyme concentration and the time that has elapsed since the beginning of the reaction. It is possible to deduce a relation of this kind if we assume that the rate of the reaction is being controlled by the rate of diffusion of the substrate to the catalyst. We have, of course, hitherto regarded this factor as of negligible importance; and the colloidal nature of most enzymes makes it rather difficult to believe that diffusion of the substrate to them, or of them to the substrate, can be a very significant factor. But it must not be forgotten that some enzyme molecules can handle their substrate molecules with an almost incredible rapidity (the "turnover number" may be several hundreds of substrate molecules per second for each enzyme molecule), so that it is not entirely inconceivable that substrate molecules may be unable to diffuse sufficiently rapidly.

On the whole, however, it would seem to be more probable that in most cases the square root law is merely a simple first approximation to a very much more complex expression. The velocity of the reaction will not necessarily be expected to vary in accordance with the logarithmic relation of a monomolecular reaction, even when the Michaelis equation is obeyed: and it may be affected by progressive inactivation of the enzyme by the products of the reaction, or by other means, and possibly towards the end of the reaction, by the presence of an appreciable reverse reaction.

Chain Reactions

We have seen in Chapter 2 that in general chemical reactions only occur between "activated" molecules—i.e. those which happen to possess at the moment of collision, more than a certain minimum quantity of energy. The products of the reaction, therefore, will also be "activated", since they possess the original activation energy as well as the energy released in the reaction, if any: and if, by some means, some of this energy could be transferred to molecules of the reactants, which would not otherwise be "active" the reaction velocity would obviously be increased. The activation energy would thus be passed along a chain of reactants and products of the reaction which would only be broken if the energy were handed to molecules which were incapable of reacting.

This conception of chain reactions was originally developed in order to account for certain anomalies in homogeneous gas reactions, but in 1931, Haber and Willstätter applied it to the activation of a substrate by an enzyme. If we denote the substrate by S, and the products of the reaction by P, and indicate activated molecules by the addition of an asterisk, the chain reaction might be represented thus:

$$\text{(enzyme)}$$
$$S \longrightarrow S^* \longrightarrow P^* \longrightarrow P$$
$$+ S \searrow$$
$$\qquad\qquad S^* \longrightarrow P^* \longrightarrow P$$
$$\qquad\qquad + S \searrow$$
$$\qquad\qquad\qquad\qquad S^* \longrightarrow P^* \longrightarrow P$$

and so on . 7.(iv)

The activation energy originally derived from the enzyme is handed to and fro between substrate and product, and the reaction continues without further intervention by the enzyme. The system, however, is not generally so simple as this. Not every molecule of the reaction product will have enough energy to activate a substrate molecule, and every now and then the energy will be "wasted" on, say, a molecule of some substance chemically related to the substrate (it probably must be adsorbed on the enzyme), or dissipated among several molecules of the reaction product. Sooner or later, therefore, the chain will come to an end. The number of links in each chain which follows the original reaction activated by the enzyme, will vary in a random fashion from zero upwards, but will have an average value characteristic of the activation energy and of the energy released by the reaction.

An expression for the velocity of a chain reaction can be deduced by postulating reactions between enzyme and substrate similar to those assumed by Michaelis (equation 7.(i), p. 311 above). The following four reactions are supposed to occur.

1. $E + S \longrightarrow S^*$

(enzyme and substrate unite and the substrate is activated)

2. $S^* \longrightarrow P + e$

(the activated substrate reacts to form the product, together with an activated substance analogous to the active group of the enzyme)

3. $e + S \longrightarrow S^*$

(a fraction of the molecules of the new activated substance unite with substrate, which is activated).

Reaction 2 is repeated, and the chain is thereby established.

4. $S^* + S \longrightarrow E + 2S$

(some of the activated substrate molecules hand their energy to other substrate molecules without reacting. The chain is broken, and the enzyme is restored; a new chain can now be initiated). A stationary state will soon be reached, in which the concentrations of the intermediate compounds, S^* and e, will be constant. Applying the law of mass action to the above reactions, and writing k_1, k_2, k_3 and k_4 for the velocity constants of reactions 1, 2, 3 and 4 respectively, and m with the appropriate subscript for the concentrations, we have:

$$\frac{d(m_{S^*})}{dt} = k_1 m_E m_S + k_3 a m_e m_S - k_2 m_{S^*} - k_4 m_{S^*} m_S = 0$$

(remembering that only a fraction, a, of the e molecules are capable of giving rise to S^* molecules).

Also
$$\frac{d(m_e)}{dt} = k_2 m_{S^*} - k_3 m_e m_S = 0.$$

Finally, the velocity of the reaction as a whole is the rate of appearance of P, so that:

$$v = \frac{d(m_P)}{dt} = k_2 m_{S^*}.$$

Eliminating m_{S^*} and m_e from these equations, we arrive at the expression:

$$v = \frac{k_1 m_E m_S}{(1-a) + \dfrac{k_4}{k_2} \cdot m_S} \qquad . \qquad . \qquad . \qquad . \qquad 7.11$$

This expression is clearly analogous to the Michaelis equation (equation 7.3) derived on a previous page, and we can identify the Michaelis constant K_m with the quantity $\frac{k_2}{k_4}(1-a)$ of the chain reaction. Further, the quantity $1/(1-a)$ is a measure of the average number of links in the chain, so that we can regard the Michaelis constant, on the chain theory, as an indication of the average chain length, rather than as an indication of the energy with which the substrate is united to the enzyme.

Suppose n initiating reactions are set up by the enzyme. There will then be an primary links in the chain $a^2 n$ secondary links, and so on. The total number of links, therefore, will be the sum of the series $n(1+a+a^2+$ etc.), or $n/(1-a)$. The average number in each chain will thus be $1/(1-a)$.

Moelwyn-Hughes has pointed out that since the Michaelis constant of the oxidation-reduction reactions is about 10^{-4} times that of the hydrolytic reactions, the average length of the chain must be about 10^4 times greater, unless the value of k_2/k_4 is also of a different order of magnitude; there is no reason to suppose that this is likely. Since the chain length in the hydrolytic reactions cannot be less than 1 (in which case $a=0$), the chain length in the oxidation-reduction reactions must be supposed to reach 10,000.

We have so far supposed that the quantity a must be less than one, so that the chains all die out spontaneously. It is possible, however, to imagine a being greater than one, so that the chains branch, and the reaction becomes progressively more rapid. This will occur if the energy available in some of the activated e molecules is so great that more than one S molecule can be activated by each. There is good reason to suppose that

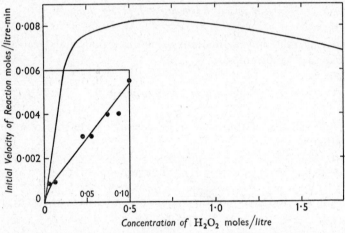

FIG. 7.5. THE INITIAL VELOCITY OF DECOMPOSITION OF HYDROGEN PEROXIDE BY LIVER CATALASE, PLOTTED AGAINST THE SUBSTRATE CONCENTRATION (pH 6·8, Temp. 20° C.)

Inset: the values at very low concentrations of the substrate plotted on a larger scale.
(After Williams, 1928.)

this does indeed occur in some gas reactions, and the result is an explosion. We cannot very well have an explosion in a system which is in aqueous solution; but some of the oxidation-reduction enzyme reactions behave in an anomalous way which can be explained on this hypothesis. As is shown in Fig. 7.5, the rate of decomposition of hydrogen peroxide, as catalysed by catalase, rises as the substrate concentration is increased, as would be expected, but then falls again at still higher substrate concentrations. In the system of hypoxanthine and xanthine-oxidase, this effect appears even more marked, and the rate of the reaction falls, as the substrate concentration is increased, even at the lowest concentration investigated. If we re-arrange equation 7.11, we can write:

$$v = \frac{\dfrac{k_1 k_2}{k_4} \cdot m_E}{1 + \dfrac{k_2}{k_4} \cdot \dfrac{(1-a)}{m_S}} \qquad\qquad . \qquad 7.11a$$

The value of the second term in the denominator will fall as the value of m_S becomes greater; but if a is greater than 1, so that this term is negative (but less than 1), the value of the whole denominator will rise as m_S becomes greater. The velocity of the reaction will fall towards an asymptotic value as the substrate concentration approaches infinity. Physically, the reason for this is that the chains are broken when the extra energy available in the activated product is handed to substrate molecules without thereby activating them (reaction (4) on p. 318 above). This process will increase in frequency as the concentration of the substrate is increased. If the chains do not branch, the effect is to prevent the rate of formation of the product from increasing indefinitely as the substrate concentration is increased; if the chains branch when the substrate concentration is small, the effect will be to reduce or abolish the branching when the substrate concentration becomes large, and so actually to reduce the rate of the reaction.

An alternative explanation of the phenomenon has been given by Haldane (1930). There is good evidence that substrate molecules may be adsorbed on many enzymes without being activated, as is the case with many inorganic catalysts—indeed, it is probable that only a small fraction of the total number adsorbed is activated. Haldane supposes that at high concentrations of substrate, the number of the "indifferently" adsorbed molecules becomes so large that they interfere with the access to the active groups of the enzyme, and so reduce the velocity of the reaction. It may be, for example, that the substrate molecule must be attached to the enzyme at two points (and the molecule thereby subjected to a strain) if the reaction is to occur. But if two separate molecules are attached, instead of one, no reaction follows. This is equivalent to the assumption that not only can the compound ES be formed, but also the compound ES_2, which is inactive. We thus have a form of competitive inhibition, in which the compound ES_2 plays the part of the inhibited enzyme EI (p. 315 above). If in equation 7.7, we replace m_I by m_S^2, we get an expression which predicts that the velocity of the reaction will fall as m_S increases, eventually approaching zero as m_S approaches infinity. It thus differs somewhat from the expression deduced from the assumption of branched chain formation.

Readers who wish to study the kinetics of enzyme action more thoroughly should consult the articles by Moelwyn-Hughes in the treatise edited by Nord und Weidenhagen (1940, vol. I, p. 220) and in that edited by Sumner and Myrbäck (1950, vol. I, part 1, p. 28), and the monographs by Haldane (1930) and by Sumner and Somers (1953).

THE ACTIVATION ENERGY IN ENZYME REACTIONS

We have seen in Chapter 2 (p. 58) that the activation energy of a chemical reaction can be deduced from the rate of change of the velocity constant

L

with temperature. Enzymic reactions are, on the whole relatively little affected by temperature, the Q_{10} value usually lying in the region of 1·4 to 2. The activation energies are thus small. Values, as calculated by the Arrhenius equation (p. 58), in some catalysed reactions are given in Table 7.2; in each case, the value for the catalysed reaction is less than that for the uncatalysed, and is less when an enzyme is used as catalyst than when an inorganic substance is used. The action of a catalyst is thus primarily to reduce the amount of kinetic energy which a molecule must acquire before it can take part in the reaction.

TABLE 7.2

Values of the Apparent Activation Energy for some Catalysed Systems
(from Moelwyn-Hughes, 1950)

Reaction	Catalyst	Activation Energy cal./mole
Hydrolysis of Cane-sugar	Invertase	8,700
	Invertase (yeast)	11,500
	Hydrogen ions	25,500
Hydrolysis of Casein	Trypsin-kinase	14,400
	Hydrogen ions	20,600
Hydrolysis of Ethyl butyrate	Pancreatic lipase	4,500
	Hydroxyl ions	10,200
	Hydrogen ions	16,800
Decomposition of Hydrogen Peroxide	Catalase	5,500
	Colloidal Platinum	11,700
	None	18,000

The apparent activation energy of an enzyme system, which is derived from the Arrhenius equation, very frequently falls as the temperature rises. After making due allowance for irregularities introduced by experimental error, this fall can be said to be directly proportional to the absolute temperature, and we can write:

$$E_A + (s-1)RT = \text{constant} = E_0 \qquad . \qquad . \qquad 2.14$$

(compare Chapter 2, p. 58), s being the total number of degrees of freedom in the system. This, indeed, might be expected with such complex systems as enzymes and relatively large organic compounds, where a considerable fraction of the total energy of the molecules must reside in internal oscillatory systems. The number of degrees of freedom, as estimated by this method, is in many cases large, and may be larger than would be expected if all the energy were in the substrate molecules. It is possible, therefore, that the active groups of the enzyme are also involved; we have already suggested (p. 291) that it is quite conceivable that some part of the energy needed for activation might be provided by the catalyst.

In some enzyme reactions, the activation energy is very small, and is little affected by changes in temperature. In these, calculation shows that the observed activation energy is little, if at all, greater than that involved in the process of diffusion of the substrate molecules to the enzyme. The reaction velocity in these cases may well be controlled by the rate of diffusion. In other reactions, again, the activation energy varies in rather an irregular fashion as the temperature changes, and sometimes passes through a maximum value. Such cases can be accounted for on the chain theory (they are chiefly found among the oxidation-reduction reactions); the different links in the chain may have different activation energies, and if so the expression relating the overall apparent activation energy to the energies of the individual links in the chain is very complex.

Care must be taken, of course, when studying the effect of temperature on the velocity of an enzyme reaction, that the temperatures used are well below the optimum. At the optimum temperature, the velocity of the reaction is independent of temperature, and the Q_{10} value is 1, but this, of course, is only apparent. Fortunately, as already remarked, the temperature coefficient of the inactivation is very large, so that the rate of inactivation becomes negligible at temperatures not very far removed from the optimum.

The activation energy of an enzyme-substrate system can be deduced without recourse to the effect of temperature on the reaction velocity, if we know the masses and dimensions of the enzyme and substrate molecules. The procedure is as follows. The total number of collisions in unit volume and unit time is calculated from the expressions developed in the kinetic theory of gases (the solution is assumed to be "ideal"); this involves the radii and masses of the enzyme and substrate molecules, and their concentrations (Chapter 2, p. 49). This number is then corrected by a factor equal to the ratio of the area of the active (prosthetic) group (assumed equal to that of the substrate) to the total cross sectional area of the enzyme, giving the number of collisions with the active group. Finally, this number is multiplied by the Maxwell-Boltzmann function, $\exp(-E/RT)$, giving the number of *activated* collisions with the active group of the enzyme. This figure is then equated to the velocity constant of the reaction, and the activation energy, E, can be calculated. The results obtained tend to be greater than those obtained from the temperature coefficients, a discrepancy which is probably to be explained by the existence of substantial numbers of internal oscillations in the molecules, as already discussed. It is very satisfactory, however, that the discrepancy is, relatively, so small.

SPECIFICITY OF ENZYMES

It is clear from such knowledge as we have as to the mechanism of hetero-geneous catalysis, that there must be some reasonably close correspondence between the molecular structure of an enzyme, and the structures of the substances whose reactions it catalyses. Just how close this correspondence must be is still uncertain. There is no doubt that many enzymes are highly specific in their actions, and appear to attack one chemical substance only; others will attack a number of substances which have somewhat similar chemical structures. Saccharase, apparently, has no action on any sub-stance except cane-sugar, while trypsin acts on all proteins. Maltase attacks α-glucosides, and emulsin attacks β-glucosides, but both these enzymes act on a great variety of glucosides of the appropriate configuration. It was at one time accepted as a doctrine of faith, by some investigators, that there must be a separate enzyme for every substance acted upon; it is now clear, however, that we need not assume dogmatically the perfect specificity of all enzymes, until experimental evidence shows that it is necessary.

The specific relations between enzyme and substrate appear to be determined by the particular arrangement of the atoms and atomic groups in the neighbourhood of the particular linkage attacked, rather than on the structure of the molecule as a whole. This particular arrangement may be found in a number of different substances, all of which are attacked by the same enzyme; while, on the other hand, two different enzymes may attack the same substances at different points, where the molecular configurations are different, and give rise to different reaction products. Thus, for example, carboxy-polypeptidase and amino-polypeptidase both remove an amino-acid from a polypeptide molecule by hydrolysing a peptide linkage; but the first removes an amino-acid with a free —COOH group, while the second removes one with a free —NH_2 group. Innumerable examples of this type of specificity are becoming available, as more and more pure enzymes are isolated.

But until the enzymes have been isolated and purified, the nature and degree of their specificity is not easily established. Suppose we have a crude enzyme preparation which will catalyse more than one kind of reaction; it may contain several specific enzymes, or only one which is relatively unspecific. If it contains only one, all the following criteria, as given by Haldane (1930), will be satisfied. (1) The normal processes of purification, crystallisation etc. must fail to separate out more than one enzyme. (2) The same agents must activate, inactivate, or destroy all the enzymic activities to the same extent. (3) The rate of reaction in a mixture of the enzyme-substrate systems must not be equal to the sum of the rates of reaction of the individual systems with the same enzyme and substrate concentrations;

this implies that one enzyme can be saturated by all the substrates. (4) Other additional criteria may be useful in certain circumstances, such as the identity of the pH-activity curves, but are not necessary or sufficient. Failure of the preparation to satisfy one or more of these criteria indicates that it contains several different enzymes; and the nature of the failure will often suggest the degree and nature of their specificities.

A general discussion of the problems of enzyme specificity will be found in the article by Helferich (1950); and with special reference to specificity as regards optical isomers, in the article by Kuhn (1940).

LITERATURE

Historical.   Berzelius (1837); Kühne (1878).
Kinetics of Catalysis.   Moelwyn-Hughes (1947—Chapter X).
Surface Catalysis.   Adam (1941—Chapter VII).
Enzymes. General Treatises. Nord und Weidenhagen (1940); Sumner and Myrbäck (1950).
   Monographs.   W. M. Bayliss (1925); J. B. S. Haldane (1930); Northrop *et al.* (1948); Tauber (1949); Sumner and Somers (1953); Dixon and Webb (1958).

8

OXIDATION AND REDUCTION

The essential reaction by which all living cells—plants as well as animals—obtain the free energy necessary for their continued existence is the reduction of molecular oxygen by means of the hydrogen contained in the foodstuffs, these being simultaneously oxidised. In the next chapter we shall discuss how, by the aid of light energy, this oxidation-reduction reaction is reversed, and the chemically stable system of $CO_2 + H_2O$ is converted back again into one of higher potential energy, carbohydrate and oxygen. But, although this system possesses considerable potential energy, it is, chemically, not a highly reactive one. Carbohydrates, or, indeed, any of the ordinary foodstuffs, do not react with molecular oxygen at a measurable rate in ordinary conditions. In living cells, therefore, there are catalytic systems which have the effect of "activating" both the oxygen and the oxidisable substrate.

Now the "object"—if we may so put it—of oxidising the foodstuffs is not, of course, merely to get rid of them, or even to generate heat, as in a steam or oil engine; as much as possible of the energy released is used to "drive" other chemical reactions which, in turn, produce the materials necessary for the formation of new living cells, for muscular movement, for secretion, and so on. In order that such *coupled reactions* may occur, the process of oxidation and reduction takes place in a large number of steps, each of a relatively small size. This is energetically advantageous, as will appear later; and the substances formed in the intermediary stages may be used in chemical reactions of importance for other purposes.

The oxidation of one substance is always accompanied by the reduction of another: oxidation and reduction are complementary to one another, and a system in which oxidation occurs will also be one in which reduction occurs, according to which components of the reaction we study. In a sequence of oxidation-reduction reactions, therefore, such as we have in the oxidative metabolism of living organisms, one and the same substance must act as an oxidising agent or as a reducing agent, according to circumstances. Our first studies, then, must be into the physico-chemical nature of these circumstances which determine which substances shall be oxidised (or reduced) by which other substances. We have then to consider the means by which the reactions which are physico-chemically possible are made to proceed at appropriate rates.

OXIDATION-REDUCTION SYSTEMS

There are three ways in which an oxidation-reduction process can occur. First, oxidation can occur by the transfer of an atom of oxygen from an oxidising agent—the *oxidant*—to some other substance which is thereby oxidised. At the same time, the oxidant becomes reduced, so that we can equally well regard the process as one of reduction, the substance oxidised being the reducing agent, or *reductant*. An example of such a process of oxygen transfer might be the oxidation of an aldehyde to a carboxylic acid by, say, silver oxide

$$R—CHO + Ag_2O \longrightarrow R—COOH + 2Ag$$

Alternatively, the oxygen may be in the gaseous state, or in free solution, as in the combustion of carbon monoxide:

$$CO + O \longrightarrow CO_2$$

Secondly, we can regard reduction as being due to the transfer of an atom of hydrogen from the reductant or *hydrogen donor*, which is thereby oxidised, to the oxidant, or *hydrogen acceptor*, which is thereby reduced. As an example we can take the oxidation of an alcohol to aldehyde by means of quinone:

$$CH_3CH_2OH + C_6H_4O_2 \longrightarrow CH_3CHO + C_6H_4(OH)_2$$

We shall see later that most of the oxidative reactions that are known to occur in living cells consist of hydrogen transfers. It is possible, indeed, that *all* oxidative reactions in solution should be regarded as hydrogen transfers; there is reason to believe, for example, that the reaction between silver oxide and an aldehyde, given above as an example of an oxygen transfer, should more properly be regarded as a transfer of two hydrogen atoms from a hydrated aldehyde to the silver oxide which is thereby reduced to metallic silver and water.

Lastly, oxidation and reduction can be regarded as essentially a process of the transfer of an electron from the reductant to the oxidant, as was suggested by Ostwald in 1890. The process of reduction consists of the gain of an electron, and the process of oxidation consists of the loss of one. Thus stannous chloride will reduce mercuric chloride to calomel:

$$Sn^{2+} + 2Hg^{2+} \longrightarrow Sn^{4+} + 2Hg^+$$

This last viewpoint is the most general one, and is probably the most fundamental. Thus we can regard the uptake of a hydrogen atom as being in reality the uptake of a hydrogen *ion* subsequent to the gain of an electron. The substance which is reduced as a result of gaining an electron becomes an anion; but its acid dissociation constant may be so small that the anion cannot exist even in the presence of an infinitesimal concentration of hydrogen ions. Similarly, the uptake of an oxygen atom is equivalent to the loss of an electron and the gain of a hydroxyl ion.

In the above examples, we have shown the reactions as proceeding only in one direction. This was only justified because, in the particular instances chosen, the velocity of the reverse reaction is negligible. If, however, in our first example, we had used a metal which is more easily oxidisable than silver, say sodium, the reaction would, in fact, be reversed: a carboxylic acid is reduced by metallic sodium with the formation of an aldehyde and the oxide (or in this case the hydroxide) of the metal. Like all other chemical reactions, the criterion as to the direction in which an oxidation-reduction reaction will proceed is determined by the change of free energy.

It is not, however, necessary that we should study the free energy changes that occur when every conceivable oxidisable substance is allowed to react with every conceivable reducible substance. As we have just seen, the essential reaction is a transfer of a hydrogen atom (or an oxygen atom, or an electron, whichever is the most convenient for the particular reaction considered) from one substance to the other. If, therefore, we know the change in free energy that occurs when each oxidisable or reducible substance gains or loses a hydrogen atom, we can at once predict whether any given oxidisable substance will reduce any given reducible substance, or whether an equilibrium will be reached between them. It is only necessary to compare the free energy changes that occur when a hydrogen atom is gained by the one or lost by the other. If these two free energy changes are exactly equal to one another, then an equilibrium will be reached in which the molar concentration of the oxidant is equal to that of the reductant.

In practice, the above argument is not infrequently reversed, and the free energy change in an oxidation-reduction process is discovered from the relative concentrations of oxidant and reductant when equilibrium has been attained. The relation between the equilibrium constant and the change in free energy was discussed in Chapter 2, pp. 69-71.

OXIDATION-REDUCTION POTENTIALS

Remembering that an oxidation can be regarded as the loss of an electron by the substance oxidised, we see that the ionisation of a metal at, say, an electrode in contact with a solution of a metallic salt, is also essentially, an oxidation. Now we have seen in Chapter 5 that the ease with which a metal loses an electron and becomes ionised can be measured in terms of the potential difference between the metal and the solution. If we apply a potential to the electrode which is less negative than the standard electrode potential, the metal goes into solution as ions. If the applied potential is more negative than the standard potential, the ions are deposited on the electrode as atoms. We also saw, in connection with our discussion on polarographic analysis, that exactly the same considerations can be applied when an electrode of some indifferent material, such as mercury or platinum, is immersed in an electrolyte solution. But since, as we have just said, the ionisation of a metal is only a special case of an oxidation-reduction reaction, we should expect that similar potentials should be discoverable when an indifferent electrode is placed in a solution of any oxidisable or reducible substance. These potentials, also, should be a measure of the ease with which an electron is gained or lost. Thermodynamically, of course, such a relation must exist. It follows from what has been said in Chapter 4 that in any electrochemical reaction, the change in free energy can be measured in terms of the E.M.F. developed at an appropriate "reversible" electrode.

It is important, in this connection, that the reader should not become confused between the two meanings which are attached to the word "reversible". A chemical reaction is considered to be reversible when the change in free energy is small and the energy which has to be supplied in order to drive it one way or the other can be easily supplied under laboratory conditions. If a reaction is not in itself reversible, in this sense, it cannot be made so by a catalyst. On the other hand, the word is used in connection with electrode reactions, with oxidation-reduction systems, and in other connections, to indicate whether a process which should, according to free energy considerations, proceed spontaneously, does in fact do so under ordinary conditions. Suppose we have three oxidisable and reducible substances A, B, and C, such that, from free energy considerations A can oxidise B and C can reduce B. If the system is a "reversible" one, then we can change B smoothly to and fro between the oxidised and reduced state by adding A or C. Such reversibility is permitted chiefly by the absence of any large activation energy, and in consequence of this, is often dependent on the presence of suitable catalysts. We shall see later, that such catalysts and reversible oxidation-reduction systems are of the utmost importance in living cells.

The absence of much activation energy is often, but by no means always, associated with "reversibility" at an indifferent electrode.

Thus the oxidising or reducing power of a given substance in solution may be precisely characterised in terms of the potential developed at an indifferent electrode, measured with respect to the potential at some standard electrode; this is, by convention, taken to be the normal hydrogen electrode (hydrogen electrode in a solution of pH O). This *oxidation-reduction potential* can only be measured directly if the system concerned is "reversible", in the kinetic sense, at an electrode. Approximate potentials may sometimes be estimated for substances which are imperfectly reversible; but for the remainder, the potential must be derived from measure-

L*

ments of the free energy change, made in other ways. It has become the accepted practice, however, to characterise oxidation-reduction systems by means of their potentials whether these can be directly measured or not.

The Influence of Hydrogen Ion Concentration on Oxidation-Reduction Potentials. Suppose some substance A in a watery solution becomes reduced, gaining an electron and becoming an ion A^-. Since there must also be some hydrogen ions present, this reduction reaction will be accompanied by an acid dissociation reaction, in which the A^- ions will combine with H^+ ions, to a greater or less extent, depending upon the stability of the A^- ions and on the H^+ ion concentration.

In the one extreme case, we may regard the acid HA as being completely dissociated into A^- ions and H^+ ions; hydrogen ions then do not take any part in the reaction, and the oxidation-reduction potential is independent of pH. In the other extreme case, the substance HA will not dissociate, electrolytically, at all, and the potential at the indifferent electrode will be determined by the concentration of the only *charged* substance that takes part in the reaction, i.e. the H^+ ions. The oxidation-reduction potential of such a substance, therefore, will vary with pH in exactly the same way as does the potential of a hydrogen electrode, i.e. will change at the rate of 58 mV. per pH unit at 20° C. (the actual potential at the two types of electrode, however, will not be the same). The reversibly oxidisable substance here, only plays the part of a catalyst, ensuring the "reversible" ionisation and de-ionisation of the hydrogen atoms.

The above relations between the oxidation-reduction potential and the hydrogen ion concentration may be treated kinetically in the following way. Suppose a substance A is reduced, by electron transfer at an indifferent electrode, to the corresponding anion.

$$\text{i.e. } A + ne \rightleftharpoons A^{n-}$$

where e represents an electron and n the number involved per molecule of A. Now the potential at the electrode with respect to that at some standard electrode is determined by the work required to carry an electron from the standard electrode to the substance A. It can be conceived, therefore, as being determined by the ratio between the concentration (or better, activity) of the free electrons in the metal electrode (which is constant) and the concentration (or activity) of the free electrons in the solution. This last is a hypothetical concept, which is useful only in the development of the equations. According to the general relations developed in Chapter 4 (p. 146), then, we can write:

$$E - E_{\mathrm{H}} = -\frac{RT}{nF} \ln [e]$$

where E_{H} is the potential of the standard electrode. (The activity of the electrons in the electrodes themselves, being constant, is included in the constant term E_H). By applying the law of Mass Action to the process of electron transfer, we get:

$$[e]^n = K_{or} \cdot \frac{[A^{n-}]}{[A]} \qquad . \qquad . \qquad . \qquad . \qquad 8.1$$

The equilibrium constant K_{or} defines the affinity of A for electrons, that is to say its strength as an oxidising or reducing agent. If, further, the n electrons concerned are accompanied by n hydrogen ions, we have the additional reaction:

$$A^{n-} + nH^+ \rightleftharpoons H_nA$$

We can write, as we did in Chapter 4, when discussing the dissociation of weak acids:

$$\frac{[A^{n-}] + [H^+]^n}{[H_nA]} = K_a$$

whence
$$[A^{n-}] = \frac{K_a([H_nA] + [A^{n-}])}{[H^+]^n + K_a} = K_a \frac{[\text{Red A}]}{[H^+]^n + K_a} \qquad . \qquad . \qquad 8.2$$

The sum of $[H_nA]$ and $[A^{n-}]$ occurs in the numerator of this expression, since this represents the *total* concentration of the substance A in the reduced state (i.e. [Red A]), and it is this that we are concerned with, rather than the concentration of either the free acid, or the acid ions, separately. Thus we have:

$$[e]^n = K_{or}K_a \frac{[\text{Red A}]}{[A]} \cdot \frac{1}{[H^+]^n + K_a}$$

and:
$$E - E_H = -\frac{RT}{nF}\left\{ \ln K_{or} + \ln \frac{[\text{Red A}]}{[A]} - \ln ([H^+]^n + K_a) + \ln K_a \right\} \qquad . \qquad 8.3$$

If, in this expression, we keep the ratio of reduced A to oxidised A constant, the potential at the electrode will vary as $\ln ([H^+]^n + K_a)$. If K_a is small compared with $[H^+]$ (i.e. if the acid is practically undissociated), the potential will vary in a linear manner with pH. If K_a is large compared with $[H^+]$ (i.e. if the acid is completely dissociated), the potential will be independent of pH. The first condition represents the type of oxidation-reduction which occurs by the transfer of a hydrogen atom: the second corresponds to that which occurs by the transfer of an electron.

Now as we have said the affinity of the substance A for electrons is defined by the equilibrium constant K_{or}. This quantity will be measured by the potential at an indifferent electrode if we adjust the conditions so that the substance A is exactly half oxidised or half reduced, i.e. so that [Red A] = [A]. In these circumstances, we have:

$$(E - E_H)_0 = -\frac{RT}{nF}\{\ln K_{or} - \ln ([H^+]^n + K_a) + \ln K_a\} \qquad . \qquad 8.4$$

For those substances which have large values of K_a, this expression reduces to

$$(E - E_H)_0 = -\frac{RT}{nF} \ln K_{or} = E_0 \qquad . \qquad . \qquad . \quad 8.4a$$

E_0 is known as the *oxidation-reduction potential*. From equation 8.1 above, we can see that the value of K_{or} increases when the affinity of A for electrons diminishes. K_{or}, therefore, is a measure of the *reducing* power of A. The value of E_0 in consequence becomes increasingly negative as we pass from mild to strong reducing agents, and decreasingly negative, or increasingly positive, as we pass towards strong oxidising agents.

If, however, K_a is small compared with $[H^+]$, equation 8.4 reduces to

$$(E - E_H)_0 = -\frac{RT}{nF} \{\ln K_{or} - n \ln [H^+]\} = E_0 - \frac{2 \cdot 303\,RT}{F} pH \quad . \quad 8.4b$$

We thus measure the true standard value of E_0 only if the solution is at pH 0. But since we are usually more interested in reactions which occur in approximately neutral solution, it is conventional also to define the relative oxidising and reducing powers of different substances in terms of the oxidation-reduction potential at pH 7. This value is given the symbol E'_0; it may be identical with E_0, or may be greater or less than E_0 by amounts which depend on the nature of the oxidation-reduction reaction. If this reaction proceeds by means of a simple transfer of hydrogen atoms as in the analysis above, E'_0 differs from E_0 by $-\dfrac{2 \cdot 303\,RT}{F} \times 7 = -0 \cdot 405$ volts at 20° C. But if the number of hydrogen ions transferred is not the same as the number of electrons transferred—i.e. if the reaction occurs partly as a result of electron transfer, and partly as a result of hydrogen transfer, the relation between E'_0 and E_0 becomes more complicated. In general, if n electrons are accompanied by m hydrogen ions, we have the relation:

$$(E - E_H)_0 = E_0 - \frac{m}{n} \cdot \frac{2 \cdot 303\,RT}{F} \cdot pH \qquad . \qquad . \quad 8.5$$

An example of this is the reduction of CO_2 to a formate anion:

$$CO_2 + 2e + H^+ \rightleftharpoons HCOO^-$$

Here $n = 2$ and $m = 1$, and the oxidation-reduction potential varies with pH at one-half the rate of variation of the potential of a hydrogen electrode, i.e. at 29 mV. per pH unit at 20° C. On the other hand, in certain systems, where the substance reduced is already an anion before reduction, an additional hydrogen ion may be transferred, over and above those which accompany the electrons. Thus in the reduction of formate (or acetate) ions to formaldehyde (or acetaldehyde) molecules, we have:

$$HCOO^- + 2e + 3H^+ \rightleftharpoons HCHO + H_2O$$

The oxidation-reduction potential of this system varies with hydrogen ion concentration more rapidly than does that of the hydrogen electrode, and at a rate of $58 \times 3/2$ or 87 mV. per pH unit at $20°$ C.

The Quinhydrone Electrode. The reaction between quinol (hydroquinone), $HO—C_6H_4—OH$, and quinone, $O=C_6H_4=O$, provides a system in which the oxidation-reduction potential varies with pH at the same rate as does the potential at a hydrogen electrode. The potential at an indifferent electrode, usually of platinum or gold, in a solution containing an equimolecular mixture of quinol and quinone (quinhydrone) can thus be used as a measure of the pH, as already described in Chapter 4 (p. 153). The necessary condition that the reduced substance, quinol, should not be electrolytically dissociated is not satisfied if the solution is more alkaline than pH 8·5; K_a then begins to be comparable in magnitude with $[H^+]$.

The rH Value. If we consider the oxidation-reduction process as a transfer of hydrogen atoms, rather than as a transfer of electrons, we can derive an alternative quantity, known as the rH value, which defines the oxidising or reducing activity of a given substance. Suppose a substance A is reduced by n hydrogen atoms to form AH_n. If the hydrogen atoms are in equilibrium with molecular hydrogen we can write the equation:

$$A + \frac{n}{2} H_2 = AH_n$$

By the Law of Mass Action,

$$[H_2]^{n/2} = K_{or} \frac{[AH_n]}{[A]}$$

or
$$(n/2) \log_{10} [H_2] = \log_{10} K_{or} + \log_{10} \frac{[AH^n]}{[A]} \qquad . \qquad . \qquad 8.6$$

As before, the value of K_{or} defines the affinity of the substance A for hydrogen, and when the conditions are such that A is half oxidised and half reduced, we have

$$\log_{10} K_{or} = (n/2) \log_{10} [H_2] \qquad . \qquad . \qquad . \qquad 8.6a$$

By analogy with the pH notation, we write $-\log_{10} [H_2] = rH$, so that $rH = -(2/n) \log_{10} K_{or}$, and is thus independent of pH. We can imagine the rH value, if we wish, as being a measure of the concentration of hydrogen molecules which is necessary to bring the substance considered to the half oxidised, half reduced, condition. By methods similar to those used in the previous section, it can be shown that we can also define the rH value of a reaction which occurs by electron transfer: we consider it as occurring by simultaneous transfer of hydrogen atoms and hydrogen ions. In such cases, accordingly, the rH value varies with the pH of the solution.

By comparison with the expression derived in the previous section for the oxidation-reduction potential (equation 8.4a), we see that at pH 0, we can write:

$$rH = -(2/n) \log K_{or} = 2E_0F/2 \cdot 303RT = E_0/0 \cdot 029$$
$$\text{(for } pH = 0 \text{ and } T = 20° \text{ C.)} \qquad . \qquad . \qquad . \qquad 8.7$$

We cannot deduce any general relation between the two quantities at any other pH, owing to the different ways in which they vary with pH in different types of oxidation-reduction system. But if we wish to compare two oxidation-reduction systems, the above relation will hold for the *differences* between the rH and the E_0 values at any pH.

The Free Energy Change. We showed in Chapter 2 that the free energy change in any reversible reaction was related to the equilibrium constant by the relation

$$-\Delta G° = RT \ln K \qquad . \qquad . \qquad . \qquad . \qquad 2.22$$

By inserting the appropriate relations between $\ln K_{or}$ and E_0 or rH respectively, we find that

$$-\Delta G° = n.F.E_0 = 46 \cdot 15 \, E_0 \text{ kcals. (for } n = 2) \qquad . \qquad . \qquad 8.8$$

$$= 2 \cdot 303(2RT/n)rH = 1 \cdot 342 \, rH \text{ kcals.}$$
$$\text{(for } n = 2 \text{ and } T = 20° \text{ C.)}. \qquad . \qquad . \qquad 8.8a$$

Interaction between different Oxidation-Reduction Systems. So far, we have been considering the potentials developed at a suitable electrode when different oxidation-reduction systems are present, in turn, all of them being in the half oxidised state. Let us now turn our attention to the potentials developed by a given system when the ratio between the oxidised and reduced forms is varied.

It can easily be seen from the expressions that have just been given, that if the ratio of reduced form to oxidised form is, say, p, then the potential observed will be given by

$$E - E_H = E_0 - \frac{RT}{nF} . \ln p \qquad . \qquad . \qquad . \qquad 8.9$$

$$= E_0 - 0 \cdot 029 \log_{10} p \text{ at } 20° \text{ C. if } n = 2.$$

Conversely, we may conclude that if the observed potential is, say $0 \cdot 058$ volts different from the standard oxidation-reduction potential of the system concerned, then $\log_{10} p = \pm 2$, and only 1 per cent. is in the oxidised, or reduced, form according as the observed potential is more or less positive than the standard value.

Proceeding a step further then, we may say that two different oxidation-reduction systems may reach an observable equilibrium with one another, if, say, not less than 1 per cent. of one is reduced or not less than 1 per cent. of the other is oxidised. This implies, from what we have just said, that the oxidation-reduction potentials of the two systems must not differ from one another by more than, say, 0·116 volts at 20° C. when two electrons are transferred per molecule. Similar reasoning shows us that this condition will also be satisfied if the rH values for the two systems do not differ by more than four units.

This simplicity of the relation between rH units and the fraction oxidised or reduced is one of the main advantages of this unit. In addition, it has the convenience in biological work of being independent of pH for systems which involve hydrogen transfer and not electron transfer.

The importance of these conclusions lies in the fact that it is reasonable to suppose that two oxidation-reduction systems may react smoothly with one another and, from a practical standpoint, reversibly, if their rH values do not differ by more than about four units. This implies, also, that the total change in free energy for the oxidation of one system by the other, must not greatly exceed 5 kcals./mole. It is important to remember, also, that two systems may not "overlap", in this sense, at some particular H ion concentration, but may do so at some other, not very greatly removed. Change in acidity may affect considerably the state of oxidation or reduction of many components of living cells.

Oxidation-Reduction Indicators. Just as there are dyes which change colour according to the degree of ionisation, so also, are there dyes which lose their colour when they accept hydrogen atoms and become reduced. Methylene blue is perhaps the best known example. Again, if we know the acid dissociation constants of the acid-base indicators, we can use their colours as a measure of the hydrogen ion concentration of a given solution: so, also, if we know the standard oxidation-reduction potentials of the oxidation-reduction indicators, we can use their colours as a measure of the oxidation-reduction potential, or rH, of a solution. In both cases, of course, the indicators must be present in such low concentration that they do not themselves disturb the equilibria of the other constituents of the solution. A range of suitable dyes has been worked out by Mansfield Clark and by Cohen; descriptions will be found in the article by Cohen (1933).

Attempts have been made to use the decoloration of dyes on reduction in order to estimate the oxidising or reducing power of living cells. The reduction of litmus by bacteria, for example, was observed by Helmholtz in 1843, and Ehrlich made many observations in 1885 with alizarin blue and indophenol blue. The development of the modern theory of oxidation and reduction, and the provision of a series of oxidation-reduction indicators, re-awakened interest, and a review of the later work will be found in an article by Chambers (1933). The results, however interesting, are nevertheless of doubtful significance and difficult to interpret. We now know that there are many oxidation-reduction systems in the living cell, whose potentials range from values at least as negative as the hydrogen electrode, to values as positive as that of the oxygen electrode. These systems are not in equilibrium with one another, but reach a steady state. The "mean" oxidation-reduction potential, as given by a suitable indicator, will depend upon the relative rates of the various reactions, on the activities of the various enzyme systems, and on the rates of supply of the various reactants.

The oxidation-reduction potentials and changes in free energy associated with a number of oxidation-reduction systems of physiological importance are given in Table 8.1.

The free energy changes $(-\Delta G')$ are reckoned from an arbitrary standard value, the free energy change in the ionisation of hydrogen being taken to be zero : they are independent of pH for those reactions for which the change in E'_0 per pH unit has the same value as that of the hydrogen electrode (0·059) over the whole range of pH considered—i.e. there is no change in the degree of ionisation of either of the substances concerned. For other reactions the values of $-\Delta G'$ at any desired value of pH may be calculated from the difference between the value of E'_0 and that of the hydrogen electrode at this pH, using equation 8.8.

Values of $-\Delta G'$ and of E'_0 for other reactions of biological interest will be found in the article by Burton (1957).

FREE RADICALS IN OXIDATION-REDUCTION REACTIONS—SEMI-QUINONES

Most of the oxidation-reduction reactions with which we shall be concerned involve the loss of two electrons, or of two hydrogen atoms from each molecule of the substance oxidised. If these are transferred to two separate molecules of the substance reduced, the reaction will be of the third order; as pointed out in Chapter 2 (p. 53), such reactions, involving collisions between three "active" molecules, will proceed very slowly, owing to the very small chance that such a collision will occur. Even if the two hydrogen atoms are both transferred to the same molecule, so that a single two-body collision is sufficient, each transfer will need its activation energy independently of the other; and if, as is likely, the molecules concerned in the reaction are large, they must be appropriately orientated at the moment of collision; "successful" collisions will thus be rare.

It seems highly probable, therefore, that such oxidation-reduction reactions will proceed in two stages, the hydrogen atoms, or electrons, being transferred one at a time. We thus have to admit the possibility that

TABLE 8.1

Free Energy Changes in Oxidation-Reduction Reactions
(at 25° C. and pH 7)

Reaction	Free Energy Change $(-\Delta G')$, kcal. per 2H	Oxidation-Reduction Potential (E'_0), volts	Change in E'_0 per pH unit
Hydrogen Peroxide $\rightleftharpoons$ Water	82	+1·36	0·0295
Oxygen $\rightleftharpoons$ Water	56·7	+0·816	0·059
$Fe^{3+} \rightleftharpoons Fe^{2+}$	34·6	+0·75	0
Oxygen $\rightleftharpoons$ Hydrogen Peroxide	32·7	+0·295	0·059
Quinone $\rightleftharpoons$ Quinol (hydroquinone)	32·0	+0·28	0·059 $(pH < 9)$
Cytochrome c reduction	30·7	+0·25	0 $(pH < 7·3)$ 0·059 $(8·3 < pH)$
Calomel electrode (satd. KCl)	30·4	+0·2443	0
Fumarate^{2-} $\rightleftharpoons$ Succinate^{2-}	20·5	+0·031	0·059 $(5·9 < pH)$
Methylene blue reduction	19·7	+0·01	0·0295 $(6·5 < pH)$ 0·089 $(pH < 5·5)$
Yellow enzyme reduction	13·5	−0·122	0·059
Oxalo-acetate^{2-} $\rightleftharpoons$ Malate^{2-}	11·45	−0·166	0·059 $(5·7 < pH)$
Pyruvate$^-$ $\rightleftharpoons$ Lactate$^-$	10·32	−0·19	0·059 $(4·4 < pH)$
Acetaldehyde $\rightleftharpoons$ Ethanol	10·0	−0·197	0·059
Riboflavin reduction	9·9	−0·20	0·0295 $(6·8 < pH < 8·5)$ 0·059 $(pH < 5·8)$
Phosphopyridine nucleotides DPN$^+$ $\rightleftharpoons$ DPNH	4·33	−0·315	0·0295
TPN$^+$ $\rightleftharpoons$ TPNH	4·11	−0·324	
Pyruvate$^-$ + CO_2 $\rightleftharpoons$ Malate^{2-}	3·83	−0·330	0·0295 $(5·7 < pH)$
Cystine $\rightleftharpoons$ 2 Cysteine Glutathione reduction	3·42	−0·34	0·059
Acetyl CoA $\rightleftharpoons$ Acetaldehyde + CoA	0·11	−0·412	0·059
Hydrogen ion $\rightleftharpoons$ Hydrogen atom (Hydrogen electrode)	0	−0·414	0·059
Acetate$^-$ $\rightleftharpoons$ Acetaldehyde	−8·5	−0·60	0·089 $(5·2 < pH)$
Acetate$^-$ + CO_2 $\rightleftharpoons$ Pyruvate$^-$	−13·12	−0·699	0·059 $(5·2 < pH)$

the bonds by which some of the atoms in these molecules were attached to each other—and will be again attached to other atoms when the reaction is complete—can remain broken for appreciable periods of time. Such groups of atoms in which some of the valencies are "unsatisfied" are known as "free radicals". As we shall see in the next chapter, they play an important part in photochemical reactions. In most of the reactions in which they occur, although they exist for a period of time comparable with the average interval between molecular collisions, this period is, of course, extremely short, only a minute fraction of a second. But in reactions which involve heterogeneous catalysis, such as enzyme reactions, the radicals may be adsorbed on the colloidal carrier, and not being strictly "free", may exist for much longer periods of time. This possibility, indeed, accounts for a large part of the catalytic action; we are not concerned with the very improbable three-body collisions, but with two successive two-body collisions.

Let us consider the oxidation-reduction reactions between two organic compounds, involving the transfer of two hydrogen atoms. As an example, let us take the oxidation of a $=CHOH$ to a $=C=O$ group. If we transfer only one hydrogen atom instead of two, we are left with a free radical, $=C—OH$, and we shall probably create another free radical from the compound to which the hydrogen atom is transferred. We should expect that such a creation of two unsatisfied valencies would require a large amount of energy, and in general, when we are dealing with substances of relatively simple constitution, this is so. Indeed, it is the difficulty with which the first hydrogen atom is transferred that makes the simple hydrocarbons, for instance, so stable at ordinary temperatures. On the other hand, the very large amount of energy contained in the partially oxidised free radical contributes largely to the violence of the reaction, when once this has been started.

When however, we turn to the more complex organic compounds, it seems that the extra energy associated with the unsatisfied valency in the free radical can, as it were, be shared out over the whole molecule, which then becomes relatively stable. That the transfer of two hydrogen atoms does, in fact, occur in two successive stages, is seen clearly in the oxidation of phenols to quinones; the half-way stage, when one hydrogen atom has been lost by the phenol being known as a "*semi-quinone*". Such free radicals, of course, have only a transitory existence. But in the oxidation of certain complex polyphenols, the semi-quinones that are formed are sufficiently stable for their presence to be readily demonstrated; in some cases, more than 10 per cent. of the total dye present is in the form of the semi-quinone. These reactions were studied extensively by Michaelis and his co-workers from 1931 onwards.

It is found, as might be expected, that those substances which form relatively stable semi-quinones also form kinetically reversible oxidation-reduction systems, and give stable and reproducible oxidation-reduction potentials. The amount of the semi-quinone, or other similar free radical, that is present at any moment depends on its stability, and this in turn depends on the energy of its formation. The more free radical there is, the more smoothly will the reaction proceed; but it can be calculated that, in fact, a reaction may proceed smoothly at room temperatures, even though the free radical is present at any moment in a quite undetectable concentration. In the living cell, it is essential that oxidations and reductions should go smoothly and without explosive violence; and it may well be that one of the functions of the complex oxidation-reduction enzyme systems by which they are brought about is to stabilise the free radicals of various kinds which are formed during the course of the reactions.

AUTOXIDATION

Certain substances, such as phosphorus, benzaldehyde and many unsaturated organic compounds, containing carbon atoms united by a double bond, will oxidise spontaneously in air. It has been known for a long time that in these spontaneous "autoxidations" a peroxide is formed in addition to the ordinary oxidation product of the substance concerned. For example, if a molecule of oxygen is taken up by an organic substance at a double bond, the compound formed has the structure of a peroxide:

$$>C=C< \ + \ O_2 \longrightarrow >\overset{\displaystyle O—O}{\underset{\displaystyle |\quad\ |}{C—C}}<$$

In all these autoxidations, a molecule of oxygen combines, in the end, with at least two molecules of the autoxidisable substance; in accordance with what has been said in the previous section, such a reaction, involving at least three molecules, will not occur in one stage. The first stage in the reaction, therefore, must be supposed to be the direct attachment of a molecule of oxygen to the oxidisable substance, forming a peroxide, as indicated above. Peroxides have oxidation-reduction potentials more positive than that of oxygen gas (compare Table 8.1), and thus require energy to form them; they are similar, in fact, to the free radicals and semi-quinones already discussed. The peroxide may then react with another molecule of the autoxidisable substance to form two molecules of a lower, and more stable, oxide; or in some circumstances with water, to form hydrogen peroxide, or with molecular oxygen, to form ozone.

The formation of a peroxide during the autoxidation of one substance may often result in the oxidation of some other substance. Thus Indigo Blue is very slowly oxidised in air, while oil of turpentine is oxidised at a considerable rate, presumably with the production of a peroxide. In a mixture of both substances, the oxygen of the peroxide is transferred to the indigo, which thus undergoes a rapid oxidation. It has been held that the oil of turpentine should be called a catalyst in this reaction, since it does not appear as a constituent of the oxidised indigo, although it is not itself in its original form at the end of the reaction. There can be no doubt that a process cannot be a catalytic one when free energy for the reaction is supplied by the agent called catalyst, and it is then better to call it a coupled reaction. In this particular case, however, the oil of turpentine provides only activation energy, since indigo blue will oxidise in air spontaneously; it is analogous to the acceleration of a spontaneous reaction by the action of light. It is difficult, therefore, to draw a precise line of demarcation between this kind of reaction and that in which the action of hydrogen peroxide on hydriodic acid is accelerated by molybdic acid (p. 289, above). The only essential difference is that in this true catalytic action, the catalyst is recovered unchanged at the end of the reaction. This must be considered to be the true criterion. If, as sometimes, the catalyst cannot be recovered intact, the change undergone must be independent of the main reaction, and merely incidental to it; the oxidation of the oil of turpentine, however, is an essential part of the reaction. It must be admitted, nevertheless, that such a distinction is not always easily made.

The process of autoxidation results, then, in the production of a peroxide and in the simultaneous oxidation of certain other substances present in the system, which may not, by themselves, react spontaneously with molecular oxygen at a measurable rate. In the presence of water, we generally find that hydrogen peroxide is formed. This, however, is not a very powerful oxidising agent. But, as was known to Schönbein in 1860, ferrous salts, in extremely small amounts, strongly accelerate the action of hydrogen peroxide on oxidisable substances. Ferrous salts, again, as also those of copper and of manganese, accelerate the oxidising action of turpentine, benzaldehyde, etc.; and it is significant that the metallic ions concerned are all capable of taking up and losing one or more electrons, and thus of being reversibly oxidised and reduced. There is reason to believe that the reduced (e.g. ferrous) ion, particularly when in organic combination, can take up two atoms of oxygen, forming a kind of peroxide, and that there is then a re-arrangement of the electrons whereby the ion is oxidised (e.g. becomes ferric), the peroxide linkage is broken, and the oxygen atoms transferred to some other substance. The result of this is that much less activation energy is needed for the simultaneous uptake of the two atoms of oxygen in a molecule, and autoxidation is thus greatly facilitated. In such a reaction, no detectable amount of free peroxide need be formed.

THE OXIDATION SYSTEMS OF THE LIVING CELL

The nature and properties of the numerous substances which take part in physiological oxidations and reductions have been the subject of much biochemical investigation, and detailed accounts are to be found in text-books of Biochemistry. The reaction systems are of great complexity; the reactions are catalysed by enzymes whose composition is incompletely known; and many of the enzymes cannot be extracted from the cells without loss of activity. Thus, although we are in possession of a large number of facts, their relation to a general theory is not at all a simple matter. We are here concerned primarily with the physico-chemical aspects of oxidation and reduction in living cells; but a brief account must first be given of some general features of the systems concerned.

On the evidence at present available, we can divide the oxidation-reduction systems of living cells into two main groups. At one end of the chain of reactions, we have a group of enzymes and carriers concerned with the reduction of molecular oxygen; these we may collect together under the term *"oxidases"*, although the term is usually given only to the enzymes and not to the carriers. At the other end of the chain—although this end is usually not to be defined precisely—we have a group of enzymes and carriers concerned with the transfer of hydrogen atoms from one substrate to another, and, of course, eventually to the oxidases. These we may collect together under the term *"dehydrogenases"*. In addition, there are enzyme-carrier systems which act as intermediaries between these two main groups; and other enzymes concerned in reactions which, although essential to the whole sequence of operations, do not involve hydrogen or electron transfer.

Oxidases

The Cytochrome System. By far the most widespread and important of the oxidase systems are the *cytochromes*. These are iron-porphyrin proteins, similar in general constitution to the red blood pigment, haemoglobin, and to the enzymes catalase and peroxidase, to be referred to later; the porphyrins, however, as well as the proteins to which they are attached, have different constitutions in all these substances. The structure of the iron-porphyrin prosthetic group is based on that of the porphin skeleton, shown in Fig. 9.2 (p. 389). Various side chains are attached to the pyrrole rings, forming the various porphyrins, and an iron atom is fitted in the middle; it is attached to the surrounding nitrogen atoms by covalencies and electrovalencies in somewhat different fashions in different compounds.

Cytochromes are to be found in the cells of all organisms which are able to reduce molecular oxygen; and there are very few kinds of cell indeed which cannot do this. Detection of the cytochromes, and study of their properties, is greatly facilitated by the fact that they have characteristic absorption spectra. These contain four relatively narrow bands in the green and yellow, provided that the compound is in the reduced state (the iron is in the ferrous condition); when oxidised (with the iron trivalent) these bands disappear, and are replaced by a shallower and broader band in the same region of the spectrum. If a suitable preparation of living cells is observed with a spectroscope, the characteristic bands of reduced cytochrome will be observed, but only so long as oxygen is rigidly excluded. As soon as oxygen is admitted these bands disappear, as the cytochrome takes up molecular oxygen; when oxygen is again excluded, the bands reappear once more, as the cytochrome system is reduced by some constituents of the cells.

The cytochromes were first observed in 1886 by MacMunn in the wing muscles of the bee, but their significance was not at that time understood, and their existence was vigorously denied by Hoppe-Seyler. They were rediscovered in 1925 by Keilin, and our knowledge of their functions and importance is due almost entirely to the work of Keilin and his co-workers from that date onwards.

Keilin's original experiments may well be described here in his own words (*Proceedings of the Royal Society*, vol. B.98, p. 319, 1925). "The oxidation and reduction of the pigment can be easily observed in yeast. If a shallow tube (30 mm. high) is half-filled with a suspension of baker's yeast in water (20 per cent.), and the suspension then examined with the Zeiss microspectroscope, the four absorption bands may be clearly seen; but when the air is rapidly bubbled through the suspension, the cytochrome becomes oxidised and the bands disappear. If the current of air is stopped, the pigment becomes reduced and the four bands rapidly reappear. . . . When, instead of air, a current of N_2 is passed through the yeast emulsion, or when the latter is shaken with N_2, the cytochrome remains in a reduced state, showing all the time its characteristic four absorption bands. Similar results are obtained with the thoracic muscles of bees or the striated muscles of a guinea-pig. But in these cases the oxidation and reduction are better seen in the broken-up muscles, which may be spread on a slide. When the muscle is exposed to air, the cytochrome is seen in its oxidised form, but when the slide is covered with another slide and the space around the muscle filled with glycerin, the cytochrome becomes reduced and the four bands appear. In these experiments, cytochrome is oxidised by O_2 of the air and reduced by the tissue itself."

More detailed examination of the cytochrome system showed that the exact positions and relative intensities of the absorption bands varied in different kinds of cell. There are, in fact, three main kinds of cytochrome, known by the letters *a*, *b* and *c*, and each of these types has again been subdivided. Each cytochrome has two bands only, like other haematin derivatives. Constitutionally, the difference lies entirely in the nature of the protein, to which the haematin derivative is attached; the prosthetic group is the same in all. Functionally, the difference lies in the ease with which they autoxidise. Cytochrome a and c, the latter being the most prevalent quantitatively, will not combine spontaneously with oxygen at all; cytochrome b does so, but only slowly. A fourth component, present in very small amounts only, known as cytochrome oxidase, however, catalyses the autoxidation of the cytochromes and is, probably, one of the cytochromes itself. Cytochrome c is the only member of the group which has so far been extracted from the living cell, and isolated in a pure state. The other cytochromes, and cytochrome oxidase, are attached to cell constituents which cannot be brought into solution without being destroyed. They are, also, destroyed at temperatures above 50° C.

Cytochrome oxidase very readily combines with carbon monoxide, cyanides, sulphides and azides, and its activity may be completely inhibited by these agents; the last three are effective in a concentration as low as M/1000. This property is responsible for the poisonous action of these substances on cell respiration. The action of carbon monoxide is of particular interest, since it competes with oxygen for combination with the prosthetic group of cytochrome oxidase, and the degree of inhibition depends on the ratio of the partial pressures of the two gases. We are reminded here of the very similar behaviour of haemoglobin. The compound of cytochrome oxidase with carbon monoxide, also, like that of haemoglobin, is dissociated by light of the appropriate wave-length—i.e. that corresponding to the absorption band of the carbon monoxide complex.

It is of some interest to note that in 1932, before the existence of cytochrome oxidase had been discovered, Warburg deduced that the oxygen uptake by living cells was dependent on the activity of some iron-porphyrin compound. He based his conclusions on the mutual relations between the partial pressures of carbon monoxide and oxygen on the rate of oxygen uptake; and on the relative effectiveness of light of different wave-lengths in inhibiting the poisonous action of carbon monoxide. On the basis of Grotthus' law, that light cannot have a photochemical action unless it is absorbed (Chapter 9, p. 372), he deduced the absorption spectrum of the hypothetical compound concerned. It is now known that Warburg's "Respiratory Enzyme" is identical with cytochrome oxidase.

The Phenol Oxidases. In the cells of plants, and of many invertebrate animals, we find enzymes which catalyse the oxidation of phenols to quinones, by means of molecular oxygen. The majority of these enzymes are concerned only with the oxidation of polyphenols, of which the di-phenol, catechol, is the most rapidly oxidised; but some tissues also contain enzymes which promote the oxidation of monophenols to the corresponding o-quinone.

The importance of these enzymes lies in the fact that small quantities of catechol can be detected in most cells which contain polyphenol oxidases; and further, that the o-quinone so formed can be reduced again by the oxidisable substrates of living cells, with the aid, it may be, of ascorbic acid (vitamin C) or of other enzyme systems. The catechol-polyphenol oxidase system can thus serve the same function as the cytochrome-cytochrome oxidase system, in bringing about the oxidation by molecular oxygen of substances which are not themselves, autoxidisable. The phenol oxidases have been shown to contain copper in their prosthetic groups: this is in the cupric state in the presence of oxygen, and in the cuprous state when the enzyme has oxidised its substrate.

The Flavo-proteins. There are, also, several oxidases which contain riboflavin (one of the B group of vitamins), together with a metal atom (copper, iron, molybdenum or manganese) as the prosthetic group. Enzymes of this type bring about the oxidation of amino-acids, aldehydes, and xanthine by molecular oxygen, and in the course of the reaction, hydrogen peroxide may be formed. The structure of riboflavin is given in Fig. 8.1; in the enzymes it occurs either as the phosphate, as shown, or as a dinucleotide with adenine, being then known as flavin-adenine dinucleotide, or FAD, the structure being generally similar to that of the di-phosphopyridine nucleotides, to be discussed below. Riboflavin has a greenish-yellow colour in solution, with a strong yellow-green fluorescence, and was accordingly called the "Yellow enzyme" when it was first isolated, in 1932, by Warburg and Christian. Other flavins, of similar structure, occur naturally, and yet others have been synthesised; some of the latter show some enzyme activity.

Peroxidases and Catalase. Such peroxides as may be formed by the action of the oxidases will not, by themselves, oxidise substances present in the cells to any significant extent; they consist either of hydrogen peroxide or of organic substances having a similar constitution. Enzymes, however, have been prepared from various plant tissues which act as catalysts for the reaction of peroxides with a number of oxidisable substances; they were called *"peroxidases"* by Bach and Chodat in 1903. As we have seen, certain metals, or compounds containing them, have the same effect, and, as already remarked, the peroxidases contain iron-porphyrin compounds as the prosthetic group. In particular, a special peroxidase has been described which catalyses the oxidation of reduced cytochrome *c*.

Peroxidases occur rarely, if at all, in animal tissues; instead, we find *catalase*, which accelerates the decomposition of hydrogen peroxide into oxygen and water, without at the same time bringing about the oxidation of any substrate. It thus inactivates any excess hydrogen peroxide that may be formed.

Peroxidase was the first oxidation-reduction enzyme to be investigated, largely on account of the fact that it is concerned in the oxidation of a convenient test substance, the gum *guiacum*; one of the constituents, guiaconic acid, becoming blue on oxidation. Benzidine, or pyrogallol, may also be used. The experimental procedure used by Bach and Chodat in the discovery of peroxidase, and its mode of action, are extremely simple. It can be established, to begin with, that guiacum is not oxidised spontaneously by the oxygen in ordinary air, nor by hydrogen peroxide without any catalyst. But if a drop of guiacum solution is applied to, say, the scrapings from the surface of a potato, a blue colour is produced. This does not occur, however, if the tissues of the horse-radish root are used, unless some hydrogen peroxide is added as well. The plant tissues, therefore, must contain something which activates hydrogen peroxide. This constituent can be shown to have the properties of an enzyme, being destroyed by heat and precipitated by alcohol, for example; and it was therefore called "peroxidase". If, now, the guiacum solution is added to the potato scrapings in the complete absence of oxygen (say in a tube in which the air has been replaced by hydrogen or coal gas) no oxidation takes place although it does so when air is admitted. The peroxidase presumably, is present as usual, but in the absence of oxygen, no peroxide is present for it to act upon.

These, and other similar, experiments led to the belief that the production of hydrogen peroxide was a general phenomenon when molecular oxygen is reduced by living tissues. The discovery of the modes of action of the cytochrome system, and of the phenol oxidases, showed that this was not so, and less emphasis is now placed on the part played by the peroxidases.

It is to be noted that, as far as is known, all the enzymes which activate molecular oxygen contain metal atoms in their prosthetic groups. It is known, also, that in some of these, at least, the prosthetic groups undergo electronic re-arrangements when they take up a molecule of oxygen, and subsequently release it in a reduced state. The oxidation-reduction reactions in which they take part thus consist primarily of electron transfers, and no hydrogen atoms need be involved.

DEHYDROGENASES

It has been known for a long time that fresh animal and plant tissues have the power of reducing nitrates to nitrites, the process being thought probably to be a catalytic one. But the existence of *reducing enzymes*, analogous to the oxidising ones, was not generally accepted until Schardinger made the observation in 1902 that fresh milk rapidly reduces methylene blue, indigo, and so on, if an aldehyde, such as formaldehyde or acetaldehyde, be present; whereas it has no such action in the absence of the aldehyde. The property is abolished by boiling, and has been used as a test to distinguish fresh from sterilised milk. It was clearly proved by Trommsdorff in 1909 that this reaction is due to an enzyme, and not to bacteria. If microbes are present, the milk, after some hours, acquires the property of reducing methylene blue without the addition of an aldehyde.

The mechanism of this reaction may be illustrated by means of a relatively simple example, which does not involve any product of a living organism: that of the spontaneous oxidation of hypophosphites in solution, in the presence of finely divided metallic palladium. In the absence of the palladium, hypophosphites do not undergo oxidation in water at a measurable rate. It appears that a molecule of hypophosphite first takes up a molecule of water, and then loses two hydrogen atoms to the palladium which acts as a hydrogen acceptor. The reaction may be represented thus:

$$\begin{array}{c}\underset{O}{\overset{H}{\diagdown}}P\underset{H}{\overset{OH}{\diagup}} + HOH \longrightarrow \underset{HO}{\overset{H}{\diagdown}}P\underset{\underset{H}{|}}{\overset{OH}{\diagup}}OH \xrightarrow{(Pd)} \underset{O}{\overset{H}{\diagdown}}P\underset{OH}{\overset{OH}{\diagup}} + 2H\,(Pd)\end{array}$$

$$2H\,(Pd) \longrightarrow H_2 + Pd$$

In this reaction, if there is no additional hydrogen acceptor to which the hydrogen atoms can be transferred, free hydrogen is evolved. The palladium thus acts as a true catalyst; minute amounts can bring about the oxidation of indefinite amounts of hypophosphite. If some easily reducible substance is present as well, the hydrogen atoms on the palladium can be transferred to it; the reducible substance thus brings about the oxidation of the hypophosphite.

Now as already mentioned, it seems likely that the oxidation of an aldehyde is, in fact, the dehydrogenation of the hydrated aldehyde. But if we take an aldehyde in place of hypophosphite, we find that the presence of metals of the platinum group does not accelerate their oxidation to any great degree. The oxidation-reduction potential of the aldehyde-carboxylic acid reaction is, apparently, not sufficiently negative to that of the hydrogen electrode, and free hydrogen cannot be evolved, at least at a measurable rate (compare Table 8.1). But if we add some easily reducible substance, with an oxidation-reduction potential substantially more positive than that of the hydrogen electrode, such as methylene blue, the aldehyde becomes oxidised and the methylene blue reduced. This reaction is of particular interest since methylene blue contains no oxygen; the additional oxygen needed to convert an aldehyde into a carboxylic acid must come from the water in which it is dissolved.

The enzyme shown by Schardinger and Trommsdorff to be responsible for the reduction of methylene blue by fresh milk in the presence of an aldehyde obviously plays a part similar to that of the platinum metals in the above reaction. Such reducing action of fresh tissues has been described by various observers, and ascribed to enzymes called "reductases" or "reducases", but now more usually called "*dehydrogenases*".

Our knowledge of the nature of the dehydrogenases results chiefly from the work of Thunberg, from 1920 onwards, and of that of subsequent workers using the very simple procedures devised by him. A complete oxidation-reduction system must include an oxidisable substrate (hydrogen donator) and a dehydrogenase, together with any co-enzymes or activators that may be needed in order to transfer the hydrogen atoms to such hydrogen acceptors as may be present. In the final stage this will be atmospheric oxygen. Most fresh tissues even when finely minced will use methylene blue as hydrogen acceptor in the same way as does milk in Schardinger's experiments. Since the reduced, or leuco-, methylene blue is colourless, it is easy to observe whether a given preparation contains a complete system of substrate + dehydrogenase + co-enzyme. Since the leuco-methylene blue becomes re-oxidised spontaneously in the presence of atmospheric oxygen, the "Thunberg tube" in which the reaction is studied is evacuated, or filled with hydrogen or nitrogen.

We find, by this method, that in the first place, boiling the minced tissue removes all reducing power: an enzyme is clearly concerned. Secondly, if the tissue is dialysed, or well washed with water, the reducing power is again very much reduced; but now, the addition of *boiled* tissue restores it. Washing, or dialysis, in fact, removes two necessary components, the substrate and a co-enzyme. If we add a number of possible substrates in turn, we can find which of them are capable of acting as hydrogen donators; and by analysis of the washings, or dialysates, it has been found possible to identify the co-enzymes. These, originally known as Co-enzymes, or Co-dehydrogenases, I and II, are now usually given the more precise names of di- and tri-phosphopyridine nucleotide, abbreviated to DPN and TPN, respectively. Each molecule contains one molecule of adenine, one of nicotinic acid amide, two or three of phosphoric acid, as the case may be, and one of a pentose sugar (*d*-ribose), as indicated in Fig. 8.1. The most important constituent of the molecule is the nicotinamide. This can be synthesised by very few animals, if any, but by several kinds of micro-organism; inadequate supplies lead to the deficiency disease known as pellagra in man, and black tongue in dogs. Nicotinic acid, or its amide, is therefore classed as a vitamin, and is included in the B group.

Both of these co-enzymes can be reversibly oxidised and reduced, provided that the appropriate protein part of the whole enzyme system is present; in its absence, they are no more reactive than are the substrates themselves. In the oxidised state, these pyridino-proteins thus act as natural hydrogen acceptors and will then reduce methylene blue, if it is present, or, in natural conditions, some other appropriate reducible substance. The oxidation and reduction involves the loss or gain of one hydrogen atom and one electron per molecule of the co-enzyme: two

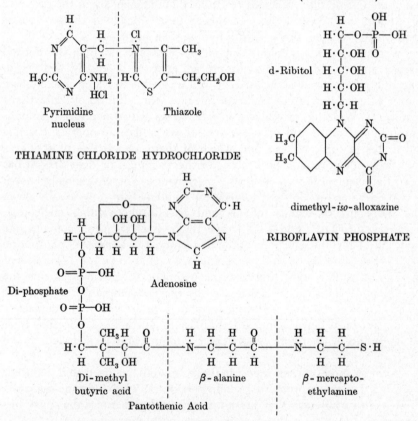

Di-phosphate

d-Ribose

Adenine

Adenosine

d-Ribose

Nicotinic
Acid Amide

DI-PHOSPHOPYRIDINE NUCLEOTIDE (COENZYME I)

Pyrimidine
nucleus

Thiazole

THIAMINE CHLORIDE HYDROCHLORIDE

d-Ribitol

dimethyl-*iso*-alloxazine

RIBOFLAVIN PHOSPHATE

Adenosine

Di-phosphate

Di-methyl
butyric acid

β-alanine

β-mercapto-
ethylamine

Pantothenic Acid

COENZYME A

Fig. 8.1. The Structural Formulae of some of the Co-enzymes and Prosthetic Groups concerned in Oxidation-Reduction Reactions in Living Cells

The structure of adenosine diphosphate may be seen in the left-hand half of that of Diphosphopyridine nucleotide, and in the upper half of that of Co-enzyme A. Adenosine triphosphate has three phosphate groups instead of the two shown.

The sulphydryl group of Co-enzyme A unites with the carboxyl group of acetic acid to form "active acetate".

hydrogen atoms may, however, be removed from one substance and handed on to another, in which case, one of them becomes oxidised to a hydrogen ion in the intermediate stage, and remains in free solution. Fig. 8.1 shows the formula of DPN in the oxidised state. The reduction of both DPN and TPN is associated with a change in the absorption spectrum, an additional band appearing at about 3400 Å., the main band, at about 2600 Å. remaining almost unchanged. This circumstance has greatly facilitated the study of the reactions in which they take part.

Most of the dehydrogenases that are known belong to the class of pyridino-proteins, but the nature of a few is uncertain, since there are some which do not require any known co-enzyme. They are all highly specific towards the substrate which is to provide hydrogen atoms, and also towards the co-enzyme. Some, such as that which operates on lactic acid in muscles, will only work in the presence of DPN, while others, such as that which operates on hexose monophosphate, require TPN. The lactic acid dehydrogenase of liver, on the other hand, and some others, needs no co-enzyme, while the glucose dehydrogenase of liver will work with either.

The pyridino-proteins, when reduced by the acceptance of hydrogen atoms from substrate molecules, cannot directly bring about the reduction of oxidised cytochrome c, still less that of molecular oxygen. The junction is effected by certain *flavo-proteins*, one of the most important being *cytochrome reductase*, which acts specifically in catalysing the reduction of cytochrome c by reduced TPN. There are, also, several other flavo-proteins, with more or less specific properties, which co-operate with each other and with various dehydrogenases and oxidases.

It seems probable that quantitatively the greater part of the oxidative metabolism of most kinds of cell is carried out by means of hydrogen atoms which are removed from the substrate molecules and transferred successively from one enzyme system to another along a chain: first, the dehydrogenases, with the pyridine nucleotides and other co-enzymes; then the flavoproteins and perhaps enzymes of other kinds not yet identified; then the oxidase system of cytochrome c and its associates; and thus finally to molecular oxygen. There are exceptions, however. The o-quinones which are formed by the action of the polyphenol oxidases can be reduced directly by most of the dehydrogenase systems, without the intervention of flavoproteins; those oxidase systems which give rise to hydrogen peroxide, or to organic peroxides, can bring about the oxidation of some kinds of substrate with the aid of the peroxidases; and there are "aerobic dehydrogenases", consisting of certain flavoproteins, or at least containing them, which can carry the hydrogen atoms from the substrate all the way to molecular oxygen. The enzyme discovered by Schardinger in milk is, in fact, one of these, since the oxidation of aldehydes will be accompanied by the reduction of oxygen, if this is present, instead of methylene blue.

THE FORMATION OF CARBON DIOXIDE

The substrates with which the dehydrogenases and other similar enzymes react, contain carbon as well as hydrogen; and it is well-established—and indeed almost common knowledge—that carbon dioxide is evolved by metabolising tissues in about the same volume as that of the oxygen absorbed. It is now known, however, that this process is not strictly an oxidation. The energy made available by oxidative metabolism in living cells is almost entirely derived from the reduction (or hydrogenation) of oxygen to water; the reactions which lead to the release of carbon dioxide are not accompanied by the release of any considerable amounts of free energy. Conversely, as we shall see in the next chapter, the main reaction in photosynthesis is the oxidation (or dehydrogenation) of water, to form free oxygen; the simultaneous reduction of carbon dioxide is, to some extent, a secondary process.

The carbon dioxide produced in oxidative metabolism is derived from the terminal groups of carboxylic acids, which may be amino-acids or keto-acids, by a process of *decarboxylation*. The greater part of the carbon dioxide produced by animals is believed to be derived from keto-acids, such as oxaloacetic acid and pyruvic acid. Amino-acids are readily decarboxylated by many bacteria, including those within the alimentary tracts of animals, with the production of the corresponding amines: most of these have highly powerful and specific actions on the tissues of animals, as for example, histamine and putrescine, so that they could only be produced by the animals themselves in extremely minute amounts. Decarboxylation reactions are catalysed by an enzyme *carboxylase*, the co-enzyme for which is di-phosphothiamine, or vitamin B_1 pyrophosphate; the structure of thiamine is given in Fig. 8.1. At least two of the enzymes with which thiamine is associated are activated by the presence of magnesium or manganese ions in addition, and the former may well form part of the co-enzyme.

In the higher animals, the reactions in which carbon dioxide is evolved are more complex than the above statements would imply. Simple decarboxylation of a keto-acid to yield an aldehyde occurs in yeast cells during alcoholic fermentation, e.g. pyruvic acid becomes acetaldehyde:

$$CH_3.CO.COOH \longrightarrow CH_3.CHO + CO_2$$

but this does not occur in animal tissues. In these, the product of decarboxylation is a carboxylic acid, e.g. pyruvic acid becomes acetic acid:

$$CH_3.CO.COOH \longrightarrow CH_3.COOH + CO_2$$

an oxygen atom being added at the same time as the carbon dioxide molecule is removed. This process of *oxidative decarboxylation* is catalysed by rather complex enzyme systems; the co-enzyme di-phosphothiamine is required, as well as magnesium ions, and, in addition, a relatively simple substance, lipoic (6-thioctic) acid. This substance contains two sulphur atoms in each molecule, and can undergo oxidation and reduction with loss or gain of hydrogen atoms. We shall refer to this again later (p. 360).

THE IMPORTANCE OF CELL STRUCTURE

The basic reaction systems concerned in oxidative metabolism have been investigated largely in disintegrated cells, or in extracts from them. In the living cell itself, we find that we must take account, also, of its "structure" by which we mean not merely the coarse structure seen under the microscope, but also the ultra-microscopic structure, of molecular dimensions, which is probably no less important.

As long ago as 1907, Fletcher and Hopkins observed that in an intact muscle, lactic acid was formed in the absence of oxygen, and disappeared when oxygen was re-admitted. If the muscle was ground with sand, the lactic acid did not disappear. Again, a fluid which is filtered off from muscles or other kinds of cell, excluding particles of more than colloidal dimensions (the so-called "press juice", since a press is used for the filtration process) is incapable of consuming oxygen; this has been repeatedly observed. Yeast juice, however, as is well known, is still able to cause alcoholic fermentation.

It appears that the pyridinoproteins and flavoproteins are largely present in the cells in a more or less free state, and so can be extracted in watery solutions. The cytochromes, however, are mainly attached to cellular inclusions, notably the *mitochondria*—small rods or threads which are just visible under a high power microscope—and cannot easily be removed intact. It is for this reason, probably, that cell extracts are unable to reduce molecular oxygen. Thin slices of some tissues will do so, and the breast muscle of pigeons, which contains much myoglobin, will consume oxygen even when minced. But, owing largely to the work of Claude in 1941 and onwards, methods are available whereby the mitochondria may be separated from the other cellular constituents. Such preparations of isolated mitochondria are able to reduce molecular oxygen: and, moreover, they contain all the enzymes and co-enzymes concerned in the complex sequence of reactions involved. It is, nevertheless, still difficult to obtain preparations to which oxygen can gain rapid access, and which will also make use of the oxygen which is available to them. For this reason, our knowledge of the anaerobic fermentations has advanced more rapidly than has our knowledge of aerobic respiration.

No discussion of biological oxidation-reduction reactions would be complete without mention of the Warburg micro-respirometer, which has proved so valuable in providing quantitative information about reactions in which a gas, notably oxygen, is absorbed or evolved. In principle, the quantity of gas taking part in the reaction in a given time is measured in terms of the change in pressure that occurs in a closed vessel, as indicated by a sensitive mano-meter; corrections being made for any unavoidable changes in the temperature of the vessel and the pressure of the atmosphere. Such an apparatus was first described by Thunberg in 1905, modified by Winterstein in 1912, and de-veloped by Barcroft and by Warburg, by whose name it is now usually known.

THE ENERGETICS OF LIVING CELLS

Experiments on whole organisms, such as those done originally by Rubner and by Benedict, show that the heat produced is identical, within the limits of experimental error, with the loss of chemical energy of the food-stuffs, The reduction of each molecule of oxygen, with the formation of two molecules of water, involves the creation of four O—H bonds, and the rupture of one $O=O$ bond. From the table of bond energies given in Chapter 2, we should expect that 322 kcals. of energy would thereby be released, when each gram-molecule of oxygen is reduced; or 161 kcals. when each pair of hydrogen atoms is oxidised. But in the oxidation process of the living cell, the hydrogen atoms are derived from carbon compounds, so that in addition, we must allow for the rupture of the C—H and C—C bonds, and for the formation of the $O=C=O$ bonds (in carbon dioxide). The final result, then, is that roughly speaking, the reduction of each gram-molecule of oxygen is attended by the release of 100 kcals. of heat.

Living cells, however, are not heat engines, but chemical engines. The energy released in metabolic reactions—for the most part in oxidative reactions—"drives" other kinds of reaction; and these, in turn, operate the "engines" in the cells of "effector" organs, for example, which perform external work, producing mechanical movement, bringing about the secretion and transport of substances in solution, generating electrical currents, and producing light. Moreover, all cells, whether performing external work or not, must continually perform internal work in main-taining their states of organisation, or "structures", both physical and chemical, in opposition to the spontaneous processes of disorganisation, as has been pointed out in Chapter 1. Whether the reactions necessary for the synthesis of the "structure" and the operation of the "engines" will proceed or not, depends on the free energy change involved. Intrinsically, all these reactions are, and must be, endergonic; they will go only when properly "coupled" to the exergonic reactions of oxidative metabolism, and supplied with energy from them. We are concerned, therefore, first with the amount of free energy which is made available in these reactions, and not with the amount of heat released; and secondly, with the way in which this energy is transferred to, and "drives" other kinds of reaction.

As already pointed out in Chapter 2, the amount of free energy released or absorbed in a chemical reaction may be greater than, equal to, or less than, the heat of reaction. The difference results from the change in entropy that may be involved; for example, if the number of individual molecules is increased during the reaction, or if the reactants are solid and the resultants gases, the whole system becomes more random, and the entropy increases. If the reaction is an exothermic one the heat content of the resultants must be less than that of the reactants by an amount equal to the heat of the reaction. The reduction in the free energy of the system, therefore, must be greater than the reduction in the heat content by an amount proportional to the increase in the entropy, as may be seen from equation 2.17 (p. 62). We have an example of this in the combustion of glucose to carbon dioxide and water. The heat of reaction is 674 kcals. per mole, but about 690 kcals. of free energy are released.

Unfortunately, heats of reaction are more easily measured than are changes in free energy, and it is often necessary to use the former rather than the latter. No serious error is likely to occur except when the heat of reaction is small: the reaction may then proceed spontaneously in the direction in which heat is absorbed. Such a reaction, in the terminology defined in Chapter 2, is endothermic but exergonic.

Spontaneous processes which are not subject to any form of regulation or control must always be associated with a gain in entropy; and in the limit, all the free energy released in such a process is degraded into heat. In order to be able to make use of the greatest amount of free energy, the process must be made to go in as reversible a manner as possible. Some form of machine is needed in order to control the process; and, indeed, the machines which we ordinarily use for converting one form of energy into another (apart from heat engines) are reversible in the sense that a hydraulic turbine could be used as a pump, or an electric motor as a dynamo. In some respects, the energetics of the living cell are less complex than this, since most of the chemical energy released by the reduction of oxygen is not converted into any other kind of energy, but is incorporated in the bond energy of new chemical compounds. Nevertheless, the principle remains the same. The "structure" of a living cell is itself necessary for the provision of the free energy required for its own maintenance, for its increase during growth of the organism, and for the performance of external work. In an intact cell, a much larger proportion of the chemical energy appears as free energy, doing work, than it does when the cell is disintegrated; most of the chemical energy obtained from oxidation is then degraded into heat.

M

There is something in the cell structure, then, with which, or by whose aid, the work of the cell is carried on. There are arrangements by which the chemical energy of the oxidation processes is caught, as it were, before it has fallen to the state of heat. If we look upon the cell constituents as chemical compounds, merely without the assistance of some organised mechanism, nothing but heat could be obtained on oxidation. In the same way, if a petrol motor is smashed up and mixed together, with its fuel, nothing but heat would be obtained by burning the mass.

It is unfortunate, but inevitable, that neither energy nor matter can be transferred from one system, or part of a system, to another at a finite rate without some "degradation" of energy; but as discussed in Chapter 2 (p. 75), the rate of entropy production in a chemical reaction increases rapidly as the concentrations of the components depart from their equilibrium values. Thus, one reaction, in which free energy is released, can "drive" another, in which free energy is absorbed, with reasonable efficiency only if the reactions are observably reversible. As already described earlier in this chapter, the oxidation processes are carried out, with the aid of a chain of enzyme systems, in a series of steps. Not only does this provide a variety of intermediate products, but, since each step is attended by a relatively small change in free energy, it is clearly of value in reducing the fraction of the energy which is degraded into heat.

The Coupling of Chemical Reactions

As Ostwald pointed out in 1900, if the energy released in one chemical reaction is to be transferred to, and "drive", some other reaction, it is necessary that there should be some molecule or radical which is common to the two reactions concerned. An exception to this rule is to be found when the energy is transferred from one reaction to another by means of radiation; but there is no evidence that this process plays any part in the living cell.

The coupling of one oxidation-reduction reaction with another may be greatly facilitated by the presence of a substance to which the name "mediator" has been given. Such a substance must itself be capable of oxidation and reduction, with a potential intermediate between those of the two reactions to be coupled; and will act most effectively if it possesses a complex molecular structure and is capable of forming a semi-quinone (in the most general sense of the word). These two properties permit the mediator to react reversibly with both substances whose oxidation and reduction are to be coupled: and the two hydrogen atoms concerned can be transferred one at a time (as already pointed out, almost all the oxidation-reduction reactions of physiological interest involve the transfer of two hydrogen atoms per molecule of substance reacting).

All the oxidation-reduction enzyme systems described in the previous section may be regarded as mediators, in a general sense. The equilibrium or steady state, condition of one oxidation-reduction system may be shifted by, say, a removal of hydrogen atoms; these may then be transferred to quite a different system, whose components are unrelated chemically to those of the first system. Such a coupling process, involving the transfer of electrons and hydrogen atoms, will be adequate for some of the reactions involved in the synthesis of the complex compounds which occur in living cells, but by no means all of them. Similarly, of the various kinds of "effector" action that are known, the production of light (bioluminescence), for example, results from the oxidation of a special substance, which consequently becomes "excited", as discussed in the next chapter; the transfer of hydrogen atoms and electrons is thus the chief requirement, although it is probably not the only one. On the other hand, the reactions which are necessary in order to bring about the "active" transport of a substance, to be discussed in Chapter 10, must, of necessity, involve many kinds of reaction other than hydrogen and electron transfer; and those which lead to shortening, or the development of tension, by the long-chain macro-molecules (Chapter 6, p. 234) in the various forms of contractile tissue—cilia and muscles, for example—while unknown in detail are certainly more complicated than simple oxidations and reductions. In these more elaborate coupling processes, a large and important part is played by the radical, or group, carriers, mentioned in the previous chapter.

Organic Sulphur Compounds. An important class of mediator consists of organic compounds whose molecules contain sulphur atoms linked directly to carbon atoms. These may exist either in the reduced state, containing the group $\equiv$C—S—H, or in the oxidised state, when two such "sulphydryl" groups join together with the elimination of two hydrogen atoms, $\equiv$C—S—S—C$\equiv$. This oxidation proceeds very readily in most compounds of this kind, and some of them are autoxidisable in the presence of oxygen and a suitable catalyst. The two —SH groups which unite in this way may be in the same molecule, or more usually, in two different molecules, which are thus joined together by the —S—S— ("disulphide") linkage, mentioned in Chapter 6. The importance of these sulphur-containing compounds, however, results not only from their ability to undergo oxidation and reduction, but also from their ability to combine with other molecules or radicals, through the sulphur atom. The stability of these linkages is bound to be affected by the oxidation-reduction potential of the system, and the extent to which the sulphydryl groups become oxidised; in the disulphide form, the sulphur atoms are "blocked" by being combined one with another, and so cannot combine with other radicals.

One of the most widespread of this class of activators and mediators is *glutathione*, the tripeptide formed by the combination of glutamine, cysteine and glycine, first discovered by Hopkins in 1921. Although its presence is essential for many kinds of reaction, the precise way in which it participates in them is still rather uncertain. We shall encounter some other important compounds which contain sulphur in the course of the subsequent discussion.

This possibility, that the state of oxidation or reduction of a substance may affect the ease with which it reacts with certain other substances, leads us to the most important of the methods by which exergonic, oxidative, reactions, are coupled with other, endergonic, reactions. The principle was first described and investigated in terms of certain peculiar properties of phosphoric acid, but there is reason to believe that certain other substances may act in a similar manner.

"Active" Phosphate. We ordinarily regard phosphoric acid as an "inorganic" substance, whose three hydrogen atoms are capable of successive ionisation. In neutral solution, however, the third ionisation does not occur at all detectably and the second ionisation is only partial; the two —OH groups concerned can then enter into covalent linkages. The whole molecule behaves rather as if it were water, with one of the hydrogen atoms replaced by the radical:

$$
\begin{array}{c}
\text{O} \\
\parallel \\
-\text{P}-\text{OH} \\
| \\
\text{O}^-
\end{array}
$$

The structure of the phosphate ion is clearly a resonating one, as can be seen from its general similarity to the carboxylate ion. But, of course, all three hydroxyl groups can take part in the resonance, and the resonance energy is likely to be large, although the exact value is not known. The formation of an ester linkage with one of the un-ionised hydroxyl groups would lead to a reduction of the resonance energy by some 10 per cent. at the most (by analogy with the carboxyl group) and most probably by less than this, since there are two other hydroxyl groups as well. Substitution of one only of the hydroxyl groups should thus go with a relatively small change in energy, as is indeed observed when the nucleoside, adenosine, is phosphorylated; the hydrolysis of adenosine monophosphate is associated with a release of only about 2 kcals. of free energy per gram-molecule. But the phosphate radical has a further important property. Like water, it will attach itself to a like radical, and so form a chain. At least, it has been shown to form such a chain of three radicals when the first is already attached to adenosine, or to certain other similar compounds belonging to the class of "nucleosides". We thus get the important compounds adenosine di- and triphosphate. The structure of adenosine, and of its diphosphate, may be seen in Fig. 8.1, forming part of the molecule of diphosphopyridine nucleotide, and of that of co-enzyme A. The great importance of these compounds arises from the fact that substitution of a second hydroxyl group in the phosphate radical leads to a considerable reduction in the resonance energy: only one hydroxyl group remains, so that the number of possible bond structures is considerably reduced, and the hydroxyl group which is esterified was previously partly ionised (compare Chapter 2, p. 66). Thus the whole bond system is associated with less energy and is less stable: the phosphate radical is easily thrown off and replaced by a hydrogen atom. By analogy with the carboxyl radical, we might expect that the change from an ionised to an esterified hydroxyl group would lead to a reduction in the resonance energy of some 12 kcals. per mole. In fact, there is evidence that the amount of free energy released in the hydrolysis of adenosine triphosphate under standard conditions at pH 7·5 is 9·4 kcals. per mole: in more "physiological" conditions, it is believed to be about 10 kcals. per mole.

Now the phosphate radical will also exchange freely with the hydrogen atom of a hydroxyl group united to a carbon atom, thereby, again, introducing a considerable lack of symmetry into the molecule. The two important examples of this are the effects of its substitution in carboxyl groups:

$$
\underset{O^- \quad O}{\overset{|}{\underset{\diagdown\diagup}{C}}} \longrightarrow \underset{\underset{(HPO_3)^-}{O \quad O}}{\overset{|}{\underset{\diagdown\diagup}{C}}}
$$

and in enol groups:

$$
\begin{array}{ccc}
H & & H \\
| & & | \\
-C\!=\!C- & \longrightarrow & -C\!=\!C- \\
| & & | \\
O & & O \\
| & & | \\
H & & (HPO_3)^-
\end{array}
$$

In the first, the resonance becomes less complete (compare the effects of esterification discussed in Chapter 2, p. 67): and in the second, the change from the enol to the keto structure, $CH\!=\!C\!-\!OH \rightleftharpoons CH_2\!-\!C\!=\!O$, is prevented; the phosphate radical cannot move freely between the oxygen atom and the carbon atom, as can the hydrogen atom which it replaces, since the direct link between carbon and phosphorus is extremely weak. In both cases, therefore, there is a gain in bond energy whenever the phosphate group is replaced by a hydrogen atom. There is no such effect, however, if the phosphate radical replaces a hydrogen atom in an alcoholic group, forming an ester type of linkage:

$$
\begin{array}{ccc}
\overset{\displaystyle \diagdown \diagup}{\underset{\diagup \diagdown}{C}} & \longrightarrow & \overset{\displaystyle \diagdown \diagup}{\underset{\diagup \diagdown}{C}} \\
H \quad O & & H \quad O \\
| & & | \\
H & & (H\overset{.}{P}O_3)^-
\end{array}
$$

and this exchange is not accompanied by any considerable change in bond energy; the standard free energy change being only some 2 to 3 kcal. per mole, as in the formation of adenosine monophosphate. Subsequent oxidation of this linkage to a ketone or carboxylic acid, then leads to the phosphate radical being thrown off at the first opportunity, since the molecule is considerably more stable in its absence. Moreover, in the absence of a suitable acceptor for the phosphate radical (in practice, usually adenosine diphosphate) there is little tendency for the oxidation-reduction reaction to proceed, since the release of energy is small.

It may be well to emphasise at this point that the essential experimental observations are that certain reactions will go when an appropriate reactant is phosphorylated, whereas they will not go otherwise: free energy is thus, apparently, made available by the phosphorylation. The term "high energy phosphate bond" has been used as a convenient "shorthand" method of describing this fact, extra energy being apparently available in certain phosphorylated compounds, to drive the phosphate group into some other combination. But according to the conventional definitions, the bond energy of, say, the phosphorylated carboxyl group is *smaller* than that of the carboxylate ion; and, moreover, the change in energy is not solely in the bond uniting the carboxyl group to the phosphate group, but in the whole system. The term "active phosphate" would seem to describe the phenomena equally well, and is less open to objection.

Just how the energy "concentrated" in adenosine triphosphate is used in the organised metabolic activities of the cell is still largely obscure. It seems undoubtedly to be used in the formation of phosphorylated compounds which are more reactive than the metabolites from which they are derived. A well established example of such an action is found in the initial stages of the oxidative metabolism of carbohydrates. The starting-point for this process, in most types of cell, is glucose, and the first stage in its oxidation is a division into two three-carbon compounds. This process, however, occurs only if the glucose molecule has previously been phosphorylated in two places, a process which in itself is endergonic, but which can be performed by means of two molecules of adenosine triphosphate. There are several intramolecular changes in addition to the phosphorylations, which we need not go into in detail, but the final result is the production of fructo-furanose 1 : 6 diphosphate. This then splits into two molecules of 3-phosphoglyceraldehyde, which can be dehydrogenated, with the eventual production of pyruvic acid, and the restitution of both of the molecules of "active phosphate" which were used to start the reaction; the necessary energy is derived from the dehydrogenation reaction. The fate of the pyruvic acid will be discussed below.

It has been established, also, that adenosine triphosphate is concerned in the synthesis of proteins from their constituent amino-acids—a reaction which is basically endergonic but which apparently goes spontaneously when certain of the reactants are phosphorylated. The details of the reaction sequence are not known.

There is no doubt that adenosine triphosphate is very closely concerned in the transfer of energy from oxidative metabolism to the structures in muscles which shorten, develop tension, and perform mechanical work; the final mechanism, however, by which chemical energy is converted into mechanical energy is still in dispute. Some processes of active transport, in which osmotic work is performed, also seem to depend upon the provision of "active phosphate" of some kind, although details are not known.

Historically, our knowledge of the important part that is played by the phosphate systems in metabolic processes began with the observations of Harden and Young in 1905. They observed that although yeast press juice would carry out alcoholic fermentation, only about one-half of the glucose that disappeared was converted into carbon dioxide and alcohol; the remainder combined with phosphate to form what is now known to be glucose 1 : 6 diphosphate. The true significance of phosphorylation only began to be realised, however, with the discovery of the peculiar properties of "phosphagen" by Eggleton and Eggleton in 1927, and of creatine phosphate (the two shown later to be identical) by Fiske and Subbarow in the same year. The properties of the adenosine polyphosphates were investigated chiefly by Lohman in 1931, although the existence of the compounds was known before. Baldwin has pointed out that it had for long been "an article of biochemical faith" that enzyme reactions should be studied in solutions which were buffered, very often by phosphates. It was not until about 1940, however, that the importance of the fact that the phosphates might be taking part in the reactions, as well as buffering the solutions, began to be fully realised. A full account of the nature and energetics of the reactions involving phosphates will be found in the articles by Kaplan (1951) and by Lipmann (1948).

"*Active*" *Acetate*. Acetic acid is an intermediary product in the oxidative metabolism of all three of the chief foodstuffs—carbohydrates, fats and proteins. It is formed in the oxidative decarboxylation of pyruvic acid, which, as we have just seen, is a stage in the metabolism of glucose and thus of other carbohydrates: it is formed in the oxidative splitting of fatty acids, known as "β-oxidation": it is formed from the glycerol of fats, since this is oxidised to glyceraldehyde and thus to pyruvic acid: and it is formed from amino-acids, since the first stage in their oxidative breakdown is the exchange of the amino group for a keto group, with the formation of keto-acids which are subsequently treated in the same way as those formed in the intermediate stages of the breakdown of carbohydrates.

The formation of acetic acid, whether from pyruvic acid or from a fatty acid, is an enzymic process, for which a special co-enzyme is needed. This is known as "Co-enzyme A", and consists of pantothenic acid, one of the B group of vitamins, attached by a peptide linkage at one end to β-mer-captoethylamine, and at the other end to the terminal phosphate radical of either adenosine diphosphate or triphosphate; the structure is indicated in Fig. 8.1. The terminal sulphydryl group will unite with the carboxyl group of acetic acid, with the elimination of water; the acetyl radical, CH_3–CO—, is then in an "active" state. Just as the phosphoryl radical can be transferred from adenosine triphosphate to other molecules, so can the acetyl radical be transferred from acetyl co-enzyme A. Moreover, the transfer of the acetyl radical, just as that of the phosphoryl radical, will occur in conditions where the acetylated (or phosphorylated) compound is, by itself, unstable.

The "active" condition of the acetyl radical is clearly related to the fact that it is joined to the sulphur atom in co-enzyme A. In a similar way, the methyl radical, attached to the sulphur atom in the methionine molecule, becomes "active" when the methionine molecule is united, at its other end, to a molecule of adenosine triphosphate. But in the formation of "active acetate" from pyruvate, an important part is played by another, relatively simple, compound which contains sulphur. In pyruvic acid we have an acetyl radical united with a carboxyl group, or, in effect, with carbon dioxide and a hydrogen atom. It seems that the acetyl radical and the hydrogen atom are first taken up by the two sulphur atoms in the substance known as *lipoic acid* (or 6-thioctic acid):

$$CH_2\text{---}CH_2\text{---}CH.(CH_2)_4.COOH$$
$$\underset{S\text{----------}S}{|\qquad\qquad|}$$

a molecule of carbon dioxide being thrown off. The acetyl radical is then transferred to co-enzyme A, owing to the fact that the hydrogen atom is taken up by triphosphopyridine nucleotide, and then transferred to other hydrogen acceptors. The lipoic acid may thus be said to act by separating the decar-boxylation reaction from the dehydrogenation (or oxidation) reaction.

It is known that acetylation—the attachment of an acetyl radical to some other molecule—is a relatively common metabolic reaction. Two such reactions are particularly relevant to our present discussion, and both proceed only when "active acetate" is available; it is probable, indeed, that all acetylations are brought about by means of acetyl co-enzyme A. The first of these is concerned with the oxidative breakdown of acetate itself; this will be discussed more appropriately in the next section. The other kind of acetylation consists in the repeated combination of acetate radicals with each other, so as to form fatty acids with long chains of carbon atoms. The number of carbon atoms in such a chain must, of course, be a multiple of two, and it has long been known that all the fatty acids found in nature do, in fact, have even numbers of carbon atoms. The conditions in which such synthesis of fatty acids occurs, rather than their oxidative breakdown, are not known; but it is obvious that since the "active acetate" that is needed may be formed from carbohydrates, the well-known fact that an excess of carbohydrate in the food results in the storage of fat is not difficult to understand.

The Sequence of Oxidative Reactions

The substances metabolised by living cells mostly possess large molecules of complex structure. The work of biochemists, particularly within the last 20 years, has brought to light much of the sequence of reactions that is involved in the oxidative breakdown of these substances. Although the sequence may be complicated, and seemingly elaborate, particularly when laid out in full, the actual chemical operations performed at each stage are relatively simple; they consist only of the removal of hydrogen atoms, and the loss of carbon dioxide from carboxyl groups. It need hardly be added that all, or practically all, the reactions to be described are catalysed by enzymes: and even though the reactions may be "generalised" for clarity of presentation, the enzymes are, mostly, highly specific. As an introduction to a more complete study of the subject, the reader should consult the little monograph by Malcolm Dixon (1949).

The dehydrogenation reactions may be considered under three headings, according to the nature of the atomic groups concerned. In the *first* type two hydrogen atoms are removed from adjacent carbon atoms, with the consequent formation of a double bond, as shown in Fig. 8.2 A (1). From the table of standard bond energies in Chapter 2 (p. 65), and assuming that the two hydrogen atoms are used to reduce an atom of oxygen, we should expect that 39 kcals. of heat should be released for each pair of gram-atoms of hydrogen removed. (This, of course, should also be the difference between the heats of combustion of the two compounds concerned, for example, succinic and fumaric acids, in which this difference is 37 kcals. per mole.) From Table 8.1, also, we can see that, taking the succinic-fumaric conversion as an example, the free energy available by taking two gram atoms of hydrogen from succinic acid to oxygen at pH 7, but otherwise in the standard state, is $(56 \cdot 7 - 20 \cdot 5 \doteqdot 36)$ kcals. per mole. We have no evidence as to how this free energy is "harnessed" by the living

M*

cell: but there is evidence that "active" phosphate may be synthesised when succinate is oxidised to fumarate. The double bond system, however, takes up a molecule of water very readily—or, more probably a molecule of phosphoric acid if this is available, as indicated in Fig. 8.2 A (2). Application of the table of bond energies shows that the uptake of water

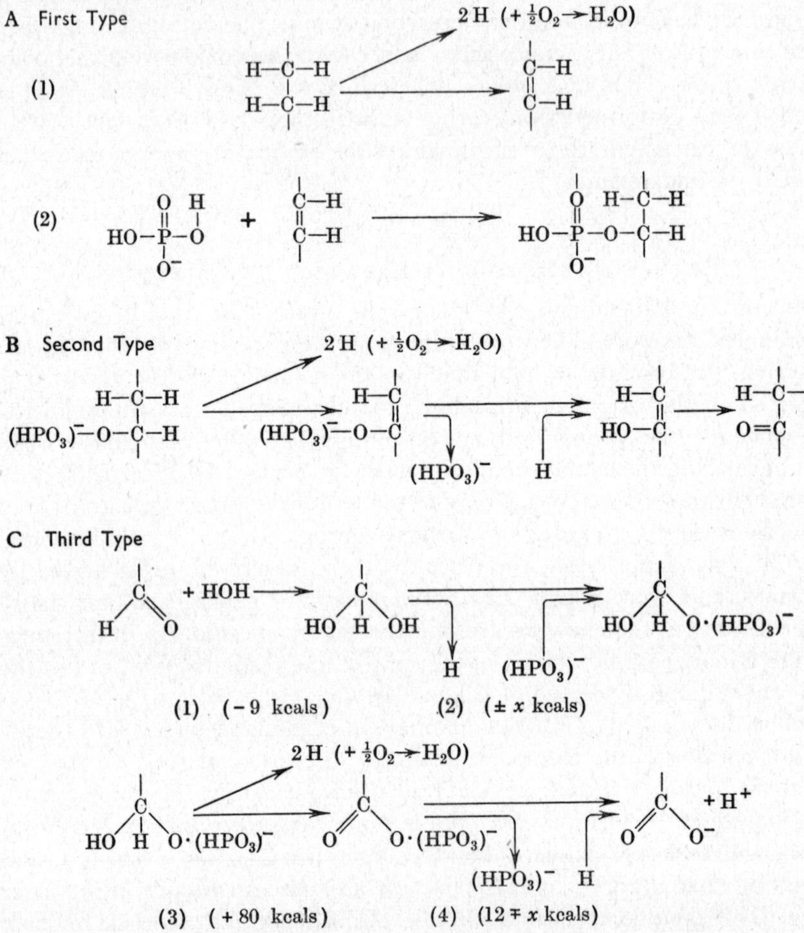

A First Type

(1)

$$2\,H\;(+\tfrac{1}{2}O_2 \rightarrow H_2O)$$

$$\begin{array}{c} H-\overset{|}{C}-H \\ H-\overset{|}{C}-H \end{array} \longrightarrow \begin{array}{c} \overset{|}{C}-H \\ \overset{||}{C}-H \end{array}$$

(2)

$$\begin{array}{c} O\;\;H \\ \| \;\; | \\ HO-P-O \\ | \\ O^- \end{array} + \begin{array}{c} \overset{|}{C}-H \\ \overset{||}{C}-H \end{array} \longrightarrow \begin{array}{c} O \;\; H-\overset{|}{C}-H \\ \| \\ HO-P-O-\overset{|}{C}-H \\ | \\ O^- \end{array}$$

B Second Type

$$2\,H\;(+\tfrac{1}{2}O_2 \rightarrow H_2O)$$

$$\begin{array}{c} H-\overset{|}{C}-H \\ (HPO_3)^--O-\overset{|}{C}-H \end{array} \longrightarrow \begin{array}{c} H-\overset{|}{C} \\ (HPO_3)^--O-\overset{||}{C} \\ \downarrow \\ (HPO_3)^- \;\; H \end{array} \longrightarrow \begin{array}{c} H-\overset{|}{C} \\ HO-\overset{||}{C}. \end{array} \longrightarrow \begin{array}{c} H-\overset{|}{C}-H \\ O=\overset{|}{C} \end{array}$$

C Third Type

$$\begin{array}{c} \overset{|}{C} \\ H \;\;\; O \end{array} + HOH \longrightarrow \begin{array}{c} \overset{|}{C} \\ HO\;H\;OH \end{array} \longrightarrow \begin{array}{c} \overset{|}{C} \\ HO\;H\;O\cdot(HPO_3)^- \\ \downarrow \\ H\;\;(HPO_3)^- \end{array}$$

(1) (− 9 kcals) (2) (± x kcals)

$$2\,H\;(+\tfrac{1}{2}O_2 \rightarrow H_2O)$$

$$\begin{array}{c} \overset{|}{C} \\ HO\;H\;O\cdot(HPO_3)^- \end{array} \longrightarrow \begin{array}{c} \overset{|}{C} \\ O\;\;\;O\cdot(HPO_3)^- \\ \downarrow \\ (HPO_3)^- \;\; H \end{array} \longrightarrow \begin{array}{c} \overset{|}{C} + H^+ \\ O\;\;\;O^- \end{array}$$

(3) (+ 80 kcals) (4) (12 ∓ x kcals)

FIG. 8.2. TYPES OF DEHYDROGENATION REACTION THAT OCCUR IN LIVING CELLS

should release 6 kcals. of heat per mole, and should thus be reversible. The uptake of phosphate does, in fact, appear to go spontaneously.

A word of caution may appropriately be inserted here. It is, of course, the change in free energy which is the important quantity in these chemical reactions, and not the heat of the reaction. But free energy changes are not easily measured; whereas the use of standard bond energies to estimate the

heat of reaction, particularly when only parts of complex molecules are reacting, provides a convenient, though rough, measure of the energy changes
involved. In these estimates, however, any contributions that there may be
from changes in the heats of hydration or ionisation are neglected. Hydration
and ionisation, of course, are also associated with changes in free energy
which in many cases, will depend on the conditions in which the reaction
takes place.

This takes us to our *second* type of dehydrogenation. This consists in
the removal of a pair of hydrogen atoms from such an alcoholic group, or
esterified phosphate, as would be produced by the reactions considered in
the previous paragraph. This leads to the formation of an enol group, and
is thus really only a variant of the first type (Fig. 8.2 B). We again
expect a heat change of 39 kcals. per pair of gram-atoms of hydrogen. But
now, in the absence of the phosphate group, we should get an immediate
molecular re-arrangement, leading to the formation of a keto group and the
loss of the double bond between the carbon atoms. From the bond energies,
we should expect a heat change of $+18$ kcals. per mole to be associated
with this re-arrangement, and this would enable the phosphate group to
combine with, say, adenosine diphosphate. The total heat change in this
second type of dehydrogenation is thus about 57 kcals. per mole. The total
free energy change in such a reaction, however, appears to be somewhat
less than the total heat change: in the conversion of malate to oxaloacetate
with the formation of water, for example, it is about -45 kcals. per mole.
We do not know the free energy change in the enol-keto transformation,
but we do know that in certain circumstances it is sufficient to add a
phosphate radical to adenosine diphosphate, which, as we have said,
requires some 10 kcals. per mole.

Thirdly, we have the oxidation of a terminal aldehydic group. As we
said earlier in this chapter, the oxidation of an aldehyde in solution is
probably to be regarded as a dehydrogenation of the hydrated aldehyde.
The sequence of reactions is shown in Fig. 8.2 C. It is to be expected
that reaction (1) in this scheme should proceed with a slight absorption of
heat (ΔH from the bond energies is about -9 kcals. per mole) and probably, also, with an absorption of free energy. There is, however, a large
concentration of water available to drive the reaction in the direction of
hydration; and, moreover, the products of the reaction are being removed
by reaction (3) as soon as they are formed. The heat and free energy
changes in reaction (2) are not known. Reaction (3), however, would
liberate about 80 kcals. per pair of gram-atoms of hydrogen, if the resonance energy in the carboxyl-phosphate were the same as that in a carboxyl-
ester. Lastly, the ionisation of the carboxylic acid, after the exchange of
hydrogen for phosphate, at reaction (4), would probably release some
12 kcals. per mole. (The resonance energy in a carboxyl-ester is 24 kcals.

per mole, that in a carboxylic acid is 28 kcals. per mole, and that in a carboxylate ion is some 36 kcals. per mole—see Chapter 2, p. 67.) The total energy released in this sequence is thus some 83 kcals. per mole. The difference between the heats of combustion of acetaldehyde (gas) and acetic acid (liquid) is 76 kcals. per mole, in precise agreement, as it happens, with the value calculated from the bond energies. But the total change in free energy when acetaldehyde is converted into acetate ions (both in solution) and water, is only $(56 \cdot 7 + 8 \cdot 5 \rightleftharpoons 65)$ kcals. per mole, as may be seen from Table 8.1; the difference is due to the entropy changes and the energies of hydration and ionisation. This figure will, of course, be different for different aldehydes and their corresponding carboxylic acids.

Lastly, there is the decarboxylation, which has already been referred to in an earlier section. In this reaction, a molecule of carbon dioxide is removed from a carboxyl group:

This process might be expected to yield about 5 kcals. of heat per mole, from considerations of the bond energies, and thus might be expected to be reversible—a fact which is of importance in photosynthesis, as we shall see in the next chapter. The free energy change in one such decarboxylation reaction, that of:

$$\text{oxaloacetate}^{2-} + H_2O \rightleftharpoons \text{pyruvate}^- + HCO_3^-$$

has been measured. The standard free energy change, ΔG_0, is -6 kcals. per mole, but under more "physiological" conditions, at pH 7, with a carbon dioxide pressure of $0 \cdot 05$ M. and with the other reactants at a concentration of $0 \cdot 01$ M., the change in free energy is -9 kcals. per mole: although the reaction may thus be considered to be reversible, the equilibrium position is well over in the direction of decarboxylation.

As an example of an oxidative decarboxylation, we may take the conversion of pyruvic acid to acetic acid; in standard conditions, there is a release of some 70 kcals. of free energy per mole, approximately equal to the sum of the free energy change in a simple decarboxylation and that in the third type of dehydrogenation.

The first type of reaction can then operate once more (provided, of course, that the molecule still has at least two carbon atoms): or, if there should already be a hydroxyl group attached to one of the carbon atoms, the second type of reaction could occur. Or, again, the new terminal carbon atom may already be attached to a hydroxyl group (as, for instance, if the first type of reaction has already occurred); the third type of reaction may then operate. In any case, sooner or later the number of carbon atoms in the molecule will be reduced to two, and acetic acid will be formed. Now it appears that few, if any living cells are able to oxidise completely substances which contain only one carbon atom. Decarboxylation of an acetate, therefore, whether simple or oxidative, would result in the sequence of oxidation-reduction reactions coming to an end before all the hydrogen atoms had been removed from the substrate molecules. This is avoided by the fact that the "active" acetate which is formed from pyruvates or fatty acids will acetylate a compound containing several carbon atoms— actually oxaloacetate, with four carbon atoms. Hydrogen atoms and carbon dioxide molecules can then be removed from various parts of the larger molecule so formed, leaving in the end oxaloacetate again. This then combines with another molecule of "active" acetate and the cycle is repeated. Oxaloacetic acid has two carboxyl groups, and on combining with acetic acid, citric acid is formed, with three carboxyl groups. The cycle is thus sometimes known as the "citric acid cycle". The first few reactions which citric acid undergoes are dehydrogenations, with the formation of other tricarboxylic acids; the cycle is thus also known as the "tricarboxylic acid cycle". It is obviously not essential that there should be a continuous synthesis of oxaloacetate, since it reappears at the end of each cycle; but it must have been formed at some time, and there may well be losses from "side reactions" which must be made good. This is done, in all probability, by a direct combination of carbon dioxide with pyruvic acid: simple decarboxylation involves only a small change in free energy, and is thus reversible, particularly when the product of the reaction, as in this case, is removed by combination with "active acetate".

More detailed discussions of these reactions will be found in the articles by Krebs (1948) and by Lynen (1952). The various enzymes and enzyme systems necessary for the different stages of the tricarboxylic acid cycle have been called by Green, the *cyclophorase complex*. The whole complex seems to be contained in the microscopic granules found in nearly all kinds of cell known as "mitochondria". (See the review by Green, 1951.)

Study of the values of oxidation-reduction potentials given in Table 8.1 shows us that the first type of dehydrogenation (as exemplified by the succinate-fumarate system) has so positive a potential that the dehydrogenation can only be performed by the cytochrome system, or by a relatively simple polyphenol-quinone system. It would appear, also, that the gap between the E'_0 values of these systems is too large for the dehydrogenation to be reversible—except, perhaps with cytochrome c in acid solution. The second type of dehydrogenation, as exemplified by the malate-oxaloacetate system, would go reversibly with flavo-proteins; or, as exemplified by the pyruvate-lactate system, with the phosphopyridine nucleotides. The third type of dehydrogenation, as exemplified by the acetaldehyde-acetate system, at first sight, has so negative a potential that no reversible reaction would seem possible with any of the oxidation-reduction enzyme systems. But we must remember that in fact, the re-action involves the phosphorylated compounds, in which the free energy change on dehydrogenation is about 10 kcals. per mole smaller than that for the aldehyde-carboxylate system. The oxidation-reduction potential would thus be at least 0·2 volts and possibly 0·4 volts more positive—i.e. positive to that of the hydrogen electrode—and reversible reactions with the phosphopyridine nucleotides would be possible. Similarly, the second type of dehydrogenation involving phosphorylated compounds which remain in the enol form, would certainly go reversibly with flavoproteins, but not, however, with the pyridinoproteins.

It is clear from the schematic presentation of the reaction sequences in Fig. 8.2 that by no means all the reactions are such that they can be coupled with the formation of an "active" phosphate; and that, of the total amount of free energy released, only a small fraction is incorporated in "active" phosphate radicals. The "efficiency" of the process would thus seem to be very small. Living cells are indeed, not highly "efficient" in their use of the energy released in oxidative metabolism, although it is not easy to put a precise quantitative meaning to the word "efficient"; so much of the energy is used in maintaining a steady state, without perform-ing any net work. The estimates of the total energy changes, however, include the amounts released in the transfer of hydrogen atoms from one oxidation-reduction system to another, and eventually to oxygen. As can be seen from Table 8.1, considerable amounts of free energy could be made available in these reactions, and coupled with the synthesis of "active phosphate". From purely energetic considerations, it would theoretically be possible for 23 molecules of some "active phosphate" to be formed when each molecule of pyruvic acid is completely oxidised to carbon dioxide and water. Actually, experimental evidence shows that 14 molecules of adenosine triphosphate may be synthesised in these conditions so that one-half of the energy is available for utilisation by the living cell. There may also be other "active" compounds, and other methods of coupling chemical reactions, which have not yet been identified.

THE RELATION OF OXYGEN PRESSURE
TO ITS CONSUMPTION

We find, as a general rule, that the supply of oxygen to small cells in intimate contact with the environment, is more than sufficient to meet the requirements of the cells: increase of its pressure (equivalent to concentration) does not lead, by mass action, to increased consumption. In larger cells, and in multi-cellular organisms, an apparent variation of consumption with pressure is often found, since at low pressure the rate of diffusion to the interior may be inadequate. On the other hand, there is also good evidence that in some types of cell, such as some bacteria and some types of blood cell, there is a genuine variation of rate of oxygen consumption with pressure, when this falls to 10 per cent. of an atmosphere or less.

Study of the oxidation-reduction potentials given in Table 8.1 shows that all the cellular oxidation-reduction systems have potentials which are much more negative than that of oxygen; they would thus become fully oxidised at very low pressures of oxygen (even cytochrome c, for example, would be 99 per cent. oxidised in the presence of 10^{-15} atmosphere of oxygen). But this is on the assumption that a true equilibrium is attained. In the steady state which is reached by a living cell, the concentrations of the various components will depend on the relative rates of the various reactions, and the relative rates at which the components can enter the cell. The whole system of reactions is proceeding steadily in one direction, and we must consider the rate of movement in this direction, rather than any position of equilibrium that might be attained. In general, we might expect that the rate of reduction of molecular oxygen would depend on the concentration of oxygen present; but there are two factors which may come in and prevent this. In the first place, the aerobic oxidases may have a very high affinity for molecular oxygen, and so become saturated at a relatively small concentration (we have discussed this saturation phenomenon in enzyme action in Chapter 7, p. 313). In the second place, the rate of supply of reducing substances may be the limiting factor, rather than the rate of supply of molecular oxygen; in other words, the overall rate of metabolism may be determined by the velocity of one of the reactions catalysed by an anaerobic dehydrogenase, rather than by that of a reaction catalysed by an aerobic oxidase.

ANAEROBIC METABOLISM

Living cells of many different kinds can continue to exist for considerable periods of time—in some cases indefinitely—and even continue to carry out their specialised activities, in the absence of a supply of molecular oxygen. The necessary energy is obtained from chemical reactions which are essentially oxidation-reduction reactions, although in the end no molecular oxygen is reduced. The chief end-products of the reaction will gradually accumulate, however, and, being non-volatile and not water, as in aerobic metabolism, will limit the duration of anaerobiosis unless they can diffuse away in the environment. The two types of cell in which these reactions have been most extensively studied are yeast cells and the skeletal muscle cells of vertebrates. The classical observations of Fletcher and Hopkins in 1907 showed that muscles would not only remain alive in the absence of oxygen, but would contract and perform external work, although only for a limited period of time; indeed many of our own muscle cells operate without a supply of oxygen when we are taking vigorous exercise. That yeasts produce alcohol, in what is now known to be their anaerobic metabolism, has been known to mankind since the earliest times of which we have any record.

The material from which energy is obtained in anaerobic conditions is, in all cases, carbohydrate—sucrose in the particular case of yeast, and glycogen in that of muscle. Both of these may be derived from, and converted into, glucose, and this may conveniently be considered as the starting-point. As already described, glucose, when being subjected to oxidative breakdown, is first split into glyceraldehyde, which is then dehydrogenated with the formation of glyceric acid; this then loses water to form pyruvic acid (we may neglect, for the moment, the phosphorylation reactions). Now the two hydrogen atoms that are withdrawn from each molecule of glyceraldehyde are temporarily accommodated on a molecule of diphosphopyridine nucleotide (at least in both yeast and skeletal muscle). In the presence of oxygen, they are then handed on, presumably through a flavoprotein, to the cytochrome system, and thence to molecular oxygen. In the absence of oxygen, however, the reduced co-enzyme will become re-oxidised by any oxidation-reduction system with a more positive potential. Study of the figures given in Table 8.1 shows at once that two very suitable systems are available. One is the pyruvate-lactate system; and skeletal muscle uses this system. The other is the acetaldehyde-ethanol system (pyruvic acid is readily decarboxylated with the formation of acetaldehyde); and yeast uses this system. Further, if the acetaldehyde is removed as fast as it is formed, by growing the yeast in the presence of bisulphite, the reduced co-enzyme then becomes re-oxidised at the expense of half the glyceraldehyde formed from glucose; glycerol is thus produced.

In muscles, therefore, the end-product of anaerobic carbohydrate metabolism is lactic acid, the reaction sequence being known as *glycolysis*. In yeasts, the end-product is ethanol, the reaction sequence being one of *alcoholic fermentation*. Micro-organisms of many kinds also make use of glycolysis (or lactic fermentation)—the fact that lactic acid is produced in milk by certain kinds of bacteria was responsible for its name. Lactic acid, again, is produced by many kinds of animal cell besides those of muscles, when deprived of oxygen, but none, certainly in the higher animals, produce ethanol; this appears to be a speciality of the plants.

The Energetics of Glycolysis and Fermentation. If we look at the overall chemical reaction that occurs when glyceraldehyde is converted into lactic acid:

$$
\begin{array}{c}
\quad\ \text{H}\ \ \text{H} \\
\quad\ |\ \ \ | \\
\text{H--C--C--C}\diagup^{\text{H}}_{\diagdown\text{O}} \\
\quad\ |\ \ \ | \\
\quad\ \text{OH\ OH}
\end{array}
\longrightarrow
\begin{array}{c}
\quad\ \text{H}\ \ \text{H} \\
\quad\ |\ \ \ | \\
\text{H--C--C--C}\diagup^{\text{OH}}_{\diagdown\text{O}} \\
\quad\ |\ \ \ | \\
\quad\ \text{H\ \ OH}
\end{array}
$$

we see that all that has occurred is an interchange of a hydrogen atom and a hydroxyl group between the two terminal carbon atoms. But in lactic acid, we have a carboxyl group which is absent from glyceraldehyde; so that we should expect a release of energy during the fermentation process, corresponding to the resonance energy of the carboxyl group, which from the bond energies should be about 30 kcals. per mole. The free energy change, however, is estimated to be only some -20 kcals. per mole. (The overall free energy changes in the formation of lactic acid are estimated as $-28 \cdot 5$ kcals. per mole from glycogen, and -25 kcals. per mole from glucose; the free energy changes in the reactions which lead to the formation of glyceraldehyde from glucose add up to about -5 kcals. per mole.) Thus in the formation of each pair of molecules of lactic acid from glycogen, there should be more than enough energy available for the synthesis of three "active phosphate" molecules. Actually, during the sequence of reactions, it is found that four are synthesised, but one is used up in the second phosphorylation of glucose, so that the net gain is, in fact, three. Thus, of the 57 kcals. of free energy released in the fermentation of each 6-carbon unit of glycogen, some 35 to 40, or nearly two-thirds, are retained in a form suitable for use in coupled reactions.

Similar computations for the alcoholic fermentation show that the amount of free energy released is much the same, i.e. about 30 kcals. per mole of ethanol formed from glucose. In addition, two phosphorylations are needed, each intrinsically endergonic, so that the net gain is only two "active phosphate" molecules, per molecule of glucose fermented. Some 25 to 30 kcals. out of the 60 kcals. released, or nearly one-half, is thus retained in a "useful" form.

LITERATURE

General Theory. Michaelis (1946, 1951).

Oxidation-Reduction Potentials. Cohen (1933); Chambers (1933); Dixon (1949).

General Biochemistry. Baldwin (1952); White *et al.* (1954).

Respiratory Enzymes. Sumner and Myrbäck (1951—vol. II, part 1); Dixon (1949); Green (1951).

Energy Coupling and "Active" Phosphate. Kaplan (1951).

Reaction Sequences in Living Systems. Krebs (1948); Lipmann (1948); Ochoa (1951); Lynen (1952); Krebs and Kornberg (1957).

9

THE ACTIONS OF LIGHT AND OTHER RADIATIONS

The whole existence of living organisms on the earth depends on the receipt of radiant energy from the sun, and it is unnecessary to stress the importance of the study of the way in which this energy is used. If it were merely converted into heat, much of the free energy would be lost in any further process of conversion into other forms of energy; the whole process would be very wasteful, as has been demonstrated in our study of the principles of energetics. A considerable part of the sun's energy is, of course, used up in warming objects on the earth, thus accelerating all chemical reactions that may be in progress. But light may also initiate chemical reactions which do not proceed at all in its absence, and which may, indeed, be intrinsically endergonic; the study of such reactions is obviously of great importance, although of some difficulty.

The amount of energy actually received from the sun may be realised by the following data. Suppose that the atmosphere were absent, and the sun in the zenith, then each square metre of the earth's surface would receive 1322 watts: this figure is known as the *Solar Constant*. The presence of the atmosphere, which absorbs and scatters part of the radiation, reduces the value to about 900 watts per square metre when the sun is at the zenith. In the temperate zones, we may consider the sun, on the average, to be at an altitude of about 30° from the horizon. The average solar power falling on each square metre of horizontal surface then becomes about 350 watts—one-third of that produced by a small electric fire. In other words, the energy received by 1 square metre in one minute would suffice to raise the temperature of 1 kilogram of water by about 5° C.

The power received from the sun on the whole surface of the earth is thousands of times greater than that at present generated throughout the world by the combustion of coal and oil; but it is difficult to make much practical use of it, since it is distributed over so wide an area. Of the sources of power which are at present used in substantial quantities, only that produced by falling water and that produced by the activities of animals, including man, are directly and continuously derived from solar radiation; the first by the evaporation of water from the sea and thus the falling of rain on the mountains; the second by the use of food materials derived from plants and synthesised by means of photochemical reactions. A relatively small amount of power is derived from the direct combustion of plant materials such as wood, alcohol produced by fermentation of sugar, and the oils pressed out of olives, palm kernels and so forth. But the stores of energy in coal and petroleum—at present the chief sources of power—also owe their origin, directly or indirectly, to the action of green plants in past ages. The reactions by means of which the chlorophyll system of green plants converts light energy into chemical energy are thus by far the most important of all photochemical reactions.

In addition to the chlorophyll system, there are other actions of light and similar radiations which are of physiological importance. Such are the process by which living organisms can detect the presence of light by means of photoreceptors, such as the eyes; and the actions of ultra-violet light and radiations of very short wave-length such as X-rays and γ-rays, to which may be added the actions of streams of high energy particles such as β-rays, α-rays, protons and neutrons. All these last, as we shall see, have an essentially destructive action on protoplasm, but they form useful tools since the destruction is highly localised. As experimental tools, also, depending on the action of light, the various photographic methods may be mentioned, as well as the various types of photoelectric cell; and, above all, of course, the human eye, although a detailed account of its mode of action is outside the scope of this chapter. In order that we may understand, as far as is possible at present, the natures of the processes concerned in these various actions of light, we must first discuss briefly the general theory of photochemical reactions.

ABSORPTION OF LIGHT

All substances absorb radiant energy to some extent; even glass which seems perfectly transparent absorbs rays of shorter wave-length than those that we recognise as light, and also those of very much longer wave-length; and water absorbs strongly in the infra-red region only just outside the limits of vision. The absorption of the radiations of very short wave-length, such as X-rays, depends on the weight of the atoms in the material concerned; that of the radiations of very long wave-length, such as wireless waves, depends on the electrical conductivity of the material; that of the radiations in the middle region—ultra-violet, visible, infra-red—depends on the particular structure of the molecules in the material, and is characteristic for each chemical substance. Thus, a part of the energy of a beam of radiation which traverses any substance is removed and held back in the substance. Something must happen to the substance; it may be merely warmed, or other forms of energy may make their appearance, chemical, electrical, and so on.

Grotthus's Law. It seems fairly obvious to us at the present time that no effect can be produced by radiant energy unless it is absorbed. The law that light must be absorbed in order to produce an effect was first clearly enunciated by Grotthus in 1819, and independently, at a later date, by Draper in 1841. It is frequently known as *Draper's Law.*

Grotthus found, for example, that ferric thiocyanate, which is red, is decolorised by green light, yellow gold chloride by blue light, blue starch iodide by yellow light. Each is attacked by light of the colour complementary to its own colour, that is, by the light which it absorbs.

The Laws of Lambert and of Beer. In order to be able to compare the amount of light absorbed by one substance or solution with that absorbed by another, it is necessary to take some standard of measurement. Bunsen and Roscoe introduced the *extinction coefficient* for this purpose. When light of a particular wave-length is absorbed by any substance, it is clear that the intensity of the light issuing from it is less than that which enters it, and that there must be some particular thickness of it which reduces the intensity of the light to one-tenth of the value it had on entering. In order that the numbers, characteristic of different substances, should rise or fall in the same direction as the absorbing power of the substance or solution, Bunsen and Roscoe defined the extinction coefficient as being the reciprocal of the depth of the solution required to reduce the intensity of light of a given wave-length to one-tenth of that which it had on entering. It is plain that the *greater* the absorbing power, the *less* the depth required; hence the advantage of the inverse value, the extinction coefficient being directly proportional to the absorbing power.

Now in practice it is the intensity of the issuing light that is measured, and it is more convenient to use a constant thickness of solution, and to measure the intensity of the light that has passed through this, than to vary the thickness of the absorbing layer. It is therefore necessary to know the laws which express the relation of the one to the other. We assume that in traversing each elementary layer of the absorbing substance, a certain amount of the incident radiation is absorbed, this amount being proportional to the thickness of the layer, and to the intensity of the radiation entering the layer, i.e. each layer is assumed to absorb a constant fraction of the incident radiation. Thus, if the incident intensity is I, then on traversing a thickness dx, an amount dI will be absorbed, and we can write:

$$-dI = a.I.dx \quad \text{or} \quad -dI/I = a.dx$$

where a is a constant depending on the nature of the material, and known as the *absorption coefficient.* On integrating this equation over a finite thickness x, we get:

$$I = I_0 \exp(-a.x)$$

or
$$\ln (I/I_0) = -a.x$$

where I_0 is the intensity of the radiation entering the absorbing substance. This relation is known as *Lambert's Law*. The ratio I/I_0 is known as the *transmission coefficient* or *transmittance* (t) and, of course, is the quantity which is actually measured. It depends upon the thickness of the absorbing substance in a logarithmic manner, and in practice, therefore, we often use the *density* (D) of the absorbent, which is defined as:

$$D = \log_{10} (I_0/I) = -\log . t$$

Now the extinction coefficient (ϵ), as already mentioned, is defined as the reciprocal of the thickness of the material (the value of $1/x$) for which $I/I_0 = 1/10$ and thus $D = 1$. We thus have:

$$\log_{10} (I_0/I) = D = \epsilon.x = (\log_{10} e) \, a.x = 0{\cdot}435 a.x$$

The optical density of an absorbing material thus increases directly with its thickness, and with the value of its absorption coefficient, or its extinction coefficient.

When light passes through a solution, it may be absorbed by the solvent or by any of the solutes present. It is only reasonable to suppose that the fraction of the incident light that is absorbed by a layer of given thickness will depend on the amount of material present which is capable of absorbing that light; the optical density of a solution, then, will depend on the *concentrations* of the absorbing components. *Beer's Law* states that the optical density is directly proportional to the concentration of the absorbing component; so that if we know the absorption coefficient, or density, for a known concentration, we can estimate an unknown concentration by measuring the absorption coefficient, or density, of the solution. This principle is the basis of *colorimetry* (which should strictly be called *absorptiometry*, since, in general, it is not the *colour* which is measured but the amount of light absorption). It must be remembered, however, that Beer's law is not of universal application. Some substances in solution, for example, change in colour as the concentration is changed, usually as a result of an interaction between the solute and the solvent (such as the change in ionisation of salts of copper and cobalt); the possibility of such an effect must be borne in mind when making use of absorptiometry.

Another, and more frequent source of error is the presence of other coloured solutes besides the particular one being estimated. This error can be overcome by using a compensating colorimeter; on one side, light is passed through the solution under analysis, and on the other, successively through a pure solution of the particular constituent with which we are concerned, and through a solution of all the other constituents, the depths of both being under control. Alternatively, we can illuminate the colorimeter with monochromatic light (or light which is nearly monochromatic, as given by suitable filters), and work with such a colour that the absorption by the substance under analysis is large compared with that of all the other constituents.

Greater accuracy, may be attained, and the analyses made less fatiguing if the intensities of the emergent light beams are observed, and matched, by means of a suitable photoelectric cell, rather than by visual observation. It is almost essential, in this case, to use light which is at least approximately monochromatic. The "light", of course, need not necessarily have such a wave-length as to be visible.

THE MECHANISM OF LIGHT ABSORPTION

Light consists of a series of periodic electromagnetic disturbances of various periods of vibration, or wave-length. When a system, such as a pendulum, has the same period of vibration as that of a series of minute impulses delivered to it, the system is set into vigorous movement by the accumulation of the effect of a large number of small impulses. We have seen in Chapter 1 that the total energy content of a molecule is associated with vibrations and rotations of the constituent atoms and electrons, and with rotation and translation of the molecule itself; all these, with the exception of the last, are periodic in nature. Consider, now, the effect of light containing many different wave-lengths, or frequencies of vibration, such as that of the sun, on a molecule which has itself, as we have seen, a number of different frequencies of vibration. Some of the frequencies of the light waves will probably coincide with those of the molecule, and will set it into resonant vibration; the amplitude of the vibration may become great enough to bring about chemical change. At the same time, those rays which have the particular frequency concerned will be absorbed, and there will be an *absorption band* in the spectrum of the substance. This will appear in a photograph of the spectrum, and will be seen by the eye, if it lies in an appropriate region of wave-lengths: and if a curve is plotted, relating the optical density of the substance (or solution) to the wave-length (or frequency) of the light used, there will be a peak corresponding to each absorption band.

Such a curve not only indicates the position of each absorption band, but also gives a measure of its density and "shape"; these can be assessed only approximately by direct observation. It is obtained by means of observations in a *Spectrophotometer*, an instrument which is effectively a combination of an absorptiometer with a spectroscope.

It is, perhaps, more correct to replace this classical view of the mechanism of light absorption by that which is based on the quantum nature of radiation. According to the quantum theory, as we have seen in Chapter 1, atoms and molecules can only change their energy contents in a series of discontinuous jumps (apart from certain exceptions, which we will consider later); the sizes of the jumps depending on the nature of the atom or molecule. The electrons in the atom, in fact, can only take up a limited number of possible configurations, each being associated with a definite quantity of energy: similarly, only a limited number of types of vibration and rotation are possible, each, again, being associated with a definite quantity of energy. Light, or any other kind of radiation, accordingly, can only be absorbed or emitted by matter in definite packets of energy, the size of each packet, or *photon*, being proportional to the frequency of the radiation (or inversely proportional to the wave-length).

The amount of energy associated with N photons, where N is the Avogadro number is often known as the *einstein*. The einstein, then, has the same relation to the photon as the gram-molecule has to the actual mass of each molecule.

Accordingly, if an atom or molecule is exposed to radiation, it can only absorb such photons as exactly fit one of its possible energy jumps. Similarly, if excited by some other means, it can only emit photons of a size, and thus frequency, equal to one of its energy jumps. We thus get, for example, the line spectra, both of absorption and emission, such as are given by sodium, mercury, and other atoms; these result from changes in the configurations of the electrons. The possible modes of vibration and rotation, particularly in complex molecules, may be very numerous, and may differ only slightly in energy content. We may thus get a large number of absorption lines very close together, giving an absorption band; and we may, indeed, be unable to resolve the individual lines, and get what appears to be a band of continuous absorption.

The amount of radiation absorbed by a given substance in given conditions, thus depends on the probability that photons will be absorbed by the molecules of the substance concerned: and the deduction of the relation between the two is a simple example of the use of the ordinary laws of chance. Suppose that the probability that a photon will be absorbed by a molecule is p. Then the probability of its not being absorbed is $(1-p)$. If there are r molecules in the path of the radiation, $(1-p)$ is the chance that it will fail to be absorbed by each molecule in turn, so that the chance of its escaping all of them will be $(1-p)^r$. Now p is a very small number (the molecules themselves occupy only a small fraction of the total cross sectional area exposed to the radiation), while r is very large: the expression thus approximates to $\exp(-p.r)$, as we have seen in Chapter 1. Thus, out of a very large number of photons incident on the absorbing material, each will have this chance of penetrating; and, on the average, the fraction penetrating will be given by the same quantity. In other words, the fraction of the radiation transmitted by the absorbing material, I/I_0, is proportional to $\exp(-p.r)$ or to $\exp(-a.x)$, as given earlier in this chapter (p. 372), since r obviously increases with the thickness of the absorbing material, and p with its absorption coefficient. If we look at the problem from the point of view of the absorbing molecules, we see that the chance of any one molecule absorbing more than one photon, say n, will be p^n. Remembering that p is very small, we see that although a large number of molecules has a good chance of absorbing a large number of photons, the chance of each molecule absorbing more than one is extremely small.

THE CONSEQUENCES OF THE ABSORPTION
OF A PHOTON

If an atom or molecule absorbs a photon, its energy is increased accordingly. It has become excited, or activated, and the extra energy will subsequently be lost again in several different ways. First, the excited atom or molecule may collide with a normal atom or molecule, and the extra energy may be shared between them in the form of kinetic energy or vibrational energy; the energy absorbed from the photon is then dissipated as heat. This, in fact, is the commonest process, but is of no special interest in our present discussion, except in so far as it reduces the "efficiency" of the other processes. Secondly, another photon may be emitted; this photon has less energy than that of the absorbed photon (it obviously cannot have more) and the light emitted has a longer wave-length than the light absorbed. This process is known as "fluorescence". Thirdly, the excited molecule may undergo chemical change, dissociating into two or more smaller molecules, or reacting with another atom or molecule, which may be normal or itself excited; the excess energy is then used up in the energy of dissociation or reaction, or in the energy of activation, or both.

Fluorescence. This belongs to the class of phenomena known as *luminescence*, a term used to describe the production of light of such a wave-length that it cannot result solely from the temperature of the system concerned—i.e. the quanta emitted are larger than those corresponding to the kinetic energy of random movement of the molecules. If atoms become excited as a result of the absorption of photons, and if the energy absorbed is radiated again only during the arrival of the exciting photons, we have *fluorescence*; if the luminescence continues for a short time after the exciting photons have ceased to arrive, we have *phosphorescence*.

Fluorescence is most obvious and striking when ultra-violet light is absorbed and visible light is emitted; this is not uncommon, and occurs, for example, with solid anthracene, solutions of quinine salts, and solutions of the dye-stuff fluorescein, and many others. The fluorescence of many kinds of inorganic crystal is of importance commercially in fluorescent lighting; in this, the ultra-violet light produced by the excitation of mercury atoms in an electric field is converted into visible light by means of the fluorescence of suitable substances on the walls of the lamp. Traces of impurities in the crystals markedly increase the efficiency of the system, which in terms of quanta may approach unity. Both fluorescence and phosphorescence may be excited by a stream of electrons as well as by a stream of photons—a phenomenon which is made use of in the cathode ray tube, such as is used in television receivers.

Chemi-luminescence.—Although not strictly relevant to the subject of this chapter, it may be added here that an atom may become excited, and emit photons with relatively large energies, not only as a result of absorbing other photons, but also as a result of absorbing thermal energy, or the energy released in chemical reactions. In the Welsbach mantle, used for incandescent gas lighting, the light emitted is of shorter wave-length than that corresponding to the temperature of the gas flame. Several organic substances may glow visibly when heated to quite moderate temperatures. Chlorophyll, for example, in a suitable solvent, when heated to about 200° C. emits an orange-red glow; in the absence of luminescence, light of this colour would not be emitted unless the temperature were raised to about 1200° C.

When the excitation is produced by the energy released in a chemical reaction, the size of the photon, and thus the wave-length of the light emitted, must depend on the amount of energy made available; but this energy will be converted into radiation only if the atoms concerned have appropriate electronic structures, and the wave-length of the light emitted will be decided by these structures. Luminescence of this kind is not uncommon when certain organic compounds undergo oxidation (few other kinds of reaction release sufficient energy) although the conditions for its occurrence are not at all well understood. It is important to the biologist owing to the fact that many kinds of living organism are luminous in the dark—the luminous bacteria, the glow-worm and the fire-fly are common examples. This luminescence results from chemical reactions which involve the reduction of molecular oxygen by means of special substrates and enzyme systems; in some cases these can be extracted from the organisms, separate from one another, and light is produced when the extracts are mixed.

Photochemical Reactions. In order that any kind of chemical change may be produced, it is necessary, to begin with, that the energy of the photon which is absorbed should be equal to, or greater than, the energy needed for any possible reaction to occur—i.e. the activation energy if the reaction is exothermic, or the sum of the activation energy and the heat of reaction, if the reaction is endothermic. In other words, if the radiation employed does not contain photons of sufficiently high frequency, we cannot get chemical reaction, but we may get fluorescence. Such a limiting frequency is known as the *photochemical threshold*. Reference to Fig. 9.1 shows that the energy per einstein is of the order of magnitude of the activation energies and heats of reaction per mole of most chemical reactions, when the wave-length of the radiation is in the region extending from the near infra-red, through the visible to the ultra-violet. It is with these wave-lengths, therefore, that we observe photochemical reactions.

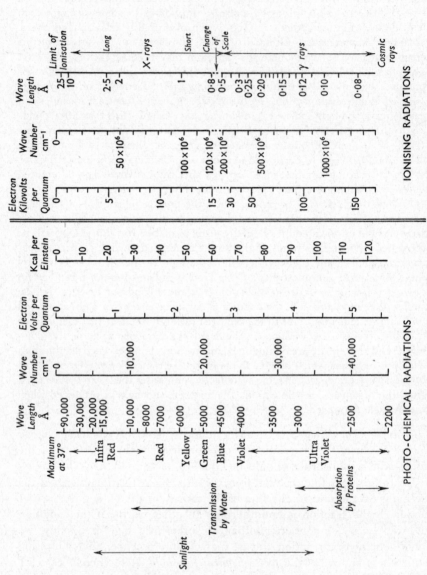

FIG. 9.1.   CHART SHOWING THE WAVE-LENGTHS AND ENERGIES PER QUANTUM OF THE BIOLOGICALLY IMPORTANT RADIATIONS

It is, of course, possible for a molecule to absorb more than one photon, but it is improbable; and it is highly improbable that it would absorb more than a very few. The precise photochemical threshold, in any given system, will depend, of course, on the nature of the particular reaction which may be brought about. Even if the radiation contains photons of sufficient energy, however, no chemical effect will be produced unless they can be absorbed by the molecules of the reactants concerned—or, if these molecules are large and complex, by appropriate parts of these molecules.

These fundamental generalisations are upset to some extent by the existence of substances known as "photochemical sensitisers", which will be discussed later. In the presence of these substances, reactions may proceed even though the incident radiation is not absorbed by the reactants themselves, and even when the frequency of the radiation is below the strict photochemical threshold; but the reduction in frequency is never large.

Ionising Radiations. If, now, we consider the effects produced by radiations of much higher frequencies, and thus with much greater energy per photon, we find the circumstances rather different. The radiations so far considered, which we have called "photochemical", have energies of a few hundred kilocalories per einstein. These lead to the excitation of an atom as a result of imparting extra energy to the electrons within it. But if the photon is associated with some ten times this amount of energy, or more, an electron can be ejected from an atom altogether. Such radiations, therefore, lead to *ionisation* of the material through which they pass. As seen from Fig. 9.1, the radiations of interest in this connection are X-rays and the γ-rays emitted by radioactive materials. The passage of high-velocity particles, such as electrons (β-rays) charged helium atoms (α-rays), protons and neutrons, which are associated with energies of the same order of magnitude, also produce ionisation in a similar way. It is conventional, when discussing ionising radiations and particles, to express their energies in the unit known as the "electron-volt" (eV). This is defined in terms of the work done by an electron moving 1 centimetre in an electrical potential gradient of 1 V/cm., and is identical with the gain or loss of kinetic energy when its electrical potential changes by 1 volt. An energy change of 1 eV per molecule is equivalent 96·5 kJ. (23 kcals.) per mole.

Photoelectric Cells. Metals contain electrons which are largely free and able to move about from place to place—this is shown by the ease with which electric currents are conducted by metals. Correspondingly, electrons can be ejected from metals relatively easily when photons are absorbed, the energy required being only a few electron-volts; the exact value depends on the nature of the metal. Thus if a metal plate is illuminated by radiation, even of wave-length corresponding to the visible or near ultra-violet regions, electrons are freed and will emerge with small energies, of some 2 to 3 electron-volts. They may then be drawn off to another, unilluminated, plate which is maintained at a positive potential with respect to the illuminated plate. Both plates must, of course, be in a vacuum, otherwise the electrons would soon be stopped by collision with the gas molecules. The photoelectric current in such cells is very small, but is strictly proportional to the intensity of the illumination. Several hundred volts are usually applied between the anode and the photoelectric cathode. Photoelectric cells for use with visible radiations are usually made with sodium or caesium cathodes, since the electrons in these metals are more easily ejected than are those in any other metal.

Greater photoelectric currents can be obtained by causing the primary electrons, ejected by the photons, to impinge on, and ionise, suitable materials within the cell. These materials may be inert gases, such as argon, at about 0·2 mm. Hg pressure (in *gas-filled* cells), or may be metallic electrodes with suitable coatings, maintained at suitable potentials with respect to the anode and cathode (in *secondary emission* or *photomultiplier* cells). One drawback to the use of gas-filled cells is that as soon as any considerable magnification of the primary photoelectric current is obtained, the total current ceases to be strictly proportional to the intensity of illumination. This drawback does not apply to the secondary emission cells.

An alternative pattern of photoelectric cell is the *photovoltaic* cell, also known as the barrier-layer, or rectifier, type of cell. This ordinarily consists of a metal plate in contact with a layer of metallic oxide—usually copper in contact with cuprous oxide. On illumination, an electromotive force is generated between the metal and the oxide, which will drive a current round an external circuit, and deflect a galvanometer. The photoelectric current, rather then the E.M.F. generated, is proportional to the intensity of illumination, so that it is desirable to use a low resistance external circuit. The resistance of the cell itself, and the E.M.F. generated, is relatively low, and they are thus less suitable for use with valve amplifiers than are the photoelectric cells proper. Under given conditions, however, the actual current delivered by a photovoltaic cell is of the order of 10 times that delivered by a vacuum photoelectric cell.

It is to be remarked that the photovoltaic cells are identical in basic construction with the elements of the metal rectifiers. The photovoltaic properties of the metal-oxide system are thus probably connected with the rectifying properties: the photoelectric current, however, flows in the opposite direction to the rectified current. Photovoltaic properties are also shown by many other electrode systems, notably by a number of metal electrodes in electrolyte solutions. These properties, therefore, are most probably of photochemical origin rather than photoelectric *sensu strictu*.

Lastly, we may refer to *photoconductivity*. A great variety of crystals show an increased electrical conductivity when suitably illuminated. This is the result of two effects: first, there is a primary current due to the release of electrons (ionisation) as a result of the absorption of photons; then, this primary current leads to an increased mobility of ions within the crystal, particularly along flaws and irregularities in the crystal structure. The secondary current is thus due to a true increase in conductivity, and in many crystals —notably those of selenium, as are most commonly used—is many times greater than the primary current, which is entirely obscured. The result of this is that the change in conductivity actually observed is not directly proportional to the intensity of illumination. Furthermore, a substantial period of time (usually seconds, and sometimes minutes) must pass before the increase in conductivity becomes fully established.

In conclusion, it is to be emphasised that the responses of all these cells —photoelectric, photovoltaic and photoconductive—depend upon the wavelength of the incident radiation as well as on its intensity. No such cell, therefore, can be used for measuring the *absolute* intensity of any radiation, without previous calibration. Absolute intensities must be estimated by absorbing the whole of the radiation in a "black body", thus converting it into heat, and measuring the rate of rise of temperature of the absorbing body, its heat capacity and rate of heat loss to the surroundings being known.

GENERAL THEORY OF PHOTOCHEMICAL ACTION

The various reactions which are brought about by the influence of light are of great variety and complexity. It is well, therefore, to dispose of a not infrequent misconception of the nature of the action of light, as being *catalytic*. The initial phase of all photochemical reactions is accompanied by the absorption of light energy, setting in motion a reaction which may afterwards proceed either with the evolution of energy, or with further absorption of light energy. We have seen in Chapter 7 that a catalyst adds no energy to a reacting system, but merely increases the *rate* at which the reaction proceeds towards an equilibrium. In many cases, a catalyst is indeed formed by the action of light, and this catalyst then proceeds, independently of the photochemical reaction proper, to perform its ordinary function of accelerating the natural course of the reaction. But in many other reactions, notably that of the decomposition of water by the green leaf, the reaction is made to proceed in the direction *opposite* to that in which it goes spontaneously, the free energy of the system being increased as a result of the absorption of the radiant energy. It is these reactions which are of the greatest interest and to which the term "photochemical" is properly applied; those reactions which are essentially spontaneous, but which are accelerated by light, may be called "photocatalytic".

In either case, however, the first event, as we have seen, is the absorption of a photon by a molecule of one of the reactants. Such an excited molecule may collide with another molecule, which may or may not be also in an excited state, and react with it; but this is found to occur only rarely, since an excited molecule only retains the energy of the absorbed photon for a very short time (of the order of 10^{-13} seconds). It is more usual for the absorbed energy to bring about dissociation of the molecule into two or more parts, either immediately, or as a result of a collision with an indifferent molecule; this molecule being neither excited nor entering into any chemical reaction.

The existence of dissociation can be inferred from the nature of the absorption spectrum. If a molecule receives enough energy to bring about dissociation, that is to take it over the potential energy barrier, as indicated in Fig. 2.1, the energy of the resultant fragments is largely kinetic, and is not quantised. The molecule can thus absorb radiant energy at any frequency, within limits, and a band of continuous absorption is observed.

The result of such dissociation is usually the formation of atoms and free radicals. These are highly reactive, and may re-combine in a wide variety of ways, according to the circumstances of the moment. Photo-chemical reactions, particularly of organic compounds, thus usually result in the formation of quite a number of different products. As an example of the formation of free radicals, we may instance the decomposition of acetone vapour by ultra-violet light. The reaction is believed to proceed in the following steps (hv represents a photon of frequency v):

1. Activation: $CH_3COCH_3 + hv \longrightarrow CH_3COCH_3{}^*$

2. Dissociation, which is, at least partly, induced as a result of a collision with an indifferent molecule:

$$CH_3COCH_3{}^* \longrightarrow CH_3CO + CH_3$$

3. Reactions between the free radicals:

$$2\,CH_3CO \longrightarrow (CH_3CO)_2 \ (\text{Diacetyl})$$
$$CH_3CO \longrightarrow CH_3 + CO$$
$$CH_3CO + CH_3 \longrightarrow C_2H_6 + CO.$$

Two methyl radicals, apparently do *not* combine directly to form ethane. At temperatures above 60° C. the CH_3CO radical is so unstable that the combination of two of them to form diacetyl does not occur.

The free radicals, of course, may re-combine to form the original compound, and such "back reactions" are very common. The velocity of the back reaction is, in many cases, dependent on the presence or absence of some indifferent substance, very often the walls of the reaction vessel, which can absorb the energy released by the forward reaction. We have already referred to this phenomenon in connection with the catalytic action of surfaces (p. 293). Without such an indifferent third body, the energy content of the molecules formed in the primary photochemical reaction may be so large that the back reaction will proceed quite rapidly.

Such a process may be of importance even in endothermic reactions, since the energy imparted by the photons may be large compared with that absorbed by the chemical reaction.

If the conditions are such that the spontaneous back reaction—or "dark" reaction—proceeds at a rate which is comparable with that of the forward photochemical reaction, a *"stationary condition"* may be reached, which simulates a chemical equilibrium. Unlike a condition of true equilibrium, however, the stationary condition is only maintained so long as there is a continuous supply of light energy; and the concentrations of the various reactants varies with the intensity of illumination. We may take as an example, the effect of illumination of anthracene by ultra-violet light, which results in polymerisation to di-anthracene. The stable condition in the dark is, at ordinary temperatures, that of pure anthracene, to which di-anthracene changes spontaneously. The rate of this reverse change is unaffected by light, but increases, by mass action, as more di-anthracene is formed by the action of the light. Under a given intensity of illumination, therefore, a condition will be reached in which as much anthracene is formed by the "dark" reaction as di-anthracene is formed by the light in the same time; a stationary condition is thus reached.

The actions of the "chemical sensitisers" may be mentioned in this connection. When, for example, a photographic plate coated with silver bromide alone is exposed to the light, a certain amount of free bromine is produced and a stationary condition is reached owing to the re-combination of silver and bromine, which is a spontaneous "dark" reaction. Such a plate would be of little use in photography, since it would be relatively insensitive to light. If, however, a substance such as gelatin is present, which combines with the bromine as it is produced, a much greater decomposition of the silver bromide is brought about by the same intensity of illumination.

The Quantum Yield

An important characteristic of a photochemical reaction is the number of quanta associated with each molecule which reacts. We have taken for granted, so far, that this figure must be unity: but in fact, experimental evidence shows that the quantum yield—or the number of molecules which are caused to react when one quantum is absorbed—may vary, in different reactions, from quite small fractions to a million or so. Now it is clear that one quantum cannot be absorbed by more than one molecule, and, while one molecule may absorb more than one quantum, this is highly improbable. The wide range of observed values of the quantum yield, therefore, is usually due to the existence of secondary processes. It must be remembered that the reacting molecules possess energy apart from that imparted to them by the photon which is absorbed. We have discussed this in connection with the activation energy of reactions. At any moment, therefore, only a certain fraction may possess enough energy, even after the absorption of the photon, to react. The number of molecules which react will then be less than the number of quanta absorbed, and the quantum yield will be less than one. The quanta absorbed, also, may not be used solely in driving the primary photochemical process, but fluorescence, de-activating collisions, back-reactions or a combination of all these, may also occur: the quantum yield will then again be less than one. On the other hand, if the quantum yield is greater than one, we usually find that the quanta absorbed are initiating a chain reaction. We have already discussed such reactions in Chapter 7, in connection with enzyme reactions, and we can regard the process as similar to that of the production of a catalyst by the absorbed radiations, which allows molecules to react even though they themselves have not absorbed the radiations. It must be remembered, however, that the "photocatalyst" may well contain the energy of the absorbed photons, and so be able to bring about reactions which are intrinsically endergonic. The decomposition of ozone into oxygen by light of wave-length less than 2700 Å., for example, has a quantum yield of at least 4; and the value depends on the amount of other gases present. It is believed that a chain reaction is concerned, the primary reaction being the photochemical decomposition of the ozone molecules into activated oxygen molecules and oxygen atoms:

$$O_3 + h\nu \longrightarrow O_2^* + O$$

This reaction is exergonic, and the energy both of the absorbed photons, and of the reaction itself, is largely retained in the products of the reaction; the oxygen molecule is thus activated. This activated oxygen will then react with a fresh ozone molecule, in the normal state

$$O_2^* + O_3 \longrightarrow 2O_2 + O$$

The oxygen atoms, both from the primary reaction, and from this secondary reaction, will also react with normal ozone molecules

$$O + O_3 \longrightarrow 2O_2^*$$

But this reaction is highly exergonic, and these oxygen molecules are also activated. A steadily increasing number of activated oxygen molecules is thus formed, and a diverging chain reaction is initiated. The chain is broken, however, and a steady state produced, by deactivating reactions between oxygen atoms and activated oxygen molecules on the one hand, and the walls of the vessel, or indifferent molecules present as impurities, on the other hand

$$2O + S \text{ (walls of vessel)} \longrightarrow O_2 + S$$
$$O_2^* + M \text{ (impurity)} \longrightarrow O_2 + M$$
$$O + O_2 + M \longrightarrow O_3 + M$$

The last of these is essentially a back reaction, catalysed by the indifferent molecules M, which absorb the excess energy.

PHOTOSENSITISATION

Suppose we have a system in which a photochemical reaction can be brought about by light of some particular wave-length—perhaps in the ultra-violet region; and suppose we add to this some substance, such as a dye, which absorbs light of some quite different wave-length—say in the visible region. We now find, if we have chosen the appropriate system and the appropriate dye, that the photochemical reaction is brought about by light which is absorbed by the dye and is not absorbed by the photosensitive system itself. The essential factor in the choice of an appropriate dye as such a photosensitiser is its ability to hand on the energy of the absorbed photons to the reacting molecules without any, or at least any considerable, dissipation into heat. Although various dyes are, perhaps, the commonest sensitisers, the action being very obvious since they absorb radiations in the visible region, the property of sensitisation in general is found in a wide variety of substances. The action is of a somewhat general nature, since there are certain reactions which can be accelerated by practically any wave-length of light, so long as a suitable dyestuff is present.

A simple experiment, due to Wager, may be given as an example. Strips of paper containing starch are soaked in a solution of methyl violet, methyl green, eosin, fuchsin or fluorescein, exposed to light and then moistened with potassium iodide solution. Iodine is liberated and stains the starch blue. It is interesting that cyanin, although bleached by light, does not act as a photosensitiser in this reaction.

One of the important practical applications of optical sensitisers is in the production of photographic plates which are sensitive to the whole visible spectrum; silver bromide itself is sensitive only to violet and ultra-violet light, but the addition to the emulsion of dyes which absorb green, yellow and red light, make it sensitive to these also. The chlorophyll system of green plants, as we shall see later, contains several auxiliary pigments which act as photosensitisers. Certain dyes, also, have the effect of sensitising living organisms to visible light, with the result that on illumination, the effects are identical with those produced by ultra-violet light in the absence of the dye.

Quite simple substances may act as sensitisers, such as mercury or cadmium vapour and the halogens in certain gas reactions; even the rare gas xenon acts as a photosensitiser in the decomposition of hydrogen molecules to hydrogen atoms. In this reaction, as in most of those in which such simple photosensitisers are involved, the frequency of the absorbed

N

radiations is greater than the photochemical threshold, but this is not a necessary condition for sensitisation.

The basic principle of photosensitisation is straightforward. A mercury atom, for example, absorbs radiation at one of its resonant frequencies, say 2537 Å.; it thus becomes excited and acquires extra energy (some 112 kilocalories per gram-atom—cf. Fig. 9.1). If it then encounters a water molecule, and can hand on this energy to the constituent atoms of the water, without its becoming converted into kinetic energy either of the mercury or the water, it is possible, energetically, for either of the following reactions to occur, at nearly every encounter:

$$H_2O \longrightarrow H_2 + O$$

or
$$H_2O \longrightarrow H + OH$$

The peculiarity of the process is that the energy can be passed from one molecule to another without loss, and that this passage can only occur between certain particular types of atom and molecule. The process is, perhaps, easier to conceive in heterogeneous reactions than in homogeneous. In the former, both sensitiser and reactants are adsorbed on some surface, possibly in a particular topographical relation to one another, and there is little likelihood of either acquiring much kinetic energy of translation. Two of the most important instances of photosensitisation, the panchromatic photographic emulsion, and the photosynthesis of carbohydrates by green plants, are both heterogeneous reactions.

PHOTOCHEMICAL REACTIONS IN SOLUTIONS

The previous paragraphs have been concerned primarily with photochemical reactions in homogeneous gaseous systems. In many respects these are the simplest, but in physiology we are concerned almost entirely with systems of aqueous solutions.

In the first place, when dealing with solutions, we have to remember that the incident radiations may be absorbed by the solvent as well as by the solute; photochemical reactions may occur in the former as well as in the latter, and there may be mutual sensitisation towards wave-lengths which are absorbed by only one of them. In the second place, an activated solute molecule is much more likely to encounter a solvent molecule during the short period of its existence, than another solute molecule. It may then react with the solvent molecule, but is more likely to lose its energy in a deactivating collision. The quantum yield of a reaction in solution is usually less than that of the same reaction in the gaseous state. Alternatively, if the activated solute molecule undergoes dissociation, the radicals formed are likely to encounter solvent molecules almost immediately and so lose energy, while still close together, and thus to re-combine.

On the other hand, if these free radicals, which often have a large kinetic energy, succeed in getting past the immediate shell of solvent molecules, and then encounter some other solute molecule, or free radical, there is an excellent chance that there will also be solvent molecules close enough to absorb the energy released in the reaction, and so to prevent the reverse reaction occurring immediately. Partly for this reason, and partly also as a result of chain reactions set up with the aid of activated solvent molecules, the quantum yield of some reactions in solution is greater than that of the same reactions in a gas.

RELATION OF VELOCITY OF REACTION TO INTENSITY OF LIGHT

Bunsen and Roscoe showed in 1862 that in order to produce a definite degree of darkening on silver chloride paper, the time required was inversely proportional to the intensity of the light. That is:

$$i.t = \text{constant}$$

where i is the intensity of the light, and t the time of action. This is known as the *Bunsen-Roscoe Law*. This relation implies that the total amount of effect produced is proportional to the total quantity of radiation absorbed. The quantum yield, in fact, must be independent of the light intensity, as is to be expected in general. There are, however, some photochemical reactions in which this law does not hold: complications may arise from dark reactions, assisting or opposing the photochemical reaction; from the products of the reaction absorbing some of the incident radiation themselves, so that the effective intensity steadily falls, although the incident intensity is constant; and from other factors. In the photographic emulsion, for example, it is rare to find an exact equivalence between intensity and duration of exposure, particularly when the blackening actually observed is produced by development, subsequent to the exposure. Schwarzschild modified the Bunsen-Roscoe law into the expression:

$$i.t^p = \text{constant}$$

where p varies according to the type of emulsion, nature of the development, etc., but ordinarily lies between 0·8 and 1·0.

Induction Period. Many, if not most, photochemical reactions which involve chain reactions do not attain the full rate of reaction immediately on illumination. This is due to the presence of impurities, either in the reactants or on the walls of the reaction vessel, which act as inhibitors, and break the chains—as indicated above; these impurities are soon removed by chemical reactions, or become saturated. The photographic emulsion shows a phenomenon similar to that of an induction period, which is known as the "inertia". There is a certain minimum duration of exposure below which no effect is produced, however intense the light; and conversely, there is a minimum intensity below which no effect is produced, however long the exposure.

An induction period is also found in the chlorophyll system, as we shall see later. This appears to result from the fact that the whole process of photosynthesis is carried out by a complex series of reactions, only one of which is strictly photochemical, the others being "dark" reactions. Some of these involve the products of the primary photochemical reaction.

PHOTOSYNTHESIS OF CARBOHYDRATES— THE CHLOROPHYLL SYSTEM

The action of green plants in making use of radiant energy from the sun in order to decompose water, reduce carbon dioxide to carbohydrates and release molecular oxygen, is without doubt by far the most important of all known photochemical reactions, and is, perhaps, the most interesting of all natural phenomena. Without it, none of the oxidative reaction sequences discussed in the previous chapter, by means of which all living cells— plant as well as animal—obtain the energy necessary for them to exist, grow and reproduce, would have any relevance to the study of biology. The foodstuffs concerned—carbohydrates, fats, proteins and other nitrogenous compounds, and above all oxygen—would not exist in nature, except perhaps as curiosities, as it were. Nevertheless, little is really known about the nature of the photochemical reactions which take place; they are heterogeneous in character and the colloidal systems concerned are of great complexity.

It has been established for a great many years, by several different kinds of experiment, that it is only those plants, or parts of plants, which are *green* that can carry out photosynthesis. From such parts of plants a green pigment, *chlorophyll* can be extracted by means of organic solvents, such as acetone. It consists, actually, of two pigments, chlorophyll *a* and chlorophyll *b*, which are very closely related chemically, but may be separated by means of partition chromatography; talcum, sugar and urea have been used as adsorbents. The bacteria possess a third kind of pigment only, known as bacterio-chlorophyll. The extracted pigments form colloidal solutions in water. In the green plant cells, the chlorophylls are associated with yellow pigments, which are *carotenoids*, and in certain kinds of algae only, with red and blue pigments, the *phycobilins*. All these are ordinarily extracted with the chlorophylls, and all are concerned in the process of photosynthesis. Many other kinds of pigment may be extracted from plant tissues of various kinds, such as, for example, the anthocyanins in flowers; but these do not concern us here.

The Chemical Nature of the Pigments

The chemical constitution of the chlorophylls has been discovered in the usual way by studying the degradation products after treatment with various reagents. It is found that the chlorophylls belong to the group of substances known as *metallo-porphyrins*—a group which is of widespread biological importance. The structures of the various porphyrins are all built up on the porphin skeleton, a set of four pyrrole rings, labelled I,

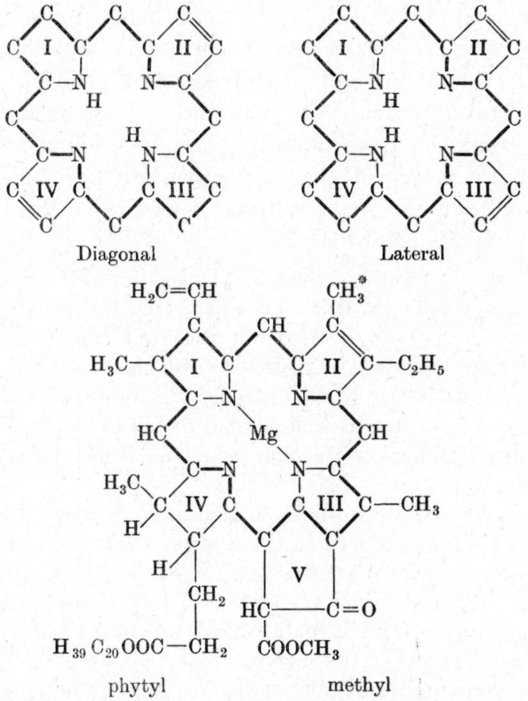

FIG. 9.2. THE STRUCTURE OF PORPHIN, SHOWING THE TWO CONFIGURATIONS (*above*); AND THE STRUCTURE OF CHLOROPHYLL (*below*)

The thick lines represent alternate double and single bonds, for which two arrangements are possible, both in the diagonal and the lateral configurations.

II, III and IV in Fig. 9.2. In the chlorophylls the metal is magnesium; if the metal is iron, and with various different kinds of porphyrin, we get *haem* which in combination with a protein forms the important blood pigment *haemoglobin*, and the oxidation-reduction enzymes and carriers, *peroxidase* and the *cytochromes*.

In the formation of the chlorophylls, the porphin skeleton is "clothed" by the addition of various side-groups and hydrogen atoms, and a magnesium atom is inserted in the middle. The dimensions of the whole ring structure are such that the magnesium atom will fit snugly into the "hole" between the four nitrogen atoms, and so will become united equally readily with any of them. Two of the side groups are acidic; and these are esterified, by a long-chain unsaturated alcohol known as *phytol*, and by methanol, respectively, as is indicated in Fig. 9.2. On treatment of chlorophyll with alkali, the methanol and phytol are removed, leaving the acid, *chlorophyllin*. An enzyme (esterase) is present in green leaves which catalyses this hydrolysis; or, if the solutions are concentrated, and little water is present, the converse esterification will be brought about. When chlorophyll is acted on by acid, on the other hand, the magnesium is split off, and a derivative called *phaeophytin* is formed. On treating phaeophytin with alkali, the methanol and phytol come off, leaving an acid called *phaeophorbin*. This substance is formed, also, if, by the action of acid, the magnesium is removed from chlorophyllin. The chlorophylls, therefore, are methyl-phytyl esters of the acid chlorophyllin, which, in turn, is formed from phaeophorbin, a porphyrin derivative, by the addition of magnesium in organic combination.

The various side groups shown in Fig. 9.2 are those present in chlorophyll *a*. In chlorophyll *b* the methyl group on ring II, indicated by an asterisk, is replaced by a methoxy group, but the two compounds are otherwise identical. In neutral solution, the phyllin from chlorophyll *a* is olive-green in colour, and that from chlorophyll *b* is red. In bacterio-chlorophyll, the double bond in ring II is reduced, as well as that in ring IV, and the vinyl group on ring I is oxidised to an acetyl group; otherwise it has the same constitution as chlorophyll *a*.

There are two equally probable configurations of the porphin skeleton, depending on the positions of the two semi-isolated double bonds; in the "diagonal" form, they are in rings II and IV (or I and III), and in the "lateral" form, they are in rings II and III (or I and IV). If the rings have different side groups, as in chlorophyll, there will be two forms of each configuration; those parts of the ring system shown in thick lines in Fig. 9.2 consist of alternate double and single bonds, as in the benzene ring, and there are two possible arrangements of these bonds, according as we place, for example, a double bond to the right or to the left of the top central carbon atom. There are thus 8 possible isomeric and mesomeric forms of chlorophyll. The "diagonal" form of the structure of chlorophyll is given in Fig. 9.2, and it is probable that two "lateral" forms also exist, but it seems likely that they would have a slightly greater energy.

The *yellow pigments*, belonging to the class of substance known as *carotenoids*, are of two kinds. One of them, *carotene*, is a long-chain hydrocarbon, with 18 carbon atoms and 11 double bonds, and an ionone ring added at each end. If the chain is split in the middle, vitamin A is formed (see Fig. 9.5). The other kinds of pigment, *xanthophylls* or *carotenols*, have structures similar to that of carotene, but with hydroxyl groups substituted in the ionone rings. There are several kinds of xanthophyll, which differ in their detailed structures; one of them is luteol, the yellow pigment also found in egg yolk; both carotene and the xanthophylls are unsaturated and autoxidisable, that is they oxidise spontaneously in the air—in plant cells probably also by enzyme action—and then become bleached. They can also be reduced by hydrogenation of the double bonds.

The *phycobilins* (*phycoerythrin*, which is red, and *phycocyanin*, which is blue) contain four pyrrole rings, as do the porphyrins, but arranged in a straight chain, instead of in a ring. They are thus similar in structure to the mammalian bile pigments, which are derived from the haem part of haemoglobin, after splitting off the iron.

It must be confessed that, so far, knowledge of the chemical constitutions of the various pigments has not been of much value in elucidating the nature of the photochemical reactions. One of the reasons for this may be that study of the structure of the plant cells in which photosynthesis occurs strongly suggests that in the living cell, chlorophyll and the associated pigments are intimately bound in a complex colloidal form. The pigments are not present in free solution, but in special granules known as *chloroplasts*, of which they form only a small part, most of the solid matter consisting of proteins and lipids. The chlorophylls are thus probably attached to a protein carrier, together with the carotenoids and probably, also, with other lipids and with carbohydrates. The chloroplasts, also, contain many kinds of enzyme system, some of which, at least, are intimately concerned in the process of photosynthesis.

Absorption of Light by Chlorophyll and Associated Pigments

Fig. 9.3 shows the absorption spectra of chlorophyll, both in the living leaf, and in its two forms in true solution. The most striking and characteristic feature is the dark band in the red, which becomes shifted slightly towards the blue when the chlorophylls go into true solution, and is further towards the blue in chlorophyll *b* than in chlorophyll *a*. There is also appreciable absorption in the blue and violet (particularly by chlorophyll *b*), extending into the ultra-violet, and slight absorption in the yellow. The chief absorption, however, is in the longer wave-lengths, and is practically in the position of the maximum energy of the solar spectrum during the greater part of the day in temperate regions.

With the sun at the zenith, and with a very clear atmosphere, the maximum energy of the solar radiation is at $0.48\,\mu$ (4800 Å.). But as the altitude of the sun diminishes, the red rays are proportionately less absorbed and scattered than are the blue and violet rays; the maximum of the spectral energy curve then shifts, towards the red, and, on the average in temperate climates,

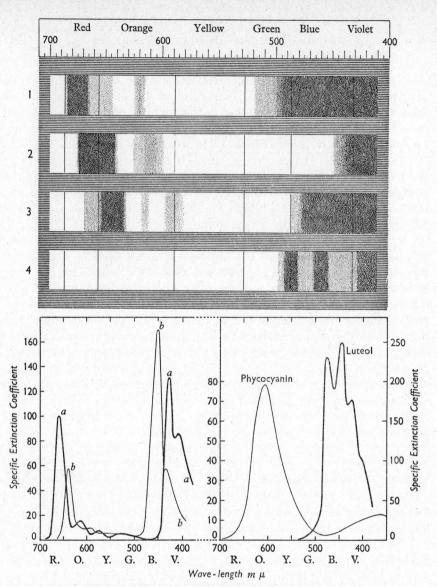

FIG. 9.3. THE ABSORPTION OF LIGHT BY CHLOROPHYLL AND SOME
ASSOCIATED PIGMENTS

ABOVE. Absorption Spectra, as observed by Willstätter und Stoll (1913). (Some of
the weaker bands have been omitted in the reproduction.) At the top, scale
of wave-lengths in $m\mu$.

1. Nettle leaf, living: chlorophyll in the colloidal state.
2. Chlorophyll a ⎫ in solution in ethyl ether.
3. Chlorophyll b ⎭
4. Carotene in solution in ethanol.

BELOW. Curves showing more precisely the relation between the Specific Extinction
Coefficient and the Wave-length.

On the left: chlorophyll a (thick line) and chlorophyll b (thin line) in
solution in ethyl ether (Zscheile and Comar, 1940).

On the right: phycocyanin (thin line) (Svedberg and Katsurai, 1929); and
luteol, one of the main carotenoids present in most kinds of plant, in
solution in ethanol (Zscheile, White, Beadle and Roach, 1942).

it is at about $0 \cdot 67 \mu$. Apart from the gaps due to the heavy absorption by water vapour in the atmosphere, at $0 \cdot 69 \mu$, $0 \cdot 725 \mu$, $0 \cdot 765 \mu$ and elsewhere in the infra-red, appreciable quantities of energy are received from the sun at all wave-lengths between $0 \cdot 30 \mu$ and $2 \cdot 3 \mu$.

Fig. 9.3 also shows the absorption spectra of carotene and of luteol which have three absorption bands in the blue-green, blue and blue-violet regions. These pigments, as we shall see, must be supposed to co-operate with chlorophyll in photosynthesis, which can, in fact, be carried out by green plants in light of any wave-length in the visible region.

When in true solution, in organic solvents, chlorophyll is *fluorescent*, the re-emitted light having, as is to be expected, the same colour as that which is most strongly absorbed. In colloidal solutions, and in the living leaf, the fluorescence is extremely weak, and, indeed, was not detected at all for many years. The fluorescence emission band is slightly to the red of that given by true solutions, just as is the main absorption band. Further, if a living leaf is killed by being immersed in boiling water, the absorption band shifts towards the blue, and marked fluorescence appears. Again, extracts of chloroplastic material can be prepared which show little fluorescence, and have the chief absorption band in the same position as in the living leaf. These solutions are colloidal in nature and are not decomposed by strong illumination, as are true solutions of chlorophyll.

It is an important fact that in the living leaf, the fluorescence band is at the same wave-length whatever wave-length is used to excite it. This strongly suggests that the energy of photons absorbed by the other pigments associated with chlorophyll can be transferred in a form which can "excite" the chlorophyll molecule. All these observations on fluorescence support the conception that in the living cell the chlorophylls and associated pigments form part of a complex colloidal system.

PHOTOCHEMICAL REACTIONS OF THE CHLOROPHYLL SYSTEM

The final result of the photosynthetic process may be represented by an equation such as:

$$x CO_2 + x H_2O + \text{light energy} \longrightarrow C_x H_{2x} O_x + x O_2$$

but this naturally gives us no indication as to how it is brought about. Now the reduction of carbon dioxide and oxidation of water is an endertgonic process, the necessary energy to drive it being supplied by the lighquanta which are absorbed. But since the reactants do not themselves absorb any appreciable amount of radiation at the wave-lengths known to be active, we must assume that the chlorophyll acts as a photosensitiser,

N*

and in this respect acts as a catalyst, since it does not disappear during the course of the reaction.

It is certain that the whole reaction does not occur in one step, but in a number of stages, in series and in parallel with one another, only some of which are photochemical. Evidence for this comes from the effect of *temperature* on the rate of absorption of carbon dioxide or of production of oxygen. Photochemical processes have small temperature coefficients (activation energy is not provided by thermal agitation), but at low temperatures and high intensities of illumination, photosynthesis has a large temperature coefficient, which reaches 6, for example, for the 10° range between $-5°$ C. and $+5°$ C. At higher temperatures, the temperature coefficient falls, and is only 1·76 for the 10° range between 20° C. and 30° C.; the velocities of the "dark" enzymic reactions have, presumably, increased so much that the rate of the whole process is now limited by that of a photochemical reaction. Similarly, in weak illumination, the temperature coefficient is small at all temperatures, since the velocities of the photochemical reactions are now less than those of the "dark" reactions, and are again the limiting ones.

Further evidence is derived from the existence of an "induction period". If a plant which has previously been in the dark, is suddenly illuminated, the rates of absorption of carbon dioxide, and of production of oxygen, are at first small, and only reach the steady values, corresponding to the intensity of illumination falling on the plant, after several minutes. The products of the primary photochemical reaction are, apparently, not released as oxygen, or used to reduce carbon dioxide, until their concentrations have been built up to the extent necessary to speed up the "dark" reactions. Again, if the intensity of illumination is fairly great, the amount of photosynthesis produced by a given amount of incident energy is increased if the illumination is made intermittent—i.e. is applied in flashes; the overall reaction apparently continues during the dark periods, making use of some of the energy absorbed during the periods of illumination. The nature of some of the "dark" reactions (which are sometimes called the "Blackman reactions", after the name of their discoverer) will appear later.

Now in all living organisms, as we know, carbohydrate is oxidised and oxygen is reduced, with the production of carbon dioxide and water. Photosynthesis, therefore, may be conceived as essentially a reversal of oxidative metabolism. This point of view is emphasised by the fact that experiments with the isotope of oxygen (^{18}O) have shown that the oxygen produced in photosynthesis is entirely derived from water, and not from carbon dioxide, as was formerly believed. In order, therefore, to release the hydrogen atoms which will reduce carbon dioxide, we must have a reducing system with a potential at least as negative as that of the hydrogen electrode, with a value, probably, of some $-0\cdot5$ V: and simultaneously, in order to oxidise the water and release oxygen, we must have an oxidising system with a potential equal to, or greater than, $+0\cdot8$ V. As may be seen from Table 8.1 (p. 337), these values are exceeded only by those of the most powerful reducing or oxidising systems, respectively.

The essential photochemical event in photosynthesis, whatever "dark" reactions may also be involved, is undoubtedly the absorption of a photon by a chlorophyll molecule which thus becomes excited: and such an excited molecule may act as a very powerful reducing agent and a very powerful oxidising agent at the same time. The electron system in one of the constituent atoms has been distorted and is associated with a far greater potential energy than usual. One of the outer electrons may, therefore, be fairly easily lost to an atom in another molecule which, in accordance with what we learnt in the previous chapter, must thus become reduced. Further, the displacement of the electron system can be conceived as leaving a "hole" into which an added electron may drop; the molecule from which this electron is derived being thereby oxidised. This part of the reaction sequence may thus be represented as:

$$Chl + h\nu \longrightarrow Chl^*$$
$$Chl^* \longrightarrow {}^-Chl^+$$

the excitation of the chlorophyll molecule being supposed to result first in a transfer of an electron from one part of it to another. The negative and positive charges will then be transferred to hydrogen and hydroxyl ions, respectively, through charged water molecules as highly unstable intermediary substances, with the production of hydrogen atoms and hydroxyl radicals. The hydroxyl radicals will then combine with one another to form oxygen; and the hydrogen atoms reduce carbon dioxide:

$$2OH \longrightarrow H_2O + O$$
$$2O \longrightarrow O_2$$
$$CO_2 + H \longrightarrow (-COOH)$$
$$(-COOH) + H \longrightarrow (-CO) + H_2O$$
$$(-CO) + H \longrightarrow (-CHO)$$
$$(-CHO) + H \longrightarrow (-CH_2O)$$

The successive products of reduction by hydrogen atoms are enclosed in brackets to show that they are not free, but attached to some other, larger, molecules. The precise sequence of reactions is very uncertain, and that given above is intended merely to be illustrative. It is not to be supposed, either, that the hydrogen atoms and hydroxyl radicals appear in the free state, except, perhaps, for infinitesimal periods of time.

That the action of light on chlorophyll is essentially one of transferring hydrogen atoms is supported by the existence of what might be called "partial" photosynthesis. There are various types of bacteria and algae, for example, which can reduce carbon dioxide by means of hydrogen derived from hydrogen sulphide or thiosulphate, various organic compounds and even molecular hydrogen, instead of from water. If this last kind of bacteria are grown in a closed vessel containing hydrogen and oxygen, the gases disappear and water is formed. If carbon dioxide is also present, it disappears and the carbon is assimilated by the bacteria. In the absence of carbon dioxide, moreover, bacteria and algae may reduce other substances by means of hydrogen obtained from water or organic substances: in this way we may get the reduction of nitrates or aldehydes. The reduction of nitrates, indeed, occurs in nearly all green plants, and is an important preliminary step in the synthesis of proteins. If we include in this generalisation the reduction of oxygen by hydrogen obtained from an organic substance, we include what is ordinarily regarded as oxidative metabolism. But we are justified in doing so, since it has been found that chlorophyll may act as a photocatalyst in this reaction. Certain bacteria, also, in the absence of any suitable hydrogen acceptor, such as oxygen, may release molecular hydrogen to the atmosphere. All these reactions may be summarised as in Table 9.1, with the designations that have been given to them by various workers.

TABLE 9.1

Reactions sensitised by chlorophyll in vivo

Designation	Hydrogen acceptor	Hydrogen donor ($R = organic\ radical$)
Photosynthesis	CO_2	H_2O
"Photoreduction"	CO_2	H_2, H_2S, H_2R, $H_2S_2O_3$, etc.
"Photoautoxidation "	O_2	H_2R
Nitrate reduction	HNO_3	H_2O or H_2R
Aldehyde reduction	C_6H_5CHO etc.	H_2O (or H_2R ?)
Photochemical liberation of hydrogen	(atmosphere)	H_2R

Granted, then, that the primary process in photosynthesis is the simultaneous generation of an oxidising agent and a reducing agent, the problem arises as to how these are kept apart, so that they react with, say, water and carbon dioxide, rather than with each other. The answer seems to be that in the living green plant cell, the cholorophyll forms part of an organised system of many different enzymes, as well as other proteins and lipids, as has already been mentioned; the radicals formed in the primary reaction are not free, but remain adsorbed, and held apart. Chlorophyll in solution is quite incapable of bringing about photosynthesis. And the fact that the intensity of fluorescence is far greater when the chlorophyll is in solution than when it is in the living cell, suggests that some substances have been removed which can undergo chemical reaction, and so accept the energy of the absorbed photon. This conception is strongly supported, also, by the existence of the "Hill reaction". Hill and Scarisbrick found in 1939 that chloroplasts, isolated by grinding up living cells and then suspended in watery solutions, could make use of light energy to oxidise water, with the production of free oxygen, but were unable to bring about the reduction of carbon dioxide. The hydrogen, or electron, acceptor in this reaction was, in their first experiments, provided by some constituent of fresh tissue extracts, but this, they found, could be replaced by organic ferric salts, and, later, by a number of other oxidising agents, such as quinone. The inability of these isolated, and probably fragmented, chloroplasts to reduce carbon dioxide is presumably due to the lack of some special enzyme system which must "fix" the carbon dioxide before it can be reduced by the chlorophyll system. They do, however, contain the system which ensures that the hydroxyl radicals shall be formed, and that they shall then give rise to molecular oxygen.

The fixation and reduction of carbon dioxide can be effected by certain protoplasmic systems by the aid of chemical energy, without the assistance of light energy. It is known, as stated in the previous chapter, that the reaction of simple decarboxylation is reversible. It has been shown, for example, by the use of isotopic tracers, that even in animal tissues, carbon dioxide is taken up by pyruvate ions to form oxaloacetate ions. But of even greater importance is the fact that *oxidative* decarboxylation may be reversed if it is coupled with a suitable exergonic reaction. Ochoa, for example, used the anaerobic oxidation of glucose-6-phosphate to reduce triphosphopyridine nucleotide, which in turn brought about the "reductive carboxylation" of pyruvate to malate; the "malic enzyme" necessary for catalysing this reaction has been found in plant tissues. It has been shown that the isolated chloroplasts, in the presence of light, can reduce the phosphopyridine nucleotide co-enzymes, but only to a small extent. Since the oxidation-reduction potential of these co-enzymes is about -0.3 V, it is clear that this system could not reduce free carbon dioxide. This difficulty will be overcome, however, if in the complete system the preliminary fixation of carbon dioxide is brought about by a suitable exergonic reaction; the oxidation-reduction potential of the compound so formed may not be too negative to be reduced by known systems. There is, indeed, good reason to suppose that such a reaction does occur, and that it involves the co-operation of "active" phosphate compounds.

We saw in the previous chapter that the energy released when a phosphoryl ester of a carboxylic acid is formed by an oxidation process is about 10 kcals. per mole less than that released when the carboxylate ion is formed from the same precursor. There will be a corresponding difference in the oxidation-reduction potentials of the two reactions; and accordingly, if the carbon dioxide, when taken up, is converted into a phosphoryl ester, it might be appreciably reduced by a system with an oxidation-reduction potential not more negative than -0.3 V. The phosphopyridine nucleotides might thus be adequate.

This may, perhaps, be made clearer by the following arguments. If an aldehyde group, to which a phosphoryl radical is attached, is oxidised to a carboxylate ion, the phosphoryl radical becomes less stable and is more easily thrown off. Conversely, reduction of, say, a carboxylate ion to an aldehyde will facilitate the uptake of a phosphoryl radical from some "active" phosphate. If, now, we have an aldehyde and a carboxylate ion in equilibrium with one another, and add an "active" phosphate compound, the Principle of Mobile Equilibrium (p. 72) states that the system will change in such a way as to remove the "active" phosphate; the equilibrium between carboxylate and aldehyde will be shifted, more aldehyde will be formed, and phosphoryl radicals taken up. The magnitude of the shift will be such that the free energy released by the loss of "active" phosphate will be equal to the free energy absorbed in the reduction of the carboxylate ion.

Direct experimental evidence as to the nature of the compounds formed when carbon dioxide is reduced during photosynthesis has been obtained, largely by Calvin and his co-workers since 1949, by the use of carbon dioxide labelled with the carbon isotope [14]C. It appears that in algae at least, the earliest intermediate compound in which ^{14}C can be detected is phosphoglycerate. On reduction, reversing the sequence of reactions described in Chapter 8 (pp. 359, 368), phosphoglycerate can be converted into triose phosphate and thus into hexose. Indeed, if photosynthesis is allowed to continue for more than a few seconds, it is found that ^{14}C subsequently appears in a wide variety of sugars, at many different points in the molecules, as well as in fats and proteins. The precursor, with which carbon dioxide combines, is not, however, a two-carbon compound, as might at first be expected, but a phosphorylated five-carbon sugar, ribulose diphosphate; each molecule of the six-carbon compound formed then splits into two molecules of phosphoglycerate. Phosphorylation of the pentose, of course, is an endergonic process, and almost certainly involves the participation of adenosine triphosphate; this is synthesised in the course of, and by means of energy released in, the ordinary oxidative metabolic reactions which are concurrent with those of photosynthesis. The pentose itself is formed by a kind of "dismutation" reaction, whereby a mixture of a hexose and a triose changes over into one of a pentose and a tetrose; it is thus derived from products of previous photochemical reactions. This fact accounts for the existence of the induction period. The organisation of the enzyme systems is presumably such as to ensure that the hydrogen atoms (or electrons) formed in the primary photochemical reaction are preferentially "captured" and used to reduce the "fixed" carbon dioxide. But unless, and until, substantial quantities of "fixed" carbon dioxide are available, the hydrogen atoms will be largely "wasted" by immediate re-combination with hydroxyl radicals. Moreover, after a period of active photosynthesis in strong illumination, when all the carbon dioxide that is taken up is immediately reduced, and none has to wait for a hydrogen atom, it would seem likely that the amount of ribulose diphosphate present will be in excess of that actually needed; this would account for the observed fact that in such conditions, the uptake of carbon dioxide continues for a short time after the light has been cut off. Again, it seems that the reaction by which carbon dioxide is taken up is specifically inhibited by the presence of cyanide ions. This would be expected if adenosine triphosphate is one of the essential reactants, formed only in the course of oxidative metabolism; cyanide in general, is found to inhibit specifically those enzymes (oxidases) which are concerned in the utilisation of molecular oxygen.

The first, and simplest, of all possible reductive carboxylation reactions is that of a molecule of hydrogen, to give formaldehyde:

$$H_2 + CO_2 \longrightarrow HCHO + O$$

It was, in fact, suggested by von Baeyer in 1870 that formaldehyde is the first product of photosynthesis, and Usher and Priestley, in 1906, found that an aldehyde is to be detected as a product of the action of light on films of chlorophyll in the presence of moist carbon dioxide. There is also reason to expect formaldehyde to be produced, since formic acid has been obtained by the action of light on carbon dioxide in the presence of uranium salts, and formaldehyde by the action of ultra-violet light on colloidal solutions of uranium hydroxide or ferric hydroxide. Moreover, formaldehyde is readily polymerised to higher carbohydrates; by the action of magnesium oxide and lead on formaldehyde at 60° C., a sugar is obtained which was shown by Emil Fischer to be inactive fructose. Formaldehyde, again, is formed by exposing a mixture of carbon dioxide and hydrogen, or of water and carbon monoxide, to ultra-violet light, or by exposing moist carbon dioxide to the silent electric discharge. In both cases, a series of intermediate reactions take place, and the conditions are, undoubtedly, rather far from those of the green leaf. These reactions, however, are interesting as suggesting possibilities by which carbohydrate might be formed from inorganic materials in the absence of green plants, or indeed, before the appearance of chlorophyll on the earth.

Now, if the aldehyde in Usher and Priestley's experiments were actually derived from the carbon dioxide present, a great step would have been taken, but there is considerable reason to doubt whether such a reaction is likely.

An aldehyde is indeed only to be obtained from chlorophyll after it has been exposed to light, but the production does not depend upon the presence of carbon dioxide, whereas oxygen must be present, and is used up. The aldehyde which is split off from the chlorophyll system must have been derived from some constituent of the chlorophyll, probably the phytol, since it is formed by light irrespective of the presence of carbon dioxide. The experiments just related, therefore, give us no information as to the most difficult part of the problem, namely how formaldehyde could be formed from carbon dioxide, if, in fact, it ever is.

A number of experimenters have succeeded in detecting the presence of aldehydes in green plants during photosynthesis, but others have either failed to do so, or have given reasons for believing that their presence was unconnected with carbon assimilation. Again, in some experiments, plants have been found to be able to produce more polysaccharides in the presence of formaldehyde than in its absence. But in other experiments, again, this has not occurred, even when the concentration of formaldehyde present has been too low for there to have been any toxic action.

We may conclude, therefore, that it is unlikely that formaldehyde is an intermediary in the formation of carbohydrates, although the possibility is not absolutely excluded. It must be remembered, also, that formaldehyde molecules which have polymerised, lose their chemical identity; and similarly, it is not to be expected that (CH_2O) radicals which are still attached to an enzyme system will possess the chemical properties of formaldehyde.

The Efficiency of the Chlorophyll System

From the point of view of the physical chemistry of the photosynthetic reaction, it is not the overall energetic efficiency which is of interest, but the *quantum yield*, the average number of molecules of oxygen released, or of carbon dioxide reduced, by each quantum of light absorbed. The inverse of this quantity is known as the *quantum requirement* of the reaction. The maximum value of the quantum yield is likely to provide information as to the nature of the reaction, and in order to discover this, we must ensure that it is the light intensity which is limiting the rate of the reaction; we must also, of course, know exactly how much of the incident light is absorbed by the chlorophyll system, and we must work with monochromatic light.

The greatest practical difficulty in obtaining reliable values of the quantum yield lies in the fact that it is highly probable—and, indeed, almost certain—that oxidative metabolism proceeds in the tissues of the green plant even when they are also carrying out photosynthesis. It is necessary, therefore, to make some assumption as to the rate at which oxygen is being consumed at the same time as it is being produced by the action of light. Evidence has been obtained by the use of isotopes of oxygen, that *in the steady state* the rate of consumption of oxygen is the same when the cells are illuminated as it is when they are in the dark. It is less certain that the rate of production of carbon dioxide is unaffected by light, owing to the complexity of the reactions involved, but there is no strong evidence to the contrary. In the *transient* conditions, of the "induction" period immediately following sudden illumination, and of the period immediately following its cessation, the rate of production of carbon dioxide, and of absorption of oxygen, are certainly not constant.

The gain in free energy in converting gaseous carbon dioxide, at the partial pressure at which it is present in the atmosphere, and liquid water to either glucose or sucrose, is almost exactly 120 kcals./g. atom of carbon. In visible light, there are some 40 to 60 kcals./einstein, so that the maximum quantum yield, from energetic considerations, will lie between 0·33 and 0·5. The experiments of Warburg and his co-workers indicate that it is possible for the actual yield to be about 0·25, not much smaller than the theoretical maximum. But in order to attain this high value, the organisms under investigation (the green alga *Chlorella*) must be "trained" by being grown in dim light and in the appropriate culture media; appropriate experimental methods must be used, and the light intensity must be very small; the quantum yield falls steadily as the light intensity rises. The observations of other workers (notably of Emerson and his colleagues) even in very weak light are not consistent with so large a value of the quantum yield, and values lying between 0·08 and 0·12 are much more usual. Some 8 to 12 quanta are thus needed for the reduction of each molecule of carbon dioxide. Under natural conditions, of course, where the light intensity is large and the supply of carbon dioxide is the limiting factor, the efficiency of photosynthesis is much smaller: only some 1 per cent. of the incident energy, or some 2·5 per cent. of the energy absorbed, is used for photosynthesis, the quantum yield then being about 0·01. A considerable fraction—at least one-quarter—of the incident radiation is either reflected from the surface of the plant tissue, or passes through it without being absorbed; and of that which is absorbed by land plants, a great part is used up in the evaporation of water, thus bringing about transpiration, and the flow of watery solutions from the roots.

In the general scheme put forward in the previous section, the reduction of a molecule of carbon dioxide, and the genesis of a molecule of oxygen, occurred in four steps, each of which resulted from the absorption of one quantum. Warburg's quantum yield of about 0·25 would thus seem to fit admirably, and one would have to suppose that the more usual, much smaller, values result from the existence of considerable "wastage" by back reactions. This, indeed, is not unlikely, and several probable reactions of this kind have appeared in the course of our discussion in the previous section. But, on the other hand, the reaction sequence involving four steps using four quanta, may be regarded as a stoichiometric minimum; in practice there may be more than four steps and more than four quanta may be concerned. If this is so, it must be presumed that in Warburg's experiments some intermediate compounds, already partially reduced as compared with carbon dioxide, are available to accept the hydrogen atoms released from water. This question is still undecided.

Chlorophyll, as is indicated in Fig. 9.3, absorbs light strongly in the violet region of the spectrum, as well as in the red, less strongly in the blue, yellow and orange, and hardly at all in the green. Nevertheless, photosynthesis will occur in light of any colour, and measurement of the quantum yield in light of different wave-lengths suggests that the yield is practically unaffected by the size of the quantum absorbed. Moreover, as already pointed out, any fluorescence which can be excited is always red in

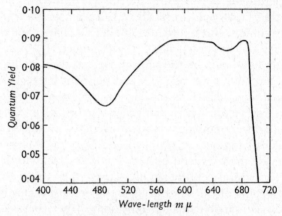

FIG. 9.4. THE QUANTUM YIELD OF PHOTOSYNTHESIS BY THE GREEN ALGA *Chlorella* IN LIGHT OF DIFFERENT WAVE-LENGTHS

The line has been drawn through the mean values obtained in 19 different experiments. (Emerson and Lewis, 1943.)

colour, and of the same wave-length as that of the main absorption band of chlorophyll *a*. It seems probable, therefore, that it is chlorophyll *a* which is primarily responsible for the photochemical reaction; chlorophyll *a*, indeed, is the only kind of chlorophyll which is found in all green plants, with the exception of the bacteria. The other pigments, including the other kinds of chlorophyll, act as secondary photosensitisers, transferring to chlorophyll *a*—and, indeed, to that part of chlorophyll *a* which is responsible for the absorption band in the red—the energy acquired when they absorb photons. It would appear, however, that this transfer, in the case of the carotenoids, is incomplete, of the order of one-half of the energy being lost. As is shown in Fig. 9.4, the quantum yield, as directly observed, is smaller in green, blue and violet light, which are absorbed strongly by the carotenoids, than in red and orange light. From the phycobilins, however, present in the red and blue-green algae, there is no such loss.

In the higher plants, the apparent quantum yields in blue and violet light may be reduced by the presence of flavone and anthocyanine pigments, which absorb the light but are useless for photosynthesis; they do not appear to be present in the alga *Chlorella*, used for the experiments recorded in Fig. 9.4.

It will be seen from the condensed account of the properties and behaviour of the chlorophyll system how far we are from understanding the process of photosynthesis. For more detailed accounts the reader is referred to the little monograph by Hill and Whittingham (1957), to the very complete treatment by Rabinowitch (1945, 1951, 1956), and to the reviews listed at the end of the chapter. The earlier work is described in the classical books of Willstätter and Stoll (1913 and 1918).

PHOTO-RECEPTORS AND VISION

Nearly all living organisms, both plants and animals, show changes in behaviour in response to the amount and direction of the illumination that falls upon them. All the animals, except a few protozoa, most parasites and a few with exceptional habitats, possess special receptor organs for detecting the amount of light falling upon them, and in the more complex animals, these have become developed into eyes, often of very complicated design, and of extraordinary efficiency. There can be little doubt that the means by which light activates all these kinds of receptor, whether simple or complicated, is through photochemical reactions. It is these reactions only that we will consider here; the structures of the complicated eyes, and the means by which the activated receptors set up nerve impulses, and thus give rise to a "sensation", are outside the scope of this chapter. The only structure which concerns us, therefore, is that known as the *retina*, the light-sensitive surface at the back of the photo-receptor, or eye, corresponding with the photographic plate or film in a camera.

Although it had been known for some time that the retina of a frog, removed in the dark, appeared to be of a red or purple colour when observed in the light, and that the colour disappeared more or less rapidly, the definite association of this pigment with vision was not made until the work of Boll in 1876, followed by the more extensive and detailed work of Kühne and his co-workers in 1878. The pigment is known as *visual purple*, or *rhodopsin*, although its colour is not exactly what most people would call purple, as it contains much more red. But, having a trace of violet in it, it is best described as a deep pink or rose colour. It can be extracted from the retinae of frogs and other animals by the use of bile salts, or better, digitonin. The colloidal solution so obtained is readily bleached by light, so the extraction must be done in the dark or in a deep red light. By the use of very weak light and very delicate apparatus, it is possible, nevertheless, to determine its absorption spectrum, which is of a simple form. Absorption is negligible at the red end of the spectrum (wave-lengths greater than about $0 \cdot 6 \mu$), rises steadily as the wave-length is reduced, reaching a maximum at $0 \cdot 505 \mu$ (blue-green) and then falling away again to about one-fifth of the maximum value at about $0 \cdot 4 \mu$ (extreme violet). It is possible, also, to measure the rate at which such a solution is bleached by light of different wave-lengths, but of constant power (quanta per second): the curve relating the rate of bleaching (*"action" spectrum*) may be superimposed with considerable precision on the absorption spectrum—an excellent confirmation of the Grotthus-Draper law.

But these facts by themselves give no evidence that visual purple has any necessary relation to vision or photo-reception in general. Such evidence is presented, first, by the fact that the *sensitivity* of the human eye (as measured by the reciprocal of the least energy in quanta which can be detected) varies with the wave-length of the light in just the same way as does the rate of bleaching or the absorption coefficient of visual purple. In animals other than ourselves, we can determine the least intensity of illumination of a given wave-length which will produce certain character-istic behaviour reactions, or certain characteristic electrical changes in the eye or in the optic nerve. The results of such investigations indicate that visual purple is one of the photosensitive substances in all the vertebrates so far examined, and in the cephalopods; and with less certainty in other molluscs, and in arthropods, both crustaceans and insects. The intensity concerned, of course, is that which actually reaches the retina, so that corrections may have to be applied for the absorption, particularly of blue and violet light, by various structures of the eye.

Such observations on the "threshold" intensity of illumination show, also, that if the duration of the illumination is small (in man, less than about $0 \cdot 01$ sec.; in the horseshoe crab *Limulus*, less than about $0 \cdot 1$ sec.), and the area illuminated is not too large (in man, subtends less than about $1°$ at the eye), the reciprocity law is accurately obeyed; the threshold is measured in terms of the total energy received on the retina. As the duration of the exposure is increased, the threshold value of the product $I \times t$ rises, and for very long exposures, the duration becomes irrelevant, the magnitude of the sensation now depending on the power, or flux, received on the retina, and not on the energy. Presumably some steady state, or stationary condition as discussed above (p. 383), is reached, either in the photo-chemical system as a result of "back" reactions, or perhaps, also, in the nervous system. As the area illuminated is increased beyond a certain value, the threshold value of the intensity-time product does not decrease in proportion. This is only to be expected; in all the more complicated kinds of eye, the photosensitive surface is not homogeneous, as, for example, is that of a photoelectric cell or photographic plate, but is divided up into a large number of units, which act independently. When the area illuminated exceeds the effective area of a receptor unit, the photochemical effects produced in different parts do not add together; each unit must receive the threshold number of quanta. In the human eye, and probably also in all the highly developed eyes, the matter is further complicated by the fact that the "effective" area of each receptor unit falls as the intensity of illumination rises. These observations are all consistent with the idea that the primary event in photo-reception consists of a photochemical reaction of some kind. As we shall see later, however, it seems probable that it should, strictly, be called photocatalytic, although this has not been definitely established.

There is reason to suppose that several other photosensitive substances are also concerned in vision, although the evidence is largely indirect. Insects, for example, seem to have a pigment whose maximum absorption is in the extreme violet or near ultra-violet. Fresh-water fishes have a pigment which has a maximum absorption at $0 \cdot 54 \mu$; this can be extracted from the retinae, and is known as *visual violet*, or *porphyropsin*. And most vertebrates must be presumed to have additional pigments associated with an alternative set of receptor cells, the *cones*, visual purple being associated only with the *rods*: only one of these, known as *iodopsin*, with a maximum absorption at $0 \cdot 56 \mu$, has so far been extracted, but there is indirect evidence for the existence of several others.

Knowledge of the chemistry of the visual pigments, and of the photo-chemistry of the reactions which they undergo, is due largely to the work of Morton and his colleagues, and to that of Wald and his colleagues, both since about 1940. The constitution of these pigments is analogous to that of the respiratory enzymes discussed in Chapters 7 and 8, with the res-piratory pigment, haemoglobin, and with the photosynthesising system discussed in the previous section—i.e. there is a large protein molecule associated with a number of prosthetic groups, or *chromophores*. They are destroyed by heat, inactivated by agents which denature proteins in general, and possess ultra-violet absorption spectra characteristic of proteins. The chromophore groups cannot be removed without destroying the pigment: but after bleaching by light, treatment with suitable organic solvents yields a substance known as *retinene*. This substance is a carotenoid, and is an oxidation product (an aldehyde) of vitamin A (an alcohol), whose structure is given in Fig. 9.5. There are two forms of vitamin A, known as A_1 and A_2, and these, on oxidation, give rise to $retinene_1$ and $retinene_2$ respectively. Both rhodopsin (visual purple) and porphyropsin (visual violet) contain the same protein carrier, but in the former the chromophore is retinene$_1$, while in the latter it is retinene$_2$. Moreover, iodopsin, like rhodopsin, contains retinene$_1$ as chromophore, but it is attached to a different protein carrier. If this same carrier is attached to the chromophore group of porphyropsin, a fourth pigment is formed known as *cyanopsin*; its absorption curve has a maximum at 0·62 μ and it may be present in some fresh-water fishes and tortoises. It is clear, therefore, that the absorption spectrum of the chromophore is modified by the nature of the carrier to which it is attached: and it seems likely that there are many different kinds of carrier in different kinds of animal.

The first product of the action of light on visual purple is an orange substance, having a single absorption band in the region of 0·46 μ to 0·47 μ. The quantum yield of this process appears to be about 0·5. This orange substance is extremely unstable, and is accordingly given the name of

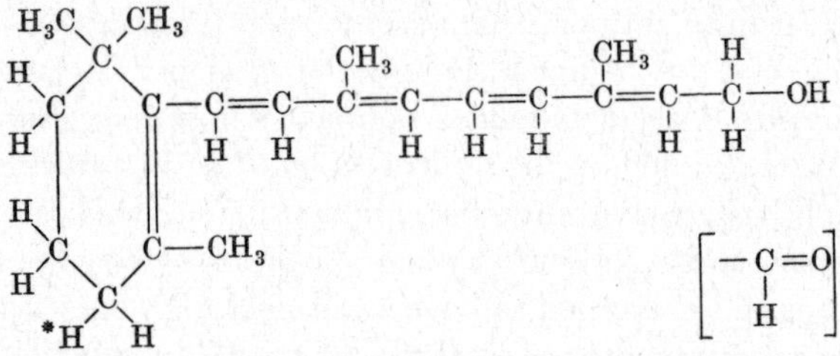

FIG. 9.5. THE STRUCTURE OF VITAMIN A AND RETINENE

Vitamin A has the terminal alcoholic group, as shown: retinene has an aldehyde group as shown beneath in brackets.

In vitamin A$_1$ and retinene$_1$, the ring structure at the other end is as shown: in vitamin A$_2$ and retinene$_2$, the hydrogen atom marked with an asterisk is missing, and instead there is a double bond between the carbon atoms in the ring.

Carotene, from which these substances, as well as the carotenoid pigments in plant cells, are derived, is a hydrocarbon formed by joining two of these chains of carbon atoms end to end, the six-membered rings being at each end of the whole chain.

transient orange: it breaks down spontaneously to a substance which is yellow in acid solution (absorption maximum at about 0·4 μ) and colourless in alkaline solution, and which is thus called *indicator yellow*. The rate of this reaction is highly dependent on temperature, and the presence of transient orange can only be detected if visual purple is bleached by light at a temperature in the region of 0° C. or below. Indicator yellow itself breaks down in acid solution, and retinene$_1$ is formed.

When a photon is absorbed by a molecule of visual purple, therefore, the prosthetic group is not entirely dissociated from the carrier molecule, but the nature of the bond between them is changed in some way, so that both the colour, and also the ionisation of the molecule, are changed. It is possible, though by no means established, that this change in ionisation is responsible for the electrical potential changes which are observed in most kinds of photo-receptor; it is these electrical effects, in all probability, that initiate the nerve impulses. Later, more profound changes may occur, and the overall reaction then appears to be irreversible. But in the whole animal, of course, the bleached visual purple must be replaced. For this, a supply of energy is needed; oxygen must be present, and probably, also, some special metabolites. In warm-blooded animals, regeneration of visual purple does not occur unless the supply of blood to the retina is intact; in the frog, there is some regeneration even in excised eyes, provided that oxygen is available. But if the bleaching process is interrupted at the stage of transient orange, some direct regeneration may occur even in solutions of extracts from retinae; it is in any case, far more complete than it is when indicator yellow is formed. This may be because the chromophore has not left the protein carrier, nor been reduced to vitamin A.

According to Wald, retinene, vitamin A and the diphosphopyridine nucleotide co-enzyme form a reaction system which, catalysed by the appropriate dehydrogenase, comes to an equilibrium in which most of the retinene is reduced to vitamin A. But if the reduced form of the co-enzyme is continuously oxidised as a result of the simultaneous presence of some other system which is undergoing oxidative metabolism, the equilibrium position is pulled in the direction of the oxidation of vitamin A to retinene. This occurs to an even greater extent if the retinene is also removed from the reaction system by combining with its specific protein carrier. Now vitamin A, and thus retinene, exist in several *cis* and *trans* isomeric forms, and only one of these—the *cis* isomer—will combine with the protein carrier: the retinene which is formed on bleaching visual purple, however, is the *trans* isomer, which will not combine. The production of the correct isomer of vitamin A must be supposed to occur only in some other part of the animal.

PHOTOCHEMICAL ACTIONS OF ULTRA-VIOLET LIGHT

Living cells, on the whole, are colourless; few of their constituents absorb light of such a wave-length as to be visible by the human eye. Most of them, however, absorb light of shorter wave-lengths, in the ultra-violet region, and will undergo photochemical reactions. In general, as remarked in a previous section, the absorption of a photon results in the absorbing molecule breaking into two parts, with the formation of free radicals; these then react with other molecules, if they do not first react with each other. It is only to be expected, therefore, that irradiation with ultra-violet light will be liable to upset the normal sequence of metabolic reactions which is necessary for the continued existence of living cells.

Study of the effects produced, however, shows that the most important constituents, from the point of view of the action of ultra-violet light, are the proteins and nucleoproteins. The latter consist of basic proteins united with nucleic acids; these, in turn, consist of chains of compounds of relatively small molecular weight containing derivatives of purine and pyrimidine (Chapter 6, p. 235). The reason for this special importance is, probably, that all enzymes are proteins, and most, if not all, the co-enzymes contain the pyrimidine ring, as may be seen in Fig. 8.1. (p. 348); this ring occurs, also, in the purines, of which adenine is probably the most important. The effects of the destruction of these substances, whose actions are catalytic, or of alteration in their properties, as a result of photo-chemical reactions, will be "amplified", as it were, into more widespread changes in the whole organism. But possibly even more important is the fact that the synthesis of the enzymes, and thus probably of all the cellular constituents necessary for the growth and reproduction of the cell, depends on the action of nucleoproteins. These occur particularly in the nuclei of the cells (hence the name) where they make up the genes. These link up to form the chromosomes, and their proper arrangement is necessary, particularly when the cell divides, and reproduces itself, for ensuring that the new cells shall be able to develop the proper metabolic systems. Destruction, or alteration, of a gene as a result of the absorption of a photon, may not affect the cell immediately, but may result in death when the cell next divides. Somewhat similar, from this point of view, is the effect of radiations on viruses. These are also nucleoproteins, and their presence within a cell may result in the production of similar nucleo-proteins, causing abnormality or death of the cell. This, however, appears to occur only when there is a specific relation between the structure of the virus and that of some particular cellular component. Absorption of a photon by a virus molecule, is likely so to change its properties that it will no longer be able to reproduce itself within the cell, and so will no longer be infective.

The action of ultra-violet light on proteins *in vitro* is chiefly one of causing the rupture of the peptide bonds, the hydrogen bonds and the disulphide bonds which hold together the constituent amino-acids and link the protein chains one with another. The quantum yield is very small (of the order of 10^{-2} to 10^{-5}) probably because the radicals formed cannot rapidly diffuse away, and so mostly re-combine. In addition, there may be deamination and decarboxylation and various oxidations and reductions owing to the production of peroxides, hydroxyl radicals and hydrogen atoms from oxygen (if present) and water; this last effect is of greater importance in the actions of the ionising radiations, to be considered in the next section. The most effective wave-length for these reactions is about 2800 Å., corresponding with the absorption band characteristic of proteins.

Irradiation of the nucleoproteins will produce similar reactions, and may cause destruction of the pyrimidine ring. Here, the most effective wave-length is about 2650 Å., corresponding with an absorption band characteristic of nucleic acids.

It has not, so far, been possible to relate the action of ultra-violet light on living cells with any definite chemical reaction. That nucleoproteins are largely involved is strongly suggested by the action spectra. The lethal action of a given amount of radiant energy on viruses, bacteria and sperm cells, depends on the wave-length in the same way as does the absorption of the radiation by nucleic acids; there is a maximum at about 2650 Å., and there is little or no action if the wave-length is greater than 3200 Å. This applies, also, to the inhibition of certain specific enzyme reactions which have been studied. In other cases, such as the lethal action on some egg cells and protozoa, and the effects produced on red blood cells, the maximum effect is produced when the wave-length is about 2800 Å., corresponding with the absorption by proteins. There is no evidence, however, that these substances themselves undergo any substantial chemical change. The relation between the amount of effect produced and the wave-length of the radiation is not always simple and definite; it is probable—and indeed to be expected—that many different substances and many different reaction sequences are affected. The general result, however, is somewhat similar to that of a rise in temperature. Amoebae, for example, on illumination with ultra-violet light, stop all movement and become spherical. Watery drops may appear on the surface, and finally disintegration occurs. It would seem that the inactivation of the enzyme systems prevents the organism from maintaining itself against the "spontaneous" reactions of disorganisation and destruction.

The actions of ultra-violet light on protoplasm have some practical importance. The lethal effects on viruses and bacteria have been utilised for the purpose of sterilising air, water and watery solutions, and the dust particles on floors. The injurious effects on all cells are familiar to everyone from the inflammation (erythema) produced in the skin when exposed to strong sunlight. This *sunburn*, if severe, may lead to the formation of oedema, blisters and loss of the superficial layers of the skin. Exactly similar effects are produced by all agents which damage the tissue cells, such as excessive heat or cold. Sunburn, however, is not an effect of heat, and it is, indeed, more liable to occur in cold surroundings, or in strong winds, perhaps partly because the heat of the sun is not noticed, and no means are taken to protect the skin. It is purely an effect of the ultra-violet components of sunlight, and can easily be obtained with artificial sources of ultra-violet light. The most effective wave-lengths for producing sunburn are between 2900 Å. and 3050 Å., and less than 2650 Å. The band of longer wave-lengths does not correspond with the maximum absorption of either protein or nucleic acid, but there is good reason for believing that the action takes place in the deeper epidermis of the skin; the light reaching this layer, therefore, must first pass through the outer layer of corneum, which is largely protein in nature. The action spectrum of erythema formation is thus determined chiefly by the absorption spectrum of the corneum, which acts as a light filter, and only slightly by the absorption spectrum of the reactive cells themselves.

In suitable people, the erythema is followed by a brown protective coloration of the skin. This pigmentation is initially due to the migration of melanin pigments from the deeper layers to the corneum. Later, the basal cells begin to produce more melanin. In addition, illumination with wave-lengths of 3100 Å. to 4000 Å.—i.e. somewhat longer than those most effective in producing erythema—results in darkening of pigment already present. These longer wave-lengths, also, are somewhat more effective in causing production of the pigment than are those most effective in causing the erythema. The sensitivity of the skin to ultra-violet radiation becomes reduced as the exposure is prolonged, even in the absence of pigmentation, owing to the progressive thickening of the corneum.

Exposure of the eyes to strong ultra-violet light results in a very painful and incapacitating inflammation, or *conjunctivitis*, also known as "snow-blindness". The condition, however, clears up spontaneously, and no permanent damage is done. The effective radiations have wave-lengths less than about 3050 Å., and those with wave-lengths less than 2800 Å. are relatively more effective in producing conjunctivitis than they are in producing erythema, possibly because it is the superficial layers, in which they are absorbed, that are damaged; whereas in the skin the superficial layers are already dead. Ultra-violet light is highly reflected by snow and ice, so that erythema and conjunctivitis are very apt to occur when the ground is snow- and ice-bound. It is apt to be forgotten that a fine mist scatters light, rather than absorbing it, and that snow-blindness may occur even when the sky is overcast, or the traveller is in a cloud. There is considerable risk of suffering from erythema and conjunctivitis when exposed to radiations, not only from the sun and sky, or an artificial source intended to produce ultra-violet light, but also from that from any unprotected arc lamp, or the hot metal during welding operations, whether by electric arc or oxy-acetylene torch.

The formation of vitamin D is probably the only beneficial action of ultra-violet light. This occurs in the tissues of the skin, from the ergosterol and other steroids which act as precursors; but under civilised conditions, it is probably better performed in a factory. The effective wave-lengths lie in the region 2500 Å. to 3150 Å.

Sources of Ultra-violet Light. (a) *Sunlight.* In outer space, beyond the earth's atmosphere, the amount of energy associated with wave-lengths less than about 4000 Å. is about 5 per cent. of the total energy of the sun's radiation, and the intensity is appreciable down to a wave-length of about 2200 Å. At the earth's surface, the total energy is reduced by absorption and scattering in the atmosphere by an amount which depends enormously on the clearness of the air and the height of the sun; some 90 per cent. may penetrate, or nearly none at all. But in all cases, the proportion of the energy in the ultra-violet region is greatly reduced, becoming 0·2 per cent. of the total or considerably less. This is due largely to the presence of ozone in the upper atmosphere (at a height of about 20 kilometres) which absorbs practically all the radiation with a wave-length less than about 3000 Å. Scattering and absorption by constituents of the lower atmosphere are also appreciable, however, so that the intensity of the ultra-violet radiation increases as one ascends above sea-level. It is the shortest wave-lengths that are affected most, and these are the most active biologically; the risk of suffering from sunburn or snow-blindness thus increases rapidly with height, as is well known to all who ascend mountains. The scattering of direct sunlight produced by the atmosphere has the effect that the total amount of ultra-violet radiation received from the whole blue sky is greater than that received directly from the sun, except when the altitude of the sun is greater than 60°. This fact is apt to be overlooked, and may be significant when a large expanse of sky is visible, as at sea.

(b) *Artificial Sources.* The most generally convenient is the mercury arc in a quartz envelope (ordinary glass does not transmit radiation at a wave-length less than about 3000 Å.). The nature of the radiation emitted depends chiefly on the pressure of mercury vapour when the lamp is operating: if the pressure is low (about 0·01 mm. Hg), some 90 per cent. of the radiant energy is concentrated in the "resonance" line of 2537 Å. wave-length; if the pressure is high (1 to 100 atmospheres), the radiant energy is distributed among a very large number of wave-lengths, including those in the visible region, about one-half being in the ultra-violet, mostly at wave-lengths greater than 3200 Å. If considerable amounts of energy are required in wave-lengths in the region just below the limits of vision (say between 3000 Å. and 4000 Å.), the carbon arc may be used, particularly if the carbons are provided with cores containing cerium, iron or certain other metals. The best source of a sensibly continuous and uniform radiation over the whole ultra-violet region, down to 2000 Å. or less, is the hydrogen arc; this is not very suitable for general illumination, but is the best source for use with a monochromator when accurately known wave-lengths are needed.

Further information as to the sources of ultra-violet light, the measurement of its intensity, its transmission by various substances and its applications, will be found in the book by Koller (1952). A detailed account of the biological actions is given by Errera (1953).

Photodynamic Sensitisation

It has been found by several observers that light which has no action by itself on protozoa, bacteria, blood or small animals such as mice and rats, produces the effects of ultra-violet light when certain dyestuffs are present. As an example, we may quote some experiments by Hertel in 1905.

Exposure of certain bacteria to ultra-violet light of 2800 Å. killed them in 60 seconds. Eosin has an absorption band in the region of 5180 Å., and in the presence of eosin, 1 part in 1200, exposure to light of this wave-length, with about the same radiant energy as the ultra-violet light, killed them in 70 to 90 seconds. In the absence of eosin, this light had no effect. Moreover, irradiation with light of 4480 Å. had no effect, whether eosin was present or not; eosin has no absorption band in this region.

Many dyes besides eosin will act as photodynamic sensitisers, haematoporphyrin being very effective; chlorophyll, riboflavin and methylene blue have also been used. There is no doubt that the dye, in these reactions, is acting as a photosensitiser. But, as already remarked (p. 385 above), the mechanism of the action is very imperfectly understood. In many cases, the presence of oxygen is necessary, and the reacting substance becomes oxidised; hydrogen peroxide may be formed. But this is by no means universal, and, for example, disulphide linkages may be reduced to sulphydryl groups.

THE ACTIONS OF IONISING RADIATIONS

If the quantum of radiation absorbed by an atom is sufficiently large, one of the constituent electrons may gain so much energy that it can leave the atom altogether, instead of merely taking up a new configuration with greater energy content. In such cases, the atom is said to become ionised. The upper limit of wave-length for such ionisation is about 25 Å.—i.e. 100 times smaller than that of ultra-violet light—corresponding to an energy content of some 500 electron-volts per quantum. The exact value depends on the atomic weight of the material concerned, and the above value may be taken as a fair average for substances of biological interest. The ionising radiations are known as X-rays, γ-rays, and cosmic rays, according to their wave-lengths, as indicated in Fig. 9.1.

Ionisation may also be produced by the products of atomic disintegration, when travelling with a high velocity. These products are: electrons, forming β-rays when emitted as a result of radioactive disintegration, and cathode rays when emitted from a metal and accelerated in a large electric potential gradient; helium nuclei, with positive charges, emitted in radioactive disintegrations (α-rays); protons (positively charged hydrogen nuclei) formed by impact of other particles with hydrogen atoms, or by accelerating gaseous hydrogen ions in an electric field; and neutrons, the uncharged particles which are released in certain nuclear disintegrations. The charged particles produce ionisation as a result of the intense electrical fields generated in the atoms through which they pass. A neutron can readily penetrate right through the electron shell of an atom, not being subject to any electrical forces, and collide with the nucleus: if the neutron has a high velocity, the nucleus will be shot away, also with a high velocity, and since in the materials of interest to biologists, the encounter is most likely to be with a hydrogen atom, a proton will be produced; if the neutron has a low velocity, it will be absorbed by the nucleus, which then becomes unstable and undergoes radioactive disintegration, with the emission of α-, β- and γ-rays, according to the nature of the nucleus encountered. Both particles and radiations may be characterised either by their energies, or by their wave-lengths or frequencies, the ratio between energy and frequency being given by the Planck constant, h (Chapter 1, p. 25). For a given amount of energy, the heavier particles (neutrons, protons and α-particles) will, of course, have a lower velocity than the very much lighter electrons or β-particles.

The methods of generating such radiations and high-velocity particles form a rather specialised branch of physics. Apart from the "ordinary" X-rays, with energies up to a few hundred thousand electron-volts, the sources of which are available commercially, the generation of high energy particles and radiations necessitates the application of very high voltages, up to 10 million or more, and may involve large scale engineering, as in the construction of cyclotrons, synchrotrons and the various similar types of machine. Low velocity neutrons are produced in enormous quantities in nuclear fission reactors, the construction of which also involves large scale engineering; these, as already remarked, when absorbed in suitable materials, will produce artificial radioactive elements, which are very convenient sources of certain kinds of ionising radiation. Text-books of atomic physics should be consulted for further details.

The absorption of a quantum of radiation of all but the longest wave-length X-rays, endows the electron with considerably more energy than is necessary just to eject it from the atom. It thus leaves with a considerable velocity and acts like a β-ray in producing ionisation in other atoms. Such *secondary ionisation* also occurs as a result of the primary ionisation produced by one of the particles mentioned in the previous paragraph. These secondary ionisations occur as "clusters" round the site of the primary ionisation and if the electrons emitted in the secondary ionisation have an appreciable range, they are often referred to as δ-rays.

An ionising particle, or quantum of ionising radiation penetrates into matter until its energy has been absorbed by the ionisations produced. The *depth of penetration* of a particle, therefore, increases with the initial energy of the particle, and decreases with its size. Conversely, the *amount of ionisation* produced by each particle per unit length of path decreases with increase in the initial energy, as shown in Table 9.2, and in Fig. 9.6. This Table also gives the amount of secondary ionisation, and it will be seen that with ionising particles of high energy, the secondary ionisation is quantitatively as important as the primary ionisation. Fig. 9.6 also shows how the ionisation produced by a high-speed particle is closely restricted to the path of the particle, with the exception of the branches made by the δ-rays. The ionisation produced by X-rays, on the other hand, is distributed at random throughout the tissue, in accordance with the random distribution of the quanta in the incident radiation.

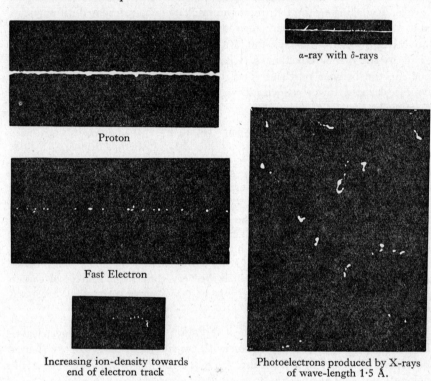

α-ray with δ-rays

Proton

Fast Electron

Increasing ion-density towards
end of electron track

Photoelectrons produced by X-rays
of wave-length 1·5 Å.

10 μ Tissue

FIG. 9.6. DISTRIBUTION OF IONISATION PRODUCED BY DIFFERENT RADIATIONS

Photographs taken of a Wilson cloud chamber: the ions formed in a gas have been made visible by the condensation of water droplets on them. The dimensions of each photograph have been adjusted so that it represents reasonably closely the distribution of ions in a piece of irradiated tissue.   (From Lea, 1946.)

The Röntgen Unit. It is important to be able to define the total quantity of ionising radiation absorbed by some material under examination. Since the effects are due to the ionisation produced, the unit ordinarily used, known as the Röntgen unit, is defined as that quantity of radiation, or of ionising particles, which produces one electrostatic unit of electricity, as a result of ionisation, in one cubic centimetre of air at normal temperature and pressure (0·001293 g.). It is a quantity which can be measured with reasonable accuracy, and is not of an inconvenient size in relation to the biological effects produced. The absorptive power of matter for ionising radiations and particles, however, depends upon its composition; and the energy of the secondary electrons ejected depends upon the frequency of the incident radiations. The total number of ionisations, and the amount

TABLE 9.2

Penetration of Charged Particles, and Amount of Ionisation Produced

Energy keV	Range μ	Number of Primary ionisations per μ ($\rho=1$)	Number of δ-ray* ionisations per primary ionisation
Electrons			
0·1	0·003	1700	—
0·5	0·02	530	0·225
1·0	0·05	224	0·52
3·0	0·31	82	0·60
10	2·52	30·6	0·69
100	141	4·7	0·86
α-particles			
1000	5·3	5210	0·72
3000	16·8	2030	0·88
7000	60·3	968	0·95
10,000	108	706	0·98
Protons			
1000	23	398	0·905
3000	147	152	0·98
7000	642	71·6	1·01
10,000	1210	52·2	1·02

* Number exceeding 100 eV energy.

of energy released, as a result of the absorption of each Röntgen unit thus depends somewhat on the nature of the absorbing material and on the nature and energy of the radiation. Roughly, 1 r. produces 1·7 (for X-rays and neutrons) to 1·9 (for α-rays and protons) ionisations in each cubic micron (10^{-12} g.) of wet tissue. The amount of energy released varies from 53 to 70 eV per 10^{-12} g. of tissue. More complete and detailed values are given by Lea (1955, Table 2, p. 8).

Chemical Effects. The ejection of an electron from a molecule, leaving it with a positive charge, or the absorption of an additional electron, giving it a negative charge, does not usually lead to immediate decomposition of the molecule. Subsequent collision with some other molecule, particularly if this is also ionised, with a charge of the opposite sign, will result in the release of energy and the formation of free radicals. It is the existence of these free radicals which is largely responsible for the chemical effects produced by ionising radiations. The extra energy in an ionised atom may also lead to electronic excitation and fluorescence in the visible region of the spectrum, as does the absorption of a photon of, say, ultra-violet light. But when we are dealing with solutions, this effect is quantitatively negligible.

In practice, one of the most valuable of the chemical reactions produced is the blackening of photographic emulsions. Photographic plates and films, therefore, can be used to detect the presence of ionising radiations of all kinds, although, of course, no optical image can be formed (except with electrons, as in the electron microscope). It was, in fact, this reaction, together with the fluorescence produced, which led to the discovery of X-rays by Röntgen in 1895.

Water is quantitatively the chief constituent of living matter, and it absorbs the ionising radiations as effectively as do most of the solutes. The actions of ionising radiations thus differ from those of ultra-violet light, which is hardly absorbed by water at all, and are due largely to the free radicals produced from the ionised molecules of water. If an electron is ejected from a molecule of water, we are left with a positive ion:

$$H_2O \longrightarrow H_2O^+ + e$$

This ion may then dissociate into a hydrogen ion and a hydroxyl radical:

$$H_2O^+ \longrightarrow H^+ + OH$$

Meanwhile, the ejected electron will probably travel an appreciable distance (in terms of molecular dimensions) before encountering any atom or molecule. It may be absorbed by a water molecule and produce a negative water ion:

$$H_2O + e \longrightarrow H_2O^-$$

This may then dissociate into a hydroxyl ion and a hydrogen atom:

$$H_2O^- \longrightarrow H + OH^-$$

Alternatively, the electron may encounter a hydrogen ion and give rise to a hydrogen atom:

$$H^+ + e \longrightarrow H$$

Both the hydrogen atoms and the hydroxyl radicals are extremely reactive, and may be expected to react with the first molecule or atom that they encounter. The most obvious reaction is one of re-combination to form water, and this, indeed, is a frequent reaction; but the hydrogen atoms and the hydroxyl radicals may be formed at some distance from each other, and there is thus a finite chance that other reactions may occur.

The separation between the water ions of opposite sign is particularly marked when the density of the ionisation, per unit length of track, is large. With all kinds of particle, the ionisations are produced initially within a cylinder whose radius is approximately 15 mμ (the edges, of course, are not sharp, and the ion density actually decreases exponentially from the centre of the track). If the particle is an electron with an energy of some 50 kV. or more, the positive and negative ions are more or less uniformly and randomly distributed along this cylinder. But if the particle is, say, an α-particle, or a very slow electron, the positive ions, and thus the hydroxyl radicals, are more densely packed within some 1 to 5 mμ of the centre of the track, and the negative ions, and thus the hydrogen atoms, are produced mainly outside this zone. Initially, in the central zone, the density of hydroxyl radicals may be 100 times that of hydrogen atoms. The radicals and the atoms, however, rapidly diffuse away from their initial positions, and the separation between them has sensibly vanished after about 10^{-7} seconds. By this time, also, the total concentration has been reduced, by re-combination and other reactions, to about 1/100 of the initial value. The life-time of these reactive units is thus extremely short. Nevertheless, they may be involved in several different kinds of reaction. We may have, for example:

$$H + H \longrightarrow H_2$$
$$OH + OH \longrightarrow H_2O + O$$
$$O + O \longrightarrow O_2$$

If dissolved oxygen is present, either from the atmosphere, or from the last of these reactions, we may have:

$$H + O_2 \longrightarrow HO_2$$
$$2HO_2 \longrightarrow H_2O_2 + O_2$$

Hydrogen peroxide seems to be formed only when free oxygen is present. It is clear from these reactions that highly oxidising and highly reducing conditions will both be produced within a relatively small volume of the solution. It is these conditions, mainly, which bring about the chemical effects of the ionising radiations on any solutes that may be present: an oxidisable substance will take up hydroxyl radicals, and the companion hydrogen atoms will be evolved as hydrogen gas; a reducible substance will take up hydrogen atoms, and oxygen will be evolved.

Study of the kinetics of a number of reactions—mostly decompositions and oxidations and reductions—has shown that unless the solution is very

o

dilute (10^{-3} M. or less), the number of molecules caused to react by each pair of ions formed by the radiation (the yield per ion-pair) is sensibly independent of the concentration. In other words, the hydrogen atoms and the hydroxyl radicals react almost entirely with the solute molecules, and there is little re-combination. In very dilute solutions, however, the yield per ion-pair becomes smaller and re-combination becomes significant. The actual value of the yield per ion-pair in most of the reactions lies between 0·1 and 2, with some values outside this range in both directions. Low values are due partly to the fact that it is not essential that every collision between an active atom or radical and a solute molecule should lead to chemical reaction; as with photochemical reactions, there are likely to be "deactivating" collisions in which the energy is released as heat, for example. In some cases, also, it is highly probable that other reactions are occurring besides the particular one whose velocity is being estimated; this is particularly likely to be true when the solute is a complex organic compound. High values of the yield per ion-pair are most probably due to the existence of chain reactions.

Now the quantity of ionising radiation necessary to produce detectable effects in living tissues of various kinds lies roughly within the limits of 50 r. and 500,000 r. This means that between 100 and 1,000,000 ionisations are produced in each cubic micron and thus about 10^2 to 10^6 molecules react. The total number of atoms present in this volume of tissue, however, is about 10^{11}; so that the biological effects are produced as a consequence of the reaction of only a minute fraction of all the atoms present. The effects of each quantum of ionising radiation, also, are limited to a volume occupied by one, or at most a few, molecules. For these reasons, the actions of the ionising radiations are apparent, even more than those of ultra-violet light, in the "catalytic" systems of living cells, such as enzymes, viruses and genes. The chemical effects produced by these radiations, moreover, are more apparent the larger is the molecule. The destruction, or chemical alteration, of one molecule among, say, 1000 similar molecules will not alter the properties of the solution to any marked extent; but the destruction of one link in the chain of 1000 which constitutes a macro-molecule, for example, is likely to affect the properties of the whole molecule. It appears, also, that the effects of "excitation" consequent on the absorption of a quantum of energy at one point in such a molecule may be transmitted, in part, to other points in the same molecule, and also, probably, to neighbouring molecules in the same micelle.

The actions of the ionising radiations on living tissues, on the whole, are thus similar to those of ultra-violet light. Enzymes and viruses are inactivated, probably as a result of some change similar to denaturation; genes, both nuclear and cytoplasmic, may be destroyed or altered in various ways, and the linkages which bind them into chromosomes may be ruptured. The chromosomes will then be abnormal, and the genetic characters of the organism may be changed (mutation); it is probably true to say that the ionising radiations are some of the most powerful tools available to the geneticist. The destructive effects produced by the ionising radiations continue for a long time and do not appear at once in their full magnitude. The effects are more serious than those of ultra-violet light, also, since not only do they appear above all in those tissues which contain many dividing cells, but the ionising radiations penetrate to much deeper tissues. Thus, in man, a very intractable form of dermatitis is produced by their action on the skin, sterility by their action on the generative organs, and serious disorders of the blood by their action on the bone marrow, lymph nodes and other tissues where the various blood cells are formed. The actively proliferating cells of cancers may be destroyed, for a similar reason; but, presumably owing to the disorganisation of the nuclear and cytoplasmic genes, cancers may also be produced. Further details, particularly of such actions of the ionising radiations, will be found in the monograph by Spear (1953).

It is reasonable to assume, at least as an initial approximation, that a single ionisation occurring within a gene, or virus, is sufficient to cause destruction. If we irradiate with a known dose of a homogeneous ionising radiation, we know the average number of ions produced per unit volume of the tissue, as already remarked. If we then apply the ordinary laws of probability, we can calculate the chance that an ionisation shall occur within a certain specified volume—that is the chance that at least one of the quanta fired into the tissue shall hit the target. In our application of the laws of chance to the absorption of radiation earlier in this chapter (p. 375), we considered the chance of a single photon being absorbed by a large number of molecules: we are now interested in the probability that each molecule (or target area) will receive at least one out of a large number of quanta fired at it. If p is now the chance that a quantum shall hit a target, and N is the number of quanta fired, we can deduce, as before, that a fraction $\exp(-p.N)$ of the incident quanta will traverse the tissue without hitting at all. Now, on the average, of the N quanta fired, $p.N$ will hit (from the definition of probability), so that if we adjust the value of N until the value of $p.N$ is unity, i.e. if the dose of radiation is just sufficient to produce, *on the average*, one ionisation per critical volume, then $\exp(-1)$, or 37 per cent., of the organisms will survive. By relating the dose of radiation to the fraction surviving, we can thus deduce the number of quanta that hit the target, and thus, from the number of ionisations produced in unit volume of the tissue, and their spatial distribution, the size of the critical target. The calculation, however, is somewhat elaborate.

It is necessary to take account of several complicating factors. (*a*) The number of ionisations per quantum of radiation must include the secondary ionisations as well as the primary; (b) account must be taken of the finite width of the ionisation track, owing to the δ-rays; (c) allowance must be made for the fact that the length of the target, measured along the ionisation track, may not be small compared with the interval between ionisations—there may be an appreciable chance of getting two ionisations in one target, or, indeed, if the target is large, this chance may become unity, and the randomness disappears in this co-ordinate.

The results of some measurements of target size are given in Table 9.3. It would appear that a single ionisation occurring anywhere within the smallest virus will bring about its destruction; the calculated target size is independent of the dose of radiation, and agrees with the size of the virus as determined by ultra-filtration. This is not so with the largest virus, however, and it is probable that there may be some hundred critical target volumes, each of some 6 mμ diameter; such inhomogeneity is also suggested by the appearance in the electron microscope. The virus of intermediate size may be homogeneous, and the apparent discrepancies may be due to the application of the simplifying assumptions necessary in calculating the target size from the inactivation dose of radiation. For a full discussion, particularly of this aspect of the effects of ionising radiations, the monograph by Lea (1955) should be consulted. The target theory, in its simplest form, can hardly be expected to apply to the actions of the ionising radiations on the larger, more complex, organisms. There are likely to be many "critical" targets, and the effects on these, with their "catalytic" action on the whole organism, will interact in many and various ways.

TABLE 9.3

Inactivation of Viruses by Ionising Radiations

Radiation	Inactivation Dose Millions of Röntgens	Target Diameter mμ	Virus	Diameter mμ
γ-rays	0·58	15·5	Phage S. 13	16
X-rays (1·5 Å.)	0·99	15·9		
α-rays (4 MeV.)	3·5	16·3		
γ-rays	0·079	31	Staph. Phage K	64
X-rays (1·5 Å.)	0·109	40		
α-rays (7 MeV.)	0·21	58		
α-rays (4 MeV.)	0·45	50		
γ-rays	0·080	31	Vaccinia	200
X-rays (1·5 Å.)	0·104	41		
α-rays (5 MeV.)	0·211	70		

LITERATURE

General Theory of Photochemical Reactions. Rollefsen and Burton (1939); Rabinowitch (1945).

Chlorophyll System and Photosynthesis. Willstätter und Stoll (1913, 1918); Rabinowitch (1945, 1951, 1956); Hill and Whittingham (1957); Calvin (1950-51); Whittingham (1955); Bossham and Calvin (1957).

Photo-receptors and Vision. Granit (1947); Collins (1954); Pirenne (1956); Dartnall (1957).

Ultra-violet Light. Koller (1952); Errera (1953); Blum (1941).

Ionising Radiations. Lea (1955); Spear (1953).

IO

THE PASSAGE OF SUBSTANCES THROUGH MEMBRANES

All living cells are surrounded by membranes which prevent their contents from mixing freely with the solutions outside them. These membranes are too thin to be visible—even under the electron microscope, they have not been seen with certainty—and their constitution must be inferred from their properties. The various organs and tissues which make up a whole living organism, also, are separated by membranes consisting of sheets of flattened cells, bedded in, and sometimes covered by, a homogeneous "matrix". The whole organism itself is, in most cases, covered by an "integument" or "skin", with much the same composition. It is essential for the proper existence of any living organism that some substances, such as the food materials, and the waste products left over after the food has been utilised, should pass easily through some of these membranes; whereas other substances, such as water and salts, at least in some kinds of animal, should be held back. Conversely, it is necessary, also, that there should be membranes relatively impermeable to food substances and waste materials, but permeable to salts. The properties of membranes, and the factors which determine the rate of penetration of substances through them, thus form important parts of physiological studies.

The passage of a substance through a membrane is essentially a process of diffusion; it is a "spontaneous" process, in which the free energy of the system decreases. The direction in which the substance moves, therefore, is determined by the direction of the chemical potential gradient, or, if the substance is electrically charged, of the electrochemical potential gradient. But the membrane forms a separate phase, distinct from the solutions on either side of it, and its structure and composition are likely to be different from those of either of these solutions. Many complicated factors may thus be concerned in determining the *rate* of passage. In living organisms, however, there are many examples of a substance passing through a membrane in the direction contrary to that expected from the apparent electrochemical potential gradient—a process known as "active transport" or "secretion". It must be inferred that work is done by some auxiliary processes on the substance concerned, with the result that the actual potential gradient within the membrane is contrary to that expected from the compositions of the two solutions on each side. Rather little is known about this at present; we can do no more than put forward certain possible physico-chemical processes which may be involved.

THE PROPERTIES OF MEMBRANES IN GENERAL

It is obvious that a membrane, being merely a thin sheet or film, may be composed of almost any substance. But, for our purpose, it is useful to classify membranes according to their behaviour towards water, and towards substances dissolved in it. In the first place, there are such things as glass or mica, which allow neither water nor substances dissolved in it to pass through. These may be called *impermeable* and have a comparatively small importance. There are also some materials which are impermeable to water, but allow certain other liquids or gases to pass through; for example, india-rubber is impermeable to water, but allows pyridine to pass through. A metal, palladium, may be regarded as impermeable to water under ordinary circumstances, but allows hydrogen to pass through.

The most important membranes for the physiologist are those which allow water to pass through, but hold back dissolved substances. There are various degrees in this respect; some membranes, such as parchment paper, gelatin, cellophane, etc., will not allow colloids to pass, but are freely permeable for crystalloids. Copper ferrocyanide, on the other hand, holds back the majority of both colloids and crystalloids, but allows water to pass. A membrane which does not permit dissolved substances to pass, although permeable to water, is known as *semi-permeable*. When we wish to speak of a membrane which allows water to pass, but not a particular given substance, we say that it is impermeable as regards that substance, and permeable as regards certain others. An ideal semi-permeable membrane, permeable to water, but completely impermeable to all substances in solution, has not yet been prepared in the laboratory, and probably does not exist; the copper ferrocyanide membrane of Traube, however, approximates to it very closely.

THE STRUCTURE OF MEMBRANES

The fact that a membrane is permeable to some substances, for example water, and impermeable to others, must result from some peculiarity in its structure. It may act as a mechanical sieve, or riddle, and possess pores of such a size that small molecules can pass through and larger ones are held back, just as a sieve will separate sand from gravel. Or, alternatively, it may refuse passage to certain molecules by reason of their being insoluble in its structure, whereas others can dissolve in the membrane, diffuse through it, and then pass out again on the other side. Or, thirdly, some constituents of the membrane may form reversible chemical, or adsorption, compounds with certain substances, which are thus enabled to penetrate. As an instance of a membrane which is permeable to a substance because of the solubility of this substance in the membrane, we may take a membrane of water, supported in some way, as in wet parchment paper. This allows carbon dioxide to pass through, but, in comparison, keeps back oxygen and nitrogen. The latter, however, are not absolutely insoluble in water, and after a sufficient time, there will be no difference in composition between the gas mixtures on the two sides of the membrane. A membrane of metallic palladium, as investigated by Ramsay, again, is permeable to hydrogen, but not to oxygen, either because the hydrogen is soluble in it, or because a reversible compound of some kind is formed on the side of the membrane in contact with the higher partial pressure of hydrogen, and dissociates on the side in contact with the lower partial pressure. As regards the membranes like parchment paper, gelatin, collodion, etc., referred to in Chapter 6, which allow water and crystalloidal substances to pass through, but hold back colloidal substances, it is practically certain that they have a porous structure. As already mentioned in Chapter 6, collodion membranes can be prepared with pores of very varying sizes; the sizes of the pores can be determined, and the membranes used to measure the sizes of colloidal particles.

A detailed investigation of the permeability of large numbers of artificial membranes was undertaken by Walden in 1892. The membranes which he used can be arranged in order of merit as regards impermeability to the substances tested. Tannin-gelatin is the lowest in the the series, being permeable to all except tannin itself; while copper ferrocyanide is the highest, being impermeable to a larger number than any of the others. A significant fact is that none of the membranes comes out of its place as regards any particular substance. That is, assuming that the pores increase regularly in dimensions from the copper ferrocyanide to the tannin-gelatine, no substance is found which diffuses through a membrane having the smaller pores while being held back by that with the larger pores, as might happen on the solution theory. The behaviour of the hydrochlorides of the three ethylamines is of interest. The copper ferrocyanide membrane is readily permeable to that of monoethylamine, slightly permeable to that of the diethylamine, impermeable to that of the triethylamine, following the increase of molecular dimensions.

The sieve conception and the solution conception have been presented here, as well as in some other books, as if they were fundamentally opposed. While this may be true for artificial membranes of considerable thickness, and impermeable only to relatively large molecules, it becomes increasingly difficult to make a hard and fast distinction as the membranes become thinner, and as the differential permeability becomes more refined. The copper ferrocyanide membrane is freely permeable to water, and, in fact, contains water in its constitution; it is not easy to understand how a substance such as sugar, which is easily soluble in the water contained in the membrane, fails to pass unless something like a sieve is present, acting as a mechanical constraint on molecules above a certain size. But even here, it might also be argued that the water within the membrane is "bound", in the sense defined in Chapter 6, and so incapable of dissolving the sugar; whereas the "free" water molecules could pass through by interchanging with the "bound" molecules.

Another point to be remembered is that the surfaces of the elements of the membrane may adsorb dissolved substances. In the filtration of salts through a gelatin filter, the first portions of the filtrate contain less salt than the original solution; this continues until the adsorption capacity of the membrane is saturated. A colloid, when adsorbed, may diminish considerably the dimensions of the pores, so that the filter becomes impermeable to substances to which it was at first permeable. Such adsorption moreover, may to some extent be reversible. A membrane which initially behaves as a sieve, may subsequently allow molecules to pass by reversible adsorption.

In the last analysis, the process of solution consists in the penetration of the solute molecules into the interstices between the solvent molecules, and thus differs only in scale from the penetration of molecules into the pores within a membrane. The forces of interaction between solvent and solute, on the one hand, are usually very considerably greater than those between the membrane and molecules penetrating it, on the other hand; but the difference is quantitative, rather than qualitative. A further, and perhaps more significant difference, however, is that a sieve-like membrane is a solid structure and the pores are of fixed size, whereas a solvent-like membrane may be liquid, so that its molecules can be pushed aside to make space for a penetrating molecule.

THE PERMEABILITY OF A MEMBRANE TO A GIVEN SUBSTANCE

The permeability of a given membrane with respect to a given substance is defined quantitatively as the number of gram-molecules of that substance which pass through unit area in unit time—i.e. the *"flux"*—produced by unit difference of activity (or for solutes in dilute solution, of concentration) across the membrane. The ordinary units of area and time are square centimetres and seconds, respectively, and there seems no good reason why these should not be used in the definition of permeability constants, although other units have often been used. The ordinary unit of concentration difference, similarly, is 1 mole per kilogram of solvent; but,

o*

as has been pointed out by Rashevsky, if the unit of concentration difference is taken to be 1 mole per cubic centimetre (or, practically speaking, per millilitre) of solution, the unit of the permeability constant becomes 1 centimetre per second; this simplification has much to recommend it, particularly when the solutions considered are all dilute.

The definition of the permeability constant is exactly analogous with that of the diffusion constant, considered in Chapter 3. The Fick equation for the diffusion of an "ideal" solution, in which activity is equal to concentration, is:

$$\phi_2 = -D\frac{dm}{dx} \qquad . \qquad . \qquad . \text{ (from 3.31)}$$

where ϕ_2 is the flux of the substance concerned, dm/dx is the concentration gradient and D is a constant. But in a thin membrane, we assume that the thickness is constant, even if it is unknown, and that the concentration gradient is uniform within the membrane. We thus write, for a membrane:

$$\phi_2 = +P(\Delta m) \qquad . \qquad . \qquad . \qquad 10.1$$

where P is now the permeability constant, and Δm is the difference in concentration between the solutions on its two sides. This equation defines the net movement of the substance, in accordance with the concentration gradient. Since, as in diffusion, the movement results from the thermal agitation of the molecules, this net movement is, in fact, the difference between two movements in opposite directions. We may thus write:

$$(\phi_2)_{in} = P_{in}m_e$$
and
$$(\phi_2)_{out} = P_{out}m_c \qquad \Big\} \qquad . \qquad . \qquad . \qquad 10.1a$$

where m_e and m_c are the concentrations of the substance considered in, say, the external solution and the contents of a living cell, respectively, and $(m_e - m_c) = \Delta m$. P_{in} will not necessarily be identical with P_{out} and will certainly not be if the substance concerned is an ion, and there is an electrical potential difference across the membrane. The "*flux ratio*" will be given by:

$$\frac{(\phi_2)_{in}}{(\phi_2)_{out}} = \frac{P_{in}}{P_{out}} \cdot \frac{m_e}{m_c} .$$

If the cell is in a steady state, there being no net gain or loss of the substance considered, the two fluxes will be equal, but not necessarily zero, and the flux ratio will be unity.

Equations 10.1 and 10.1a are, of course, valid only in the conditions in which equation 3.31 may be used for defining the diffusion constant. Apart from the neglect of activity coefficients, it is obvious that the permeabilities P will not be true "constants" unless the flux is proportional to the concentration difference across the membrane; this may not be true in all circumstances, as will be discussed later.

When considering the penetration of water (or other solvent) it is common to take unit osmotic pressure difference (usually derived indirectly in terms of freezing point lowering, or even of total solute concentration), or unit hydrostatic pressure difference (or the algebraic sum of the two) instead of unit activity difference; it is convenient, and justifiable, also, to consider 1 millilitre as the quantity diffusing, instead of 1 gram-molecule. But if we consider a hydrostatic pressure to be precisely equivalent to an osmotic pressure, we are tacitly assuming that the flux results only from the corresponding activity gradient; the effect of the hydrostatic pressure being indirect, only, through its effect on the activity of the water. This is not, in general, true, since the hydrostatic pressure may well produce a viscous flow through pores in the membrane, and this may be large compared with the movement due to diffusion under the activity gradient. The velocity with which a molecule diffuses through a relatively large pore is independent of its distance from the wall; but the velocity of a molecule which is being carried through by a mass flow of the fluid increases from zero if it is at the wall, to a maximum if it is on the axis. Thus the rate of flow under a hydrostatic pressure head depends both on the total area of pores in unit area of membrane, and on the radius of each pore; whereas the rate of diffusion under an activity gradient depends only on the total pore area, the radius of each pore being of importance only when it is not very large compared with that of the diffusing molecules (say less than 10 times greater), so that the diffusion becomes "restricted". In the limit, of course, when the pores become so small that the diffusing substance can only enter the membrane as single molecules—or, perhaps, single molecular complexes—there can be no mass flow, and the driving force must be the partial free energy of the molecules.

In applying equation 10.1, it must be remembered that it is assumed that the rate of passage of the substance considered through the membrane is very small compared with its rate of arrival at the membrane on one side, and of its dispersal from the membrane at the other; diffusion within the solutions is assumed to be relatively rapid, or the solutions on both sides are assumed to be well stirred.

The permeability of an ideal sieve-type membrane to various substances whose molecules are considerably smaller than the pores, will be defined by the normal laws of diffusion, i.e. the permeability will be inversely proportional to the square root of the molecular weight (Chapter 3, p. 110). Care must be taken, however, in applying this rule, to ensure that there is no flow of solvent through the membrane, such as would result from the existence of a hydrostatic pressure difference; the solvent will then flow through the pores, carrying with it all the solutes that are able to penetrate.

With a solvent-type of membrane, on the other hand, the permeability would be expected to depend on the partition coefficient of the diffusing substance within the membrane—i.e. with the ratio of the concentration within the membrane to the concentration in the solution on each side. I for example, the concentration of a solution on one side of the membrane were two units, and that on the other side were one unit, the fall of concentration, or driving force for diffusion, would be one unit. But if the membrane had a partition coefficient of, say, 3, the concentrations within the membrane on each side would be 6 and 3, and the driving force would be 3 units. Actually, however, as we shall see in a later section, with most membranes, and particularly with those of biological interest, the matter is more complicated than this.

It should be noted that the permeability constants of two membranes towards a given substance are not necessarily a sure indication of their relative permeabilities towards a different substance. No account is taken of the thickness of the membrane in the definition, so that a difference in the permeabilities of two membranes may be due to differences in the thickness. If this were so, we should have no justification in concluding that the membrane with the greater permeability constant would pass larger molecules, for example, than the membrane with the smaller permeability; nor can we necessarily conclude that the substance considered was more soluble in the membrane with the larger permeability than in the one with the smaller permeability. Again, on the sieve conception, we can imagine the permeability of a membrane being increased as a result either of the formation of a greater number of pores of the same size, or of an increase in the size of the existing pores. In the first case, the limiting size of molecule which would just pass is unchanged, and in the second case, it is increased. Conversely, of course, we can imagine two membranes with pores of different sizes, but in which the total pore area per unit area of membrane is the same. The permeabilities of the two membranes would be the same towards a substance whose molecules were smaller than the pores of the finer membrane, but very different towards a substance whose molecules were larger than these pores, but smaller than those of the coarser membrane.

Permeability should always be regarded quantitatively. It is very rare to encounter a membrane which is absolutely impermeable to any substance, although there are membranes which approach this condition very closely. This is due largely to the fact that the pores in an artificial membrane, and indeed, in most living membranes, are not all of the same size. The flux of a given substance through the membrane will depend on the number of pores, per unit area, whose diameter is greater than that of the molecules or particles of the substance concerned; this number will diminish progressively as the particles become larger. Similarly, a condition of absolute insolubility is unknown. If given sufficient time, even substances which at first appear to be entirely insoluble in the membrane, will eventually pass through.

Permeability to Electrolytes. Some complications may arise when the permeability of a membrane to an electrolytically dissociated substance is investigated. If, for example, it is found that such a substance is unable to penetrate, one cannot assume that the membrane concerned is impermeable to *both* the ions. As was pointed out by Ostwald in 1890, if one ion can pass, but the other cannot, the electrostatic attraction between them will prevent the permeable ion from travelling further than such a distance at which the diffusion force balances the electrostatic force. Copper ferrocyanide is permeable to both ions of potassium chloride; when, therefore, it is found to be sensibly impermeable to calcium chloride and to potassium sulphate, it must be the calcium ions, on the one hand, and the sulphate ions on the other hand, that are held back.

Such differential permeability to ions of different sign is, in fact, relatively common, and is to be expected when the interface between the substance of the membrane and the solutions in contact with it is electrically charged. We will return to this later. It is important to note at this point, however, that if a membrane separates two electrolyte solutions, and is selectively permeable to ions of one sign rather than to those of the other, a diffusion potential will be set up, as already discussed in Chapter 4. This potential, in turn, will assist the passage of ions in one direction, and oppose the passage in the other direction. There will thus be a condition of irreciprocal permeability, and the permeability constants of the ions will appear to be different according to the direction in which they are traversing the membrane. It is not, of course, necessary that the membrane should be absolutely impermeable to any ions; but in the limiting condition, in which this is so, there will be a Gibbs-Donnan equilibrium across the membrane. As we have seen in Chapter 5, the concentration of, say, cations on one side of the membrane (A) is greater than that on the other side (B); but since there is a state of dynamic equilibrium, the actual number of cations traversing the membrane from A to B must be the same as that traversing from B to A. The permeability constant, or rate of penetration for unit concentration difference, must, therefore, be greater in the direction B——>A than in the direction A——>B. Conversely, of course, the permeability constant for anions will be greater in the direction A——>B than in the direction B——>A.

It would thus be more logical to define the permeability constants for ions in terms of the electrochemical potential gradient, rather than in terms of the activity, or chemical potential, gradient only (in practice, replaced by the concentration gradient). The electrochemical potential of an ion in, say, the solution surrounding a living cell, is defined (p. 143) as:

$$RT \ln (m_e \gamma_e) + zFE \qquad . \qquad . \qquad 4.19 \text{ and } 3.7$$

where m_e is its concentration, z its valency, γ_e the activity coefficient, and E the electrical potential above some arbitrary zero; R, T and F have the usual meanings. This may be written in the form:

$$RT \ln \{m_e \gamma_e . \exp (zFE/RT)\}$$

In the absence of any electrical potential, the force producing diffusion, or penetration through a membrane, is the chemical potential only, i.e. $RT \ln (m_e \gamma_e)$ (Chapter 3, p. 106), and it is from this, neglecting activity coefficients, that the relation $(\phi_2)_{in} = P_{in} m_e$ (equation 10.1a) is derived. If we include, now, the electrical potential, we derive, accordingly, the relation:

$$(\phi_{\pm})_{in} = P'_{in} m_e \gamma_e . \exp (zFE/RT)$$

and similarly, we shall have:

$$(\phi_{\pm})_{out} = P'_{out} m_c \gamma_c . \exp [zF(E - \Delta E)/RT]$$

$$\left. \begin{array}{c} \\ \\ \end{array} \right\} \qquad . \quad 10.2$$

where the subscript c indicates that the concentration and activity coefficient refer to the contents of the cell, and ΔE is the potential difference across the membrane. We thus get:

$$\frac{(\phi_{\pm})_{in}}{(\phi_{\pm})_{out}} = \frac{P'_{in}}{P'_{out}} . \frac{m_e \gamma_e}{m_c \gamma_c} \exp (zF.\Delta E/RT) \qquad . \qquad . \quad 10.2a$$

There may, however, be practical difficulties in applying this equation, since is is not always easy—or even possible—to measure the electrical potential difference across the membrane, even though it is possible to measure the flux which results from a chemical potential gradient.

Just as the electrical force may either assist or oppose the diffusion force, so also, conversely, may the diffusion force assist or oppose the electrical force. The membrane, in such conditions, will conduct electricity more readily in one direction than in the other, and will thus act as a rectifier of alternating current.

This effect can be demonstrated by using a salt, of which one ion only is in the colloidal state, enclosed within a membrane of parchment paper, collodion or cellophane; a suitable substance is the sodium salt of the dye Congo-red, but there are many other substances which may be used. On the other side of the membrane is placed a weak solution of some crystalloidal electrolyte. An electrical potential difference is established across the membrane by placing electrodes, one on each side of the membrane, connected to a suitable battery through a milliammeter. Suppose, first, that the electrode in the colloidal solution is the positive one. The current will be carried by positive ions (chiefly sodium ions) passing through the membrane, out of the colloidal solution, in the direction in which they would naturally diffuse were they not held back by the colloidal anions. On the other hand, if we reverse the polarity of the electrodes, the flow of current would be such that negative ions would pass out of the colloidal solution; since most of these are colloidal, and cannot penetrate the membrane, the flow of current will be much smaller.

It will be clear from the discussion which has been given in the previous pages, that the permeability constant, as defined in equation 10.1 or equation 10.2, is a complex property of both membrane and penetrating substance. In the case of a solvent type membrane, the permeability is obviously determined by the nature of the interactions, chemical and electrical, between the molecules within the membrane structure and the molecules which are penetrating. In the case of a sieve type membrane, the permeability will be determined by the fraction of the total area which is occupied by the pores—a property of the membrane only; by the relative diameters of the pores and of the penetrating molecules, and by any forces acting between the walls of the pores and the penetrating molecules, and affecting their rate of passage—i.e. the interactions, again both chemical and electrical, between the membrane and the penetrating substance; and finally, by the resistance to relative movement of the penetrating molecules within the pores—a property of the penetrating substance only. In the extreme case of a solution passing through pores of relatively large diameter, this last factor may be identified with the viscosity of the solution; the second factor is unimportant in this case, and it is thus possible to discover the properties of the membrane itself.

Measurement of Permeability Constants

In principle, all that is necessary is to set up a concentration gradient of the substance in which we are interested, across the membrane concerned, and to measure the flux which results. The flux, however, is almost always measured in terms of the rate of change of the concentration of the solution on one or other side of the membrane, the volume of this solution being known, and constant. Unless special arrangements are made, the concentration gradient thus changes during the course of the experiment. This can be allowed for, without difficulty, by making appropriate calculations; but it is necessary to assume that the permeability constant is independent of the concentrations of the substance concerned on each side of the membrane, or varies in some known and relatively simple manner. Such assumptions, as we shall see later, may not be justified unless the changes in concentration are very small.

One must, of course, ensure that the properties of the membrane, or of the system as a whole, are not significantly changed as a result of the establishment of the concentration gradient. This applies particularly when permeabilities are investigated in living systems; the introduction of some "foreign" substance, not ordinarily present, or a substantial change in the concentration of a substance already present, may disturb the existing steady state in many different ways.

These difficulties are largely avoided by the use of *isotopes*. The concentration of a radioactive isotope is readily measured even when it is present in very small quantity; the concentration of some "foreign" substance which is suitably "labelled" by the presence of some radioactive isotope in its molecule can thus be kept small. Moreover, when the permeability of a membrane to a "normal" constituent is being investigated, a known fraction may be replaced by some easily detected isotope, whose flux through the membrane is then measured in terms of the rate at which it appears on the opposite side. There is no change in the *total* concentration of the substance, and the change in the isotope concentration may be kept very small.

Suppose, for example, a living cell, or group of cells, is placed in a solution containing some identifiable substance *S. Then the rate of change of its concentration within the cell is given by:

$$\frac{d[*S]_c}{dt} = P_{in} \cdot \frac{A}{V}[*S]_e = k_{in}[*S]_e$$

where square brackets denote concentrations, and the subscripts c and e refer to the cell contents and the external solution respectively; P_{in} is the permeability constant and V and A are the volume and surface area of the cell, or cells, respectively. When the investigations are concerned only with changes in the permeability of a particular kind of cell, or whenever the absolute values of the permeability constants are not of importance, it is convenient to replace the quantity $P_{in}.A/V$ by the "rate constant", k_{in}. Similarly, if the cells are allowed to accumulate the substance *S, and are then placed in a solution from which it is absent, the isotope concentration within the cell will fall at a rate given by:

$$-\frac{d[*S]_c}{dt} = P_{out} \cdot \frac{A}{V}[*S]_c = k_{out}[*S]_c$$

Thus, in general:

$$\frac{d[*S]_c}{dt} = \frac{A}{V}\{P_{in}[*S]_e - P_{out}[*S]_c\} \quad . \qquad . \qquad . \quad 10.3$$

These equations are, of course, derived directly from equation 10.1 defining the permeability constant. If we know the total concentration of some substance S within the cells and in the external solution, as well as the concentrations and fluxes of the corresponding isotope *S, we can deduce the total inward and outward fluxes, which are given by $P_{in}[S]_c$ and $P_{out}[S]_e$ respectively.

In principle, therefore, the measurement of permeability constants is very simple; and if radioactive isotopes are used, the measurement of their concentrations is also very simple, the necessary apparatus being available commercially. (The principles on which the methods of measurement are based have been discussed in Chapter 2, pp. 43-44.) But it is by no means so simple to ensure that the concentrations measured are in fact those of the cell contents, and that the conditions of the experiment are such that these simple equations can be applied. One important point is that in whole tissues—portions of plants or the muscles or nerves of animals, for example —there are intercellular spaces, outside the cells but within the tissue as a whole. The concentration of the substance *S in the whole tissue is not, in general, identical with that within the cells themselves; and, moreover, it is not always certain that the substance investigated will reach the membrane whose permeability is to be measured at a rate which is large compared with that at which it penetrates the membrane. Further, in the deduction of the total inward and outward fluxes, it is assumed that the flux of an isotope is truly representative of the flux of the corresponding unlabelled substance—that the one is, as it were, a "scale model" of the other. There is reason to believe, however, that in the penetration of some substances through some kinds of membrane, this may not be true. Experimental studies have not yet been very extensive, but it is probable that discrepancies of this kind are not very common.

When investigating the permeability of a given membrane to *water*, the flux can often be conveniently measured in terms of the rate of change in volume (or sometimes pressure) of the solution on one or other side of the membrane. The "concentration" gradient should, strictly, be replaced by the activity gradient, as measured by the vapour pressures of the solutions; but it is ordinarily sufficient to use measurements of the total molar concentration, if we restrict ourselves to dilute solutions, or to small differences in activity across the membrane. Equation 10.1, defining the permeability constant, may now be written in the form:

$$dV/dt = RT.P_1.A\{\Sigma(m_c) - \Sigma(m_e)\} . \qquad . \qquad . \qquad 10.4$$

where $\Sigma(m_c)$ and $\Sigma(m_e)$ are the total molar concentrations within the membrane—e.g. in the contents of a living cell—and in the external solution, at any moment; V and A are the volume and surface area of the cell at that moment; and P_1 is the permeability constant for water. Moreover, we can write:

$$\Sigma(m_c) = \{\Sigma(m_i)\}(V_i/V) . \qquad . \qquad . \qquad 10.4a$$

where $\Sigma(m_i)$ is the total concentration within the cell, and V_i is its volume initially, before any swelling or shrinking has occurred. The value of $\Sigma(m_i)$ is taken to be equal to that of $\Sigma(m_e)$ when the conditions are such that the volume of the cell remains constant at the value V_i. The surface area of the cell will not, in general, remain constant, but will increase as the cell swells; if the cell is spherical, its surface area will be given by:

$$A = 4\pi r^2 = 4\pi(3V/4\pi)^{2/3} = (36\pi)^{1/3}V^{2/3}$$

A further correction can be made for the fact that the thickness of the membrane will probably become smaller as the surface area becomes larger.

Equations of the form given in equation 10.4 describe reasonably accurately the observations which have been made on the swelling of the eggs of *Arbacia* (a sea urchin), and of other marine animals, in diluted sea water. In some cases, however, the permeability constant is found to be appreciably greater when the cells are shrinking than when they are swelling. To some extent, this difference is accounted for by the assumption made in developing the equation that the activity of the water within the cell varies directly as the total cell volume, rather than as the volume of free water within the cell $(V-b)$, where b is the volume of dissolved and suspended substances. Even after this correction has been made, however, water still appears to leave the cell at a significantly greater rate than it enters, the known driving forces being equal in both cases. Some of Lucké's observations on the eggs of *Ostraea* (the oyster) and of *Chaetopterus* (a marine worm) are plotted in Fig. 10.1 in a form designed to test the accuracy of equation 10.4 after integration; the fit is quite satisfactory.

The penetration of water into and out of certain kinds of living cell provides an example of a process in which the movement of an isotope apparently does not represent accurately the movement of the corresponding unlabelled substance. The permeability constants for water of the frog's skin, and of the surface membranes of several kinds of egg cell, measured by observations on the rate of swelling and shrinking, as just described, may be many times greater than the values obtained from observations on the rate of entry of heavy water (D_2O). The origin of this discrepancy is not certain; it may be that the molecules of water, for some reason, cannot move independently, by simple diffusion, but only in mutually interacting groups, as chains in single file, for example. This will be referred to again later.

So far, it has been tacitly assumed that all the solutes present, both within the cell and in the external solution, pass through the membrane at a rate which is negligible compared with the rate at which water passes. If this condition is not satisfied, the changes in volume will be more complicated. If, for example, we add to the external solution some substance which penetrates slowly through the cell membrane, the cell will at first shrink, since water is drawn out by the excess concentration outside. But as the substance added penetrates into the cell, the concentration difference will fall, and eventually vanish, and the volume of the cell will return towards its initial value. Alternatively, if the penetrating substance is made to replace part of the non-penetrating solutes, so that the total concentration remains constant, there will be no preliminary shrinkage, but the cell

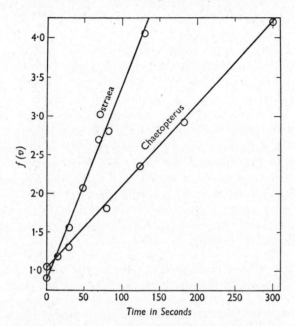

FIG. 10.1. SWELLING OF THE EGGS OF *Ostraea* AND OF *Chaetopterus* IN A DILUTE EXTERNAL SOLUTION

Normally the eggs live in sea water; for the experimental observations they were placed in sea water the total concentration of which had been reduced to 50 per cent. (*Ostraea*) and to 60 per cent. (*Chaetopterus*), respectively, of the normal value by the addition of fresh water. The quantity plotted as ordinates, $f(V)$, is an expression obtained by integration of equation 10.4: and the relation between $f(V)$ and time should theoretically be a straight line. The slope of the line is a measure of the permeability constant of the cell membrane for water.   (Re-drawn from Lucké, 1940.)

will swell steadily, just as if the external solution had been made more dilute. In both cases, the rate of change of volume will depend on the permeability constant of the membrane for the penetrating substance as well as that for water. Records indicating these points will be found in Fig. 10.3, below.

For the penetration of the added solute, we can write:

$$\frac{dn_2}{dt} = RT.P_2.A(m - n_2/V) \qquad . \qquad . \qquad 10.5$$

where n_2 is the number of moles of the solute that have penetrated in time t; V is the volume of the cell at this time, and A its surface area, which may be a function of V; m is the concentration of the solute in the external solution, assumed constant; and P_2 is the permeability constant for the given solute. For the penetration of water, we have:

$$\frac{dV}{dt} = RT.P_1.A\left\{\frac{\Sigma(n_2{}^*)_c + n_2}{V} - (\Sigma(m_e) + m)\right\} \qquad . \qquad 10.6$$

where $\Sigma(n_2{}^*)_c$ is the total number of osmotically active gram-molecules in the normal cell, and $\Sigma(m_e)$ is the total molar concentration of the external solution, before the addition of the solute under investigation. No general solution of the two simultaneous equations is possible, but Jacobs has succeeded in deriving numerical solutions for a number of special cases, so that with the aid of tables and charts, given in his original papers, and in the monograph by Davson and Danielli (1952), the value of P_2/P_1 can be derived from the time taken for the cells to reach some pre-determined volume, as compared with that taken to reach the same volume in the absence of the penetrating solute; or, in appropriate cases, the time taken to reach the minimum volume. The value of P_1 is separately determined by means of observations made in the absence of the penetrating solute, and P_2 can then be calculated.

The initial volume of a spherical cell, and the volume at any moment, may be determined by measuring the diameter with an ocular micrometer. Alternatively, the average diameter of all the cells in the suspension may be estimated from the dimensions of the diffraction pattern produced by illumination with parallel monochromatic light from a point source. If d is the average diameter of the cells, λ is the wave-length of the light, and θ the angular displacement of the nth dark (or light) band from the central image, we have:

$$d.\sin\,\theta = \lambda.z(n)/\pi$$

where $z(n)$ is a constant depending on the value of n, and on whether the band observed is dark or light. A more detailed description of the method is given by Ponder (1948). Both these methods suffer from the disadvantage that the volume of the cells is proportional to the cube of the diameter, which is measured; the observational errors are thus correspondingly magnified.

The average volume of a large number of cells, of whatever shape, freely suspended in a suitable solution, may be measured by throwing them down in a centrifuge, and measuring the volume of the packed mass; the suspension is ordinarily centrifuged in a tube of uniform bore, and the volume of the cells measured in terms of the length of tube occupied by the solidly packed mass. Such tubes are often known as "haematocrit" tubes, since this method was first used for measuring the volume of the red cells in a given volume of mammalian blood. It is usually necessary, for greater precision, to make a small correction for the volume of suspending fluid which is trapped between the packed cells. Alternatively, a known quantity of some "reference substance" may be added to a known volume of the suspension of cells, and its concentration in the suspending fluid measured after centrifuging off the cells. It is necessary, of course, that the reference substance should not penetrate into the cells, or be adsorbed on their surfaces; and its concentration must be very small, otherwise the volume of the cells would change. It must be possible, therefore, to measure its concentration accurately, and if possible simply, even in very dilute solution. It is very doubtful if any substances exist which satisfy these criteria perfectly, although there are some colloidal dyes which are reasonably satisfactory when used with red blood cells. Suitable radioactive isotopes have also been used. A rapid and convenient method for measuring the volume of the cells in a suspension is that suggested by Ørskov in 1935, although it is probably not applicable to all kinds of cell. A dilute suspension of the cells (red blood cells are ordinarily used) becomes more transparent as the cells take up water and swell; the optical transmittance, as measured by a photoelectric cell, for example, can be related accurately to the average volume of the cells by preliminary calibration, using salt solutions of known concentration.

Mammalian red blood cells are particularly convenient for permeability studies, since little or no change occurs in the surface area when the cells swell; normally each cell has a bi-concave shape, and on becoming spherical, the volume increases some two and a half times without change in the surface area. Further increase in the volume leads to failure of the cell membrane, with discharge of the haemoglobin into the suspending fluid—a process known as *haemolysis*; this is very readily detected owing to the strong colour of haemoglobin. This property has been made use of by Jacobs and others, the rate of swelling being measured in terms of the time taken for a pre-determined fraction of the cells—usually 75 per cent.—to swell so far as to haemolyse. A separate series of experiments, in which suspensions of cells are allowed to come into equilibrium with external solutions of known concentration, defines the concentration within the cells, $\Sigma(m)_h$, at which this fraction of the cells burst. The permeability constant is then calculated from equation 10.4, which is integrated in a form which gives the time taken for the internal concentration of the cells to fall from $\Sigma(m)_i$ to $\Sigma(m)_h$.

A somewhat similar procedure has been used with plant cells, although, so far, only semi-quantitatively. In such cells, the large central vacuole contains a solution which is more concentrated than that outside the cell; it takes up water, swells, and develops a hydrostatic pressure so that the cytoplasm is pressed tightly against the cellulose wall. If the external solution is made sufficiently concentrated, this pressure will fall, and the cytoplasm can be seen under the microscope to shrink away from the wall—a process known as "plasmolysis". The rate at which this occurs can be used as a rough measure of the rate of penetration of water. If the solute in the external solution is capable of penetrating through the cytoplasm into the vacuole, the plasmolysis will eventually be reversed; the time taken for this to occur is an indication of the rate of penetration of the solute.

THE KINETICS OF PENETRATION
THROUGH A MEMBRANE

As has already been remarked, penetration through an "ideal" sieve type membrane occurs by simple diffusion of the molecules of the penetrating substance through the pores in the membrane. The only property of the membrane which is concerned in such ideal conditions is the total cross sectional area of the pores per unit of the membrane. If, however, the molecules of the penetrating substance interact with those of the membrane in any way, such as occurs when the diffusion becomes "restricted", and, more particularly, when exchanges of chemical, electrical or solvation energy are involved, the whole process becomes more complicated.

In discussing these processes, we assume in all cases that the rate of approach of the molecules to the surface of the membrane is large compared with the rate of passage through it. This is justified, since even if diffusion through the solution is not very rapid compared with that through the membrane, we can suppose that the solution is stirred. We consider therefore, a molecule at the surface of the membrane on the side at which the concentration is the greater. This molecule must first pass across the interface between the solution and the membrane, then traverse the substance of the membrane, and finally pass across the interface between the membrane and the solution on the other side.

ACTIVATED PENETRATION

Before the penetrating molecule can traverse either of the interfaces, it will, in general, have to surmount some kind of a potential barrier; the magnitude of this will depend upon the nature of the membrane and the chemical constitution of the molecule. If the membrane is an "ideal" sieve, with pores large compared with the size of the molecule, the barrier is negligible; if the membrane is electrically charged, and we are considering the passage of an ion, the potential barrier will be partly electrical in origin; if the molecule has to become dissolved in the membrane, the potential barrier will be determined by the relative solubility of the molecule in the membrane compared with that in the solution in contact with it. Thus if we consider a case which is probably very usual in living systems, that of a membrane of a fatty, or generally lipoid, nature, in contact with a watery solution, a molecule with many polar groups, such as sugar or glycerol, will require a considerable amount of energy in order to break these groups away from the water molecules; the activation energy for entry into the membrane will be large. On the other hand, a non-polar molecule, such as benzene, will require little activation energy before it can pass into the membrane, since there are no hydrogen bonds or similar forces holding it to the water molecules. The polar molecule, of course, will pass out of the membrane, on the other side, very easily, since it will be sucked, as it were, by the hydrogen bonds which unite it to the water molecules. The non-polar molecule will have no such assistance, and will

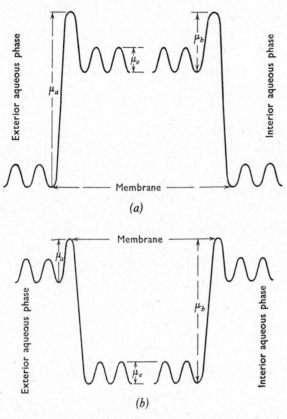

FIG. 10.2.   POTENTIAL ENERGY DIAGRAMS OF A LIPOID MEMBRANE

(a): for a polar molecule such as glycerol ;
(b): for a lipoid soluble (non-polar) molecule such as benzene.

(Davson and Danielli. 1952.)

have to break its way among the water molecules as a result of its kinetic energy only. In the interior of the membrane, both types of molecule will pass from one side to the other by diffusion, and since the penetrating molecule will not be very large compared with the molecules of the membrane, we must consider the process as one of activated diffusion.

The potential barriers can be represented diagrammatically as in Fig. 10.2, a and b, for polar and non-polar molecules respectively. μ_a is the activation energy for entering the membrane, μ_b is that for leaving it, and μ_e that for surmounting the successive barriers within the membrane. The concentration of the solution on the external side of the membrane is m_e and that of the solution on the internal side is m_c; just within the membrane, before the first diffusion barrier, the concentration is m_o, and just within the membrane on the other side, after the pth diffusion barrier has been crossed, the concentration is m_p. Then, following the treatment adopted by Danielli, and according to the principles of activated diffusion, discussed in Chapter 3 (p. 109), we can write:

$$\phi_2 = a.m_e - b.m_o = b.m_p - a.m_c$$
$$= \frac{a}{2}(m_e - m_c) - \frac{b}{2}(m_o - m_p)$$

a and b being exponential functions of μ_a and μ_b of the form $A \cdot \exp(-\mu/RT)$; and ϕ_2 being the flux of the substance considered through the membrane. But, from equation 3.33, we have:

$$\phi_2 = \frac{e}{p}(m_o - m_p)$$

Eliminating $(m_o - m_p)$ from these equations, we get:

$$\phi_2 = \frac{\dfrac{a}{2}(m_e - m_c)}{1 + \dfrac{p}{e} \cdot \dfrac{b}{2}}$$

$$= \frac{a.e}{p.b + 2e}(m_e - m_c)$$

But, by definition, if P is the permeability constant:

$$\phi_2 = P(m_e - m_c)$$

Thus
$$P = \frac{a.e}{p.b + 2e} \qquad \cdot \qquad \cdot \qquad \cdot \qquad \cdot \qquad \cdot \quad 10.7$$

This expression can be simplified for two special cases.

(a) If $p.b$ is small compared with $2e$—i.e. if μ_b is large compared with μ_e or if p is small (the membrane is very thin), the expression reduces to:

$$P_a = a/2 \qquad \cdot \qquad \cdot \qquad \cdot \qquad \cdot \qquad \cdot \quad 10.7a$$

This condition is satisfied for a number of substances which penetrate very thin membranes (such as those at the surfaces of living cells) very slowly. Physically, it is clear that if the rate at which the substance traverses the membrane is large compared with the rate at which it penetrates the interface from the membrane to the solution outside—i.e. if the distance over which diffusion has to occur is small, or if the activation energy for diffusion within the membrane is much smaller than that for penetrating the interface—then the concentration within the membrane will be sensibly the same at both interfaces. Even though the value of μ_b may be large, its precise value will not affect the rate of penetration; the actual number of molecules passing *out of* the membrane in unit time will be the same at both interfaces, into both the external and internal solutions. The permeability constant will thus be determined almost entirely by the difference between the rates of passage *into* the membrane from the two solutions, respectively.

(*b*) Conversely, if the value of $p.b$ is large compared with that of $2e$, we can write:

$$P_b = \frac{a.e}{b.p} = \frac{B}{p} . e \qquad . \qquad . \qquad . \qquad 10.7b$$

where B is the partition coefficient of the substance considered between the membrane and the watery solutions. For a given membrane, p is constant, and the permeability thus depends only on the "resistance" to diffusion within the membrane as determined by the quantity e, together with the actual concentration gradient within the membrane, as determined by the partition coefficient, B. Moreover, if the viscosity of the membrane substance is not very large, the value of e will be sensibly the same for a number of different substances, as we have seen in Chapter 3. In these special circumstances, then, the permeability coefficient should be approximately proportional to the partition coefficient of the substance considered between the membrane and the solution. This, indeed, is what is to be expected from a simple "solvent" type membrane.

The condition that $p.b$ is large compared with $2e$ may be satisfied either if p is large, and the membrane thick, or if b is large (the activation energy μ_b is small); there will then be only a small concentration difference across each interface. In either case, there will be a large concentration difference within the membrane, and the overall rate of penetration may be expected to depend upon the values both of b and e. This last condition is found to apply to many molecules which penetrate relatively thin membranes very rapidly.

It is to be noted that if we write the quantities a and e in equations 10.7a and 10.7b in full, we have expressions of the form:

$$P = k\sqrt{\frac{RT}{2\pi M}} . \exp(-\mu/RT)$$

μ being given the suffix $_a$ or $_e$ as the case may be (compare equation 3.35; the quantity k includes the factors λ and r'). A theory based on a conception of permeability by solution in the membrane thus leads to the conclusion that the permeability constant will be related to the square root of the molecular weight of the penetrating substance (M), as might at first sight be more appropriate to a sieve conception. The partition coefficient turns out to be the major determining factor only in certain conditions, when the "resistance" to the penetration of the interfaces is small compared with that to the penetration of the membrane substance. The effect of molecular size, however, is relatively small and uniform; there are no "restriction" effects, as with a sieve type membrane, in which the permeability constant falls very rapidly, and almost discontinuously, to zero as the diameter of the penetrating molecules approaches that of the pores.

The Effect of Temperature on the Permeability Constant. The full expression for the permeability constant P, as given in the previous paragraph, may be written in the form:

$$\ln\left(\frac{P\sqrt{2\pi M}}{k\sqrt{RT}}\right) = -\frac{\mu}{RT}$$

If, therefore, we plot log ($P/\sqrt{T}$) against $1/T$, we should get a straight line, whose slope will be a measure of the total amount of activation energy involved, and whose position will depend on the molecular weight of the substance penetrating, and on the value of the constant k. If the penetration were by simple diffusion, the activation energy being negligible, we should expect that the permeability constant P would be proportional to the square root of the absolute temperature, $\sqrt{T}$.

Further, if at a temperature T, the permeability constant has a value P, and at another temperature ($T+\Delta T$) it has a value P' ($=P+\Delta P$), we have:

$$\frac{P'}{P} = \sqrt{\frac{T+\Delta T}{T}} \cdot \frac{\exp\left(-\mu/R(T+\Delta T)\right)}{\exp\left(-\mu/RT\right)}$$

$$\risingdotseq \exp\left(\frac{\mu}{RT} \cdot \frac{\Delta T}{T}\right) \text{ if } \Delta T \text{ is small compared with } T.$$

Thus:
$$\left(\frac{P'}{P}\right)^{T/\Delta T} \risingdotseq \exp\left(\frac{\mu}{RT}\right) = \frac{k\sqrt{RT}}{2\pi P\sqrt{M}}. \quad . \quad . \quad 10.8$$

or
$$2\pi P\sqrt{M} \cdot (P'/P)^{T/\Delta T} \risingdotseq k\sqrt{RT} \quad . \quad . \quad 10.8a$$

If the interval of temperature, ΔT, is $10°$ C., then the ratio P'/P is defined as the Q_{10} value of P. This relation shows that the effect of temperature on the rate of penetration of a substance through a membrane may be large or small according as it penetrates slowly or rapidly, and according as its molecules are small or large. The actual processes by which penetration occurs are, nevertheless, the same. If we were to consider the temperature coefficient only, therefore, the penetration of a substance through a membrane might appear to be either a "physical" process or a "chemical" one, according to circumstances. For a given value of T, moreover, the quantity on the left of equation 10.8a should be constant for all substances for which the same value of k is appropriate; in practice, this means that they must penetrate the membrane slowly, so that equation 10.7a can be applied, and they must have reasonably symmetrical molecules.

These expectations have been tested, in so far as adequate data are available. Study of the effect of temperature on the rate of penetration of many different substances through several kinds of living cell membrane shows that there is a linear relation between $\log (P/\sqrt{T})$ and $1/T$; substantial amounts of activation energy are clearly required. For the penetration of certain suitable non-electrolytes into red blood cells of the ox, and into egg cells of the sea urchin *Arbacia*, the quantity $P\sqrt{M} . (P'/P)^{T/\Delta T}$ is found to be constant, within the reasonable, but rather large, limits of experimental error.

It is important to remember, however, that in this analysis it is tacitly assumed that the membrane is homogeneous. We have considered the passage of a molecule at one spot in the membrane, and have assumed that all molecules penetrate all spots under the same conditions. Now if the membrane is not homogeneous, we should have to derive different values of the permeability constant, and of its rate of variation with temperature, for each spot, and then add them together in order to get the total permeability, and the overall temperature coefficient, which would be observed experimentally. In these circumstances, the quantities $P\sqrt{M}$ and $(P'/P)^{T/\Delta T}$ would not necessarily be related inversely, as is required by equation 10.8. Indeed, one of the uses to which Danielli has put these expressions is to test for homogeneity of the membrane investigated.

A more extensive discussion of the theory of activated penetration, and its application to the permeabilities of living cell membranes, will be found in the monograph by Davson and Danielli (1952).

FACILITATED PENETRATION

It has been tacitly assumed so far that the forces acting between the molecules of the membrane and those of the substances passing through it are the relatively unspecific ones which are involved in the interaction between any solute and its solvent. There may, however, be more specific "chemical" forces in addition. particularly when the membrane has a complex physico-chemical structure, as has that surrounding a living cell. If there is some form of chemical combination, or chemisorption, between the penetrating substance and some component of the membrane, the penetration will occur by a process of facilitated diffusion.

Suppose, for example, that some particular penetrating substance S combines with, or is specifically adsorbed by, some component of the membrane, C; this component is often referred to as the "carrier" substance. Then at the two interfaces between the membrane and the solution, we shall have a reversible adsorption, or chemical reaction, which may be represented:

$$C + S \rightleftharpoons CS$$

We suppose that the substance S can penetrate the membrane only when it is attached to the carrier C. Let $[S]_e$ and $[S]_c$ be the concentrations of S in the solutions on the two sides of the membrane; let $[CS]_e$ and $[CS]_c$ be the concentrations of the combined, or "loaded" carrier at the interfaces between the membrane and the two solutions; and let the total concentration of carrier, assumed constant throughout the membrane, be $[C]$, so that the concentrations of unloaded carrier molecules will be $[C] - [CS]$. The net flux of S through the membrane, ϕ, will be equal to the net flux of the loaded carrier, CS. If this passes through the membrane by simple (or activated) diffusion, we shall have:

$$\phi = \frac{D}{t}([CS]_e - [CS]_c) . \qquad . \qquad . \qquad . \qquad 10.9$$

where D is the diffusion constant and t is the thickness of the membrane. A net flux in the direction side "e" to side "c" is considered positive. The ratio $[CS]/[S]$ is, of course, the "partition coefficient" of the penetrating substance between the membrane and the external solution; it has a particularly large value when the membrane contains the particular carrier C, and the solution contains the particular substance S. It is not, in fact, necessary to suppose that the carrier molecules, loaded or unloaded, actually traverse the membrane. They might form a chain of fixed sites, over which the molecules of the penetrating substance pass by a series of jumps from one to the next. An equivalent system would consist of channels or pores able to admit the molecules of the penetrating substance, but, for some reason, unable to admit those of any other substance—at least of those ordinarily present. Even if this specificity resulted only from the size of the channels, or the presence of electric charges, the effect would be much the same as that produced by a carrier system; it is reasonable, therefore, to consider the penetration as facilitated.

The molecules of the penetrating substance would pass over such a chain of carrier molecules, or through such a system of channels, primarily by a process of activated, or restricted, diffusion. But there is the additional complication that a given molecule will not always be able to move to another site on the chain, or position in the channel, whenever it has the necessary energy of thermal agitation. It may have enough energy to leave its own site, but not enough to remove another molecule from a different site; it will be able to move only if there happens to be a vacant site within reach. If most of the sites are occupied at any moment, the molecules will rarely be able to move singly, but will all have to move together, and all will have to possess the necessary energy at the same moment—a relatively unlikely event. One consequence of this necessity for the molecules to move in single file along a fixed path, is that the inward and outward fluxes, as measured by the use of isotopically labelled substances, will not be independent of one another. If the inward flux is increased, for example, by increasing the concentration of the external solution, the outward flux will be impeded by the stream of molecules moving inwards, and will be reduced; the inward flux conversely, will increase more than in proportion to the increase in concentration. If the molecules could move freely in any direction, the opposing fluxes would be independent of one another. An effect of this kind has been observed in the movement of radioactive potassium ions $^{40}K^+$ through the surface membranes of giant nerve fibres of the cephalopod *Sepia*.

Again, if all the sites on the chains are occupied, the molecules leaving the membrane on one side, in any short period of time, will not all be identical with those entering it on the other side. This, however, is of no consequence, since one molecule cannot be distinguished from another, unless they are labelled in some way; indeed, a large part of the flux, both inwards and outwards, will ordinarily be made up of molecules which have progressed only a short way along a chain of sites. But suppose, on the other hand, that all the molecules on one side of the membrane are labelled and all those on the other side are not. It is only those chains which are completely filled with labelled molecules that will deliver a labelled molecule when one is taken up at the other end, and so will contribute only to the flux of labelled molecules. Similarly, it is only those which are completely filled with unlabelled molecules which will contribute only to the flux of unlabelled molecules; a chain which contains equal numbers of both, for example, is as likely to deliver the "wrong" kind of molecule as the "right" one. The chance that a given chain should receive a labelled, or an unlabelled, molecule is proportional to the concentration of labelled, or unlabelled, molecules, respectively; that it should receive, say, n molecules, all of the same kind, will be proportional to the nth power of the concentration. Thus the ratio of the number of "pure" labelled chains to the number of "pure" unlabelled chains—and thus the flux ratio—is proportional to the nth power of the concentration ratio, and not to the concentration ratio itself, as is the case when none of the molecules are labelled. If, as is usual, the labelled molecules are present in smaller concentration than the unlabelled ones, the flux ratio, ϕ_{in}/ϕ_{out}, and the net flux of the labelled molecules, will be reduced disproportionately, and the calculated permeability constant will be erroneously low. This may be one source of the discrepancy between the permeability of certain membranes to ordinary water and to heavy water, respectively, already referred to (p. 434 above). A similar effect is observed in the flux of potassium ions through the membranes of *Sepia* giant nerve fibres in an electrical potential gradient.

The entry of the penetrating substance into the membrane, and its subsequent discharge—i.e. the loading and unloading of the carrier molecules—may be regarded either as a reversible adsorption process, of the type considered by Langmuir (Chapter 5, p. 185), or as a reversible chemical reaction (Chapter 2, p. 47); the treatment is essentially the same. The rate of loading (adsorption or chemical combination) will be proportional to the number of S molecules which strike the membrane per second—and thus to the concentration of S—and to the number of unoccupied carrier molecules per unit area—i.e. to the concentration of free carrier molecules. Similarly the rate of unloading (or dissociation) will be proportional to the number, or concentration, of loaded carrier molecules. If the system is in a steady state, the concentration of CS at the interface will be constant. We assume that the rate at which S penetrates the interface and is taken up by, or discharged from, the carrier, C, is large compared with the rate at which the loaded carrier, CS, traverses the membrane. We may thus equate the rates of loading and unloading, and get:

$$k_u[CS] = k_l[S]([C] - [CS])$$

where k_l and k_u are the rate constants of loading and unloading respectively. Thus:

$$[CS] = \frac{[C] \cdot [S]}{k_u/k_l + [S]} \qquad . \qquad . \qquad . \qquad . \quad 10.10$$

This same equation could obviously be derived by assuming that the reaction $C + S \rightleftharpoons CS$ reached equilibrium at the interfaces, and by applying the law of mass action; the ratio of the rate constants k_u/k_l may then be replaced by the equilibrium constant K. Equation 10.10 will apply to the interfaces on both sides of the membrane, and we thus have:

$$\phi = \frac{D}{t}[C] \left\{ \frac{[S]_e}{K + [S]_e} - \frac{[S]_c}{K + [S]_c} \right\} \qquad . \qquad . \quad 10.11$$

It will be noticed that if $[S]_c$ is zero, this equation is identical with the Michaelis equation for the velocity of an enzyme reaction (equation 7.3, p. 311); it has, indeed, been derived on precisely the same assumptions. As in the enzyme reactions, also, it is important to consider two limiting conditions.

(a) If $[S]_e$ and $[S]_c$ are both small, and can be neglected in comparison with K, we may write:

$$\phi = \frac{D}{t} \cdot \frac{[C]}{K} \{[S]_e - [S]_c\} = P\{[S]_e - [S]_c\} \qquad . \qquad .10.11a$$

where P is a permeability "constant". The kinetics of the penetration will thus be the same as that of a substance which passes through the membrane by simple diffusion.

(*b*) Suppose, on the other hand, the value of $[S]_c$ is kept constant, and that of $[S]_e$ is progressively increased. Eventually it will reach a value which is large compared with K. We then have:

$$\phi = \frac{D}{t} \cdot \frac{C}{K} \{K - [S]_c\} \qquad . \qquad . \qquad . \qquad . \; 10.11b$$

The rate of penetration is now independent of the concentration gradient, and the system has become "saturated". The value of the permeability "constant", calculated as $\phi/([S]_e - [S]_c)$ will fall as the value of $[S]_e$ increases. A "saturation" effect of this kind has, indeed, been observed in the penetration of certain particular substances through the wall of the small intestine, and through the cell membranes of mammalian red blood cells. In Fig. 10.3, for example, are shown the results of some observations made on the penetration of two sugars, sorbose and galactose, into human red blood cells. The penetration of the sugar was measured in terms of the change in volume of the cells brought about by the accompanying entry of water (compare p. 433 above). It will be seen from the lower record that the flux of sorbose is directly proportional to the concentration in the external solution, as would be expected if it resulted from simple or activated diffusion. The flux of galactose, however, which is also proportional to the concentration in the external solution when this is small, reaches a "saturation" value and subsequently increases no further.

The relation between the flux of galactose and the concentration in the external solution is not precisely that to be expected from equation 10.11. It will be noticed in particular that when the external concentration becomes large, the flux actually *falls* with increasing concentration; this effect is shown even more markedly when glucose is used. The reduction in reaction velocity observed in certain enzyme reactions when the substrate concentration is made large (Chapter 7, p. 320) may be recalled in this connection, and the two phenomena may have similar causes. But in addition, it is possible that the inward flux may become limited by the rate of supply of unloaded carrier molecules to the outer surface of the membrane. Lefevre, also, has suggested that the *rate* constants of loading and unloading (k_l and k_u) are not the same at both interfaces of the membrane (their ratio, or the equilibrium constant, must be the same, but not necessarily their individual values). The effect would be similar to that of supposing that the total carrier concentration was not the same at both interfaces, provided that the "resistance" to penetration of the interfaces is not negligible, and that an appreciable activation energy is required.

The possibility of saturation of the carrier substance has a further consequence. If two substances are present, S_1 and S_2, both of which can combine with the same carrier, an increase in the concentration of either of them is likely to have the effect of reducing the flux of the other. Such

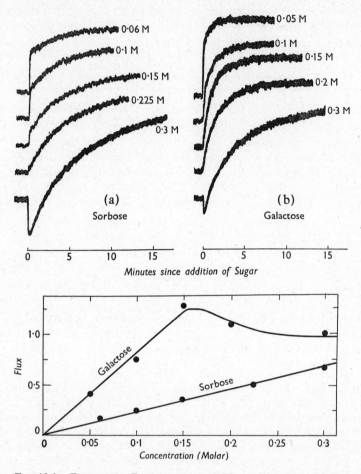

FIG. 10.3. FACILITATED PENETRATION INTO HUMAN RED BLOOD CELLS

Upper Records show the changes in volume of the red cells in very dilute suspension, as measured in terms of the light transmittance, subsequent to the addition of a small volume of a solution of a sugar, such as to produce the final concentration indicated against each curve. The initial rapid deflections, upwards or downwards, are due to the dilution of the suspension and to the passage of water consequent on the sudden change in the total concentration of the suspending fluid. The subsequent slower upward changes are due to the swelling of the cells consequent on the passage of water which accompanies the inward passage of the sugar. The permeability constant for water is very much greater than that for the sugar.   (Lefevre and Davies, 1951.)

Lower Record. The change in volume of the red cells during the first minute after addition of the sugar is plotted, in arbitrary units, against the concentration in the suspending solution; this change in volume is proportional to the initial flux of the sugar. The flux of sorbose is proportional to the concentration over the range studied, and appears to result from simple diffusion. The flux of galactose, greater than that of sorbose when the concentration is small, reaches a maximum value, and results from facilitated diffusion.

"competition" effects have, in fact, been observed. The flux of sorbose into the mammalian red blood cells, for example, illustrated in Fig. 10.3, is reduced if glucose is present in the solution as well. It may be that the carrier is more nearly saturated in the presence of both substances than in the presence of one alone; but in addition, one substance may have a greater affinity for the carrier than the other has, and may thus displace it from the membrane. It has been observed, also, that the rates of penetration of certain substances—and of these only—through several kinds of "living" membrane may be considerably affected by such agents as the acidity of the solution, and the presence of "narcotics", and "poisons" such as iodoacetate, cyanide and certain heavy metals. Such effects have been observed in the intestinal epithelium, the tubules of the kidney and the red blood cells. These agents presumably block the reaction of the carrier substance with the penetrating substance in the same general way as they block the reaction of an enzyme with its substrate. We are now, however, approaching closely the problem of "active" transport, which will be discussed later.

The essential features involved in the penetration of a membrane by means of simple, activated and facilitated diffusion, and the relation with "active" transport and "secretion", are illustrated diagrammatically in Fig. 10.4.

THE PENETRATION OF IONS

Since, as we have seen in Chapter 5, almost every interface is the seat of an electric charge, an ion penetrating into a membrane is likely to encounter an electrical potential gradient. Whether this will affect the rate of penetration *through* the membrane depends upon the nature of the membrane. Consider, first, a sieve-type membrane. There will be an electrical (Helmholtz-Gouy) double layer on the walls of the pores: and, whether it is produced by orientated dipoles, preferential adsorption or electrolytic dissociation, there will be a layer of solution containing an excess of ions of one sign (say cations) and from which ions of the opposite sign (say anions) are more or less excluded. If the radius of the pores is comparable with the thickness of the double layer, cations (in the case considered) in the solution outside the membrane will be able to exchange with those in the double layer, and so penetrate the membrane; while anions will do so much less readily. Reversal of the sign of the charge on the membrane will, of course, reverse the preferential permeability. Now the thickness of the double layer is determined by the quantity $1/\kappa$ in the Debye-Hückel theory (Chapter 4, p. 129); and this depends upon the ionic composition of the electrolyte solution (Table 5.2, p. 208). The difference in permeability of a sieve-type membrane towards ions of opposite sign will thus depend both on the charge on the interface and on the composition of the

P

solution in contact with it; and it will, in fact, be related to the ζ-potential, rather than the charge density.

Turning now to the solvent-type membrane, we find that the conditions are somewhat different. The ions must now penetrate into the substance of the membrane, and must thus overcome an electrical potential barrier in addition to that due to the van der Waals and similar forces,

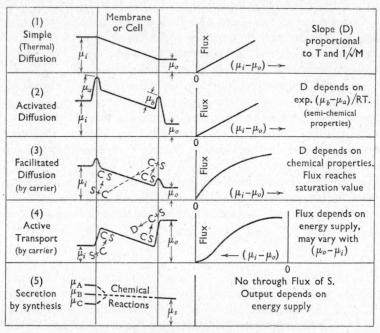

FIG. 10.4. DIAGRAMS ILLUSTRATING VARIOUS PROCESSES BY WHICH SUBSTANCES MAY PENETRATE MEMBRANES

On the left, in each case, is plotted diagrammatically the changes in the electrochemical potential (μ) of the substance as it penetrates the membrane or living cell.

On the right, is plotted the relation between the flux and the difference in electrochemical potential across the membrane or cell. The ratio between the flux and the difference in potential, constant in (1) and (2), gives the diffusion, or permeability, constant D. In (3) and (4) this ratio is not constant, and may be regarded as defining the apparent permeability.

(L. E. Bayliss, 1956. From *Modern Views on the Secretion of Urine*, edited by F. R. Winton. London: J. and A. Churchill Ltd.)

considered earlier in this chapter. The electrical potentials—positive on one side of the interface and negative on the other—will only extend for short distances, of the order of molecular dimensions, from the surface of the membrane: and in general, therefore, they will be symmetrical on the two faces of the membrane and thus have no effect on the rate of penetration of an ion right through from a solution on one side to a solution on the other. But if the membrane is only a few molecules thick, the electrically charged regions within its two surfaces will join in the middle. Ions of one sign will be attracted into the whole membrane, while those of the opposite sign will be repelled. The partition coefficient, B in equation 10.7b, will thus be greater for, say cations, than for, say anions, and the permeability constant will be greater also.

A more precise and quantitative approach to the problem is that made by Teorell in 1935 and by Meyer and Sievers in 1936, independently. In this "fixed charge" theory, the membrane is considered to contain watery spaces through which the ions penetrate, but apart from this, to be essentially homogeneous, the ionising groups of the membrane structure being uniformly distributed. The concentration of ions of any one species in the surface layers of the membrane will be related to that in the solution in contact with them according to the Gibbs-Donnan relation (as in the surface layers of a colloid, discussed in Chapter 5, p. 216). Referring back to the treatment of the Gibbs-Donnan equilibrium given in Chapter 5 (p. 203), we see that the concentrations just within the membrane, at each interface (m'), will be related to those in the bulk solutions (m), neglecting activity coefficients, by the relations:

$$m'_+/m_+ = r \text{ and } m'_-/m_- = 1/r \qquad . \qquad . \qquad . \quad 5.13$$

for cations and anions, respectively. Within the membrane, at any point, the system must be electrically neutral, so that we must have:

$$m'_+ + m'_- + \omega \bar{X} = 0$$

where $\bar{X}$ is the number of fixed ions attached to the membrane structure, per unit volume of the membrane, and ω is their average valency, positive for a cationic membrane and negative for an anionic one; $\omega \bar{X}$ is thus the membrane charge per unit volume. We can thus deduce that:

$$r = \sqrt{1 + \left(\frac{\omega \bar{X}}{2m'}\right)^2} - \left(\frac{\omega \bar{X}}{2m'}\right) \qquad . \qquad . \qquad . \quad 10.12$$

In deriving expressions for the ionic fluxes through a charged membrane, Teorell assumes that the appropriate distribution ratios of the ions in the surface phases are reached very rapidly, and are maintained in all circumstances. The "resistance" to the passage of the ions is assumed to lie entirely within the membrane and to be determined by the concentration difference set up as a result of the Gibbs-Donnan equilibrium at the interfaces, and the electrical potentials developed by the diffusing ions. This assumption seems to be entirely justified for the relatively thick artificial membranes with which the theory has been tested experimentally. It is probably not justified for the very thin membranes which cover living cells, where, except perhaps in special cases, the "resistance" to penetration of the interfaces may be significant, as pointed out in the section on

Activated Penetration. In conditions where the assumption is valid, however, the net ionic flux through a membrane in a given kind of electrolyte solution will depend on the value of $(m'_c - m'_d)$, where the subscripts refer to the more concentrated and more dilute solutions, respectively. This can be written:

$$\left. \begin{array}{l} (m_+)_c r_c - (m_+)_d r_d \\ (m_-)_c / r_c - (m_-)_d / r_a \end{array} \right\} \qquad . \qquad . \qquad . \qquad 10.13$$

or

for cations and anions respectively. For an anionic membrane, for example, the value of r is greater than 1 and the diffusion gradient for all cations will be greater than that for all anions, and their rate of penetration correspondingly increased. If the sign of the charge on the membrane is reversed, the rate of penetration of anions will be increased, and that of cations reduced. The penetration of ions may thus be regarded as a rather unspecific process of "facilitation", which acts on all kinds of cation (or on all kinds of anion, according to the sign of the membrane charge); the electric charges on the membrane substance acting as the "carrier" substance. This effect is illustrated in Fig. 10.5: with the membrane negatively charged, the flux of chloride ions is small, and that of potassium ions large; whereas when the membrane is positively charged, the flux of potassium ions is small and that of chloride ions large. The final result is that the net flux of potassium chloride falls progressively as the membrane charge increases, whether the sign is positive or negative. The net flux of potassium ions, of course, must be equal to that of chloride ions, and the diffusion potential within the membrane takes up a value such as to ensure this. We shall return to this point in the next section.

The ionic distribution ratios between the surface phases and the bulk solutions may depend, not only on the existence of a Gibbs-Donnan equilibrium, but also, partly, on a specific adsorption of certain kinds of ion by the membrane structure—as occurs, apparently, in some ion exchange resins. If this were so, the membrane might be more permeable to certain kinds of ion than to others, and the "facilitation" would be more specific.

A further inference may be drawn from this treatment. The values of both r_c and r_d in equation 10.13 will approach unity as the electrolyte concentrations on each side of the membrane become large compared with the concentration of the membrane charge—as may be seen from equation 10.12. Thus the concentration difference across the membrane itself will approach that between the two bulk solutions, and for a given value of the latter, the net flux—and thus the apparent permeability constant—will not be independent of the absolute values of the two concentrations.

A similar effect may be of importance in connection with the use of isotopes for measuring the permeability of a charged membrane. In such an experiment, the total electrolyte concentration is usually the same on both sides of the membrane, only the isotope concentration being different. Thus $r_c = r_d$, and the flux of the isotope, for a given concentration difference, may not be the same as it would be if there were the same difference in the total electrolyte concentration.

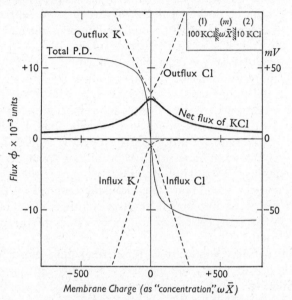

FIG. 10.5.   THE RELATION BETWEEN THE ELECTRIC CHARGE ON A MEMBRANE AND THE PERMEABILITY TO CATIONS AND ANIONS

The arrangement of the system considered is shown in the inset at the top right-hand corner of the diagram. The curves show the fluxes of potassium and chloride ions (broken lines), the net flux of potassium chloride (thick line) and the potential difference across the membrane (thin line). They are calculated from the "fixed charge" theory.

Note that when the membrane is negatively charged, it is permeable to potassium ions, but only slightly permeable to chloride ions, as shown by the large values of the flux of potassium ions in both directions, and the small values of the flux of chloride ions. Conversely, when the membrane is positively charged, the flux of chloride ions is large and that of potassium ions small. The net flux of potassium chloride consequently falls as the membrane charge increases in either direction.

The membrane potential is zero when the membrane is uncharged (the mobilities of potassium and chloride ions are very nearly the same) and approaches the theoretical limit of ± 58 mV. when the membrane is highly charged, the sign being determined by that of the ion which can penetrate—compare, also, Fig. 10.6.

(Re-drawn from Teorell, 1953.)

The Membrane Potential. If a membrane separates two electrolyte solutions of different composition, or concentration, it will form an interface between these solutions, and, as discussed in Chapter 5, there will, in general, be an electrical potential difference across it. The magnitude and stability of this potential difference will depend on the permeability of the membrane to the ions present in the solutions. Suppose, to begin with, that the permeability of the membrane for all kinds of ion except one is

zero. The potential difference across the membrane will then be affected
by changes in the concentration of this ion only, and its magnitude will be
determined by the ratio of the activities (or approximately concentrations)
of this ion inside and outside the membrane—as was demonstrated in
Chapter 4 (equation 4.18). A metallic membrane separating two solutions
of one of the salts of the same metal, or the glass membrane used for
determining hydrogen ion activity, would be examples of such membranes.
This fact is illustrated, also, by the curves in Fig. 10.5. As the charge on
the membrane is increased, in either direction, and the membrane becomes
progressively more impermeable to either potassium ions, or to chloride
ions, the potential difference across it approaches the theoretical value of
58 mV. (the concentration ratio of potassium chloride is 10) and its sign
is determined by the sign of the ions which can penetrate. In a less extreme
case, such as that originally postulated by Conway as defining the properties of living cell membranes, the permeabilities are all zero except for
one kind of cation and one kind of anion. We again have a condition of
equilibrium, and the membrane potential is determined by the chemical
potentials of the permeable ions in the two solutions in contact with the
membrane, and is independent of the exact values of the permeability
constants.

Lastly, in the more general case, the permeability constants are finite
for two kinds of cation (say sodium and potassium) and for one kind of
anion (say chloride). If this is so, the system cannot be in equilibrium, and
the electrical potential difference will eventually vanish unless a steady
state is maintained by the continuous expenditure of energy in transporting
some of the ions. Assuming that there is some form of "active" transport,
maintaining a steady state, we have to consider two possible organisations
of the system. In the first, the active transport takes place through the
membrane under examination, and across which the electrical potential
difference is measured. This implies that there must be "active" regions
in the membrane, but we assume that they are distributed among the
"passive" regions, and are too small to be detected, separately, by the
methods used for measuring electrical and chemical potentials. Thus,
taking the membrane as a whole, if the compositions of the solutions on
each side of the membrane, and the electrical potential difference, are not
changing, the flux of any particular kind of ion in one direction must be
equal to its flux in the other direction. This, however, is the criterion used
in deriving the Gibbs-Donnan relation (Chapter 5, p. 203). The potential
difference across the membrane will be related to the activity ratio of those
ions whose flux is proportional to the electrochemical potential gradient
in the same way as it would if the system were in true equilibrium; and it
will be independent of the activity ratios of those ions which are subjected
to active transport, and on which work is performed. This appears to be

the state of affairs at the external membranes of many kinds of living cell, sodium ions being actively expelled from the cells, and potassium and chloride ions being free to diffuse and take up the concentrations required by the equilibrium conditions, i.e. such as to have the same electro-chemical potential on both sides of the membrane. It is to be noted, how-ever, that if the diffusion of some kind of ion is facilitated, its flux may not be proportional to the concentration gradient; there may then be a steady state, even though the electrochemical potential of this kind of ion is not the same in both solutions.

In these conditions, the potential difference, and the activity (or con-centration) ratio, will not, of course, be determined by the activity, concentra-tion, and total charge, of the indiffusible electrolyte, as in a true Gibbs-Donnan equilibrium. Indeed, there may be no indiffusible electrolytes at all, since the "active" process may be supposed to transport ions until the com-bined electrical and chemical potential difference across the membrane is sufficient to cause diffusion in one direction at a rate which is equal to that of the active transport in the other direction.

In the second possible organisation of the system, the active transport takes place by some route which does not involve the passage of the ions through the particular membrane studied. In a large-scale model, for example, the "cell" may be open at one end, and electrolytes added continually by some form of pump. In living systems, there is reason to believe that the surface membranes of secretory cells may have different properties in different regions which can be distinguished microscopically; some of these may, perhaps, be "active", and some "passive". In these circumstances, even though the system is in a steady state, the potential difference across the "passive" part of the membrane will be the same as it would be if there were no active transport in some other part of the membrane, and the system were neither in equilibrium nor in a steady state. (With the methods available, at present, it is doubtful if the potential difference across the "passive" part of the membrane could, in fact, be distinguished from that across the "active" part, even in secretory cells; but in principle the difference may be important, as will be seen in a later section.) It would appear, also, that many kinds of isolated tissue, after removal from the organism are not, in fact, in a steady state. The electrical potential difference, in these circumstances, depends not only on the chemical potentials of the various ions in the two solutions, but also on the permeability constants of the membrane for these ions, and on the electrical asymmetry of the membrane. The only restriction on the magnitudes of the various ionic fluxes through the membrane, now, is that in the absence of any applied electromotive force, there must be no net flow of current through the membrane. Assuming, again, that there is a linear relation between flux and electrochemical potential, the electrical potential difference between, for example, the contents of a living cell and the external solution, in terms of the activity (or concentration) ratios and the permeability constants of the various kinds of ion concerned, may be derived from equation 4.14 (p. 140). We will consider the case of a "cell" (which need not be a living one) containing an electrolyte solution, surrounded by a membrane, and immersed in an "environment" which is also an electrolyte solution. The total electrolyte concentrations in the two solutions may be the same, but their compositions are supposed different.

The current carried by any particular kind of ion through unit area of membrane will be determined by its velocity multiplied by its concentration (i.e. its flux), multiplied by its electrical charge. Thus:

$$i = F.\phi = m'u'[\pm zF(dE/dx) + RTd(\ln a)/dx] \quad . \quad \text{(from 4.13)}$$

m' and u' being the concentration and mobility of the ion considered *in the membrane*, and the electrical term being taken as positive or negative according as we are considering cations or anions. We may restrict ourselves, for simplicity, and with very little loss of usefulness, to univalent electrolytes; the valency term, z, may thus be omitted. Replacing activity by concentration and activity coefficient, we get:

$$i = RT.m'u'\left[\pm \frac{F}{RT} \cdot \frac{dE}{dx} + \frac{1}{m'} \cdot \frac{dm'}{dx} + \frac{1}{\gamma} \frac{d\gamma}{dx} \right] \quad . \quad \quad 10.14$$

If, now, we assume that the ionic mobilities are independent of their concentrations, and that the electric field (potential gradient) within the membrane is uniform (compare Chapter 4, p. 141), replacing dE/dx by $\Delta E/d$, where d is the thickness of the membrane, this equation can be integrated with respect to x, between the limits of 0 and d, and between m'_c and m'_e the concentrations of the ion considered, within the membrane, on the cell side and the external solution side, respectively; we may assume that the activity coefficients are the same throughout the membrane. We thus get the following expressions:

for cations:

$$i_+ = -\frac{Fu'_+ \Delta E}{[1 - \exp(-\Delta E.F/RT)]d} \cdot [(m'_+)_e - (m'_+)_c \exp(-\Delta E.F/RT)] \quad 10.15$$

and for anions:

$$i_- = \frac{Fu'_- \Delta E}{[1 - \exp(-\Delta E.F/RT)]d} \cdot [(m'_-)_c - (m'_-)_e \exp(-\Delta E.F/RT)] \quad 10.15a$$

But since the total current through the membrane is zero, we must have:

$$\Sigma\{u'_+(m'_+)_e - u'_+(m'_+)_c \exp(-\Delta E.F/RT)\}$$
$$+ \Sigma\{u'_-(m'_-)_c - u'_-(m'_-)_e \exp(-\Delta E.F/RT)\} = 0$$

whence :

$$\Delta E = \frac{RT}{F} \ln . \frac{\Sigma\{u'_+(m'_+)_e\} + \Sigma\{u'_-(m'_-)_c\}}{\Sigma\{u'_+(m'_+)_c\} + \Sigma\{u'_-(m'_-)_e\}} \qquad . \qquad 10.16$$

Now, as already remarked earlier in this chapter, the permeability constant is defined in terms of the concentration gradient only; and, neglecting activity coefficients, the flux of the ions diffusing under the concentration gradient only may be seen from equation 10.14 above to be:

$$\phi = \frac{RT}{F} u' . \frac{dm'}{dx} \quad \text{or, on integration,} \quad \phi = \frac{RT}{F} u' . \frac{(m'_c - m'_e)}{d} .$$

But, from the definition of the permeability constant, the flux of any substance is given by $\phi = P(m_c - m_e)$, where m_c and m_e are the concentrations in the bulk solutions on each side of the membrane. If we assume that the concentrations within the membrane are proportional to those in the solutions in contact with it, we have: $m' = \beta.m$, and thus: $P = (RT/Fd)u'.\beta$, where β is a constant and may be regarded as a "partition coefficient". Inserting these relations into equation 10.16, we get:

$$\Delta E = \frac{RT}{F} \ln \frac{\Sigma P_+(m_+)_e + \Sigma P_-(m_-)_c}{\Sigma P_+(m_+)_c + \Sigma P_-(m_-)_e} \qquad . \qquad 10.17$$

The solutions of most interest to physiologists contain chiefly sodium, potassium and chloride ions, the other constituents being of minor importance quantitatively, and largely incapable of penetrating the cell membranes at any considerable rate. In these circumstances, the electric potential difference across the membrane would be given by the simpler expression:

$$\Delta E = \frac{RT}{F} \ln \frac{P_{Na}(m_{Na})_e + P_K(m_K)_e + P_{Cl}(m_{Cl})_c}{P_{Na}(m_{Na})_c + P_K(m_K)_c + P_{Cl}(m_{Cl})_e} \qquad . \qquad 10.17a$$

The above analysis is essentially that given by Goldman. There is no doubt, however, that the "constant field" assumption, on which it is based, is a simplification which is only warranted in certain circumstances. A more complete analysis is possible on the basis of the "fixed charge" theory, as has been shown by Teorell. According to this conception, the total electrical potential difference across the membrane is the algebraic sum of the two potential differences at the interfaces, arising from the Gibbs-Donnan equilibrium (π_c and π_e) and the diffusion potential set up within the membrane by the electrolyte as it passes across (E_D). As was shown in Chapter 5 (p. 203) we can write:

$$\pi_c = -(RT/F) \ln r_c; \text{ and } \pi_e = (RT/F) \ln r_e \qquad . \quad 5.12 \text{ and } 5.13$$

(univalent electrolytes, only, being considered), where r_c and r_e are the Gibbs-Donnan equilibrium ratios, as considered in the previous section.

P*

Thus $m'_+ = m_+.r$ and $m'_- = m_-/r$, and the "partition coefficient", β, in the "constant field" theory will not be the same for cations as for anions; this, however, is of no consequence, since its value is incorporated in the "permeability constant", P. But, as we have already seen, the value of r depends upon the ratio of the membrane charge concentration to the total electrolyte concentration; r_c will only be equal to r_e (so that both can be equated with β) in two special circumstances. Either the membrane must be sensibly uncharged (in relation to the electrolyte concentration of the solution), or the total electrolyte concentration within the cell must be the same as that in the environment. This condition is, in fact, satisfied, at least approximately, in the tissues of animals, but is usually not satisfied in those of plants.

The evaluation of the diffusion potential, as stated in Chapter 4, involves, in general, complicated mathematics. We may, however, again limit our treatment to the two simple cases considered in that chapter. In the second of these, in which the total concentration is the same on both sides of the membrane, or interface, but the composition is different, the value of the diffusion potential is given by equation 4.17 (p. 142). In this case, the two Gibbs-Donnan equilibrium potentials (π_c and π_e) are equal and opposite and so cancel out, and the total potential difference across the membrane is equal to the diffusion potential. If, in equation 10.17a, we put $(m_{Cl})_c = (m_{Cl})_e = m_{Cl}$; $m_{Na}/m_{Cl} = q$; and $m_K/m_{Cl} = (1-q)$ in both numerator and denominator, with appropriate suffixes, it becomes identical in form with equation 4.17; we have already seen that the "permeability constants", P, are directly proportional to the mobilities, u. In the special circumstances which are applicable to the cells of animals, then, the "fixed charge" theory leads to the same conclusions as the "constant field" theory.

The first of the two special cases considered in Chapter 4, that of a single electrolyte in greater concentration on one side of the membrane than on the other, leads to quite different conclusions. On the "fixed charge" theory, the total potential difference across the membrane depends largely on the relation of the electrolyte concentration to the membrane charge, as is illustrated by the curves in Fig. 10.6. These represent the total potential difference across a negatively charged membrane when the electrolyte concentration ratio across it is constant at a value of 10, but the ratio of charge to electrolyte concentration (the quantity $\omega \bar{X}/a$) on the more concentrated side varies from 10^{-4} to 10^2. When the membrane is relatively highly charged, the total potential difference is determined almost entirely by the Gibbs-Donnan equilibrium potential, and approaches the theoretical value of 58 mV., as already remarked. When the membrane possesses relatively little charge (and in the limit may be considered uncharged), the Gibbs-Donnan equilibrium potential vanishes and the total potential difference is determined only by the diffusion potential; this, as can be seen, may be of the opposite sign to the Gibbs-Donnan potential. The diffusion potential in this case is given by an equation identical in form with equation 4.16 (p. 141), but is somewhat more complicated, owing to the presence of the membrane charge and to the fact that the

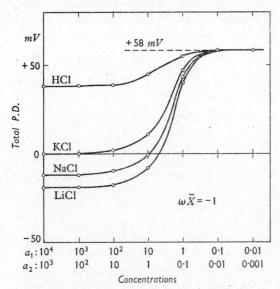

FIG. 10.6. THE EFFECT OF ELECTROLYTE CONCENTRATION ON THE POTENTIAL DIFFERENCE ACROSS A CHARGED MEMBRANE

The abscissae represent the electrolyte concentrations on the two sides of the membrane (a_1 and a_2) in arbitrary units, the ratio between them being kept constant and equal to 10. The membrane is negatively charged, with a "concentration" of 1 in the same units.

On the right of the diagram, the membrane is highly charged in relation to the electrolyte concentration, and the membrane potential for all kinds of electrolyte approaches the equilibrium value of 58 mV., corresponding to the concentration ratio. On the left of the diagram, where the electrolyte concentrations are large, the membrane is, in comparison, sensibly uncharged, and the potential difference across it is determined by the diffusion potential; this, in turn, is determined by the difference in mobility between cations and anions, and so varies with the nature of the electrolyte.

The curves are calculated from the "fixed charge" theory.

(Re-drawn from Teorell, 1953.)

concentrations within the membrane may be different from those in the bulk solutions. It may be written, neglecting activity coefficients, as:

$$E_D = \frac{RT}{F} \cdot \frac{(u_+ - u_-)}{(u_+ + u_-)} \ln \left\{ \frac{(m_+)_c r_c u_+ + (m_-)_c u_- / r_c}{(m_+)_a r_a u_+ + (m_-)_a u_- / r_a} \right\} \qquad . \quad 10.18$$

In order to discover whether a system is in a steady state or not, it is necessary to measure the net flux, or the flux ratio, of each kind of ion which is present; in living systems, as a rule, this can only be done by the use of isotopes. For univalent ions, for example, the flux ratio will be given by:

$$\frac{(\phi_\pm)_{\text{in}}}{(\phi_\pm)_{\text{out}}} = \frac{m_e\gamma_e}{m_c\gamma_c} \exp\left(\pm F.\Delta E/RT\right) \qquad . \qquad . \qquad 10.2$$

assuming that $P_{\text{in}} = P_{\text{out}}$. This equation will apply in all circumstances. But in the equilibrium, or steady state, conditions, as already remarked, the electrical potential across the membrane will be defined by:

$$(\Delta E)_s = \frac{RT}{F} \ln \frac{m_c\gamma_c}{m_e\gamma_e} \qquad . \qquad . \qquad 4.18, \, 5.12$$

We can thus write:

$$(\phi_\pm)_{\text{in}}/(\phi_\pm)_{\text{out}} = \exp\left\{[\Delta E - (\Delta E)_s]F/RT\right\} \qquad . \qquad 10.19$$

If the measured electrical potential difference across the membrane, ΔE, differs from that calculated from the activity ratio of some particular kind of ion $(\Delta E)_s$, the system is probably not in a steady state with respect to this kind of ion. On the other hand, it must be remembered that equation 10.2 is based on the assumption that the flux of the ion concerned is proportional to the electrochemical potential gradient. The system may be in a steady state, and the observed flux ratio unity, and yet ΔE may differ from $(\Delta E)_s$; we then infer either that the ion under consideration is being actively transported; or that its penetration is facilitated in some way, the word being used very generally, to indicate that the flux is not directly proportional to the electrochemical potential gradient.

The conclusion that in many kinds of living cell, there must be an active transport of sodium ions out of the cell interior and into the external solution, is based on evidence of this kind; the measured membrane potential is ordinarily very far from the equilibrium potential for sodium ions, and observations with isotopes indicate that the system is in a steady state. There is good evidence, also, that in such cells part of the flux of potassium ions is linked, stoichiometrically, with the flux of sodium ions, and has little or no relation to the electrochemical potential; the concentration ratio of potassium ions is not, as a rule, quite that to be expected from the membrane potential, although it is usually not far from it.

The Membrane Conductance. Since every ion of a given kind possesses the same electric charge, the flux of such ions through a membrane can be observed in terms of the electric current passing. Moreover, ions may be made to pass through the membrane by applying an *electrical* potential gradient, instead of, or as well as, a chemical potential gradient. The resistance to the passage of the ions will be the same whether the driving force is chemical or electrical, and whether the flux is measured in chemical or electrical terms. The *conductance*, therefore, or the ratio of the electric current to the potential difference producing it, will be determined by the permeability of the membrane to the particular ions concerned.

When the membrane is permeable to several different kinds of ion, complications arise. If, as is likely, it is not equally permeable to all the kinds of ion that are present, it will act as a rectifier of electric current, as discussed on p. 430 above; the membrane conductance will depend on the sign of the electric potential which is applied. According to the "fixed charge" theory, the magnitude of the rectification effect (the ratio of the maximum values of the conductance in the two directions) rises in proportion to the magnitude of the internal diffusion potential. In addition, a complex system such as a semi-permeable membrane is likely to be "non-ohmic", and the current will not be proportional to the applied electromotive force, in either direction. Thus we cannot use the simple definition of conductance, just given, but must define it as the rate of change of current with change in the applied E.M.F., under conditions such that the actual flow of current is negligibly small—i.e. as $\partial i/\partial E$ when i becomes zero. The relation of the conductance, $\bar{G}$, to the permeability constants and ion concentrations can thus be derived by differentiating the equations for the cation and anion currents (equations 10.15 and 10.15a)—and hence the total current—with respect to the membrane potential; we will do no more than quote the final equation reached. This is:

$$\bar{G} = \frac{F^3}{(RT)^2} \varDelta E \cdot \frac{N \cdot D}{(N-D)} \qquad . \qquad . \qquad . \quad 10.20$$

where N and D are given by the equation for the membrane potential (equation 10.17) given above, written in the form:

$$\varDelta E = \frac{RT}{F} \ln \cdot \frac{N}{D}$$

This equation for the total membrane conductance, of course, will apply only in the conditions where the "constant field" assumptions are justified. For other conditions, even more complicated expressions are needed.

The current carried through a membrane by each kind of ion will be given by its net flux multiplied by its charge, i.e. $i = F(\phi_{in} - \phi_{out})$, the ion being assumed to be univalent. That part of the total conductance contributed by this particular kind of ion, G, will be given by $\partial i/\partial E$, and may be obtained by differentiating equation 10.19. But if the system is at least approximately in a steady state, we have $\phi_{in} \doteqdot \phi_{out} \doteqdot \phi$, and in these conditions, as Hodgkin has pointed out, we get:

$$G = \frac{F^2}{RT} \phi \quad \text{and thus:} \quad \bar{G} = \frac{F^2}{RT} \Sigma \phi \quad . \qquad . \qquad . \quad 10.21$$

where ϕ is the ionic flux for each kind of ion that is carrying current, inwards or outwards, and $\bar{G}$ is the total conductance. It is thus possible to relate the electrical measurements of conductance with the flux measurements obtained by the use of isotopes, for example. Equation 10.21, it must be emphasised, can be applied only when the system is in, or not far from, a steady state; there is no such limitation to the validity of equation 10.20.

The flux of potassium ions into and out of some kinds of living cell in certain conditions, is found to be proportional to the nth power of the electrochemical potential, as if the penetration were along chains or through long narrow pores (as discussed on p. 445 above). The isotopic flux ratio ϕ^*_{in}/ϕ^*_{out} will then be the nth power of ϕ_{in}/ϕ_{out} as given by equation 10.2, and the conductance, measured electrically, will be n times that deduced from the flux by equation 10.21. In the giant nerve fibres of *Sepia*, for example, n has a value of about 2·5.

Membrane Reactance. When ions are made to move through a membrane as a result of the application of an external electromotive force, their distribution within the membrane will be changed, and so, also, in all probability, will be the conductance. The new distribution will not necessarily, or usually, be taken up instantaneously, and the conductance may initially be smaller or greater than that eventually reached. The membrane may thus appear to possess "reactance", either capacitative or inductive, respectively. Such effects have, in fact, been observed in artificial membranes as well as in living systems. There is reason to suppose, however, that the membranes of living cells contain elements which are electrical insulators and act as true dielectrics; they will thus possess a true capacitative reactance as well as the apparent reactance produced by what has been called the "delayed rectification" effect.

The Measurement of the Membrane Conductance and the Membrane Potential. It is clear from the above analyses that measurements of electrical conductance, or of potential difference, cannot in general give any immediate measure of the permeability of the membrane to any given species of ion; both measurements, however, are very valuable for indicating rapid changes in the ion permeability. But if conductance and potential measurements can be made not only when the cells are in their normal environments, but also when placed in solutions of different, and known, compositions, estimates may be obtained of the permeability constants at least for the ions present in the larger concentrations. Measurements of the membrane conductance and membrane potential have, indeed, provided very valuable information as to the nature of the cell membrane.

When dealing with artificial membranes, or with sheets of living cells which can be arranged to form a dividing wall between two solutions, no great practical difficulties are encountered. The electrodes must, of course, be non-polarisable, and any potentials generated at the electrodes themselves, or anywhere in the system other than the membrane, must be allowed for. When measuring conductances, it is preferable to use two pairs of electrodes. A measured current is passed through the membrane by means of one pair, and the potential difference across the membrane is measured by means of the second pair; these last may be quite small, and are placed as close to the membrane, on each side, as possible; the current electrodes must be large, but may be some distance from the membrane.

If, however, we are concerned with the surface membranes of the cells themselves, the measurements are more difficult. Measurements of the *potential differences* across cell membranes, and of the variations when the composition of the external medium is changed, can be made accurately only when it is possible to insert one electrode into the interior of the cell. This can be done without very great difficulty (unless the cell has a tough outer coat): but, unless the observations are restricted to a few kinds of very large cell, the electrodes must be very small. Extremely fine glass or quartz tubes (less than 1μ diameter) are used; they may contain a fine silver wire, or they may be filled with a saturated solution of potassium chloride and connected to a wider tube containing a silver-silver chloride electrode. A second "indifferent" electrode, not necessarily very small, is placed outside the cell. Owing to the very high internal resistance of most of these micro-electrodes, proper precautions must be taken to use only appropriately designed electrical circuits for measuring the potential differences.

Measurements of the *conductance* of the cell membrane, also, are best made on single cells into which a micro-electrode can be inserted; a known potential difference is applied between the electrodes, and the resulting current measured. Allowance must be made, of course, for the resistance of the micro-electrode itself; and since this may be very large, it is better, when possible, to use two micro-electrodes, one for delivering the current, and the other for measuring the potential difference. Although simple in principle, this procedure may give unexpected results; the electrical properties of most cell membranes are apt to undergo marked changes when electrical currents are passed through, unless these are very small—a property which is responsible for their "excitability".

In some circumstances, it is possible to derive a value for the membrane conductance from observations on suspensions of isolated cells, or on a tissue composed of many cells embedded in a connective tissue matrix. The specific resistance of a suspension of conducting particles in a conducting medium can be deduced theoretically, as was done by Maxwell in 1873. If the specific resistance of the suspended particles is r_c, and that of the external suspending fluid is r_e, the whole suspension will have a specific resistance $\bar{r}$, defined by the relation:

$$\frac{1-r_e/\bar{r}}{q+r_e/\bar{r}} = a \cdot \frac{1-r_e/r_c}{q+r_e/r_c} \qquad . \qquad . \qquad . \qquad 10.22$$

where a is the fraction of the total volume which is occupied by the particles, and q is a factor depending on the shape of the particles; for spheres, $q=2$, but for other shapes, its value depends on the ratio of the resistance of the particles to the resistance of the suspending fluid, and on the orientation of the particles, if any. In the general case, the analysis is so complicated that it is useful only when the particles are considered to be sensibly non-conducting; the method is thus of little use for discovering the membrane conductance except in special cases. Even so, however, a further difficulty arises from the fact that the resistance of most kinds of living cell is large compared with that of the fluid by which they are surrounded; as can be seen from equation 10.22, measurements of $\bar{r}$ and r_e will then yield accurate estimates of r_c only if the value of a is known very accurately. This, however, is technically impossible; and, in fact, one cannot establish definitely that the resistance of cells immersed in sea-water, for example, is not infinite. If the cells are such that they can be immersed in fresh water, on the other hand, their resistance is not very large compared with that of the water, and reasonably accurate measurements, can be made, particularly if the cells occupy a large fraction of the total volume (a single large plant cell, or even a frog's egg, in a total volume only just large enough to contain it, has been used). It is possible, nevertheless, to detect and measure *changes* in the membrane conductance in quite a wide variety of conditions: the relative volume of the cells and the "shape factor" can be assumed to be constant, and their values need not be known.

In the particular case of a cell which is very long and thin, such as a nerve or muscle fibre, the membrane conductance may be measured by the use of electrodes so disposed that the current flows *along* the fibre—a procedure which at first sight might seem futile, since the current would not flow through the membrane at all. This, however, is not so; the interior of the cell and the external solution constitute two conductors in parallel, united throughout their lengths by the membrane, and the flow of current will be divided between the interior and the exterior in a rather complicated way, depending on the membrane conductance. A fibre such as a nerve or muscle behaves, in fact, as if it were a "coaxial cable" or "core conductor". The electrical properties of such a cable are of great importance to electrical engineers, and have been worked out mathematically. As applied to the particular case of a nerve fibre, the mathematical treatment will be found in the paper by Hodgkin and Rushton (1946). The distribution of the current in the various components of the fibre depends on a quantity known as the "space constant" or "characteristic length", λ. This is defined by the equation:

$$\lambda = 1/\sqrt{g_m(r_e + r_c)} \qquad . \qquad . \qquad . \qquad . \quad 10.23$$

where g_m is the membrane conductance, and r_e and r_c are the resistances of the external fluid and the cell contents, respectively, all per unit length of the fibre. In order to make practical use of the equations developed in the theoretical analysis, observations must be made in certain restricted conditions. The current used, of course, must be kept small, as already emphasised.

(1) If a steady current is made to pass along the fibre between two electrodes applied to its surface, then the potential V_A at the surface of the fibre at a point A will be related to that at a point B, at a distance l from it, neither point lying between the electrodes, by the relation:

$$l/\lambda = \ln (V_A/V_B) \qquad . \qquad . \qquad . \qquad . \quad 10.24$$

In the presence of a finite membrane resistance, and thus of a finite value of the space constant, the potential at the surface of the fibre falls logarithmically as we pass away from the region beneath, and between, the electrodes; in a simple conductor, it would remain constant. Measurement of the surface potential at two points on the fibre thus provides a measure of λ.

(2) If the two polarising electrodes are a long way apart, in terms of the space constant, the lines of current flow inside and outside the fibre will be sensibly parallel, and no current will flow through the membrane. In this region, then, the voltage gradient is given by the product of the total current flow, I, and the resistance of the external and internal solutions in parallel. Thus:

$$(\partial V/\partial x)_{x=\beta} = I.r_e r_c/(r_e + r_c) = m.I \quad . \qquad . \qquad . \quad 10.25$$

where $\beta \gg \lambda$.

(3) The potential at one of the electrodes, the other being a long distance away, is related to the magnitude of the polarising current by the equation:

$$V_E = I(m\lambda/2)(r_e/r_c) \qquad . \qquad . \qquad . \qquad . \quad 10.26$$

From these three equations, involving g_m, r_e and r_c, all three quantities may be evaluated.

So far, we have assumed the presence of a cell membrane, with electrical properties distinct from those of the cell contents; apart from the fact that the space constant has a finite value, the results of the electrical measurements could, however, be interpreted without this assumption. But if a membrane is present, it will, as stated on p. 462 above, almost certainly possess a capacitance, as well as a conductance. The electrical properties of the system will thus be expected to depend on the rate of change of the applied current used to investigate them, or, if alternating currents are used, on the frequency. By using alternating currents, we measure the *impedance* of the system, which is a complex sum of the resistance and the reactance. If the system contains capacitance, the reactance will fall as the frequency is increased, but the resistance will remain constant.

If the cell is considered as a coaxial cable, we find that it has, in addition to the space constant, a time constant, or characteristic time, τ_m, given by the ratio C_m/g_m, where C_m is the membrane capacitance per unit length of the fibre. If the current applied through the electrodes is suddenly started at time 0, then the potential at one of the electrodes at time t, $(V_E)_t$ is related to the steady potential reached after infinite time $(V_E)_\infty$ according to the equation:

$$(V_E)_t = (V_E)_\infty \, \mathrm{erf}\left[\sqrt{t/\tau_m}\right] \qquad . \qquad . \qquad . \quad 10.27$$

where the symbol "erf" stands for the "error function"; for any function z, we have:

$$\mathrm{erf}\ z = \frac{2}{\sqrt{\pi}} \int_0^z \exp . \, (-y^2) \, dy.$$

The relation between $(V_E)_t$ and t is thus S-shaped; from this relation, we can deduce τ_m, and thus, knowing g_m from the steady state measurements, as already described, we can deduce C_m.

If we have a number of cells of known shape, each consisting of an electrolyte solution surrounded by a relatively non-conducting envelope, and suspended in a second electrolyte solution, we can measure the impedance of the suspension at various frequencies, and then deduce the capacitance of the cells. At very low frequencies, the impedance of the cells will be large, since the reactance approaches infinity and current can only pass through them by traversing the resistive part of the envelope. As the frequency is raised, current will pass through the capacitative part of the envelope in addition, the cell impedance will fall, and will be largely capacitative. At very high frequencies, the reactance of the membrane will approach zero, the cell impedance will become mainly resistive once more, and will be determined by the resistance of the cell contents. The circuit diagram of an "impedance bridge", by means of which such measurements can be made, has been given in Fig. 4.1 (p. 120).

Imagine a flock of sheep at one side of a field and that they start to run to the other side; the amount of wool (=electricity) which arrives at the other side in unit time depends on the number of sheep and the speed at which they run. Suppose that there are a number of pens in the middle of the field, each fenced round and separated from the neighbouring pens by narrow passages; the number of sheep now getting across in unit time will be much less than before, because they have to wait for each other to get through the openings, or are held up at the pens and fail to complete the course. We may say that less wool passes across per unit time, or in electrical terms, the conductance is less. Further, matters would not be improved if the closed pens were full of sheep, since these sheep would not be able to help in the transport. But suppose now that the sheep are induced to move alternately backwards and forwards across the field, and that we are interested in the total amount of wool which, in unit time, crosses an arbitrary line drawn across the field. The inducement to move to and fro acts on the sheep within the pens as well as on those free in the field: as external sheep congregate at one of the walls of a pen, the internal sheep will congregate on the opposite wall; there will be a press of sheep on one side of each wall and a withdrawal from the other. Part of the flow of wool across the arbitrary line will therefore be due to this piling up of sheep at the boundaries of the pens; this is the capacitative current that results from the presence of the non-conducting cell membranes. If the frequency of oscillation is made very great, however, there will be insufficient time during each half-cycle for any considerable press to build up; the total flow of wool across the field will then be the same whether the walls of the pens are there or not.

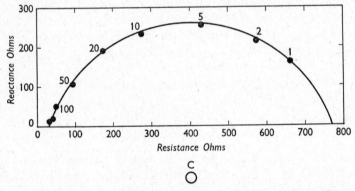

FIG. 10.7. THE RELATION BETWEEN THE REACTANCE (ORDINATES) AND RESISTANCE (ABSCISSAE) OF A FROG'S SARTORIUS MUSCLE AT DIFFERENT FREQUENCIES

The electrodes were placed so that the current flowed across the muscle fibres. Each point shows the values observed at a frequency indicated by the figure (in kilocycles per second) placed above it. The points lie on a circle whose centre is at the point C.

(Cole and Curtis, 1936.)

Measurements at very high frequencies have proved that electrolytes are in free solution in the cell interior; measurements at intermediate frequencies have provided measures of the capacitance of the membrane and hence estimates of its thickness; and extrapolation of the measurements at low frequencies to zero frequency provides an estimate of the membrane conductance. This electrical behaviour is illustrated in Fig. 10.7, in which the ordinates represent the capacitative reactance of a nerve, and the abscissae the resistance. Each circle represents the values obtained at a frequency given by the number placed above it, in kilocyles per second. It will be seen that as the frequency is reduced, the resistance rises steadily, and at zero frequency has a value some 2000 times as great as that at infinite frequency; the reactance, however, at first rises from zero, and then after reaching a maximum value, falls again to zero. The points lie quite accurately on the arc of a circle, facilitating extrapolation to zero frequency. The centre of the circle should lie on the axis of abscissae; the fact that it does not may be accounted for by assuming that the membrane capacitance is not independent of the frequency, as is that of a "perfect" condenser.

The theory of the impedance of suspensions of capacitative particles is complex and difficult. A brief account, and references to the original papers, will be found in the article by K. S. Cole (1940). The suspension will have a time constant τ, given by

$$\tau = \left[\frac{1+q.a}{q(1-a)} r_e + r_c \right] C_m.a \qquad . \qquad . \qquad . \quad 10.28$$

where a is the radius of the cell, and the other symbols have the same meanings as in equation 10.23; the shape factor, q, has the value 2 for suspensions of spheres, and 1 for a tissue consisting of parallel cylindrical cells, such as a nerve or muscle. We can derive the resistance, r, and the capacitative reactance, x, of the suspension at any frequency, $\omega/2\pi$, in terms of the resistances at infinite and zero frequency, r_∞ and r_0, as extrapolated from curves such as that in Fig. 10.7, and the time constant, τ:

$$\left. \begin{aligned} r &= r_\infty + (r_0 - r_\infty)/(1 + \omega^2\tau^2) \\ -x &= r(r_0 - r_\infty)\omega\tau/(1 + \omega^2\tau^2) \end{aligned} \right\} \qquad . \qquad . \qquad . \quad 10.29$$

As before, therefore, we must know the relative volume occupied by the cells and the value of the shape factor; in addition, we must know the radius of the cells.

ANOMALOUS OSMOSIS

When two solutions of different concentration are separated by a membrane which is more permeable to the solvent than to the solutes, there will be an initial movement of solvent from the more dilute solution to the more concentrated, as discussed in Chapter 3, p. 93. When the solute is an electrolyte, and the membrane is electrically charged, very anomalous effects may be obtained, which differ appreciably from those which would be expected from the difference in concentration on the two sides of the membrane.

The permeability of an electrically charged membrane to cations, as we have seen, may be very different from that to anions; as the electrolyte diffuses through the membrane, an electrical potential difference, possibly of considerable magnitude, is generated. If the membrane has a pore structure, the solution within the pores will be electrically charged, and will move in the electric field generated by the diffusing ions—i.e. will undergo electro-osmosis, as discussed in Chapter 5, p. 205. The electro-osmotic flow of solution is thus superimposed on the pure osmotic flow. Suppose we take a solution of some non-electrolyte, such as sucrose, of known concentration, and place it within a membrane which is not entirely impermeable to sucrose, such as a collodion sac. When placed in water, there will, at first, be a flow of water into the sac, and the pressure within it will rise. This *initial rate of diffusion*, as Loeb has called it, is determined, in any particular sac, by the partial free energy of the water in the solution, and so should be the same for all solutions of the same activity, or to a first approximation, the same molar concentration. If, however, we replace the solution of sucrose by one of an electrolyte, in which the activity of the water is the same, we find, if we have chosen suitable concentrations for our solutions, that the initial rate of diffusion is not the same as it was before. Moreover, we now find that the initial rate of diffusion depends on the valencies of the ions in the solution. If, as is generally the case, the membrane takes up a negative charge in contact with the solution, the initial rate of diffusion will rise as the valency of the anion is increased, but will fall as that of the cation is increased. This behaviour is the direct consequence of the existence of an electro-osmotic flow of solution within the pores of the membrane. Multivalent ions travel more slowly than do univalent ions, so that the magnitude of the diffusion potential increases as the valency of one of the ions is increased; its sign, moreover, is reversed by changing from a multivalent anion to a multivalent cation, so that the direction of the electro-osmotic flow is also reversed. If the sign of the charge on the membrane is reversed, so as to be positive with respect to the solution, the initial rate of diffusion is now increased by multivalent cations and decreased by multivalent anions. The general nature of the effect is shown in Fig. 10.8. If we take a solution of an acid, such as hydrochloric, the diffusion potential may be so large that with a positively charged membrane, water is driven out through the membrane by electro-osmosis faster than it enters by simple osmosis. The expected osmotic flow is thus actually reversed.

This type of phenomenon has been investigated extensively by Teorell in relation to the "fixed charge" theory of membrane permeability. Not only is the movement of the solvent anomalous, in systems involving the diffusion of an electrolyte through a charged membrane, but so also is that of other kinds of ion which may be present. Cations will tend to move preferentially towards the negative side of the membrane, and anions towards the positive side. In a particular example studied by Teorell, a solution of potassium bromide was placed on each side of a charged membrane, the concentrations of potassium and bromide ions thus being

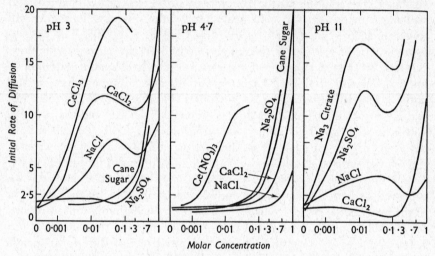

FIG. 10.8. INITIAL RATE OF DIFFUSION OF WATER THROUGH GELATIN-COATED
COLLODION MEMBRANES

Abscissae: concentration of solution within the membrane (logarithmic scale).

Ordinates: average rate of diffusion during the first 20 minutes, expressed as the rise in level of a manometer connected to the solution within the membrane.

When the solution is at *p*H 3, the membrane is on the acid side of its iso-electric point and is thus positively charged: the magnitude of the anomalous flow increases with increase in the valency of the *cation*, and decreases with increase in the valency of the anion.

When the membrane is negatively charged (the solution is at *p*H 11), the anomalous flow increases with increase in the valency of the *anion*, and decreases with increase in the valency of the cation.

At the iso-electric point of the membrane (*p*H 4·7) little or no anomalous flow is shown by univalent or bivalent electrolytes (the curves run close to the curve for cane sugar), but trivalent cations appear to impart a positive charge to the membrane, probably by adsorption.   (Re-drawn from data of Jaques Loeb, 1921.)

initially the same throughout. If hydrochloric acid was added to the solution on one side, and allowed to diffuse through, concentration gradients of both potassium ions and bromide ions developed, the potassium ions becoming more concentrated on the side from which the hydrochloric acid was diffusing, and the bromide ions becoming more dilute. Such phenomena may well be concerned in some cases in which there is an apparent "active" transport of water and electrolytes across membranes in living systems.

ACTIVE TRANSPORT AND SECRETION

The essential feature of active transport and secretion is that substances move from one place to another, and chemical changes occur, in a direction contrary to that expected from the apparent physico-chemical conditions of the system. The processes are intrinsically endergonic, and will not occur unless they are coupled with some exergonic processes. Indeed, experimental evidence shows that in most cases, secretion by living cells ceases when oxidative metabolism is blocked; although in some, it may continue so long as glycolysis and fermentation can occur. No system has yet been constructed which imitates exactly the process of secretion by a living cell; but it is possible to imagine artificial systems which would behave in a very similar manner.

The term "active transport" is applied to the type of secretion illustrated in Fig. 10.4 (4), p. 450, in which some substance enters a membrane of some kind from a solution on one side, and leaves it again into a solution on the other side, its electrochemical potential having been increased in the process. The membrane concerned may consist of living cells associated together so as to form a sheet, which may for example cover the outer surface of a more or less spherical cavity or "alveolus", or form the wall of a tube; or it may consist of the surface membrane of a single cell, the transport then taking place to or from the internal protoplasm of the cell, and from or to the external solution in which the cell lies, or, particularly in plant cells, an internal vacuole.

In the other type of secretion, which may be called "secretion by synthesis", the substance secreted into the solution on the "delivery" side of the membrane, does not occur in the solution on the "entry" side, but is synthesised within the membrane from other substances which have entered, as indicated in Fig. 10.4 (5). The chemical reactions concerned must be endergonic, proceeding only if a suitable source of free energy is available. The term "secretion" is not used when the reactions concerned are exergonic, and proceed spontaneously; as, for example, when glucose undergoes anaerobic glycolysis and lactate ions diffuse out. Secretion by synthesis occurs only, as far as is known, when the membrane concerned consists of an association of cells; synthesis is not known to occur within the surface membrane of a single cell. In this type of secretion, the substance secreted leaves the cells and enters the solution in contact with them by some form of diffusion. It might appear, therefore, that it is fundamentally different from active transport; but actually, it is fairly certain that a substance which is actively transported undergoes chemical reaction within the membrane, by which its electrochemical potential is raised, and then leaves by a process of diffusion.

It will be noted that according to this definition of secretion by synthesis, the formation of carbohydrates by photosynthesis in the green plants, and their transfer from the synthesising cells to the conducting channels in the phloem and xylem, is to be regarded as a process of secretion. It is not, however, conventional to apply the term to this process; indeed the word "secretion" is used more by animal physiologists than by plant physiologists.

An important point to bear in mind when considering the problem of active transport is the possibility of what has been called "secondary" transport. If a substance appears to move in the absence of any diffusion gradient, or in a direction contrary to that expected, it must not be immediately assumed that it is, itself, being actively transported; its movement may be a necessary consequence of the active transport of some other substance. One of the commonest examples of secretion by synthesis is to be seen in the formation of digestive "juices" by glands associated with the alimentary canals of animals, such as the salivary glands and the pancreas. The chief components of most of these juices are the enzymes which they contain, and which are synthesised in the secreting cells; but these enzymes are dissolved in water, and are accompanied by other substances in solution, such as sodium chloride and sodium bicarbonate. These solutes, and the water, may be actively transported, but they may also accompany the enzymes passively, by a process of osmosis; just as a colloidal solution within a collodion sac will draw in water and crystalloidal solutes, from the external solution. Again, suppose we have a system in which one kind of ion, say a particular kind of cation, is being actively transported. Since electric charge is being transferred from one side of the membrane to the other, an electrical potential difference will be generated; the consequent electric force will transport all kinds of anion in the same direction as the actively transported cation, and all other kinds of cation in the opposite direction. These will move in a direction contrary to the gradient of chemical potential, but *not* contrary to that of the electro-chemical potential. In such systems, it is often by no means easy to make certain which kinds of ion are being actively transported, and which are following passively.

Little is known about the actual chemical reactions that bring about secretion. The enzymes secreted by the glands associated with the alimentary canal, and also, for example, into the food vacuoles of protozoa, and by certain special cells of the insectivorous plants, are proteins; so also are many of the hormones elaborated by the cells of the glands of "internal" secretion, while some others are polypeptides. All these are, presumably, synthesised by reactions which are similar to those in which the other proteins are synthesised; that is, the appropriate kinds of amino-acid are joined together in the correct sequence, as determined, apparently, by the presence of the proper kind of nucleoprotein acting as a "template". Even

less, however, is known about the reactions which lead to the formation of
other kinds of hormone.

As regards active transport, although again there is little detailed and
precise information, there are some general considerations which are
important, and some reasonable hypotheses which may be discussed. It
seems probable that we can regard active transport as being brought about
as a result of a combination of the transported substance, S, with a
"carrier" substance, C, as in facilitated penetration discussed in a previous
section (p. 443). We now suppose that the carrier has a large affinity for
the transported substance, so that the reaction:

$$C + S \rightleftharpoons CS \qquad . \qquad . \qquad . \qquad . \quad 10.(i)$$

is driven well to the right, and S is taken up almost completely, even from
a very dilute solution. The compound CS will pass across to the opposite
interface of the membrane, or to the opposite side of the cell. Here we
suppose that it meets with a reaction system by which the uncombined
carrier C, is converted into some different substance D; it may be, for
example, that there is an enzyme system which catalyses the spontaneous
decomposition of C, or that there is some substance, or radical, X, with
which C combines irreversibly. We have, therefore,

$$\text{either:} \qquad C \xrightarrow{X} D \quad \left.\right\} \qquad . \qquad . \qquad . \qquad . \quad 10.(ii)$$
$$\text{or:} \qquad C + X \longrightarrow D$$

In either event, C is removed completely from the reaction system; CS
will then dissociate completely, and S will be released at a relatively high
concentration and diffuse out into a solution in which its concentration
exceeds that in the solution from which it is derived. The substance D may
diffuse back to the "entry" side of the membrane or cell, and be re-con-
verted to the carrier C by a reaction analogous to that in which it was
formed, i.e.:

$$D + Y \longrightarrow C \qquad . \qquad . \qquad . \qquad . \quad 10.(iii)$$

The existence of such a closed circuit for the carrier system is not essential
to the scheme; C may be created from metabolic precursors, and D destroyed, as rapidly as the substance S is transported. If there is a closed
cyclic conversion of C into D, and D back again into C, the system is
symmetrical; D can act as a carrier as well as C, and the transport by means
of C of some substance S_1 in one direction, will be linked with the transport
by means of D of some other substance S_2 in the opposite direction. There
is, in fact, evidence that two different transport systems may be linked
together.

The energy necessary for the active transport is supplied through the

reactions by which C is formed, either from D or from some other precursor, and by which it is removed. This is an essential feature of the
reaction system, and in putting forward suggestions as to the possible
nature of the substances concerned as carriers, this must not be forgotten.
It may be, for example, that the carrier C, or the substances X or Y, are
"active" compounds or radicals, formed, as is adenosine triphosphate, in
the course of oxidative metabolism. It would, indeed, seem not at all
improbable that adenosine triphosphate should play an important part in
active transport, since it acts as a "carrier" of free energy in so many
metabolic reactions. In particular, as was suggested by Wilbrandt, it
might be that glucose is transported by being converted quantitatively into
hexose phosphate, by reacting with adenosine triphosphate, and that the
hexose phosphate subsequently dissociates into glucose again, and inorganic phosphate ions. Both reactions are known to occur in living systems
and each is catalysed by a specific enzyme, so that they might occur only
in specific regions of the living cell, or on different interfaces of a membrane; it is known, also, that the inorganic phosphate can be replaced, as
an "active" radical, in adenosine triphosphate, in the course of oxidative
metabolism. Free energy released in oxidation reactions would thus be
made available to the active transport process by means of the exergonic
reaction: "active" phosphate——→inorganic phosphate. There is indeed
experimental evidence indicating that the active transport of many substances, ceases, or is greatly reduced, when the formation of "active"
phosphate radicals is prevented by reason of a lack of oxidative or
glycolytic reactions, for example, or in the presence of specific enzyme
poisons (notably dinitro-phenol, DNP). But so far, attempts to show that
adenosine triphosphate is directly concerned, as a specific carrier substance,
have been unsuccessful.

As already discussed in Chapter 3, the partial free energies, or chemical
potentials, of the components of a solution may be increased by raising the
pressure or the temperature. It is possible, therefore, at least theoretically,
that solutes or water might be actively transported through a membrane by
means of some process which raises the pressure or temperature on one side
of the membrane. The use of pressure to bring about a forced passage of
water, or other solvent, through a membrane which some of the solutes present
cannot penetrate, is familiar enough; it is not ordinarily regarded as an
"active" transport, however, but as an "ultra-filtration". It has been shown
theoretically, also, that differences in temperature which could be imagined
to occur in living systems, would be capable of bringing about an active
transport of significant magnitude; but since they might be localised in very
small regions of cells which are themselves small, their detection is likely to be
difficult. It may be remarked, however, that in a living cell the necessary rise
in temperature must, presumably, be produced by means of an exothermic
chemical reaction; it would be energetically more efficient to make use of the

free energy change in the reaction, by means of some such system as discussed above, rather than the heat change.

The Transport of Electrolytes

In the transport of electrolytes, as already remarked, we are concerned not only with chemical potentials, but also with electrical potentials. We have, thus, an additional source of information about the processes involved, and one which is, often, more readily investigated experimentally. Little is actually known about these processes, in spite of extensive investigation; it has been possible, however, to exclude several hypothetical processes, otherwise apparently quite reasonable, as a result of electrical, energetic and stoichiometric measurements.

An active transport of certain kinds of ion might be conceived as being brought about as a result of their combination with a specific carrier substance by means of covalent bonds or with the formation of a co-ordination compound (Chapter 2, p. 37). The molecules of this compound may be uncharged, or even have charges of the opposite sign from those of the ions transported; they will thus be unaffected by any electrical potential gradient across the membrane concerned, or may even travel "up" the gradient as defined in terms of the ions carried. On reaching the other side of the membrane, the carrier may be supposed to undergo a chemical change of such a nature that it will no longer combine with the ions concerned; these are therefore released into the solution. Organic compounds are known which have more or less the properties necessary for ion carriers of this kind; many of them could be imagined as acting as carriers for, say, calcium or magnesium ions; few, however, would be suitable for transporting sodium ions and not potassium ions, for example, or *vice versa*. Their presence within living cells has not been demonstrated.

It is to be noted that in the transport of, for example, a particular kind of cation, positive charges are removed from the solution on the "entry" side, and generated in the solution on the "delivery" side. It is obvious that there can be only an infinitesimal transport of one kind of ion unless, also, ions of the opposite sign are carried in the same direction, or ions of the same sign are carried in the opposite direction. These ions may travel passively, under the influence of an electrical potential gradient, as in the frog's skin, where chloride ions accompany an active transport of sodium ions; or they may be transported specifically by the "energised" carrier molecules, as in the surface membranes of many kinds of living cell, where, it seems, a potassium ion travels back on each carrier molecule which has transported a sodium ion. There is, however, an alternative method by which the compensating electric charges can be carried. Electrons may be gained and lost by atoms or radicals which are released in the various metabolic reactions which are proceeding in the living cells concerned; indeed, as we saw in Chapter 8, such electron transfers are characteristic of oxidation-reduction reactions. Thus, as Krogh pointed out, the existence of oxidative metabolic reactions provides a continuous source of hydrogen ions on the one hand (and thus of ammonium ions by combination with ammonia made available in de-amination reactions); and of hydroxyl ions on the other hand (and thus of bicarbonate ions by combination with carbon dioxide made available in de-carboxylation reactions). These ions will be available for exchanging with, or accompanying, ions which are transported by a specific carrier.

But, further, a continued production of ions in metabolic reactions is likely to lead to the development of diffusion potentials, both chemical and electrical. These, in turn, may bring about the movement of other kinds of ion, and thus to an active transport which is a direct consequence of the electron transfers in the oxidation-reduction reactions. For this to occur, however, it is essential that there should be an appropriate organisation of the cellular structure, notably in respect of the distribution of oxidation-reduction enzyme systems. It has been implicit in earlier paragraphs that an essential feature of secreting and transporting cells is their "polarisation"; there is an "entry" side, or face, which is to be distinguished from the "delivery" side, or face. At this point, however, we will refer to "end A" and "end B" of the secreting cell, since the direction of transport with respect to the organisation of the oxidation-reduction systems depends on the nature of the substance transported.

Suppose, then, that at end A the enzyme systems necessary to complete the oxidative breakdown of carbohydrates beyond the stage of, say, pyruvic or acetic acids, are lacking. These acids will thus accumulate in this region of the cell. Suppose, also, that the cell membrane at this end is impermeable to pyruvate or acetate ions, as the case may be, but permeable to hydrogen ions and, say, sodium, potassium and chloride ions. As the hydrogen ions accumulate, they will diffuse out, accompanied by chloride ions or in exchange for sodium or potassium ions. There will, of course, be a tendency for the system to approach a condition of Donnan equilibrium, and the concentration of sodium or potassium ions within the cell will be greater than that in the external solution, and the concentration of chloride ions less; but this, in itself, will not, and cannot, produce a continued transport. The pyruvate or acetate ions will, however, diffuse across the cell towards end B, electric neutrality being preserved by a flux of chloride ions in the opposite direction, or of sodium and potassium ions in the same direction. If, on the way across, they encounter the necessary enzyme systems, oxidative metabolism will be completed, and they will reach end B in the form of bicarbonate ions, able to diffuse out into the external solution. Two kinds of active transport may then occur. If the cell membranes at either or both ends are relatively impermeable to sodium and potassium ions, there will be a flux of chloride ions into the cell at end B, in exchange for bicarbonate ions, and out of the cell at end A accompanied by hydrogen ions. Such a secretion of hydrochloric acid is brought about, for example, by certain cells in the walls of the stomachs of most kinds of vertebrate. The bicarbonate ions will react with hydrogen ions in the external solution in order to maintain the equilibrium conditions of the reaction:

$$H^+ + HCO_3^- \rightleftharpoons H_2CO_3$$

The final overall result of the process may thus be regarded as a removal of hydrogen ions from the solution outside end B of the cell, and their transport to the solution outside end A. But if, on the other hand, the cell membranes are highly permeable to either sodium ions or potassium ions, or both, there will be a continuous flux of the relevant cation into the cell at end A, in exchange for hydrogen ions, and out of the cell at end B, accompanied by bicarbonate ions. Such a cation exchange process occurs, for example, in the tubules of vertebrate kidneys.

It is easy to see that if the hypothetical substance whose further metabolism is blocked at end A were a cation instead of an anion, chloride ions (and perhaps other kinds of anion) would be taken in at end A, in exchange for bicarbonate ions, and would leave at end B accompanied by hydrogen ions. There is reason to believe that in the absorption of salts from the soil by the roots of plants there is a primary active transport of anions, and a secondary flow of cations, chiefly potassium ions. If we had a mixed assembly of cells which worked with "non-penetrating anions" and cells which worked with "non-penetrating cations", the overall result would be the transport of, say, sodium chloride from one solution to the other, the hydrogen and bicarbonate ions, which also appear in each solution, combining to form carbon dioxide.

There are no fundamental objections in principle to such a scheme, and there may be secretory systems in which it operates. But in others, the results of experimental observation have shown that for quantitative reasons it cannot be accepted. Consider, first, the secretion of hydrochloric acid in the vertebrate stomach. The fluid secreted may contain hydrochloric acid in a concentration as great as 0.17 M; the hydrogen ion concentration within the cell will have to be at least as great as this, and the metabolite which gives rise to the hydrogen ions must have such an acid dissociation constant, and be in sufficient concentration, as to be at least partially dissociated. Reference to the table of acid dissociation constants given in Chapter 4 (Table 4.3, p. 161) shows that all the acidic substances which are known to be formed in the intermediate stages of carbohydrate metabolism are relatively weak acids. Taking the strongest of those listed, pyruvic acid, and applying the Ostwald dilution law, we can calculate that in order to obtain a hydrogen ion concentration of 0·17 M, the total concentration of the pure acid would have to be some 5·5 M, a most improbable value. Further difficulties arise when simultaneous measurements are made on the number of hydrogen ions secreted, or cations transported, and the number of oxygen molecules reduced. Each ion secreted or transported, on the above hypothesis, is derived from one molecule of, say, pyruvic acid; the subsequent oxidation of which is accompanied by the reduction of three molecules of oxygen. The minimum value of the ratio of oxygen molecules reduced to cations transported is thus 3; and no reasonable assumption as to the nature of the acid concerned will allow this value to be reduced to less than 1. There are many experimental observations, however, which show that in the transport of hydrogen and other cations, and in that of anions, the ratio of the number of oxygen molecules reduced to the number of ions carried may be substantially less than 1, though rarely, and perhaps not certainly, less than 1/4.

In order to see how this difficulty may be overcome, we must consider the oxidation-reduction process in terms of electron transfer, as discussed in Chapter 8, p. 327. For the reduction of molecular oxygen, we write:

$$O_2 + 4e \longrightarrow 2O^{2-} \qquad . \qquad . \qquad . \qquad 10.(iv)a$$

followed immediately by:

$$2O^{2-} + 2H^+ \longrightarrow 2OH^- . \qquad . \qquad . \qquad 10.(iv)b$$

the necessary electrons being supplied from some suitable "donor" in the shape of an oxidation-reduction enzyme or co-enzyme; this might, for example, be one of the cytochromes, in which the iron atoms would change valency, so:

$$(-Fe^{++}) \rightleftharpoons (-Fe^{+++}) + e \qquad . \qquad . \qquad . \qquad 10.(v)$$

For the oxidation of hydrogen atoms in some metabolite, we write:

$$4(-H) \longrightarrow 4H^+ + 4e \qquad . \qquad . \qquad . \qquad 10.(vi)$$

the electrons lost being taken up by an "acceptor" which may, of course, be the oxidised form of the enzyme system which has donated electrons in reaction 10.(iv)a; reaction 10.(v) would then go in the reverse direction. Ordinarily, of course, the oxidation of the hydrogen atoms and the reduction of the oxygen atoms occur close together, and the hydrogen ions and the hydroxyl ions immediately combine to form water. But if, owing to some particular organisation of the secreting cell, the two reactions are made to occur at, say, the opposite ends of the cell, there will be a production of hydrogen ions at, say, end A and a production of hydroxyl ions at end B. In this case, the hydrogen ions needed to form the hydroxyl ions in reaction 10.(iv)b will be derived from water: $2HOH \rightleftharpoons 2H^+ + 2OH^-$, the number of hydroxyl ions produced being, in the end, the same as the number of hydrogen ions. The hydroxyl ions may be presumed to combine with carbon dioxide and form bicarbonate ions; and the overall result is identical with that produced in the previous scheme. But it will be seen, now, that the formation of each hydrogen ion, and thus the transport of each cation, is accompanied by the reduction of only 1/4 of a molecule of oxygen, a figure which is no greater than most of the values obtained experimentally.

The necessary condition for this scheme to operate is the "polarisation" of the secreting cell in respect of different kinds of oxidation-reduction system. Those which activate the hydrogen atoms in the substrate molecules (the dehydrogenases) must occur solely, or at least predominantly, at the end of the cell where hydrogen ions are delivered; those which activate molecular oxygen (aerobic oxidases) must occur predominantly at the end where bicarbonate ions are delivered. It is not essential, as might at first appear, that the substance which donates and accepts the electrons should travel to and fro across the cell. If there were a chain of such substances from one end of the cell to the other, each member could undergo cyclic changes in valency and the electrons would be handed from one to the next, and so travel across the cell from the hydrogen atoms to the oxygen molecules. The general scheme for the active transport of hydrogen ions, and thus, by exchange processes, of other kinds of ion, has been called the "redox pump" by Conway and the "electron cycle" by Davies.

In this process, only a fraction of the energy released by the reduction of the oxygen molecules is actually transferred to the hydrogen ions transported. In the frog's stomach, for example, the hydrogen ions are derived from a solution with a pH of about 7 and delivered to one with a pH of about 1. From the fundamental relation between partial free energy and activity (equation 3.7, p. 83), we can readily calculate that in order to raise the activity of hydrogen ions from a pH of 7 to a pH of 1, we should have to supply about 8·5 kcals. of free energy per gram-ion, or per mole of hydrochloric acid (compare, also, equation 10.33 below). Some energy, also, is needed to bring about the passage of water, and the theoretical work required for the production of each mole of hydrochloric acid comes out to be some 9 kcals. The total amount of free energy released in the reduction of a mole of oxygen, is, as we have seen, some 110 kcals.; the theoretical maximum ratio of hydrogen ions transported to oxygen molecules reduced, from energetic considerations, is thus about 12. In the "redox pump", this ratio is limited, by stoichiometric considerations, to 4. It has been suggested that the "efficiency" of the process could be increased by making use of the "active" phosphate radical as a "carrier", somewhat as in the scheme proposed for the transport of glucose. The energy required to raise the electrochemical potential of the hydrogen ions is derived from that released in the conversion of "active" phosphate to inorganic phosphate, and is calculated to be sufficient for the transport of about 2 hydrogen ions per molecule of "active" phosphate. This energy, as we have seen in Chapter 8, is derived, in the last analysis, from the reduction of oxygen; but the same molecules of oxygen which accept the electrons in the "redox pump" may also be used in the reactions which generate "active" phosphate. It is of interest in this connection that the amount of carbon dioxide used to neutralise hydroxyl ions may be greater than that produced in metabolism; gastric mucosa which is secreting very actively may *absorb* carbon dioxide from the surroundings. It would seem that more hydrogen ions may sometimes be generated than can be derived from the hydrogen atoms in the metabolite from which carbon dioxide is released; the additional ions must, presumably, come from water.

Returning now to the initial scheme, in which ions are supposed to be carried in temporary combination, without their electric charges, we may write the general equations of the "energised carrier" system (p. 473 above) in the form:

$$C^{2-} + Na^+ \longrightarrow (C.Na)^- \qquad . \qquad . \qquad . \ 10.(i)a$$

for the uptake of the cation, say sodium, by the carrier C^{2-}, the combination thus possessing a negative charge. At the "delivery" side of the cell, we have:

$$C^{2-} \xrightarrow{\ X\ } D + 2e \qquad . \qquad . \qquad . \qquad 10.(ii)a$$

where e represents an electron. In consequence, we have:

$$(C.Na)^- \longrightarrow C^{2-} + Na^+$$

And at the "entry" side, the cycle is closed by the reaction:

$$D + 2e \xrightarrow{\ Y\ } C^{2-} \qquad . \qquad . \qquad . \qquad 10.(iii)a$$

If a steady state is to be maintained, the electrons released on the "delivery" side must be transferred back to the "entry" side, so as to compensate for those removed. This transport of electrons may occur over a chain of oxidation-reduction systems, as just discussed. But, further, we may imagine that the transfer of electrons to and from the carriers C^{2-} and D is associated with the oxidation of hydrogen atoms and the reduction of oxygen atoms. In conjunction with equation 10.(ii)a, we have, at the "delivery" end of the cell:

$$\left. \begin{array}{l} (-O) + 2e \longrightarrow (-O^{2-}) \\ (-O^{2-}) + H^+ \longrightarrow OH^- \end{array} \right\} \qquad . \qquad . \qquad 10.(ii)b$$

and

and in conjunction with equation 10.(iii)a , at the "entry" end, we have:

$$2(-H) \longrightarrow 2H^+ + 2e \qquad . \qquad . \qquad . \qquad 10.(\text{iii})b$$

(The oxygen and hydrogen atoms are both likely to be attached to enzyme systems, or to be constituents of metabolite molecules). The complete reaction sequence, from beginning to end, is then identical with that in the "redox pump", except that electrons are transferred by means of the carriers C and D, instead of the chain of oxidation-reduction systems. It should be emphasised, however, that it is not essential that the reactions of C and D should be so intimately linked with the reduction of oxygen and the oxidation of hydrogen.

Moreover, when cation transport is brought about by the "non-penetrating anion" process, or by the "redox pump", the precise nature of the ions transported depends, as we have seen, on the ionic permeability of the cell membrane at one end or the other. When this permeability must be supposed to be specific towards one particular kind of ion, it must also be supposed that penetration is "facilitated" by the presence of some particular carrier substance. The various schemes for the active transport of ions are thus seen to differ little in principle; attention is merely directed to different aspects of the phenomenon.

Electrical Potential Differences. Active transport of an electrolyte, as already remarked, will in general lead to the development of an electrical potential difference across the membrane, or sheet of cells, through which the transport occurs. But the magnitude, and even the sign, of the potential observed will depend on the process by which the transport is brought about, and on any specific ionic permeabilities that the various membranes may possess.

(1) If, say, cations are transported from one solution to another in which they are more concentrated, by means of a carrier with which they form an un-ionised compound, it is to be expected that the "delivery" side will be electrically positive to the "entry" side, since positive charges are being removed from the latter and transferred to the former.

(2) On the other hand, if there is an exchange transport, in which cations are exchanged for hydrogen ions and which results from the presence of indiffusible anions and an approximation to a Donnan equilibrium at the side at which the cations enter, the external solution will be positive to the interior of the membrane or cell at this end; at the other end of the cell, where the cations leave in company with bicarbonate ions, there is likely to be a diffusion potential which may be of either sign, but probably smaller in magnitude than the "equilibrium" potential at the "entry" side. The solution to which the cations are transported will thus be electrically negative to that from which they are derived. Similarly, if there is an exchange transport of anions by an analogous process, there

Q

will be an electric potential difference opposite in sign to that produced by the exchange transport of cations. In the hypothetical system of mixed cation and anion exchanging cells, producing an active transport of both ions of an electrolyte, there will be no net potential difference across the membrane; the effects of adjacent cells, or groups of cells, neutralising one another.

(3) With the "redox pump", one might expect that the electrical potentials would be those corresponding to the difference in oxidation-reduction potential between the two sides of the membrane or cell. Suppose, for example, that the electrons were being accepted and donated by a system involving a valency change, such as that between ferric and ferrous ions. Suppose that the concentration ratio of ferric ions to ferrous ions were, say, 100 at one end of the cell and 0·01 at the other end; there would be a difference in oxidation-reduction potential of some 240 millivolts (Chapter 8, p. 334), the electrode at the end where hydrogen is oxidised, and hydrogen ions delivered or other cations taken in, being negative to that at the other end. The potential, however, might be greater or less than this, according to the concentration of the reducible substrate, the concentration of free oxygen, and the nature and concentrations of other oxidation-reduction systems that may be present.

It by no means follows, however, that the potential that would actually be measured by means of external electrodes and electrical measuring instruments would be that expected from any of the above considerations, since it would depend on the nature of the system and of the electrodes used. Take, for example, the acid secreting cells of the stomach, and suppose them to be secreting 0·1 M. hydrochloric acid (pH 1) at one end, and to be in contact with 0·1 M. sodium chloride (pH 7) at the other end. (*a*) We should observe the oxidation-reduction potential (supposing the transport were being carried out by a "redox pump") if we were to use appropriate reversible electrodes in contact with the actual reaction systems. (*b*) If we inserted hydrogen electrodes into the two solutions, each in equilibrium with one atmosphere of hydrogen, we should expect the potential difference to be, approximately $(6 \times 60 = 360)$ millivolts (the electrode in the acid solution being positive to that in the neutral solution) *minus* the diffusion potential set up in the region where the acid and the salt solutions are in contact; this will be smaller than the electrode potential, and the electrode in the acid solution will be positive to that in the neutral solution, though not by the full 360 millivolts. (*c*) If we were to use chloride electrodes (such as calomel electrodes) we should expect to find only the diffusion potential, since the chloride concentration is the same in both solutions. (*d*) Now suppose that the contact between the two solutions were made at a membrane which was permeable only to hydrogen ions. The membrane potential set up would be identical with the electrode potential between the two hydrogen electrodes, as demonstrated in Chapter 4, p. 155, but reversed in sign. We should observe no potential with the hydrogen electrodes, and the full 360 millivolts with the calomel electrodes, the acid solution now being negative to the neutral solution. Any intermediate condition is, of course, possible. (e) Measurements are most usually made, however, in conditions where the two electrode potentials are the same, irrespective of the ionic compositions of the solutions in contact with them; as, for example, by using calomel electrodes in potassium chloride solutions, connected to the living cells (in this case, those of the gastric mucosa) by means of saturated potassium chloride bridges. We should then observe only the diffusion potential, or, if a membrane is present, only the membrane potential, and the acid solution will be negative to the neutral solution. As a further complication it is possible that the membrane might be specifically permeable to, say, sodium ions, rather than hydrogen ions; since the concentration ratio of sodium ions is roughly the inverse of that of hydrogen ions, the observed potential difference will have the same value as that calculated above, but the acid solution will be positive with respect to the neutral solution.

In this discussion, it is important to remember, the membrane has been assumed to be entirely passive, though discriminatory; the solutions on each side of it are supposed to be either in equilibrium or in a steady state of diffusion "pseudo-equilibrium". It is clear, therefore, that electrode potentials, membrane potentials and diffusion potentials of many kinds may be superimposed on any potentials which may be generated by the active transport itself. The interpretation of the observed overall electrical potential difference is thus apt to be difficult, and several different interpretations, all equally valid, are often possible.

The situation, however, may be considerably simplified by the use of the "short-circuited" membrane, where this can be done, as first introduced by Ussing for the frog's skin. If we arrange that the two solutions in contact with the two sides of the membrane are kept constant, and identical, in composition, there can be no chemical potential gradient across it, and thus, at first sight, no diffusion or membrane potentials. If, however, there is any active transport of ions, there is likely to be an electrical potential gradient, and this may produce movements of ions, and generate potential differences, within the membrane. We now provide an external source of electromotive force, and pass an electric current through the membrane in such a direction and of such a magnitude that it generates a potential difference equal and opposite to that generated by the active transport. There will then be neither a chemical nor an electrical potential gradient across the membrane (the current is, in fact, adjusted until there is no potential difference between two suitably placed electrodes): in these conditions, there can be no net flux of ions apart from that produced by the active transport. Referring back to equation 10.2 (pp. 430 and 460), we see that $m_e\gamma_e = m_c\gamma_c$ and $\Delta E = 0$. The flux ratio would be unity in the absence of any active transport. Ussing, therefore, introduced an additional potential difference, ΔE_{tr} in order to express in electrical terms the force bringing about active transport. ΔE_{tr} is defined and measured in terms of the flux ratio, as determined by means of isotopes, i.e.

$$\Delta E_{tr} = \frac{RT}{F} . \ln\left(\frac{\phi_{in}}{\phi_{out}}\right) \quad \text{(for univalent ions).}$$

(Compare, also, equation 10.19, p. 460.) We can then deduce an "apparent conductance" of the membrane, given by:

$$G' = \frac{F^2(\phi_{in} - \phi_{out})}{RT . \ln(\phi_{in}/\phi_{out})} \qquad . \qquad . \qquad . \quad 10.30$$

Such partial "conductances" can be calculated for several different kinds of ion, and the sum compared with the overall conductance as measured electrically. The comparison may give some information as to the nature of the transport process.

Finally, there is one relatively simple point which must be emphasised. If ions of any particular kind are observed to travel from one solution to another in which their concentration is greater, the transport can be passive only if there is an electrical potential difference between the solutions which is of such a sign as to cause the ions to travel in this direction. Moreover, its magnitude must be such that the electrochemical potential of the ions in the solution towards which they travel is no greater than, and preferably appreciably less than, that in the solution from which they are derived. In the frog's skin for example, the sign of the electrical potential difference across the skin indicates that cations must be actively transported; and it is of sufficient magnitude to bring about a passive transport of chloride ions against the observed chemical potential difference. In the mucosa of the stomach, on the other hand, the sign of the electrical potential difference is such that there must be some active transport of chloride ions, even though, as already stated, the chemical potential difference is zero, or at least very small; its magnitude, however (some 50 to 100 mV.), is not sufficient to bring about a passive transport of hydrogen ions.

THE TRANSPORT OF WATER

As already remarked, the active transport of solutes of any kind may be expected to be accompanied by a secondary transport of water whenever the membrane, or sheet of cells, is permeable to water. It is highly probable that in many cases the water in which secreted or transported substances are dissolved is carried through in this way; it is not, strictly, to be regarded as an "active" transport, since the chemical potential, or activity, of the water is smaller in the secreted fluid than in the solution from which it was derived. There are, however, examples of secretion and active transport in which the activity of the water becomes increased; the secreted solution is more dilute than the normal extra-cellular fluid, and its hydrostatic pressure may be greater.

Suppose that at one end of a secreting cell, the sequence of oxidative metabolic reactions ceases at a stage at which some substance is formed which has a relatively low molecular weight, but which is unable to penetrate the cell membrane; water will be drawn in from the solution outside the cell. If, further, as in the scheme for the exchange transport of electrolytes discussed above, this substance (now supposed to be a non-electrolyte) becomes completely oxidised to carbon dioxide and water as it diffuses across the cell, the water drawn in at one end will pass out at the other end, accompanied only by carbon dioxide and carbonic acid in solution. The total concentration of the solution into which the water passes may approximate to that of the cell contents, less the contribution of the dissolved carbon dioxide, which diffuses through the cell membrane almost as rapidly as does the water. The total concentration of the solution from which the water is drawn may approximate to that of the cell contents together with that of the indiffusible metabolite. The water thus passes from a solution of greater solute concentration to one of less, contrary to it own activity gradient. Such a process, however, is energetically very wasteful, and, in fact, may be ruled out for this reason.

In the distal tubules of the mammalian kidney, there are cells which transport water into the blood from the solution within the tubules, which is thus made more concentrated than the blood. Experimental observations suggest that in the kidneys of an ordinary man this active transport of water amounts to about 2 to 3 ml./min. From histological preparations, it can be calculated that the total surface area of the cells in the distal tubules is about 2000 sq. cm. It is not known what fraction of all the cells present are concerned in this transport, but it is unlikely that all of them are. As a rough estimate, therefore, we may conclude that the rate of water transport is, say, 3×10^{-5} ml./sec. through each square centimetre of membrane. The permeability to water of the membranes of many different kinds of cell has been measured by the methods discussed in an earlier section; in most, the values lie between about 5×10^{-7} and 2×10^{-6} ml./sec.$^{-1}$ cm.$^{-2}$ for each atmosphere of pressure head. If we take an average figure of 1×10^{-6}, the pressure head required within the cells of the distal tubules becomes 30 atmospheres, corresponding to a concentration difference, provided by the non-penetrating metabolite, of close on 1500 mM. Clearly, therefore, each millilitre of water traversing the cell must be accompanied by about 1·5 millimoles of the solute; and this quantity must then be fully oxidised. There is thus a necessary stoichiometric relation between the rate of oxygen consumption and the rate of water transport, depending on the chemical nature of the osmotically active solute. Even with the most favourable assumptions, it is calculated that the active absorption of water alone would use as much oxygen in a given time as is observed to be used by the whole of both kidneys, leaving none for the many other kinds of secretion known to be occurring.

This particular stoichiometric difficulty is avoided in the "osmotic diffusion pump" suggested by Franck and Meyer in 1947. In this, the osmotically active solute, formed at one end of the cell, loses its osmotic activity at the other end, not by being broken down into very small molecules which diffuse out with the water, but by being synthesised, or polymerised, into much larger molecules. These then diffuse back to the "entry" side, where they are split into the original substance again. Either the polymerisation, or the splitting of the polymer, or both, must be endergonic and "driven" by associated reactions involving the reduction of molecular oxygen; there is no necessary stoichiometric relation between the quantity of oxygen reduced and the quantity of the "carrier" substance polymerised or split, although there must be an energetic limiting value.

There is still, however, another serious quantitative difficulty which is common to all types of osmotic water transport, whether the "carrier" substance is polymerised or metabolised. This substance is supposed to diffuse across the cell, carrying with it the water molecules which are transported. Clearly, as already implied in a previous paragraph, the rate at which it diffuses across should, for efficient operation, be appropriately related to the rate of water transport, and the concentration difference, against which the transport occurs. Actually, however, the rate of diffusion per unit cross-sectional area, will be determined by the diffusion constant, the concentration difference between the two ends of the cell, and the length of the cell. The rate of water transport, on the other hand, will be determined by the effective concentration difference across the semi-permeable membrane, or membranes, and their permeability constants for water. There will be no necessary relation between the rate of diffusion and the rate of water transport. If we take any reasonable values for the quantities involved, we find that the rate of diffusion is some 1000 times greater than the optimum value corresponding with the rate of water transport. Moreover, the metabolic processes must proceed at a rate sufficient to maintain the steady state of concentration difference across the cell, in spite of this large rate of diffusion; the metabolic rate of each transporting cell, on any reasonable assumptions, is thus calculated to be some 1000 times greater than that of any living cell known. Either, therefore, the "osmotic" process of water transport is impossible, or it must be supposed that the rate of diffusion of the "carrier" substance is reduced, by a factor of 1000 or so, as a result of the presence of some impeding structures. It might be, for example, that the carrier substance has to pass

along these structures from one point to another, and that at each point there is a large "energy barrier"; only those molecules which possess an exceptional amount of activation energy can pass.

As was first suggested by Engelmann in 1872, it is possible that *electro-osmotic* effects may play a part in the transport of water. We have good evidence that the materials of which the various membranes in living organisms are composed are such as to take up an electric charge in contact with watery solutions. And not only do we know that there are potential differences between different parts of living organisms, which might be impressed across a membrane, but we know that such potential differences are necessarily associated with the active transport of electrolytes, and, indeed, are quite regularly found in secreting glands. The transport of fluid by electro-osmosis, however, involves the passage of an electric current, and not merely the presence of a potential difference. So long as there is a flux of ions, active or passive, there will also be a flow of current; electric charges carried by water molecules will contribute to this current just as do those carried by ions.

If the membrane concerned is permeable to water, but not to any electrolytes, the flow of charged water molecules will not affect the primary ion transport from which, ultimately, it is derived; indeed, it might be so arranged as to provide a path for the compensating flow of electrons, where this is necessary. In general, however, the source of the charge on the water molecules is likely to be less intimately related to the energised ion carrier system, being derived from any of the sources of interfacial potential discussed in Chapter 5. The water molecules may then be regarded as moving in the electric field, like all the ions which are subjected to secondary transport. The electro-osmotic transport of water need not, and probably will not, occur through the same parts of the membrane as does the active transport of the ions. Indeed, it may occur in the membranes of different cells altogether, or through the "cement" substance which lies between the cells. There is no necessity, also, that the membrane should be impermeable to all solutes. But if it is permeable to the particular kind of ion which is actively transported, there will be a "leakage" of this ion by diffusion, which may be accentuated by the movement of the water.

The conditions, then, are exactly analogous to those which lead to "anomalous osmosis" discussed in the previous section. The electromotive force driving the charged water molecules may, as has been assumed so far, be derived from the active transport of certain kinds of ion. But it may equally well be derived from the back diffusion of these ions, the active transport serving to maintain the steady state; in the systems in which anomalous osmosis has been studied, a steady state might similarly be maintained by some form of "active" return of the diffusing electrolyte into the more concentrated solution from which it comes.

Quantitatively, it seems rather doubtful whether electro-osmotic effects can play very much part in the transport of water. Exact calculations are impossible, since we have insufficient information as to the precise nature of the system concerned; but an estimate of the order of magnitude of the electro-osmotic flow to be expected can be derived as follows. Suppose the charge on any given membrane is such that the electro-osmotic velocity is u cm./sec. for a potential gradient of 1 V/cm. Then the total electro-osmotic flow, assuming that there is no hydrostatic pressure across the membrane, will be this quantity, multiplied by the effective cross-sectional area of the pores. Suppose that this is p square centimetres per square centimetre of total membrane area. Let t be the thickness of the membrane, and let the potential difference across it be E. The potential gradient is thus E/t, and the electro-osmotic flux is given by:

$$\phi_\omega = E.u.p/t \qquad . \qquad . \qquad . \qquad 10.31$$

The following values may be taken for the quantities concerned:
  (i) the electro-osmotic velocity, $u = 1 \, \mu$/sec. for 1 V/cm. potential gradient (the electrokinetic velocity of many kinds of red blood cell, in solutions of about the correct ionic strength).
  (ii) the membrane potential difference, $E = 50$ mV.
  (iii) the thickness of the membrane, $t = 10 \, m\mu$;
  (iv) the effective pore area per square centimetre of membrane, $p = 10^{-6}$ cm.^{2}. (This value is very uncertain, and probably varies considerably from one kind of cell to another. Estimates derived from the permeability constants for water, together with likely values of the diameters of the pores, and from the electrical conductance of cell membranes, lie on the whole between 10^{-6} and 10^{-8}. The larger the value, however, the smaller, probably, will be the potential difference across the membrane. We take 10^{-6} in order to derive a generous estimate of the magnitude of the electro-osmotic flux.)
  We thus find that:

$$\phi_\omega = \frac{50 \times 10^{-3} \times 10^{-4} \times 10^{-6}}{10^{-6}} = 5 \times 10^{-6} \text{ ml./sec.}^{-1} \text{ cm.}^{-2}.$$

We concluded above that the rate of active absorption of water in the distal tubules of the human kidney is about 10 times larger than this value.

Although the electro-osmotic flux through such a system seems likely to be small, it is possible that appreciable hydrostatic or osmotic pressures may be created. In general, we should expect that if the cell were closed, a pressure or concentration would build up inside it until there is, in consequence, a flow of water, or solution, either in the axial regions of the pores, or in pores which do not possess an electric charge, which is equal in magnitude to the electro-osmotic flow. As a very rough estimate of the possible order of magnitude of this pressure, consider a cell whose membrane is rather impermeable to water, and in which the permeability constant might be about 10^{-7} ml./sec^{-1} cm.$^{-2}$ atm.$^{-1}$. If, as above, the electro-osmotic flow is 5×10^{-6} ml./sec.$^{-1}$ cm.$^{-2}$, the steady state pressure will be of the order of 50 atmospheres. This is doubtless a very generous estimate, and may well be 100 times too large; but even so, the effect might be significant in certain kinds of cell.

THE THEORETICAL WORK DONE IN SECRETION AND ACTIVE TRANSPORT

Secretion by Synthesis (Chemical Work). In the production of the special constituents of any secretion, chemical work must be done by the secreting cells. The theoretical minimum value of this work may be calculated immediately from the standard free energy changes in the reactions involved, if these are known—or less exactly from the changes in the standard bond energies—together with the concentrations (or better activities) of the substances concerned in the fluid secreted and in the environment of the cells. But more usually than not, the constituents of the secretion have large and complex molecules, such as those of enzymes, and the free energy changes involved are difficult to discover.

As an illustration of the problem, we may quote some calculations made by Butler of the free energy change involved in the synthesis of a protein. This may be divided into two parts: (1) the free energy involved in creating the peptide bonds between the constituent amino-acids; and (2) the free energy involved in aggregating and arranging the amino-acids in such a way as to form a particular kind of protein. The magnitude of the first is about 7·5 kcals. per peptide bond. The second is made up of a heat content change of some 0·3 kcals. per bond and an entropy change of some 1·5 kcals. per bond: this last term arises from the decrease in probability consequent on making one particular arrangement of amino-acids, and is calculated by means of statistical considerations. The total free energy change is thus some 8·5 to 9 kcals. per amino-acid residue, or say about 0·1 kcals. per gram of protein. Since there are at least several hundred, and often several thousand, amino-acid molecules in each protein molecule, the total supply of free energy required for the formation of each gram-molecule of protein would appear to be measured in thousands of kilocalories. It is to be remembered, however, that the rate of production of new protein molecules is quite small. In a man, for example, the daily production of digestive enzymes amounts to less than 1 millimole, and the total daily "turnover" of protein to only a few millimoles. The energy required for the synthesis of proteins may thus amount to some 2·5 kcals. out of a total daily consumption of some 2500 kcals.

Ultra-filtration. The process of forcing out the solvent, with or without some of the solutes, through a semi-permeable membrane results in an increase in the concentration of the solutes that remain; it is thus exactly

R

analogous to the process of compressing a gas, which was discussed in Chapter 1, p. 20. The work done can thus be written:

$$W = \int_{V_1}^{(V_1 - V_f)} \Pi \, dV$$

where V_1 is the initial volume of the solution, V_f is the volume of the ultra-filtrate formed, and Π is the osmotic pressure exerted by those solutes which cannot pass through the membrane. We can relate the osmotic pressure to the volume at any moment by the approximate relation:

$$\Pi = RTm \ . \qquad . \qquad . \qquad . \qquad 3.19a$$

where m is the molal concentration, i.e. the number of moles of osmotically active solutes per kilogram of solvent. In practice, we are rarely concerned with ultra-filtration except in connection with solutions of colloids. In such solutions, we can consider the total volume of the solution at any moment, V, to be approximately equal to the sum of the volume of the solvent, and that of the colloid; this latter may also be regarded as sensibly equal to the mass concentration of the colloid (in, say, grams per litre) multiplied by the initial volume of the solution. (This implies that the density of the colloid, in solution, is unity; if the true density is known, the appropriate correction can easily be applied.) The volume of the solution at any moment is thus given by $V - c.V_1$, where c is the initial concentration of the colloid. The number of gram-molecules of colloid in the system is $c.V_1/M$, where M is the molecular weight; this quantity, of course, is constant. We can thus write:

$$\Pi = \frac{RT.c.V_1}{M(V - c.V_1)} \ .$$

Consequently, in the formation of a volume V_f of ultra-filtrate from an initial volume V_1 of a colloid solution, the work done will be given by:

$$W(V_f) = \frac{RT.c.V_1}{M} \int_{V_1}^{(V_1 - V_f)} \frac{dV}{V - c.V_1}$$

$$= \frac{RT.c.V_1}{M} \ln \frac{V_1(1 - c)}{V_1(1 - c) - V_f} \qquad . \qquad . \qquad 10.32$$

Active Transport (Osmotic Work). The work done in bringing about any change in a system is always equal to the change in free energy of that system. When we are concerned with the active transport of a single solute, as for example, that of hydrochloric acid by the cells of the gastric mucosa, considered above (p. 479), the calculation is straightforward. In general, however, the formation of a secreted fluid consists in the separation of solvent and of certain solutes from one solution (solution A) and of transferring them to another solution (solution B) of different composition. The total work done, therefore, must be equal to the sum of the changes in the partial free energies of the components of the solutions that are concerned. We can introduce the concept of activity, instead of partial free energy, and thus can write, for the solvent:

$$W_1 = n_1\, RT \ln \frac{(a_1)_B}{(a_1)_A} \qquad \cdot \qquad \cdot \qquad \cdot \qquad 10.33$$

and for each solute:

$$W_2 = n_2\, RT \ln \frac{(a_2)_B}{(a_2)_A} \qquad \cdot \qquad \cdot \qquad \cdot \qquad 10.34$$

where W_1 is the work done in transferring n_1 moles of solvent, and W_2 is the work done in transferring n_2 moles of any particular solute, from solution A, where the activities are $(a_1)_A$ and $(a_2)_A$ respectively, to solution B where the activities are $(a_1)_B$ and $(a_2)_B$ respectively. The total work, therefore, will be given by:

$$W_1 + \Sigma(W_2) = RT \left\{ n_1 \ln \frac{(a_1)_B}{(a_1)_A} + \Sigma \left(n_2 \ln \frac{(a_2)_B}{(a_2)_A} \right) \right\} \qquad \cdot \quad 10.35$$

the summation signs indicating that we have to consider separately the work done in transferring each kind of solute.

This expression is thermodynamically exact, but of no practical use unless we know how the activities of the solvent and of the solutes vary with concentration; it is the concentrations that we determine by chemical analysis of the two solutions. In the first place, we can always identify the activity of the solvent with its partial vapour pressure; this can be determined directly, or by means of freezing point depression or osmotic pressure measurements. We thus have:

$$W_1 = n_1 RT \ln \frac{(p_1)_B}{(p_1)_A} \qquad \cdot \qquad \cdot \qquad \cdot \qquad 10.33a$$

This treatment, however, has the disadvantage that n_1 is usually large, while $(p_1)_B$ and $(p_1)_A$ are not very different from one another; unless they are measured with considerable accuracy, large errors may be introduced. If the solution is sufficiently dilute to be approximately "ideal", however, we have the relation:

$$-\Delta(\ln a_1) = \frac{\Delta n_2}{n_1} = \frac{\Delta m.M_1}{1000} \qquad \cdot \qquad \cdot \qquad 3.10a$$

where Δm is the solute concentration and M_1 is the molecular weight of the solvent. If more than one solute is present, we must take the sum of the molar concentrations of all the solutes. We thus have, approximately, when m is small:

$$W_1 = RT \, n_1 \frac{M_1}{1000} [\Sigma(m)_A - \Sigma(m)_B] \quad . \qquad . \qquad . \; 10.33b$$

If we are not justified in considering the solutions to be "ideal", we may introduce the "osmotic coefficients" in order to relate the solvent activity to the solute concentration. Strictly, however, the osmotic co-efficient is an unknown function of the total solute concentration, and we cannot express the change in free energy of the solvent in passing from solution A to solution B merely as the difference between the products of the concentration in each solution and the appropriate osmotic co-efficient; we should integrate the successive steps in the process, intro-ducing at each step the appropriate value of the osmotic coefficient. The integration must either be performed graphically, or an empirical relation found between the osmotic coefficient, in the particular solution con-sidered, and the concentration.

There is the further difficulty that the osmotic coefficient of each solute, and particularly of the electrolytes, will be affected by the presence of other solutes. We can make an approximate allowance for this interaction by calculating the ionic strengths of the solutions A and B, and then the concentration of each solute which would produce, if present by itself, a solution of the same ionic strength as that of the whole solution; the values of the osmotic coefficients to be introduced are those appropriate to these calculated conditions. The use of osmotic coefficients is, in any case, inadvisable unless the values in the two solutions between which transport is occurring are not very different from one another; in this case, the elaborations introduced by the changes in the values with changes in the concentrations may be neglected. In other conditions, it is best to use vapour pressure, or freezing point depressions in order to calculate the solvent activity.

We will now consider the case of the solutes. We can introduce activity coefficients and concentrations in place of activities, and obtain the expression:

$$\Sigma(W_2) = RT \{ \Sigma[n_2 \ln (m_B/m_A) + n_2 \ln (\gamma_B/\gamma_A)] \} \quad . \qquad . \; 10.34a$$

where m is the molal concentration of each solute considered, and γ is the activity coefficient at this concentration. Again, as with the use of osmotic coefficients, we should, strictly, allow for the fact that the activity co-efficient of each solute varies continuously as the concentration changes from that in solution A to that in solution B. If the solute is an electrolyte, we may use the Debye-Hückel relation (equation 4.7, p. 130); or if the solutions are too concentrated for this to be justified, we may use one of the more complex forms of this equation, or the empirical relation (equation 4.4). This refinement, however, is rarely necessary or justified. For non-electrolytes, the activity coefficients may be taken as unity in most systems of biological interest.

The equations can all be simplified by considering the work done in the formation of that quantity of solution B—i.e. of secretion—which contains 1000 grams of solvent. If the solutions can be assumed to be reasonably dilute, this quantity does not differ significantly from a litre of solution B. n_1 is thus the number of moles of solvent in 1000 grams, and is thus identical with $(1000/M_1)$. We thus get:

$$(W_1) \text{ unit vol.} = RT \left[\Sigma(m)_A - \Sigma(m)_B \right] \qquad . \qquad . \quad 10.36$$

Moreover, we are now carrying across from solution A enough of each solute to form a kilogram of solution B; hence $n_2 = m_B$. For an ideal solution, therefore, in which we can assume the osmotic and activity coefficients to be nearly unity, we get the final expression:

$$(W) \text{ unit vol.} = RT \{ \Sigma(m)_A - \Sigma(m)_B + \Sigma[m_B . \ln (m_B/m_A)] \} . \quad 10.37$$

This expression gives us the work done in the formation of each kilogram (or litre) of secretion; and if we wish to know the rate at which work is performed, or the power exerted (which is often of greater interest than the work per unit volume of secretion), we must multiply by the rate at which secretion is occurring. If Q_1 is the rate of transport of the solvent, in, say, litres per minute, and q_2 is the rate of transport of any one solute, in, say, moles per minute, we have, for the solvent:

$$(W_1) \text{ unit time} = Q_1 RT \{ \Sigma(m)_A - \Sigma(m)_B \}$$

and for the solutes:

$$(W_2) \text{ unit time} = RT \{ \Sigma[q_2 \ln (m_B/m_A)] \}$$

But the concentration of each solute in the secreted fluid must be given by the ratio of the rate at which it is transported itself to the rate at which the solvent is transported. Thus $q_2/Q_1 = m_B$. Inserting this relation, we get:

$$\left. \begin{aligned} (W) \text{ unit time} &= Q_1 RT \{ \Sigma(m)_A - \Sigma(m)_B + \Sigma[m_B . \ln (m_B/m_A)] \} \\ &= (q_2/m_B) RT \{ \Sigma(m)_A - \Sigma(m)_B + \Sigma[m_B \ln (m_B/m_A)] \} \end{aligned} \right\} . \quad 10.38$$

When the two solutions A and B do not differ very markedly in composition, the relevant osmotic and activity coefficients may be inserted in this expression without greatly increasing its complexity. As may be seen from Figs. 3.2 and 4.2 (pp. 104 and 132) the osmotic coefficients of the more important electrolytes (from the point of view of the physiologist) change little over the range of concentrations found in most kinds of protoplasm —say between 0·1 M. and 0·5 M.—and even the activity coefficients do not change very greatly. Except for approximate calculation, however, they should be taken into account when considering the relations of the proto-plasm, and the extracellular fluid, of fresh-water organisms with their environments.

LITERATURE

General.   Davson and Danielli (1952); Pappenheimer (1953); E. J. Harris (1956)

Volume and Pressure Changes in Cells.   Lucké (1940); Jacobs and Co-workers (1931, etc.—references in Davson and Danielli, 1952); Ponder (1948).

Membrane Conductance and Potential—Penetration of Ions.   Cole (1940); Hodgkin (1951); Teorell (1953).

Anomalous Osmosis.   Höber (1945—Section 8).

Secretion and Active Transport.   Krogh (1946); Robinson (1953); Davies (1951); Rosenberg (1954); Ussing (1949, 1954); Wilbrandt (1954); Lundegårdh (1954); Conway (1954).

SOME NUMERICAL CONSTANTS

$\pi = 3 \cdot 1416$ e (exponential) $= 2 \cdot 718$ $\ln . x = 2 \cdot 303 \log_{10} . x$

$1 \mu = 10^{-4}$ cm. $1 \text{ Å.} = 10^{-8}$ cm.

1 calorie $= 4 \cdot 18$ joules $= 4 \cdot 18 \times 10^7$ ergs
$\qquad\qquad = 0 \cdot 427$ kilogram-metres

1 atmosphere pressure $= 1 \cdot 013 \times 10^6$ dynes per square centimetre

1 mm. Hg pressure $= 1335$ dyne cm.$^{-2}$

1 litre-atmosphere $= 24$ calories $= 101 \cdot 3$ joules

1 electron-volt $= 1 \cdot 60 \times 10^{12}$ ergs

1 kilowatt-hour $= 860$ kilocalories $= 2 \cdot 25 \times 10^{25}$ electron-volts

1 ml. O_2 consumed per sec. $=$ approx. 5 cals./sec. $=$ approx. 21 watts

R (gas constant) $= 0 \cdot 0821$ litre-atm. per degree for 1 mole of gas
$\qquad\qquad = 8 \cdot 31$ joule deg.$^{-1}$ mole^{-1}
$\qquad\qquad = 1 \cdot 99$ cal. deg.$^{-1}$ mole^{-1}

N (Avogadro's number) $= 6 \cdot 023 \times 10^{23}$ atoms, or molecules, per mole

Volume occupied by 1 mole of perfect gas at N.T.P. $= 22 \cdot 4$ litres

Osmotic pressure of 1 M. solution (ideal) at $0°$ C. $= 22 \cdot 4$ atm.

F (ionic charge) $= 96{,}490$ coulombs per equivalent
$\qquad\qquad = 23 \cdot 07$ kcals. per volt-equivalent

k (Boltzmann's constant) $= R/N = 1 \cdot 380 \times 10^{-16}$ erg. deg.$^{-1}$ mole^{-1}

e (charge on electron) $= F/N = 4 \cdot 80 \times 10^{-10}$ e.s.u.

h (Planck's constant) $= 6 \cdot 625 \times 10^{-27}$ erg. sec.

c (velocity of light) $= 3 \cdot 00 \times 10^{10}$ cm. sec.$^{-1}$

Frequency, v, of radiation of wave-length λ cm. $= c/\lambda$ sec.$^{-1}$

Energy per quantum (photon) $= h . v$ ergs.

T °C.	2·303 RT		2·303 RT/F volts
	cals./mole	joules/mole	
0	1250	5225	0·0542
15	1320	5510	0·0572
25	1365	5705	0·0591
37	1420	5935	0·0615

BIBLIOGRAPHY

ABRAMSON, H. A. (1934)—*Electrokinetic Phenomena and their Application to Biology and Medicine*. New York: Chemical Catalog Co.

—, Moyer, L. S. and Gorin, M. H. (1942)—*Electrophoresis of Proteins*. New York: Reinhold Publishing Corporation.

ADAIR, G. S. (1929)—"The Thermodynamic Analysis of the Observed Osmotic Pressure of Protein Salts in Solutions of Finite Concentration." *Proc. Roy. Soc.* Series **A, 126**, 16-24.

ADAM, N. K. (1941)—*The Physics and Chemistry of Surfaces*. 3rd edition. Oxford: Clarendon Press.

ALEXANDER, A. E. and JOHNSON, P. (1949)—*Colloid Science*. 2 vols. Oxford: Clarendon Press.

ARRHENIUS, SVANTE. (1887)—"Ueber die Dissociation der in Wasser gelösten Stoffe." *Z. phys. Chem.* **4**, 226-248.

—— (1907)—*Immunochemistry*. London: Macmillan and Co. Ltd.

—— (1914)—"The Theory of Electrolytic Dissociation." Faraday Lecture. *Trans. chem. Soc.* **105**, 1414-1426.

ASTBURY, W. T. (1947)—"On the Structure of Biological Fibres and the Problem of Muscle." Croonian Lecture. *Proc. Roy. Soc.* Series **B, 134**, 303-327.

BALDWIN, E. (1957)—*Dynamic Aspects of Biochemistry*. 3rd edition. Cambridge: University Press.

BARR, G. (1931)—*A Monograph of Viscometry*. Oxford University Press, London: Humphrey Milford.

BATEMAN, J. B. (1945)—"Large Molecules: their physico-chemical properties and their architectural and functional significance in living matter." In *Physical Chemistry of Cells and Tissues* by R. Höber. Section 2, pp. 93-216. Philadelphia: Blakiston Co.; London: J. and A. Churchill Ltd.

BATES, R. G. (1954)—*Electrometric pH Determinations. Theory and Practice*. New York: John Wiley and Sons Inc.; London: Chapman and Hall Ltd.

BAYLISS, L. E. (1952)—"Rheology of Blood and Lymph." In *Deformation and Flow in Biological Systems*, ed. by A. Frey-Wissling. Part C, Chap. VI, pp. 355-418. Amsterdam: North Holland Publishing Co.

BAYLISS, W. M. (1925)—*The Nature of Enzyme Action*. London: Longmans, Green and Co. Ltd.

BERTHOLLET, CLAUDE LOUIS (1799)—"Recherches sur les lois de l'affinité." Mémoires Nat. Inst. (1799), Egypt. In book form in 1801. Reprinted in Ostwald's *Klassiker der exakten Wissenschaften*. No. 74. Leipzig: W. Engelmann.

BERZELIUS, J. J. (1837)—*Lehrbuch der Chemie*. 3te. Auflage. **6**, 22. Dresden und Leipzig: Arnoldschen Buchhandlung.

R*

BINGHAM, E. C. (1922)—*Fluidity and Plasticity*. New York and London: McGraw-Hill Book Co. Inc.

BLAIR, G. W. SCOTT (1949)—*A Survey of General and Applied Rheology*. London: Sir Isaac Pitman and Sons Ltd.

BLOCK, R. J., DURRUM, E. L. and ZWEIG, G. (1955)—*A Manual of Paper Chromatography and Paper Electrophoresis*. New York: Academic Press Inc.

BLUM, H. F. (1941)—*Photodynamic Action and Diseases caused by Light*. New York: Reinhold Publishing Corporation.

BOOTH, F. (1953)—"Recent Work on the Application of the Theory of the Ionic Double Layer to Colloidal Systems." *Progress in Biophysics*, ed. by J. A. V. Butler and J. T. Randall. **3**, 131-194. London: Pergamon Press, Ltd.

BOSSHAM, J. A. and CALVIN, M. (1957).—*The Path of Carbon in Photosynthesis*. Englewood Cliffs, N.J.: Prentice-Hall Inc.

BOYS, C. V. (1912)—*Soap Bubbles*. London: S.P.C.K.

BULL, H. B. (1951)—*Physical Biochemistry*. New York: John Wiley and Sons Inc.; London: Chapman and Hall Ltd.

BURTON, K. (1957)—"Free Energy Data of Biological Interest." (Appendix to article by H. A. Krebs and H. L. Kornberg.) *Ergebn. Physiol.* **49**, 275-285.

BUTLER, J. A. V. (1946)—*Fundamentals of Chemical Thermodynamics*. London: Macmillan and Co. Ltd.

CALVIN, M. (1950-51)—"The Path of Carbon in Photosynthesis." *Harvey Lectures*. Series XLVI, pp. 218-251.

CHAMBERS, R. (1933)—"An Analysis of Oxidation and Reduction of Indicators in Living Cells." *Cold Spr. Harb. Symp. quant. Biol.* **1**, 205-213.

CLARK, W. MANSFIELD (1928)—*The Determination of Hydrogen Ions*. Baltimore: Williams and Wilkins Co.

—— (1952)—*Topics in Physical Chemistry*. 2nd edition. Baltimore: Williams and Wilkins Co.; London: Baillière, Tindall and Cox, Ltd.

COLE, K. S. (1940)—"Permeability and Impermeability of Cell Membranes to Ions." *Cold Spr. Harb. Symp. quant. Biol.* **8**, 110-122.

COHEN, B. (1933)—"Reversible Oxidation-Reduction Potentials in Dye Systems." *Cold Spr. Harb. Symp. quant. Biol.* **1**, 195-204.

—— (1933)—"Reactions of Oxidation-Reduction Indicators in Biological Material." *Cold Spr. Harb. Symp. quant. Biol.* **1**, 214-223.

COLLINS, F. D. (1954)—"The Chemistry of Vision." *Biol. Rev.* **29**, 453-477.

CONWAY, B. E. (1952)—*Electrochemical Data*. Amsterdam, Houston, London and New York: Elsevier Publishing Co.

CONWAY, E. J. (1954)—"Some Aspects of Ion Transport through Membranes." *Symp. Soc. exp. Biol.* **8**, 297-324. Cambridge: University Press.

COULSON, C. A. (1952)—*Valence*. Oxford: University Press.

DANIELLI, J. F. (1944)—"The Biological Action of Ions and the Concentration of Ions at Surfaces." *J. exp. Biol.* **20**, 167-176.

DARTNALL, H. J. A. (1957)—*The Visual Pigments*. London: Methuen and Co. Ltd.; New York: John Wiley and Sons Inc.

DAVID, F. N. (1953)—*A Statistical Primer*. London: Charles Griffin and Co. Ltd.

DAVIES, R. E. (1951)—"The Mechanism of Hydrochloric Acid Production by the Stomach." *Biol. Rev.* **26**, 87-120.

DAVSON, H. and DANIELLI, J. F. (1952)—*The Permeability of Natural Membranes*. 2nd edition. Cambridge: University Press.

DAWES, E. A. (1956)—*Quantitative Problems in Biochemistry*. Edinburgh and London: E. and S. Livingstone Ltd.

DIXON, M. (1949)—*Multi-enzyme Systems*. Cambridge: University Press.

— and WEBB, E. C. (1958)—*Enzymes*. London, New York and Toronto: Longmans, Green and Co. Ltd.

ELFORD, W. J. (1937)—"Principles Governing the Preparation of Membranes having Graded Porosities." (Discussion on "The Properties and Functions of Membranes, Natural and Artificial.") *Trans. Far. Soc.* **33**, 1094-1106.

ERRERA, M. (1953)—"Mechanisms of Biological Action of Ultra-violet and Visible Radiations." *Progress in Biophysics*, ed. by J. A. V. Butler and J. T. Randall, **3**, 88-130. London: Pergamon Press Ltd.

FARADAY, MICHAEL (1834)—"Experimental Researches in Electricity." VI. "On the Power of Metals and Other Solids to Induce the Combination of Gaseous Bodies." *Philos. Trans.* (1834), 55-76. VII. "On Electro-chemical Decomposition." *Philos. Trans.* (1834), 77-122.

—— (1839-44)—"Experimental Researches in Electricity." Reprinted from *Philos. Trans.* and other Journals. 3 vols. London: R. and J. E. Taylor.

—— (1858)—"Experimental Relations of Gold (and other Metals) to Light." *Philos. Trans.* **147**, 145-181.

FINDLAY, A. (1955)—*Introduction to Physical Chemistry*. 3rd edition. London, New York and Toronto: Longmans, Green and Co. Ltd.

FISHER, R. A. (1954)—*Statistical Methods for Research Workers*. 12th edition. Edinburgh and London: Oliver and Boyd.

FLEMING, SIR AMBROSE (1938)—*Elementary Mathematics for Electrical Engineers*. London: George Newnes Ltd.

FRANCIS, G. E., MULLIGAN, W. and WORMALL, A. (1954)—*Isotopic Tracers*. University of London, The Athlone Press.

FREUNDLICH, H. (1926)—*Colloid and Capillary Chemistry*. 3rd edition of *Kapillarchemie*, translated by H. S. Hatfield. London: Methuen and Co. Ltd.

—— (1930-32)—*Kapillarchemie*. 4te. Auflage, 2 Bände. Leipzig: Akademische Verlagsgesellschaft.

GLASSTONE, S. (1947)—*Thermodynamics for Chemists*. New York, Toronto and London: D. van Nostrand Co. Inc.

—, LAIDLER, K. J. and EYRING, H. (1941)—*The Theory of Rate Processes*. New York: McGraw-Hill Book Co. Inc.

GRAHAM, THOMAS (1850)—"On the Diffusion of Liquids." Bakerian Lecture. *Philos. Trans.* (1850), 1-46.

—— (1861)—"Liquid Diffusion applied to Analysis." *Philos. Trans.* **151**, 183-224.

—— (1876)—*Chemical and Physical Researches*. Edinburgh: Printed for Presentation.

GRANIT, R. (1947)—*Sensory Mechanisms of the Retina*. London, New York and Toronto: Oxford University Press.

GREEN, D. E. (1951)—"The Cyclophorase Complex of Enzymes." *Biol. Rev.* **26**, 410-455.

GUGGENHEIM, E. A. (1957)—*Thermodynamics*. 3rd edition. Amsterdam: North Holland Publishing Co.

— and PRUE, J. E. (1955)—*Physico-Chemical Calculations*. Amsterdam: North Holland Publishing Co.

GULDBERG, C. M. et WAAGE, P. (1867)—"Recherches sur les affinités chimiques." Christiania: Brögger and Christie. Reprinted in Ostwald's *Klassiker der exakten Wissenschaften*. No. 104. Leipzig: W. Engelmann.

HAGUE, B. (1957)—*Alternating Current Bridge Methods*. 5th edition. London: Sir Isaac Pitman and Sons Ltd.

HALDANE, J. B. S. (1930)—*Enzymes*. London, New York and Toronto: Longmans, Green and Co., Ltd.

HARRIS, E. J. (1956)—*Transport and Accumulation in Biological Systems*. London: Butterworth's Scientific Publications.

HILL, R. and WHITTINGHAM, C. P. (1957)—*Photosynthesis*. 2nd edition. London: Methuen and Co., Ltd.; New York: John Wiley and Sons Inc.

HITCHCOCK, D. I. (1953)—*Physical Chemistry for Students of Biology and Medicine*. 3rd edition. Springfield, Ill. and Baltimore, Md.: Charles C. Thomas.

HODGKIN, A. L. (1951)—"The Ionic Basis of Electrical Activity in Nerve and Muscle." *Biol. Rev.* **26**, 339-409.

— and RUSHTON, W. A. H. (1946)—"The Electrical Constants of a Crustacean Nerve Fibre." *Proc. Roy. Soc.* Series **B**, **133**, 444-479.

HÖBER, R. (1945)—*Physical Chemistry of Cells and Tissues*. Philadelphia: Blakiston Co.; London: J. and A. Churchill Ltd.

HOFF, J. H. VAN'T (1900-03)—*Vorlesungen über theoretische und physikalische Chemie*. 2te. Auflage, 3 Teilen. Braunschweig: Friedrich Viewig und Sohn.

JACOBS, M. H. (1935)—"Diffusion Processes." *Ergebn. Biol.* **12**, 1-160.

JAEGER, J. C. (1951)—*An Introduction to Applied Mathematics*. Oxford: Clarendon Press.

JOHNSON, F. H., EYRING, H. and POLISSAR, M. J. (1954)—*The Kinetic Basis of Molecular Biology*. New York: John Wiley and Sons Inc.; London: Chapman and Hall Ltd.

KAMEN, M. D. (1957)—*Isotopic Tracers in Biology*. New York: Academic Press Inc.

KAPLAN, N. O. (1951)—"Thermodynamics and Mechanism of the Phosphate Bond." In *The Enzymes*, ed. by J. B. Sumner and K. Myrbäck, Vol. II, Part 1, pp. 55-113.

KOLLER, L. R. (1952)—*Ultraviolet Radiation*. New York: John Wiley and Sons Inc.; London: Chapman and Hall Ltd.

KOLTHOFF, I. M. and LAITENEN, H. A. (1941)—pH *and Electro Titrations*. 2nd edition. New York: John Wiley and Sons Inc.; London: Chapman and Hall Ltd.

— and LINGANE, J. J. (1952)—*Polarography*. 2nd edn. 2 vols. New York: Interscience Publishers Inc.

KREBS, H. A. (1948)—"The Tri-carboxylic Acid Cycle." *Harvey Lectures*. Series XLIV, pp. 165-199.

—— and KORNBERG, H. L. (1957)—"A Survey of the Energy Transformations in Living Matter." *Ergebn. Physiol.* **49**, 212-298.

KROGH, A. (1946)—"The Active and Passive Exchanges of Inorganic Ions through Surfaces of Living Cells and through Living Membranes generally. Croonian Lecture. *Proc. Roy. Soc.* Series **B, 133**, 140-200.

KÜHNE, WILLY (1878)—"Erfahrungen und Bermerkungen über Enzyme und Fermente." *Untersuch. physiol. Institut Heidelberg*, **1**, 291-326.

KUHN, R. (1940)—"Optische Spezifität von Enzyme." In *Handbuch der Enzymologie*, ed. by F. F. Nord and R. Weidenhagen. Vol. I, pp. 187-219.

KYNCH, G. J. (1955)—*Mathematics for the Chemist.* London: Butterworth's Scientific Publications.

LANGMUIR, I. (1939)—"Molecular Layers." Pilgrim Trust Lecture. *Proc. Roy. Soc.* Series **A, 170**, 1-39.

LEA, D. E. (1955)—*The Action of Radiations on Living Cells.* 2nd edition. Cambridge: University Press.

LEDERER, E. and LEDERER, M. (1957)—*Chromatography. A Review of Principles and Applications.* 2nd edition. Amsterdam, London and New York: Elsevier Publishing Co.

LEWIS, G. N. and RANDALL, M. (1923)—*Thermodynamics.* New York and London: McGraw-Hill Book Co. Inc.

LINGANE, J. J. (1953)—*Electroanalytical Chemistry.* New York: Interscience Publishers Inc.

LIPMANN, F. (1948)—"Biosynthetic Mechanisms." *Harvey Lectures.* Series XLIV, pp. 99-103.

LOEB, J. (1924)—*Proteins and the Theory of Colloidal Behaviour.* 2nd edition. New York and London: McGraw-Hill Book Co. Inc.

LOWRY, T. M. and SUGDEN, S. (1952)—*A Class Book of Physical Chemistry.* 2nd edition. London: Macmillan and Co. Ltd.

LUCKÉ, B. (1940)—"The Living Cell as an Osmotic System and its Permeability to Water." *Cold Spr. Harb. Symp. quant. Biol.* **8**, 123-132.

LUNDEGÅRDH, H. (1954)—"Anion Respiration: the Experimental Basis of a Theory of Absorption, Transport and Exudation of Electrolytes by Living Cells and Tissues." *Symp. Soc. exp. Biol.* **8**, 262-296. Cambridge: University Press.

LYNEN, F. (1952)—"Acetyl Coenzyme A and the 'Fatty Acid Cycle'." *Harvey Lectures.* Series XLVIII, pp. 210-243.

MASSART, L. (1950)—"Enzyme Inhibition." In *The Enzymes*, ed. by J. B. Sumner and K. Myrbäck, Vol. I, Part 1, pp. 307-389.

MELLOR, J. W. (1912)—*Higher Mathematics for Students of Chemistry and Physics.* London, New York and Toronto: Longmans, Green and Co. Ltd.

MICHAELIS, L. (1946)—"Fundamentals of Oxidation and Reduction." In *Currents in Biochemical Research*, ed. by D. E. Green. New York: Interscience Publishers Ltd.

—— (1951)—"Theory of Oxidation-Reduction." In *The Enzymes*, ed. by J. B. Sumner and K. Myrbäck, Vol. II, Part 1, pp. 1-54.

MOELWYN-HUGHES, E. A. (1940)—"Physikalische Chemie und Kinetik." In *Handbuch der Enzymologie*, ed. by F. F. Nord und R. Weidenhagen, Vol. I, pp. 220-288.

—— (1947)—*The Kinetics of Reactions in Solution.* Oxford: Clarendon Press.

MOELWYN-HUGHES, E. A. (1950)—"Physical Chemistry and Chemical Kinetics of Enzymes." In *The Enzymes*, ed. by J. B. Sumner and K. Myrbäck, Vol. I, Part 1, pp. 28-78.

—— (1956)—*Physical Chemistry*. London, New York and Paris: Pergamon Press.

MOORE, W. J. (1956)—*Physical Chemistry*. London, New York and Toronto: Longmans, Green and Co. Ltd.

NERNST, W. (1923)—*Theoretical Chemistry*. Revised by L. W. Codd. London: Macmillan and Co. Ltd.

NORD, F. F. und WEIDENHAGEN, R. (1940)—*Handbuch der Enzymologie*. 2 Bände. Leipzig: Akademische Verlagsgesellschaft.

NORTHROPP, J. H., KUNITZ, M. and HERRIOTT, R. M. (1948)—*Crystalline Enzymes*. 2nd edition. New York: Columbia University Press.

OCHOA, S. (1951)—"Biological Mechanisms of Carboxylation and Decarboxylation." *Physiol. Rev.* **31**, 56-106.

OSTER, G. (1950)—"Scattering of Visible Light and X-rays by Solutions of Proteins." *Progress in Biophysics*, ed. by J. A. V. Butler and J. T. Randall, **1**, 73-84. London: Butterworth-Springer.

— and POLLISTER, A. W. ed. by (1955, 1956)—*Physical Techniques in Biological Research*. 3 vols. New York: Academic Press Inc.

OSTWALD, WILH. (1912a)—*Der Energetische Imperativ*. I. Leipzig: Akademische Verlagsgesellschaft.

—— (1912b)—*Die Energie*. Leipzig: Barth.

OSTWALD, WO. (1922)—*Grundriss der Kolloidchemie*. 7te. Auflage, Dresden: Theodor Steinkopf.

PAPPENHEIMER, J. R. (1953)—"Passage of Molecules through Capillary Walls." *Physiol. Rev.* **33**, 387-423.

PAULING, L. (1948)—*The Nature of the Chemical Bond*. 2nd edition. Ithaca, N.Y.: Cornell University Press; London: Humphrey Milford.

PERRIN, JEAN (1923)—*Atoms*. Translated by D. U. Hammick, London: Constable and Co.

PIRENNE, M. H. (1956)—"Physiological Mechanisms of Vision and the Quantum Nature of Light." *Biol. Rev.* **31**, 194-241.

PONDER, E. (1948)—*Haemolysis and Related Phenomena*. London: J. and A. Churchill Ltd.

PRIGOGINE, I. (1955)—*Introduction to Thermodynamics of Irreversible Processes*. Springfield, Ill.: Charles C. Thomas.

RABINOWITCH, E. L. (1945-56)—*Photosynthesis*. Vol. I (1945); Vol. II, part 1 (1951); Vol. II, part 2 (1956). New York and London: Interscience Publishers Inc.

RAMSAY, J. A. (1949)—"A New Method of Freezing-point Determination for Small Quantities." *J. exp. Biol.* **26**, 57-64.

REILLY, J. and RAE, W. N. (1940-48)—*Physico-chemical Methods*. 3 vols. London: Methuen and Co. Ltd.

ROBINSON, J. R. (1953)—"The Active Transport of Water in Living Systems." *Biol. Rev.* **28**, 158-194.

ROBINSON, R. A. and STOKES, R. H. (1955)—*Electrolyte Solutions*. London: Butterworth's Scientific Publications.

ROLLEFSON, G. K. and BURTON, M. (1939)—*Photochemistry and the Mechanism of Chemical Reaction*. New York: Prentice-Hall Inc.

ROSENBERG, T. (1954)—"The Concept and Definition of Active Transport." *Symp. soc. exp. Biol.* **8**, 27-41. Cambridge: University Press.

ROUGHTON, F. J. W. (1952)—"Diffusion and Chemical Reaction Velocity in Cylindrical and Spherical Systems of Physiological Interest." *Proc. Roy. Soc.* Series B, **140**, 203-229.

RUDALL, K. M. (1950)—"Fundamental Structures in Biological Systems." *Progress in Biophysics*, ed. by J. A. V. Butler and J. T. Randall, **1**, 39-72. London: Butterworth-Springer.

SADRON, C. (1953a)—"Dilute Solutions of Impenetrable Rigid Particles." In *Flow Properties of Disperse Systems*, ed. by J. J. Hermans. Amsterdam: North Holland Publishing Co.

—— (1953b)—"Methods of Determining the Form and Dimensions of Particles in Solution: a critical survey." *Progress in Biophysics*, ed. by J. A. V. Butler and J. T. Randall, **3**, 237-304. London: Pergamon Press Ltd.

SHERRINGTON, C. S. (1946)—*The Endeavour of Jean Fernel*. Cambridge: University Press.

SPEAKMAN, J. C. (1955)—*An Introduction to the Electronic Theory of Valency*. London: Edward Arnold (Publishers) Ltd.

SPEAR, F. G. (1953)—*Radiations and Living Cells*. London: Chapman and Hall Ltd.

SUMNER, J. B. and MYRBÄCK, K. (1950-51)—*The Enzymes—Chemistry and Mechanism of Action*. 2 vols. 4 parts. New York: Academic Press Inc.

— and SOMERS, F. G. (1953)—*The Chemistry and Methods of Enzymes*. 3rd edition. New York: Academic Press Inc.

SVEDBERG, T., PEDERSEN, K. O. and others (1940)—*The Ultra-centrifuge*. Oxford: University Press.

TAUBER, H. (1949)—*The Chemistry and Technology of Enzymes*. New York: John Wiley and Sons Inc.; London: Chapman and Hall Ltd.

TEORELL, T. (1953)—"Transport Processes and Electrical Phenomena in Ionic Membranes." *Progress in Biophysics*, ed. by J. A. V. Butler and J. T. Randall, **3**, 305-369. London: Pergamon Press Ltd.

TYNDALL, JOHN (1870)—*Faraday as a Discoverer*. 2nd edition. London, New York and Toronto: Longmans, Green and Co. Ltd.

USSING, H. H. (1949)—"Transport of Ions across Cellular Membranes." *Physiol. Rev.* **29**, 127-155.

—— (1954)—"Active Transport of Inorganic Ions." *Symp. Soc. exp. Biol.* **8**, 407-422. Cambridge: University Press.

WALLWORK, S. C. (1956)—*Physical Chemistry for Students of Pharmacy and Biology*. London, New York and Toronto: Longmans, Green and Co. Ltd.

WENNER, R. R. (1941)—*Thermodynamical Calculations*. New York: McGraw-Hill Book Co. Inc.

WEST, E. S. (1956)—*Text-book of Biophysical Chemistry*. New York: The Macmillan Co.

WHITE, A., HANDLER, P., SMITH, E. L. and STETTEN, DE WITT (1954)—*Principles of Biochemistry*. New York etc.: McGraw-Hill Book Co. Inc.

WHITEHOUSE, W. J. and PUTNAM, J. W. (1953)—*Radioactive Isotopes. An Introduction to their preparation, measurement and use*. Oxford: Clarendon Press: London: Oxford University Press.

WHITTINGHAM, C. P. (1955)—"Energy Transformation in Photosynthesis and the Relation of Photosynthesis to Respiration." *Biol. Rev.* **30**, 40-64.

WILBRANDT, W. (1954)—"Secretion and Transport of Non-electrolytes." *Symp. Soc. exp. Biol.* **8**, 136-161. Cambridge: University Press.

WILLSTÄTTER, R. und STOLL, A. (1913)—*Untersuchungen über Chlorophyll*. Berlin: Springer.

—— (1918)—*Untersuchungen über die Assimilation der Kohlensäure*. Berlin: Springer.

ZSIGMONDY, R. (1920)—*Colloids and the Ultra-microscope*. Translated by J. Alexander. London: Chapman and Hall Ltd.

INDEX

Figures in **bold type** refer to pages on which illustrations or tables occur.